GEOLOGY AND ENGINEERING

INTERNATIONAL SERIES IN THE EARTH SCIENCES

Robert R. Shrock, *Consulting Editor*

"Nature, to be commanded, must be obeyed."

Francis Bacon.

This portrait of "The Father of British Geology"—who was also an eminent civil engineer—is reproduced as a tribute to his memory, and as a fitting introduction to this study of what was his life's work, more than a century ago, work which is still an inspiration to geologists and to civil engineers in many countries of the world.

Wᵐ Smith
Civil Engineer

15 Buckingham Street
York Buildings
London

June 1818

GEOLOGY AND ENGINEERING

ROBERT F. LEGGET

DIRECTOR, DIVISION OF BUILDING RESEARCH
NATIONAL RESEARCH COUNCIL
OTTAWA, CANADA

With a foreword by
P. G. H. BOSWELL, D. Sc., F.R.S.

Professor Emeritus
Imperial College of Science and Technology, London

SECOND EDITION   1962

McGRAW-HILL BOOK COMPANY, INC.

New York   San Francisco   Toronto   London

GEOLOGY AND ENGINEERING

37059   THE MAPLE PRESS COMPANY, YORK, PA.

TO MY WIFE

GEOLOGY may be defined as that branch of natural science devoted to the study of the physical features of the earth, the composition and structure of the rocks composing it, the forces at work in altering it, and the record of the animals and plants that have lived on its lands and inhabited its seas.

CIVIL ENGINEERING was originally the counterpart of military engineering; its origins are thus rooted in the depths of antiquity. One of the first attempts to define its scope was embodied in that splendid phrase still found in the charter of the Institution of Civil Engineers—"the art of directing the great sources of power in Nature for the use and convenience of man." A more modern description of the art is that it includes the design and construction of all structures other than simple buildings, and the investigation, design, and construction of all systems of transportation, of natural power development, of water supply and sewage disposal, as well as the direction of natural forces for the use and convenience of man.

GEOLOGY AND CIVIL ENGINEERING. It is with the application of the science of geology to the art of civil engineering that this volume is concerned. To this end, a brief outline of the science precedes a review of the application of geological studies to the several main branches of civil engineering that involve geological problems. Appendixes bring the volume to a close by recording in convenient form reference information which may be useful to the civil engineer engaged in geological study.

It is hoped that, in addition to being of service to practicing engineers and geologists, this book will prove useful as a text for students. Instruction in geology, in the usual college course, generally precedes the student's introduction to civil engineering practice. The consequent inadequate appreciation of the relevant value of geology is unfortunate and can be obviated only if students are able, while they are studying pure geology, to see evidence of its applications in engineering work. This book is an attempt to provide such evidence in convenient form, not only as an aid to students, but also as a "casebook" to serve as a general guide to the application of geology in the practice of civil engineering.

ix

FOREWORD

WHEN THE first edition of this book was completed the author gave me the opportunity to provide a Foreword. On that occasion, influenced by experience with the geological side of engineering undertakings, I ventured to express strong support for the view that the proper background for a discussion of the services that geology could render to the engineer should be engineering rather than geological. Mr. Legget's activities, not only as author and university professor, but also as consultant and the first Director of Building Research for the Dominion of Canada, are some justification, I think, for my early contention.

It is to be expected that, with the added experience of the past twenty years, the author should find it necessary to rewrite much of the book, since engineering technique and geological knowledge have both advanced considerably. This is not the place to review that progress, but I should like to refer to one most important development, namely, the increased significance that has come to be attached to the presence and nature of the single abundant constituent of the earth's crust that exists mainly in the liquid state, to wit, water.

The quantity of water contained in particular rocks and also the properties of the water at various localities have a profound effect on the behavior of those rocks when they have to be shifted or subjected to other treatment; and the presence or absence of water in a region determines the extent to which any particular country possesses reserves of power and the ability to support a population against famine and thirst. In its frozen state, water gives rise to the problems of the permafrost areas. These areas are now being developed for human occupation, and the author's experience in their development has been extensive and peculiar.

Living in a period of climatic amelioration, as we now appear to be, we are able to witness the retreat of the polar ice sheets and of the upland glaciers of the continents. These changes are already bringing fresh problems, and if continued, they will have serious repercussions, since the engineer will be called upon to overcome the effects of the changing incidence of power production and of the water supplies essential for industry and domestic purposes. The possibility of the submergence of maritime areas, now becoming heavily industrialized and populated, under a rising sea level caused either suddenly by earthquake waves or gradually by the melting of the polar icecaps, will be ever present in the mind of the engineer with vision.

The growth of communities on the relatively low-lying areas bordering seas, estuaries, and lakes, where the foundations often consist of unconsolidated deposits of comparatively late geological age, has given impetus to the new branch of knowledge termed "soil mechanics" (and now included in geotechnics). Studies of the properties and behavior of such materials in the natural state and in the laboratory have been greatly extended during the past two or three decades. The author was early in the field to give his support: it is therefore appropriate that he should direct special attention to them in the following pages. The subject is one of considerable complexity, however, for it involves branches of science concerned with states of matter and flow phenomena which have not yet been adequately investigated.

While these new techniques were being developed, engineering undertakings of more familiar kinds were increasing rapidly in size and number, helped by improved methods of geological and geophysical exploration. The scale of impounding schemes, tunneling, building, reclamation, and recharging of strata has actually been limited only by nongeological factors, such as strength of materials, time available, and cost.

In these days of rapid change the cooperation between the engineer and the scientist tends to become ever closer, and we should do well to maintain a clear notion of their respective roles. This has already been stated so succinctly by one of our leading authorities in the geotechnical field, Dr. H. Q. Golder, that we cannot do better than use his words: "The scientist is interested in the right answer, the engineer in the best answer now."

P. G. H. Boswell*

---

* Professor Boswell died on December 22, 1960 while this book was in preparation.

PREFACE

THE PROGRESS made in the practice of civil engineering and in the development of the science of geology in the two decades since the first edition of this book was published has been steady but not spectacular except, perhaps, in the scope of some of the more recent achievements of civil engineers. Within the same period, however, soil mechanics has achieved mature status as a well-accepted part of civil engineering, leaving far behind its fledgling position in 1939. Partly because of this significant development, but probably for other reasons too, geology is now more generally accepted by civil engineers and contractors as closely related to the design and construction of civil engineering projects than it was before the Second World War.

There still remains, however, much to be done before geology is fully appreciated in the practice of civil engineering, as construction problems and occasional failures make very clear. Although this edition represents an almost complete rewriting and rearrangement of the original text, essential features have been retained. Background material on geology is presented as a prelude to a treatment of subsurface exploration; separate chapters on each of the main branches of the work of the civil engineer then follow. Case histories are used to illustrate principles whenever possible; many of them are new, but many that appeared in the first edition are included. The basic principles of sound design and safe construction change not with the years; the value of many notable examples is timeless. With one of my more eloquent friends, I agree fully that "newness is not a criterion for truth."

It is desirable to emphasize that this book deals only with the interrelationship of geology and civil engineering. Apart from the simple outlines in Chaps. 2, 3, and 7, the book does not deal with the principles or methods of geology. Discussion of engineering problems and works stops when questions relating to ground conditions have been answered. There will therefore be found no "formulas" in these pages, although their absence from the first edition was decried by one critic. The practice of civil engineering in the field is an art, requiring experience and sound judgement for the solution of every problem of ground conditions, no two of which are ever exactly alike. It is to this field of interest that attention is directed, a field that will continue to pose problems—despite all advances in structural design—as long as civil engineering works are undertaken. Even spaceships to the moon (to mention only one popular proposal) will require the very best in foundation design and construction for their launching bases before they can start on their starry journeys.

The claims of official duties, following the imperative of war, have been responsible for the regrettable delay in the appearance of this long-needed revision of the original book. These same duties, however, have necessitated travel to far places. They have required visits to many engineering works, some of great geological interest, and of more importance, they have required meetings with many persons expert in this special field of interest, from all of whom I have learned something of value. It would be almost impossible for me to list all the engineers, geologists, librarians, and public officials who have so generously answered my queries and allowed me to use the valuable information that they have provided. In the case of photographs, acknowledgment of their source is made in the text. To everyone who has given me assistance and information, I have attempted to express my thanks by personal communication, but I hope that this general and public acknowledgment of my gratitude will be accepted by all who have so helped me as if it applied individually to each of them.

Despite the care with which this information has been used and with which all references have been checked, it is probable that some errors still remain in the finished work. If those who note mistakes and omissions in the text will advise me of them, I shall be grateful, as I shall be also for any suggestions for amendments or improvements to what is here presented. Should any information have been used without due acknowledgment or without application for permission to the proper authorities, I ask those concerned to accept my apologies and my assurance that any such error has been made unwittingly.

Many have helped me with the actual preparation of this revision by favoring me with constructively critical comments on the first edition, answering my queries, and even reading parts of the text as it was under preparation. To all I am grateful, as I have attempted in all cases to say personally. To Mrs. A. Lapp and her associates and to Miss J. Sandys and Mrs. P. E. Neal I am greatly indebted for the preparation of the finished typescript.

Some of the senior friends who encouraged me with the writing of the original book, notably Dr. Charles P. Berkey, have passed on in the years between. It is a privilege again to be able to record my gratitude to Dr. J. J. O'Neill for his help when we were both residents of Montreal and to be able to repeat, in only slightly amended form, the closing words of the original preface

My lifelong interest in geology was naturally aroused by my first instruction in it, instruction that enabled even an impatient engineering student to realize that this branch of pure science was intimately associated with the practical work of his chosen profession. For that initial inspiration, for continued encouragement in all my ensuing studies of the subject, for the original suggestion that this book should be written, and for sage advice regarding this revision, I am indebted to Prof. P. G. H. Boswell, F.R.S., who has done me the honor of examining much of the revised book in manuscript form. To Professor Boswell I owe a debt that I cannot easily repay, save only by work in the field described in this book, a field in which I still hope long to be an inquiring student.

Robert F. Legget

CONTENTS

xvii

Chapter 1

THE CIVIL ENGINEER AND GEOLOGY

Geology stands to [civil] engineering in the same relation as faith to works. . . . The success or failure of an undertaking depends largely upon the physical conditions which fall within the province of geology, and the "works" of the engineer should be based on the "faith" of the geologist.

Boyd Dawkins, F.R.S.[1.1]

EVERY BRANCH of civil engineering has some contact with the surface of the earth, since the works designed by the civil engineer are supported by or located in some part of the earth's crust. The practice of civil engineering includes the design of these works and the control and direction of their construction. Geology is the name given to that wide sphere of scientific inquiry which studies the composition and arrangement of the earth's crust. This book is concerned with the application of the results of this scientific study to the art and practice of the civil engineer.

The relation of the science to the art is at once so obvious and so intimate that general comment upon it might appear to be uncalled for; unfortunately, this is not the case. It may well be that the very intimacy of the relationship has been the main reason for its frequent neglect. Whatever the cause, the fact remains that, for a considerable period, civil engineering work was carried on in all countries with little conscious reference to geology or to geologists.

In the early years of modern engineering, at the start of the nineteenth century, when engineering had not become the highly specialized practice known today, many civil engineers were also active geologists. William Smith is the outstanding example of these pioneers. Robert Stephenson combined geological study with his early work in railway construction, as is related in Chap. 8; and other well-known figures in the annals of engineering history were distinguished in both spheres.

There is a steadily growing appreciation of the vital importance of the science to those who practice the art. Geology is now a usual feature in

[1.1] All references thus noted will be found listed in Appendix D, under chapter numbers.

1

courses of training for civil engineers; current civil engineering papers contain frequent references to the geological features of the sites of works described; and the generally accepted scientific approach to soil studies (soil mechanics) provides a common meeting ground for civil engineer and geologist which has already done much to foster their co-operation. The divorce of the science from the art persisted for so long, however, that their complete correlation may not be realized for many years; some thought may therefore be given to general aspects of the contacts between them before the subject is considered in detail. Thus, the reader may have at the outset a clear idea of their fundamental relationship.

1.2. The Science and the Art. Frequently in the past, geological considerations have featured prominently in the study and discussion of failures of civil engineering works; in fact, to some engineers geology may still be thought of as merely a scientific aid to the correct determination of the reasons for some of the major troubles that develop during or subsequent to construction operations. Valuable as is the assistance rendered by geologists and by the study of geological features in such "post-mortem" considerations, the very fact that geological features may have had something to do with the failures seems to suggest, with abundant clarity, that the best time to consult a geologist or to study geological features is before construction begins. In this way, the science can serve the art in a constructive rather than merely a pathological manner. It will later be seen, as such applications of geology are considered in some detail, that not only can this constructive service of the science prevent possible future troubles but it can also suggest new solutions to engineering problems and often reveal information of utility and economic value even in preliminary work.

The more obvious effects of geological features on major civil engineering works may be seen in the underground railway services in London and New York. In London, owing to the fact that the city is built on a great basin of unconsolidated material including the well-known London clay, tube railways—located far below ground level, easily and economically excavated in the clay—have provided an admirable solution to one part of the city's transportation problems. In New York, on the other hand, since the surface of Manhattan Island on which the city is located is underlain to a considerable extent by Manhattan schist, underground railways had to be constructed in carefully excavated rock cuttings just below surface level, as the innocent visitor to that great city learns if he happens to stand on a ventilation grating when a train passes in the subway below.

Many similar instances of the profound effect of local geological characteristics upon major civil engineering works could be cited, but all would serve to emphasize the same point—how closely the science and the art are related and how dependent civil engineering work generally must be upon geology. It is, indeed, no mere figure of speech to say that the science of geology stands in relation to the art of the civil engineer in just the same way as do physics, chemistry, and mathematics. The importance of these sciences to the civil engineer is never questioned; they are always considered the necessary and inevitable background to civil engineering training. It would be inconceivable for any engineer worthy of the name to be unfamiliar with the chemistry of simple materials. So should it be in respect to the nature of the materials on which or in which the civil engineer is to construct his works.

There is a minor point of difference to be noted when thinking of the relation of geology and of parallel sciences to civil engineering. The latter sciences are utilized directly by the engineer himself, since mathematical and physical methods are important in many branches of design work. Geology, however, renders a service to civil engineering in that the findings of the pure science are applied to the specific problems of the engineer. In the case of construction problems, for example, it is the task of the geologist to state the probable difficulties, and that of the engineer to overcome them; in the case of materials of construction, it is for the geologist to say where they may be found, and for the engineer to obtain them and put them to use.

This is a minor point of difference, but it leads to another thought of some importance. The geologist has the whole of the earth's surface as his laboratory, and in every locality he encounters purely local problems that may not be duplicated elsewhere. Thus, every application of the results of the science, or its methods, to engineering work will likewise be in some respect unique. In this sense, too, there is a difference between the relationships with civil engineering of geology and of associated sciences. Although local characteristics may vary, the fundamental geological principles applying to them do not. And these guiding principles constitute the basis of geological study—study that will, it is hoped, be seen as an essential part of the training of every civil engineer.

1.3. Training in Geology. As most civil engineers who enter upon their professional careers do so by way of a university or technical college education or the equivalent course of study leading to the examinations of a national professional society, considerations of the training of civil engineering students in geology may for convenience be confined to university courses. It will be noted that reference is made to training in geology and not to training in civil engineering geology or some such suggested course. There is no special brand of geology applicable to civil engineering. There is, however, a special course of study possible and desirable in considering the application of fundamental geological principles and methods to civil engineering problems, and this must be complementary to the study of geology, as such. This important distinction is emphasized in the title of this book; a study of the curricula of many universities and colleges will show that it is generally appreciated in university work.

The training in geology necessary for civil engineers must obviously be general; it must enable students to obtain a good grasp of the nature of the subject and of the character and interrelation of various branches of geology. Thereafter, in the usual college course, time does not permit detailed study of all branches of the subject, nor does such study seem desirable. Attention has to be concentrated on those branches of geology the applications of which are of special importance in civil engineering practice. These include physical geology, structural geology, and petrology. Study of geological maps and sections can be a valuable laboratory aid to the first two of these branches, and examination of rock slides in the petrological microscope is an essential complement to lectures on petrology. The actual making of rock sections is something that the student will never have to do in engineering practice and need only be touched upon in laboratory work. Similarly, it does not seem advisable that civil engineering students should spend much time on the examination of fossils, although an introduction to practical paleontological work will be a valuable stimulus to their interest in this branch of study.

Of fundamental importance in all training is experience in the field. It may be said with propriety that no course in geology for civil engineers can be regarded as in any sense complete without a reasonable period of time spent on geological survey work. Local conditions will dictate how field work must be arranged; but a continuous period (of 1 or 2 weeks) spent in a suitable locality will usually be more effective than any number of short periods fitted into a regular schedule. Unfortunately, local circumstances usually conspire to make it impossible to combine a geological field camp with the usual topographical survey camp; a combination of the two would be an ideal arrangement.

It has been suggested that the second part of geological training for civil engineers should be an introduction to the study of the applications of what has been learned of the science to the problems encountered in actual engineering practice. The word "introduction" is used advisedly, as this note refers specifically to college work. The average student will have had little experience on outside civil engineering work and will therefore have much to learn with regard to civil engineering construction. If, however, he can start to do this in association with an introductory study of the applications of geology to such work, a double purpose will be served to great advantage. The usual college course does not permit the student to devote much time to practical subjects, but courses on foundations and construction methods present opportunities for instruction of the kind indicated.

Instruction in the classroom is but a cursory introduction to what is a lifelong study for the majority of civil engineers; considerations of the applications of geology to their work are either consciously or unconsciously an essential part of that basic experience which is the most prized possession of all members of the profession. How much easier this experience can be gained if the engineer possesses at the outset a fundamental knowledge of geology will be evident from what has already been written. Without a correct attitude of mind toward geology, no civil engineer will benefit from instruction in the science, no matter how well it may be presented. Indeed, the development of this mental attitude should be the principal aim of those charged with instructing engineering students in geology. The task is no easy one, because the students will not have had any opportunity to learn to appreciate the vital importance of geological features in actual construction work.

Fortunately, appreciation of the science as an important aid to the civil engineer is steadily becoming more general. Perhaps the best indication of this change is to be found in the papers describing civil engineering work presented to engineering societies. If one examines papers which were presented some decades ago, one will find little mention of the geology of the site of the works described. But if one studies papers of recent years, one will find few that do not include at least a brief reference to the local geology affecting the works described. Frequently, entire sections of engineering papers are devoted to geological considerations; many examples of this kind will be mentioned in later chapters. This development is of real significance and is encouraging, for the presentation of any description of an engineering structure without some reference to foundation-bed conditions or other corresponding geological data is equivalent to presenting a paper on a bridge without mentioning the loading used in design or without referring to the materials used in construction.

1.4. Practical Experience. An appreciation of geological features and, particularly, of the characteristics of the materials that make up the earth's crust is not acquired solely by training in geology. Many engineers, especially those who have spent much time on construction, possess this appreciation unconsciously as a product of their wide practical experience. There have been many engineers, and there probably still are some, who have never troubled to find out what geology is; yet they know instinctively many of the matters herein discussed solely in geological terms. This point is emphasized, since the dividing line between what may truly be called practical experience and a cultivated appreciation of geological features is quite indeterminate. For the sake of convenience, references throughout this book are confined to this trained attitude of mind toward geological features, but it is always to be understood that the practical experience of engineers unversed in geology is included, although not stated, in such references.

This knowledge derived from wide experience is not so common as some people suggest. It is almost intuitive in nature and certainly it is much more than merely factual knowledge derived from long observation. Some men could not acquire such intuitive judgment even after a lifetime of outside experience; others acquire it easily and early in their lives. The suggestion may therefore be advanced that all so-called "practical experience" may not prove to be this sound intuitive judgment. Sometimes the so-called "practical man" is the one who practices the theories of 30 years ago.

Whether the civil engineer gains an appreciation of geology by training or by intuition, it can serve him well in the field. Thus equipped, he will be able to perceive the beauties of scenery more fully; and in his topographical work, he will understand the reason for the many special features that he is called upon to survey. He will be able to direct his exploratory work more accurately, since he will know, at least to some degree, what lies hidden beneath the surface of the ground. And on construction, every step taken in connection with excavation and foundation work will have a new and added significance for the resident engineer who has had his interest awakened to all that geology can mean in his supervision of such work.

1.5. Employment of Specialists. One of the most important results of a desirable attitude toward geology should be that civil engineers will know when to call for the services of an expert geologist. As a general rule, engineers cannot hope to be more than amateur geologists, familiar with the science and its methods, appreciative of its value, but not fully qualified to carry out detailed investigations either in the field or in the laboratory. On small jobs and in routine civil engineering work, this general familiarity with the science will enable the engineer to tackle practically every problem that he faces. On large jobs, however, and for special work, specialists must be consulted, and a realization of the necessity of consultation can be taken as one of the hallmarks of a true engineer, rather than the reverse, as is sometimes erroneously believed.

On occasion, the engineer may meet with opposition when he suggests consulting a geologist. The leading argument against such a course is that similar works have been carried out successfully in the past without the special aid and additional expense of a geologist. So, it is asked, why not carry on the work without this extra assistance? Superficially, such an argument may appear to be difficult to refute unless thought is given to the parallel case of fire insurance premiums. There was a time when building owners never thought of paying out extra money for fire insurance, and owners then continued to live and prosper. But how many today would neglect to take advantage of fire coverage, despite the adequacy of modern fire-fighting equipment?

Thus may the argument be answered in economic terms. Of far more importance, however, and particularly for the engineer's own satisfaction, is the impressive record of services already rendered to the art by geologists, known and unknown, a record to which the examples cited in this book pay some tribute. How many disasters have been prevented through the use of geological advice can never be estimated, but the record of failures that have occurred when such advice has not been taken is at least an indication of what this constructive contribution has meant to civil engineering achievement. The important work of Dr. C. P. Berkey and his co-workers in connection with the Catskill Aqueduct for the water supply of the city of New York is a telling example. The geological investigations associated with the tunnels that now exist under the Mersey River at Liverpool, England, and particularly the work of Prof. P. G. H. Boswell in connection with the great vehicular tunnel offer similar evidence. The Hoover Dam on the Colorado River in the United States and many other successful dams testify silently to the value of the assistance that civil engineers have obtained from specialist geological advisers.

These few names could be extended to fill many pages, but the examples of cooperative work quoted throughout this book will be even more impressive. Usually, geologists are called upon to assist on engineering work in the capacity of consultants; the practice of having a geologist as a member of the official board of consultants so often followed in North American work is a most satisfactory arrangement. During the years immediately prior to the Second World War a few major engineering organizations added geological units to their permanent staffs. Experience during the war years, in both civilian and military engineering work, acted as a catalyst in this regard, as in many others, so that today almost all large civil engineering organizations have their own engineering geological staffs. Notable examples in North America, and pioneers in this practice, are the United States Corps of Engineers, the Tennessee Valley Authority, and the U.S. Bureau of Reclamation, while the United States Geological Survey has its own Engineering Geology Branch with headquarters in Denver, Colo. This practice is widespread tday, but the organization noted not only were early in the field but have, through the work and the publications of their staffs, made significant contributions from which the entire engineering profession benefits. On smaller works, the individual consulting geologist can give similarly useful service. Geological surveys in all countries are willing to assist when staff is available and conditions appropriate. And the geological departments of universities are often willing and able to assist through the service of their specialist staff members.

1.6. Geologists and Civil Engineering Work. This book is not intended primarily for the use of geologists, and it would be invidious for the author to comment upon the attitude of geologists toward civil engineering work. It may, however, be useful for engineers to note that geologists welcome the opportunity to cooperate on civil engineering work; their only regret is that the opportunity does not occur more frequently. This suggestion is confirmed by the contributions made by geologists to the discussion of engineering papers, such as the following statement by Dr. T. Robinson of the Geological Survey of Great Britain during discussion of a paper at the Institution of Civil Engineers, London:[1,2] "The records of the Geological Survey showed conclusively that closer co-operation between the geologist and the engineer would be greatly to the advantage of both, and it was a pity that there was no very direct way in which geologists could be kept informed of the progress of important excavations."

Practically the only way geologists can learn of new exposures made by civil engineering operations is through the engineer in charge of the work. May it be urged, therefore, that, whenever possible, civil engineers advise the director of the appropriate geological survey and the head of the geological department of the nearest university of all excavation work of interest under their charge, so that geologists may at least have an opportunity to see the exposures before they are covered up. This courtesy demands little of the engineer, but it may lead to scientific information of great value.

When geologists are called in to advise upon civil engineering work, they will have to act in conjunction with the engineers responsible for the work. Thus arises the need for cooperation between the civil engineer and the geologist, the practical builder and the man of science. Their cooperation may lead to a valuable partnership, and it often proves to be of considerable personal pleasure. This partnership is, in some ways, a union of opposites, for even the approach of the two to the same problem is psychologically different. The geologist analyzes conditions as he finds them; the engineer considers how he can change existing conditions so that they will suit his plans. From his analysis, the geologist cites problems that exist and suggests troubles that may arise; the engineer has to solve the problems and overcome the troubles. The final responsibility for the decisions involved must always rest with the engineer; but in coming to his conclusions, he will be guided by and will probably rely upon the factual information given to him by the geologist.

This joint work, therefore, calls for a fine degree of real cooperation. The geologist has to remember that what the engineer wants is a clear picture of the geological conditions related to his work, presented to him as concisely as possible and with their practical utilization in view. On the other hand, the engineer must remember that the geologist *is* a geologist, not an engineer, and he need not expect to receive from the geologist the kind of report that he would receive from another engineer. In many cases, the most effective results can be achieved if the engineer is able to give to the geologist, at the outset of his work, a list of specific questions which he hopes to have answered. The questions may relate to geological conditions, to the necessity for and the location of further exploratory works, such as boreholes and test pits, and to similar matters. The engineer should also be willing to cooperate with the geologist by allowing him to pursue, within reasonable limits, any aspects of purely scientific interest that may develop in the course of the main task.

1.7. The Pattern of Civil Engineering. When a new project comes up for consideration, the civil engineer will initially require some firsthand knowledge of the locality in which the work is to be carried out; preliminary investigations and studies will then be made; and when these are approved, complete contract drawings and specifications will be prepared. When financial arrangements are made, tenders will be called for, a contract awarded, and construction begun; when the project is complete, it must be periodically inspected and maintained in good order. Brief comment on the application of geology to each of these main divisions of civil engineering procedure will be made.

The civil engineer will generally obtain information about an area in which work is to be carried out by visiting the area, even if only for a hurried tour of inspection, and by studying descriptive literature on the district. If geological reports are included in the literature selected, and if the topography of the area is studied with due regard to the significance of the local geology, then the engineer will get a more vivid and more accurate picture of the district than if the geology were neglected. Since an elementary study of the geology of an area will demonstrate its relation to local scenery, a civil engineer trained in geology can visualize, after the necessary inspection and investigation, the general structure of the ground with which he is concerned and the origin of leading features of the local topography that will be of importance in his work.

As an example of broad concepts of local geology, the following extract may be quoted from a lecture by Dr. H. E. Gruner of Switzerland on "Hydro-electric Power Development on the Rhine":[1.3]

In the stretch which concerns us, the Rhine cuts through the jurassic system, the tertiary system, the lower layers of trias, the gneiss massive of the Black Forest and some layers of the permian system. The power-plants are founded on each of the different layers, and the results have proved favourable in every case. Of still greater importance in their effect on the longitudinal profile of the Rhine, and thus upon its character as a source of energy, are the historical occurrences during its origin. Even in pre-glacial times the Rhine flowed through the same valley as it does today, but owing to the enormous quantities of gravel that the glaciers deposited during their retreat, the Rhine lost its old course and was partially forced into a new bed. Whilst scouring out its new bed it eroded the underlying rock, which it took more time to carry off than the gravel. This produced the different falls and rapids as we find them at Neuhausen, Reckingen, Schwaderloch, Laufenburg, Ryburg-Schworstadt, Rheinfelden and on the Kembsersill. . . . The soundings and geological studies that were needed for the different power-plants, enabled us to determine the old river-bed for almost its entire length. These pre-glacial river-beds of the Rhine are technically important in many ways; they always carry water and are thus well suited for water-supply works. During the construction of power-plants they may also become the source of disagreeable surprises if they are not thoroughly examined at first.

This descriptive note gives a general picture of the geology of the sites of the plants described by Dr. Gruner; it could not, of course, have been written without a study of relevant geological reports. Although it is general, it indicates some of the geological problems that had to be faced during the construction of the Rhine water-power plants, and it suggests the kind of preliminary exploratory investigations that had to be undertaken.

Preliminary studies may be made in more detail if civil engineering work is to cover a large area. General reconnaissance surveys will probably have to be made, and general topographic maps either prepared or checked. Simultaneously with this work, geological reconnaissance can always be carried out with advantage; the local geology can be studied in more detail and correlated (although still in a general way) with engineering requirements. It is not often that civil engineers will be called upon to undertake extensive work of this nature. When the need does arise, special organizations are usually recruited to undertake the work. The subject will not be discussed here in detail, but the reader may wish to glance at a statement of the results of one important geological reconnaissance which covered an area of 40,000 sq miles—that under the control of the TVA in the United States. Although prepared and first published a quarter of a century ago, at the outset of the great TVA construction program, Table 1.1 remains one of the best and most concise statements of its kind known to the writer. It shows clearly the character of the various rock types in the valley of the Tennessee River, and illustrates, if only by inference, the interrelation of topography and geology. The suggestions made in the table will be fully confirmed by examples quoted later in this volume from the engineering and construction work of the TVA.

Having obtained a general idea of the district in which his work is to be done, the civil engineer will next proceed with his preliminary plans and estimates. Gradually these will be evaluated and discussed, until finally an accepted scheme or design is evolved which can then be prepared in detail. All this work can properly be carried out only if the engineer possesses an adequate and detailed knowledge of the ground in which his work is to be located and of the natural materials available at or near the site. This essential information will be obtained by means of detailed geological field work and by exploratory investigations such as boreholes and test pits. The preliminary exploratory work is so important that it is considered in detail in Chap. 6; it is mentioned here in order to show the logical association of geology with this leading phase of civil engineering work.

1.8. Contract Plans and Specifications. The final design of the civil engineer will usually be incorporated in a set of contract plans and specifications, on the basis of which tenders for performing the work involved will be called for from contractors. In those projects which are carried out by direct administration, instead of by contract, a complete set of drawings equivalent to a set of contract plans will still be necessary, and the equivalent of a contract specification will be needed for the guidance of the engineers in actual charge of construction operations.

The preparation of these documents marks a definite change in the engineer's work and in his responsibilities. When issued to a successful tenderer and made the basis of a formal contract, they become legal documents, entitling the contractor to certain rights and taking control of construction operations to some extent out of the hands of the owner and of the engineer as his representative. If, therefore, the application of geology can in any way assist in making the preparation of contract documents more effective and less open to question, the science will be rendering particularly valuable service. It would appear probable, from considerations already advanced, that there are several ways in which assistance can thus be rendered.

It has already been mentioned that the chief aim of preliminary exploratory work and associated geological studies is to provide accurate information about subsurface conditions at the site of the proposed work and about the availability of suitable construction materials in the vicinity. The subsurface conditions will affect the design made by the engineer and also the construction methods adopted by the contractor; the availability of materials may have some bearing on the design adopted, especially from the economic angle, and will have an appreciable effect on construction planning. It is clear, therefore, that the engineer should include in his contract documents as much information regarding the site and the available materials as is possible.

On the contract plans, the engineer can do this by giving full details of the records of boreholes, test pits, and other subsurface explorations. These should be given not only in section but also in a general plan that shows their correlation with the location of the work to be constructed. It is difficult to imagine a set of civil engineering contract drawings (apart from those showing only superstructures) on which the presence of borehole or similar records is not essential; only with these records on hand can the contractor take advantage, if he is so minded, of all the information relative to his work that the engineer has available. In many

Table 1.1. Engineering Geology of the Four TVA Subregions

Age of rocks	Pre-Cambrian and metamorphic (the oldest rocks)	Cambrian, Ordovician, Silurian, Devonian, and Mississippian	Pennsylvanian (Coal Measures)	Cretaceous, Tertiary, Recent (the youngest formations)
Prevailing rocks.........	Gneisses, schists, granites, and other igneous rocks, chiefly slate, quartzite, marble in outliers and along west flanks of mountains	Shales, limestones, sandstones	Shales, sandstones, conglomerates	Sand, gravel, clay, chalk
Geologic structure........	Usually steep dips to southeast. Faulting common but not noticeable	East of Coal Measures close folds, chief dip southeast. Faults numerous and often large. West of Coal Measures dips flat, normally southwest; faults rare and small throw	Dips flat except along east edge of coal plateaus where steep dips and faulting are common	Dips low to west or southwest. Faults rare and unimportant from engineering standpoint
Stone supplies...........	Ample supplies of granite, diabase, gneiss, and slate; local supplies of marble. Sand and gravel in local stream deposits only	Extensive supplies of limestone; widespread though less abundant supplies of sandstone. Chert gravels extensive west of coal fields	Sandstones abundant and locally furnish attractive building stone	No real stone in whole area. Very extensive sand and gravel beds in several formations
Clay supplies............	Common clays rather scarce; kaolins common in certain areas	Brick and tile clays common in river flats; good shales available for similar products	Brick clays rare. Fire clays common in all coal fields	Extensive clay deposits for all types of clay products
Cement supplies..........	No cement material. No lime material except in the marble regions. No gypsum or slag	Extensive supplies of limestone, slag, etc., for portland and slag cement. Lime abundant. Gypsum extensive in southwest Virginia	No lime, cement, or plaster materials anywhere	Lime supplies scarce except clayey chalks in Cretaceous. No gypsum or slag

Surface waters.............	Runoff rapid. Waters soft, usually fairly pure	Runoff is moderately rapid. More so than the slopes indicate, because the surface is tight. Waters usually very hard and rarely pure	Runoff rapid. Waters soft, usually moderately pure	Waters soft, rarely pure. Runoff usually slow
River topography.........	Narrow gorges with frequent falls and rapids. Occasional small flats with relatively narrow flood plains. Gradient high	Streams mostly bordered by low flood plains, increasing in area from north to south and west. Gradient moderate at north; low at southwest	Narrow gorges with frequent falls and rapids. Flood plains and flats very rare and narrow. Gradient high	Streams bordered by low and very broad flood plains. Gradient very low
Caves and sinks...........	No sinks and no real caves	Caves and sinks common and extensive in several of the purer limestone formations	None originating in Coal Measures, but solution of underlying limestone causes rare sinks	No caves or sinks
Underground waters......	Underground supply limited; localized along cleavage planes or other fracture surfaces	Underground supply extensive but often contaminated. Occurs in solution channels in the limestones and in sandstones	Underground supply limited by smallness of gathering area; in sandstones and usually pure	Extensive underground supplies in several sand formations
Soil erosion..............	Erosion slight except in the deeply weathered granite areas and on the Piedmont	Erosion extensive in most pure limestone areas. Slight in shales and nonexistent in sandstones	Erosion slight	Extensive gullies form rapidly in many clay and sand areas

SOURCE: Reproduced, by permission, from E. C. ECKEL, Engineering Geology and Mineral Resources of the T.V.A. Region, Knoxville, Tennessee, T.V.A. Geol. Bull. 1, 1934.

cases, and when possible, it will be advisable to show accurately the nature of the geological structure adjacent to foundations, instead of the usual pictorial representation of rock or unconsolidated material. In certain special cases, such as tunnel work, it will be desirable to show on the profile drawings full details of the geological formations that are anticipated along the line of the work to be built.

The same criterion should be aimed at in the preparation of civil engineering specifications. As a general rule, the opportunity to use geological information in specifications will arise in one or more of four ways:

1. In the provision for possible alterations in design due to variations encountered in subsurface conditions

2. In the provision of information relating to available materials of construction

3. In the clauses relating to methods of construction to be adopted

4. In reference to the measurement and payment for excavation

The first of these divisions is closely related to preliminary exploratory work and so may conveniently be considered in Chap. 6. The second calls for the clearest and fullest explanation of all the facts known relative to the materials available; it will also be referred to in later chapters. The third touches upon a most important matter but one that is generally and advisedly left to the selection of the contractor, usually with such a qualification as this: "The contractors are to submit to the engineers a statement with drawings showing how they propose to carry out the works, but any approval of the engineers is not to relieve the contractors of any liability that devolves upon them under this contract."

This provision, as indeed the whole essence of a civil engineering contract, makes the engineer morally responsible for giving the contractor all available information which may assist him in his construction planning and methods; at the same time, it leaves the contractor free to apply his accumulated experience and special skills to the most efficient prosecution of the work in view. Information included in the specifications, in addition to that shown on the contract drawings, will assist in fulfilling this obligation: therefore, the fullest use should be made of the opportunity thus provided.

1.9. Earth and Rock Excavation. The fourth division, relating to excavation, is of such importance that it will be considered in some detail. Contracts for civil engineering projects are designed in such a way that the work being carried out will be to the satisfaction of the owner, will fulfill the requirements of the engineer, and will provide due safeguards for the contractor. General conditions define the scope of the contract; specifications and contract drawings detail the design of the engineer; and quantities and unit prices (in the usual contract) define the extent of the contractor's operations and his remuneration. Great care is always exercised in preparing these contract documents in order to avoid disputes, but success is not always achieved, as the record of court cases regarding engineering contracts makes clear. It is probably safe to say that no one feature of civil engineering contracts has been responsible for more disputes than the classification of material to be excavated as "earth" or "rock" and consequent payment for this part of the work performed. As unit prices for rock excavation may be ten or twelve times as much as the corresponding unit prices for earth excavation, the possibility of disputes arising from questionable classification of material removed will be obvious.

The excavation of solid rock which has to be drilled and blasted is rarely questioned in this connection; similarly, the removal of loose sand and gravel or soft clay is rarely discussed. But in between these two extremes there may be materials that cannot easily be classified as either earth or rock unless a reference basis was adopted before the contract operations began. Such doubtful material is often termed "hardpan." The use of this word should always be avoided by engineers, if they wish to obviate trouble. It is essentially a popular term and is sometimes applied to special local gravel deposits whose unusual hardness has been caused by partial cementing of the rock fragments. Hardpan has been the subject of many lawsuits, mainly because the best definition one can give to it is that it is material that proved harder to excavate than the contractor had anticipated. It is a name not generally recognized in geological nomenclature, and there are no satisfactory definitions of it in engineering literature. Boulder clay is often described as hardpan, but in this case—as in practically all others—the material can be more accurately described as compact gravel, sand, and clay with boulders (or a modification of this). If material of this kind has to be removed during construction operations, an indication of the methods necessary for its excavation should accompany the description.

It might be thought that this is a situation in which a direct application of geological terminology would be of assistance. Unfortunately, this is not true, although an appreciation of the geological character of the materials involved will be of great assistance to the engineer. In geology, the term "rock" is used to describe all the solid constituent materials of the earth's crust (as explained in Chap. 2); thus, before going any further into geological terminology, one can see that it is inapplicable. As a general rule in excavation work, the engineer is not interested in the type of rock that has to be excavated—and the contractor less so—but only in its character in relation to excavation methods. Engineers have on occasion attempted to utilize geological information available to them in describing materials to be excavated, sometimes with unfortunate results. An example of this is the use of the term *cemented Triassic formation* in connection with an important contract for the construction of 6,000 ft of the outfall of the Passaic Valley Sewer in New York Harbor. This term was said to be a good description of glacial drift, but it was held by the courts to be misleading, as the contractor encountered varieties of sand and clay that were not cemented; these led to construction troubles which finally became the subject of legal action.[1.4]

Thus, the use of geological terms in connection with excavation work may not be helpful, and the detailed divisions of the main geological rock types sometimes suggested in this connection need not therefore be considered. How, then, may the problem be resolved? The following suggestions may point to a satisfactory solution:

1. Prior to the completion of contract plans, a careful study should be made—by means of boreholes, etc.—of all material to be excavated.

2. If any material intermediate between loose soils and compact rocks is discovered, special tests should be conducted to discover its character in so far as excavation is concerned. (This can be done in connection with test boring by an experienced crew.) Special care should always be taken to investigate the effect of water upon such material, since frequently, compact soil mixtures may be quite hard when dry but will disintegrate in the presence of water.

3. In the specifications, the words used to define different classes of excavation should be rigidly stated in terms of the methods to be used to excavate the material.

4. These engineering definitions should, if possible, be correlated with the geological descriptions of the materials to be encountered. The geological descriptions should be written in the correct terminology which was used in connection with the test-boring results; no indefinite and questionable terms like "hardpan" should ever be included.

5. The designations used for describing the material to be excavated should be as few and as simple as possible, e.g.:

Hard-rock excavation (excavation of granite and limestone which has to be drilled and blasted)
Loose-rock excavation (excavation of blocky limestone which does not require blasting but which cannot be removed by hand shovels or picks)
Soft-rock and earth excavation (excavation of disintegrated granite, clay, sand, and gravel which can be handled with shovels and similar tools)

It may finally be noted that throughout the rest of this book, the term "soil" will refer to unconsolidated natural materials, and the term "rock" will refer to solid bedrock, either in place or excavated.

1.10. Construction Operations. Every cubic yard of excavation that is removed during construction, every unusual loading that is applied to a natural foundation bed, every pile that is driven into the ground—in fact, every operation in construction in which the existing condition of the earth's crust is affected—is associated with geological features of some kind. Preliminary investigations of the relevant geology should therefore be of considerable value not only to the resident engineer on construction work but also to the contractor who is undertaking the work. Throughout this book, most of the examples mentioned will confirm in one way or another the vital importance to contractors of advance geological information.

The geological information available at the beginning of a job can be fully effective, however, only if it is constantly compared with actual geological conditions as they are revealed during the progress of construction. It is essential, therefore, on all civil engineering construction work that a regular and constant watch be kept on geological formations as they are revealed and that an adequate and complete record of leading geological features be kept in addition to the usual construction progress records. This can easily be done if one of the engineers on the job has been trained in geological field work; in some cases, geological training has been made a prerequisite for appointment to a resident engineer's staff.

Geological information obtained as construction progresses has a threefold value. In the first place, it acts as a check on the assumptions made with regard to geological conditions in the preparations of the final designs for the works being constructed; thus, any variation from these assumed conditions can usually be incorporated into the design before it is too late. In the second place, the revelation of the actual geology of the working site enables the contractor to keep check on the suitability and efficacy of his construction plans and plant. Finally, if the geological progress record is kept in a satisfactory manner, it may prove of inestimable value at some future time if further work has to be carried out at the same location.

Brief reference may be made to the last point, and mention made of a significant confirmation in connection with some cement grouting work carried out in parts of the famous Severn Tunnel in the southwest of England. This tunnel, which carries a main line of what used to be the Great Western Railway (now the Western Region of British Railways) under the river Severn, was started in 1873 and completed only after a fight against tremendous difficulties by the contractor, T. A. Walker. Mr. Walker kept a complete geological record throughout the construction of the tunnel, which pierces the Trias and Coal Measures of England; the rocks encountered varied from marl and shale to limestone and sandstone.[1.5] The existence of this valuable and complete record assisted the engineering authorities of the railway company almost 60 years later when they wished to undertake the extensive cementation program.[1.6] On the other hand, many examples could be given of the trouble and expense caused by the lack of comparable records for other works. A well-known tunnel in the United States, for example, had to be resurveyed, within 7 years of its completion, in connection with the installation of a concrete lining, since no records were then available of the timber sets used or of the final tunnel cross sections.

Finally, all civil engineering works have to be regularly inspected and maintained in good condition by such measures as may be called for as a result of the inspection. This routine work must always be most carefully carried out. Therefore, not only must man-made structures be regularly inspected but also the ground adjacent to that on which they rest. Inspection of bridge piers, to check against scouring, and of dams, to check against erosion of foundation-bed material caused by leaks, are two of the more important branches of such work in which geological features may be of special significance, and reference will be made to them in later chapters. References will also be made to the regular checking and maintenance of other structures and works in which careful attention to geological features can add appreciably to the value of their inspection.

1.11. Two Examples. A few cases from actual practice have been briefly mentioned to illustrate the thesis herein advanced regarding the close interrelation of geology and civil engineering. The logic of the suggestion is well seen as soon as study is made of examples from the far-flung coverage of civil engineering work throughout the world. Much of this book consists of records of case histories selected to show also the advantages to be gained by a proper appreciation of geology in civil engineering work and the troubles that may be caused by its neglect. Although examples are given from more than a score of countries, the majority are somewhat naturally from North America. Since the examples have been chosen to illustrate the various chapters into which the main subject has been divided, each one has a somewhat specialized interest. It seems appropriate, therefore, to illustrate the general theme of this volume at the outset by two examples, typical in character but drawn from parts of the world other than North America. Both are hydroelectric schemes; such projects often include a wide variety of types of civil engineering work. These examples have been chosen because they illustrate well, but in no unusual manner, the contribution that geology can make to civil engineering enterprises. Since the writer had the privilege of visiting both projects during their construction stages, he can pay personal testimony to the lessons they demonstrate.

The Snowy Mountains Scheme. About 100 miles southwest of Canberra, national capital of Australia, and midway between Sydney and Melbourne, the Snowy Mountains stand as the highest part of the Great Dividing Range which lies on the border of the states of New South Wales and Victoria. A central belt, 15 to 20 miles wide, trends north-northeast and is over 4,500 ft above sea level; it includes Mount

Kosciusko, 7,314 ft, the highest point in Australia. To the west, it is bounded by great fault escarpments that lead rapidly to the lowlands at an elevation of about 1,000 ft above sea level; the headwaters of the Murray River and its tributaries, the Geehi and Tooma, and the Tumut River provide the main drainage. To the east, the high plateau descends more gradually to a tableland at 3,000 and 4,000 ft above sea level, drained mainly by the Snowy River and its tributaries, the Eucumbene and Crackenback. The Snowy Mountains are dissected by many streams that have cut themselves deep valleys as much as 2,500 ft below the plateau surface. A masterly engineering plan, involving the construction of eight large and several small dams, more than 100 miles of large-diameter tunnels, and more than 80 miles of pipe aqueducts, is transforming the entire drainage pattern of this mountainous area. Water is being diverted through 10 power stations (several of them underground) with a total installed capacity of 3 million kw; after being used to generate power, the water is available, in the amount of 2 million acre-ft annually, for irrigation in the famous Murray and Murrumbidgee Valleys, and is diverted westward under the Range. Australia is the driest continent in the world; its average annual rainfall is only 16½ in. (half that of California) and its total runoff is about equal to that of the Columbia River, although the area of the country is about the same as that of the United States. Thus, the economic significance of the Snowy Mountains scheme is immediately apparent. Much of the limited rainfall falls on the Great Dividing Range, and the eastward flowing waters run to the sea to waste; by turning the Snowy River westward, the Snowy Mountains Hydro-Electric Authority is eliminating much of the waste from the part of the Range which has the highest rainfall.

The geology of this region was first known in broad outline only as recently as 1948. Systematic mapping of the geology started in that year as a joint venture, so that there was a little geological information available when the planning of the Snowy Mountains scheme started. As an early step, the Authority established an Engineering Geology branch which eventually included nine geologists and one geophysicist. The branch initiated detailed studies of sites under consideration for engineering works; along with the general mapping program that has continued, these studies obtained accurate information on the geology of this interesting area. Mount Kosciusko and about 400 sq miles of high land around it, extending down to 4,800 ft above sea level, constitute the only part of Australia that was glaciated; three phases of glaciation have been recognized, and all the main features of glaciated country can be seen in this small area. The greater part of the region consists of intrusive granites and granitic gneisses, hard metamorphic rocks that often show remnants of sedimentary bedding. The rest of the area is largely composed of highly folded sedimentary and metamorphosed sedimentary rocks generally of Ordovician age. These were originally muds, silts, sands, and some volcanic ash, subsequently compacted, cemented, and sometimes recrystallized. Belts of cavernous limestone have also been found. Sedimentary and volcanic rocks of Devonian age overlie Silurian rocks, mainly gently folded, along the middle section of the Tumut River where two of the major projects are located. Scattered areas of almost horizontal beds of basalt lava flows, of early Tertiary age, occur in one district and cap some of the highest ground. Limited deposits of alluvium along existing streams complete the geological picture of this unusually complex area. Because of the variety of rocks, the engineering of the Snowy Mountains scheme has had to contend with most of the major types of geological problems encountered in other countries over much greater areas. Careful study of the geology has been an essential part of the preliminary work for all the individual engineering projects. The remarkable progress made with the initial stages of the Snowy Mountains scheme (an earth- and rock-fill dam 381 ft high completed 2 years ahead of schedule, and a world's record for tunneling progress of 590 ft driven from one heading in a 6-day week, and 697 ft in 7 consecutive days' work) is not unrelated to the accurate geological information available for both design and construction purposes.

One of the most serious geological problems encountered on this project was the extent and nature of weathered rock. Much of the area is covered with a mantle of residual soil of great thickness, derived from the weathering in place of the bedrock. It is unusual to find such soil in close proximity to glacial deposits, but this is merely one of the geological features that distinguish this enterprise. Determination of the extent of the rock weathering was naturally a problem to be faced in connection with every dam site, every tunnel route, and every potential powerhouse location. Investigations showed at an early stage that unfortunately the type of rock most susceptible to weathering is one of the most abundant in the area, a medium- to coarse-grained gray granite with a high content of biotite mica (up to 20 per cent). It was frequently found to be weathered for depths of 100 ft below the surface, but might then pass abruptly to relatively fresh rock. Even in completely weathered zones, large residual boulders of fresh or only slightly weathered granite surrounded by completely weathered material were often found; since they sometimes occurred in clusters, their detection by test drilling was unusually difficult. Weathering was naturally more prevalent in faulted zones than in solid rock; the Snowy Mountains contain many faults, though few are to be seen at the surface, and this further complicated subsurface exploration. Even the gneiss was extensively weathered in places; at the Tooma Dam, weathering extended to a depth of 140 ft at the left abutment, and bands of moderately weathered rock were found in drill holes at a depth of 290 ft below the surface.

Preliminary investigations for the project started with reconnaissance geological mapping to a scale of 4 in. to 1 mile. This was followed by detailed geological mapping to a scale of 1 in. to 200 ft for tunnel routes and of 1 in. to 50 ft for dam sites. Diamond-core drilling then followed;

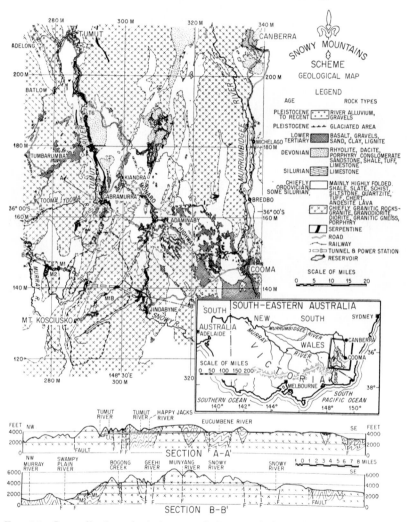

Fig. 1.1. Generalized geological map of the area being utilized by the Snowy Mountains project in New South Wales and Victoria, Australia. (*Reproduced by permission of the Snowy Mountains Hydro-Electric Authority.*)

all holes were located by the geologists on the basis of their mapping work. After the geological structure was revealed, most of the diamond-drill holes were subjected to high-pressure water tests, and thus were put to further use. With the aid of rubber packers, holes were tested in sections, and any losses of water were carefully measured and correlated with the structure revealed from the core. Finally, holes were logged electrically by means of a single-electrode electric logger. An instrument at the surface recorded, as the logger was lowered down the hole, the electrical resistivity and the changes in self-potential. Naturally, this logging could be carried out only in water-filled holes that were uncased, but it proved to be a valuable supplement and was easy to use; several hundred feet could be logged within the space of an hour. The resistivity

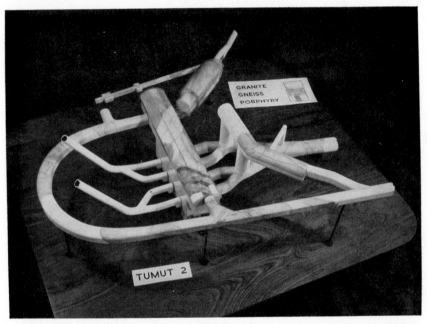

Fig. 1.2. One of the geological models used on the Snowy Mountains project, Australia, to illustrate subsurface conditions before excavation commenced, showing the Tumut 2 underground power station and connecting tunnels. (*Reproduced by permission of the Snowy Mountains Hydro-Electric Authority.*)

of weathered granite is considerably less than that of fresh granite, as is also the resistivity of clay seams or faulted zones; all these features showed up clearly on the recorded electrical logs. Geophysical methods of subsurface investigation, especially seismic refraction, were also used where appropriate. Study of the petrography of rock samples in the laboratory was a useful supplement to field investigations. Careful correlation of all preliminary investigation work, even though the area covered was almost 5,000 sq miles, gradually built up a general picture of the geology of the entire region that became increasingly valuable as the work progressed.

Specific examples will be cited later in this book (see pages 213 and 236), but as illustrative of the application of the geological studies, the Tumut Pond Dam site may be mentioned. This site was carefully studied in the manner described and good rock conditions were obtained, even though weathering extended to a depth of 60 ft and limonite staining extended down to 170 ft in test holes. Just upstream of the dam site, however, a fault zone had been detected by a careful study of aerial photographs and of the actual topography of the site. Upstream of the fault plane, a zone of crushed and sheared granite extended for about 300 ft; this and associated features of the fault severely limited the choice of the intake for the Tumut 1 pressure tunnel which was to convey water impounded by this dam. The machine hall of Tumut 1 power station, 77 ft in maximum width, 104 ft high, and 306 ft long, is 1,100 ft underground and located in closely jointed granitic gneiss and less-jointed granite. Following the preliminary geological studies, a site was selected which avoided the major faults of the region, and following the more detailed studies, the machine hall was sited chiefly in the less-jointed granite with a favorable orientation with respect to the joint pattern. Study of available rocks for use as concrete aggregate was another urgent preliminary; the biotite-rich granite gave reasonable concrete for the Guthega Dam and Tunnel (the first parts of the scheme to be completed), even though the biotite mica was found to be freed from its matrix by crushing in the fine aggregate. Other granites also proved to be satisfactory, but crushed diorite was used as a main supply for Tumut Pond Dam and tunnel lining from a source convenient to the works. These are but typical examples of what geology has contributed to this greatest of engineering projects of the Southern Hemisphere and, indeed, one of the outstanding multiple-purpose engineering projects of the world.[1.7]

The Glen Shira Project. Different in scale but similar in significance is the Glen Shira hydroelectric project of the North of Scotland Hydro-Electric Board, located in the Highlands of Scotland close to the ancient town of Inveraray near the head of Loch Fyne. As a part of the progressive development of the water power available from even the relatively small rivers and streams of the Highlands, the flow of the river Shira and a number of adjacent streams has been controlled by dams and intakes; the resulting water is conducted by a pressure tunnel across a small divide in such a way as to take advantage of a sudden drop to sea level, giving a combined total head of about 1,100 ft. The main dam, a buttress structure of mass concrete 2,250 ft long and 133 ft in maximum height, impounds the flow of the river and local streams from a catchment of just over 13 sq miles. (An average annual rainfall of 105 in. makes this small catchment understandable.) Local topography dictated a two-stage scheme; the consulting engineers took advantage of this to make the upper station, just below the main dam, a combined power-generating and pumping station; excess water is pumped back when available into the main reservoir from the lower reservoir which is formed by two dams separated by a large rock knoll. One of these is a concrete overflow section, 400 ft long and 58 ft high; the other is an earth-fill dam 600 ft long and 53 ft high. The pressure tunnel leads from the lower reservoir and is 21,050 ft long; it has two main sections driven from four portals and one subsidiary entrance section; connections are made by the use of steel-pipe crossings over the streams that intersect the tunnel line with their valleys. The tunnel, 10 ft in finished diameter, leads to an inclined shaft, steel-lined and with decreasing finished diameter (6 ft minimum), that conveys the water to the small Clachan power station on Loch Fyne at sea level. The upper (Sron Mor) station generates 8,000 hp under 138 ft head; the Clachan station 56,000 hp under 960 ft head.

The ingenious way in which topographical features were put to good use in planning the two-stage arrangement of the project, the use of the buttress type of dam, and the fact that the Clachan station was the first underground power station to be completed in Scotland distinguish the Glen Shira scheme as another example of first-class British civil engineering practice. In addition, the project is located in the Scottish Highlands, and all geologists know that the geology of the Highlands has presented some of the most baffling of all geological problems from the scientific point of view. Geology, therefore, might be expected to have played an important part in the successful prosecution of the Glen Shira works. This was certainly the case. The geology of every part of the works having been most carefully studied, geological difficulties were generally overcome. They revealed themselves, however, in one most unexpected way before the completion of the project. The area, part of the Dalradian metamorphic complex, is typical of the Grampians. Rocks consist in the main of phyllites, schists, and some epidiorite masses; there are thin intrusions of igneous rocks and a large zone of limestone north of the area covered by the works. The phyllites are soft and fissile and generally form poor foundations; the schists, on the other hand, are, on the whole, sound and massive.

Foundations for the main dam, on a site dictated generally by topography, consisted of soft phyllites, some bands of quartzite, and an extensive zone of limestone. Loading tests were performed at the site because of the poor and varying bearing capacity of the foundation beds, and unit loads up to 25 tons per sq ft gave acceptably small deflections. Pressure grouting was carried out beneath the dam; the average intake was 0.67 lb of cement per sq ft of curtain. Under the concrete spillway part of the second dam, cement intake during grouting was 1.2 lb per sq ft; this showed the variability of the character of the rock, since the two dams were less than half a mile apart. A special stilling basin had to be incorporated in the spillway structure because of the nature of the bedrock and the necessity of avoiding its erosion. Material conveniently available for the construction of the earth dam was from a glacial moraine. Study showed this to be essentially weathered mica schist, the particle size of which went down to rock flour. Its character was therefore very variable, and due allowance had to be made for this in the cross-sectional design. Owing to the high rainfall (an average of 15 in. of rain fell for 4 successive months during the construction period), construction of a rolled-fill dam was not easy; therefore a special installation of pore

Fig. 1.3. General view of the two impounding dams of the Glen Shira hydro-electric project, showing typical Scottish Highland topography. (*Reproduced by permission of Babtie, Shaw and Morton, Consulting Engineers, and the North of Scotland Hydro-Electric Board.*)

pressure gauges was included for continued observation of the behavior of the morainal material when in place and on rapid draw-down of water level in the reservoir in operation. Correspondingly, and because of the character of the earth fill, a thin flexible reinforced-concrete core wall was used, ingeniously hinged and sealed at the bedrock in the cutoff trench, from which pressure grouting was also carried out.

The pressure tunnel was carried through a variety of geological formations, the anticipated nature of which dictated the decision to make it circular in cross section. Only 5½ per cent of the total length required steel-rib supports. Overbreak averaged 7 per cent on excavation, but this increased somewhat before concrete was completed because of weathering of the exposed rock. On the average, 5½ lb explosives were used per cubic yard of rock excavated. The inclined shaft leading to the powerhouse was excavated through quartz schist with some igneous intrusions. The bedding planes were fortunately normal to the axis of the shaft; therefore, excavation was not a difficult operation, and dry working was obtained throughout. The steel liners were lowered into the shaft and concreted in when excavation was complete; finally pressure grouting was carried out in the surrounding rock through plugs left in the lining. As this grouting was proceeding, a bulge in the steel lining suddenly developed about halfway down the shaft and the steel plate was deflected inward by 7 in. Since it was essential to get the station into commission, this part of the lining was temporarily stiffened and after a careful study was made of the situation, the water was admitted. After about 6 months of successful operation, the tunnel was dewatered and the bulge was examined. The affected section was cut out and replaced. Observations at that time showed that possibly excessive pressure had been used for grouting, but a small trickle of water was also noticed. This was checked back and correlated with the geological section. It was then found that a fissured intrusion of epidiorite upstream of the point where the bulge occurred permitted a little ground water to percolate as far as the quartz-schist zone downstream. Since this zone was more impervious, a build-up of hydrostatic pressure equivalent to the static head from ground surface occurred as ground water accumulated. Figure 1.4 shows how this detail of geological structure could create the unexpected water pressure which had such an unfortunate effect. After repairs had been completed, a gauge that had been fitted to the lining at this point recorded water pressure up to 100 psi, a figure corresponding exactly with the static head.

Decision to locate the power station, a relatively small building containing only one generating unit, underground was taken on the basis of careful economic studies linked with knowledge of the rock to be encountered. The decision was also in keeping with the stringent requirements for minimum interference with the local scenery, so justly famous. The rock is mica schist, including several crushed zones, and has a dip to the north-northwest of 30 to 40°. Although rock conditions necessitated a longer roof span than was originally contemplated, this was easily achieved in the design of the thin reinforced-concrete arch used as the roof, since its soffit was close to the surface. Provision of the necessary aggregate for the job also called for careful geological study. The nearest sand was 45 miles away. Investigation of the properties of the various types of rock available on the job showed that epidiorite could best be used. Therefore, 500,000 tons of this rock, obtained from an outcrop close to the main dam, were crushed in a special plant that gave not only crushed rock for coarse aggregate but also appropriately graded rock

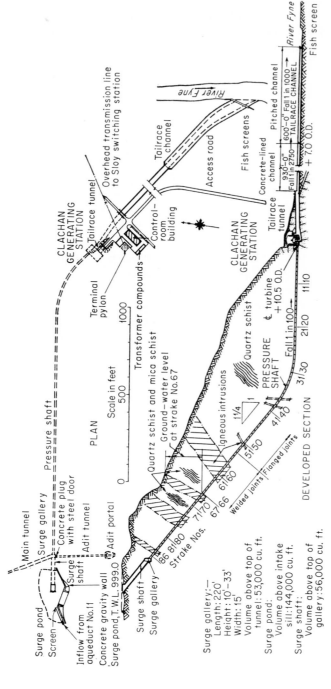

Fig. 1.4. Cross section through the surge shaft and pressure shaft of the Glen Shira hydroelectric plant in Scotland. (*Reproduced from reference 1.8 by permission of the Institution of Civil Engineers.*)

sand. The project was completed in 1957 and is now supplying 80 million kwh per year to the Scottish electrical grid; it is being operated as a peak-load station to take full advantage of its water-storage possibilities.[1.8]

1.12. In Time of War. It is easy to forget that civil engineering was originally an outgrowth of military engineering. Military engineering today has its own special demands. As practiced in two world wars, it also gained from the application of geology, even under the imperative of front-line action. Since further corroboration of the utility of geological applications in engineering work can be gained by a brief review of their use in time of war, this additional preliminary note may be helpful. And since there is a fairly general impression that geology was used as an aid to military engineering for the first time during the war of 1939–1945, attention may be paid to a rather neglected chapter in the story of engineering geology, that is, its use during the First World War. The long campaign in Northwest Europe was probably the greatest ground battle that the world has ever known (and may it always keep this distinction). Desperate as it was, and high the toll of lives that it took, it has much of value to show from the point of view of geology.

In 1914, no military geological establishment of any sort existed in the British Army; it is believed that the same was true of all the Allied armies and probably of those of the opposing powers. In April, 1915, Lt. W. B. R. King was appointed to work with the British War Office on geological problems, on the nomination of the director of the Geological Survey of England. Later Captain King, he worked throughout the war on the staff of the chief engineer in France. Meanwhile, in far-off Australia, suggestions were advanced that this member of the British Commonwealth might contribute a special corps of geologists and miners, and an official offer was accepted at the end of 1915. In May, 1916, the Australian Mining Corps, organized as a battalion for service in Gallipoli, but too late for service there, arrived on the Western front. Major T. W. E. David, who served as adviser on matters of military mining and geology in positions of increasing importance as the war progressed, accompanied this battalion. By the time of the armistice, five geologists were attached to the British General Headquarters; these men naturally received much assistance from French and Belgian geologists. In 1917, after the entry of the United States into the war, Lt. Col. A. H. Brooks, previously director of the Geological Survey of Alaska, was appointed geologist to the American Army in France; later an assistant geologist was also appointed. At the time of the armistice, plans had been made to increase this small American staff to a total of 17 geologists; most of them were actually appointed, though they were not called upon to serve.[1.9]

In the record which he prepared of this wartime work, Lt. Col. Brooks said: "The success of the British in gaining control of the underground situation must in large measure be credited to the refinement of the geological studies and their interpretations made by Lt. Col. T. Edgeworth David."[1.10] All who know anything of the 1914 war, or who have studied it, will appreciate the significance of this tribute in relation to the military operations in France, and in a minor way in relation to the thesis of this book. A necessarily impersonal treatment of geology and engineering may, therefore, be tempered for one paragraph in order to record something of this great pioneer in the field, still relatively little known outside his own Australia. Born in Wales in 1858, David went to Australia in 1882, and was appointed to the chair of geology at the University of Sydney in 1891. He retired in 1922 and died in 1934 as Professor Sir T. Edgeworth David, D.S.O.; he had received many other honors and was widely revered and respected. Some indication of his character is shown by the fact that he became a member of Shackleton's Antarctic Expedition at the age of forty and led the party of three that first reached the South Magnetic Pole. It was at the age of fifty-seven (and when a grandfather) that he volunteered for service with the Australian forces in France. To read of his wartime activities, begun at an age now sometimes regarded as suitable for retirement, gives some slight indication of the inspiration that he must have been to his students and to all who worked with him. The official records show how he applied his unusual geological skill to the needs of military engineering. Only in his private writing is one privileged to see that, even in the midst of the war, he never forgot his scientific calling. In the winter of 1917–1918, a fossil mammoth was discovered in an unusually deep dugout. The Germans captured this location in their offensive of March, 1918. In a letter written to his home at that time, David said "The beastly Bosche has gone and captured my fossil mammoth, blast him! But the E. in C. promises to get it back again in a year." The site was actually recaptured 4 months later, but the Germans had removed the bones; David was most annoyed.[1.11]

An important part of the work of King and David was to assist with mining operations under the enemy's lines. One of the most important projects of this kind was that at Vimy Ridge. Figure 1.5 shows a section of the tunnel that was driven; the geological information was obtained from French maps and scientific papers and checked by shallow borings carried out under the most hazardous conditions. Since the tunnel was driven under the enemy's lines in the Louvil clay, noise was reduced to a safe minimum and the work was undetected. The attack on Vimy Ridge was launched on April 9, 1917, when the end of the tunnel was still 70 ft away from the critical location. If the attack had been delayed 1 week, a much more successful military operation would have been achieved, with what eventual results cannot now be imagined.[1.12]

In similar tunneling at Messines Ridge, ground water encountered at

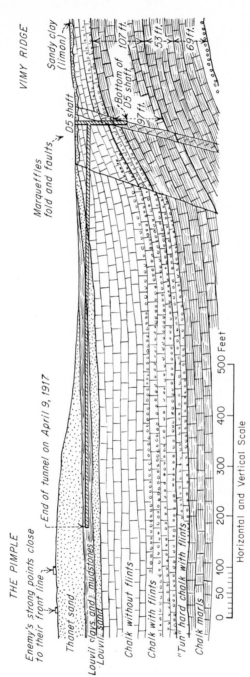

FIG. 1.5. Geological section showing the mining operations carried out during the First World War at Vimy Ridge; the tunnelling was kept in clay as far as possible to ensure silent working. (*Reproduced by permission of the Institution of Royal Engineers, England, from "Geological Work on the Western Front."*)

one point threatened the success of this immense mining project. David examined the working face 70 ft below ground level, and deduced that an old river bed was being pierced. He advised dropping a shaft some distance back from the face, and then retunneling 20 ft below; this was done and the water problem was solved. It was in this location that the greatest explosion ever used in ground fighting was set off, after 18 months' work by tunneling companies, guided by geological advice. There is on record a wonderful letter from David explaining how he checked on some uncertain geological feature by operating a light test-boring rig with two privates in a small heading in the chalk at 114 ft below the surface.[1.13] Natural tunnels were also used for military purposes. Caves were discovered in the Arras district, for example, and as many as 100 were adapted and used at various times for sheltering Allied troops. New Zealand troops occupied 25 caves that gave warm and comfortable accommodation for 11,000 men. Geological examinations were always made in advance of using caves and prior to drilling the necessary ventilation shafts (for which 6-in. boreholes were often used). It was found that the caves were really old quarries from which unweathered chalk had been removed in the seventeenth century for the rebuilding of the city of Arras.

Geology assisted in a different direction when, in 1918, the British government complained to the Dutch government that a lot of Rhine gravel used in the construction of German pillboxes was being brought in by way of Dutch canals that were supposed to be neutral waters. This protest was passed on to the German government, which replied that such gravel was being used for peaceful purposes only. King and David then went to work, obtained samples of the aggregate from actual pillboxes, and found it to be a peculiar sort of basaltic rock which occurs only at Niedermendig on the Rhine above Cologne; this was later checked by more detailed studies in England.[1.14] An even more remarkable detection was made during the war of 1939–1945 by a paleontologist (K. E. Lohman) on the staff of the American Military Geology Unit headed by W. H. Bradley. Lohman was able to determine the exact location of the launching sites of the small balloons sent up by the Japanese (so many of which reached the West Coast of North America) by a study of the diatoms recovered from sand used as ballast in the balloons; the accuracy of the deduction was checked after the end of the war.[1.15]

The great mobility of military operations in the Second World War set a different pattern for the application of geology, recognized from the outset as an essential aid to military intelligence and engineering. Trafficability maps assumed considerable importance and were produced in great numbers. Geologists studied the existing geological records of the countries involved and were aided by the results of aerial reconnaissance and, occasionally, by actual field investigations. Prior to the invasion of France, for example, geologists checked through French geological records and found that the beaches proposed for the landings appeared to be sandy but really had clay close to their sandy surface. This was first suggested, apparently, by one of Field Marshal Montgomery's scientific advisers who had spent a holiday on the Bay of the Seine before the war and had noticed the clay. Study of French records (including a paper in the *Bulletin de la Societé Prehistorique Française*, noted by an official at the British Museum) confirmed these suspicions. The clay areas were then located on aerial photographs. By means of special commando raids, actual samples were brought back to England for study. A beach with similar clay was located in Norfolk, England, and the new heavy tanks were tried out there, but became bogged down. A new device was therefore developed which enabled a tank to lay its own path across a clay patch and to leave it in place for following tanks. In the actual invasion, the first tank out of each LCT was fitted with this special device, and so the beaches were crossed.[1.16] Shortly afterward, however, geology appeared as an aid on the opposing side, for in the terrible fighting around Caen, any possibility of a surprise attack by the British was eliminated because the cavernous limestone of this area acted, in effect, as a sounding board for heavy vehicles. General Dietrich of the German Army said that he could observe the movement of British tanks merely by putting his ear to the ground, a trick he had learned in Russia.[1.17]

These incidents demonstrate the important role that geology can play, in one way or another, in actual combat. There remains for mention another military by-product in the field of engineering geology, but one of lasting value and of direct application to the needs of civil life. Soon after the entry of the United States into the First World War in 1917, a subcommittee of the Council for National Defense suggested to the geological surveys of those states in which military cantonments were located that they might well prepare a bulletin on the topography and military geology of the areas around each cantonment; the subcommittee even gave an outline of what it thought such a bulletin might contain. So far as is known, only one major bulletin of this type was ever produced, although doubtless many interim studies and reports were prepared. The published volume is Bulletin 23 of the Geological Survey of Ohio, a volume of 186 pages, issued in 1921.[1.18] It describes the geology of the Camp Sherman Quadrangle, in which the small city of Chillicothe is located; this historic town was once the capital of the Northwest Territories (of the United States, not Canada), and later still, an early capital of the state of Ohio. The volume presents a clearly written appreciation of the topography of the area under review, of its geology, and of the significance of topographical and geological features; the volume is directed toward the military needs of Camp Sherman but would be useful for any civil engineering work carried out in the area. Even today, this bulletin remains a little classic of its kind.

1.13. Conclusion. As in time of war, so also in peace, geology has a vital role to play in all engineering operations concerned in any way with the ground, and thus with the entire field of civil engineering. Most of the chapters of this volume are therefore arranged to illustrate this connection in relation to major branches of civil engineering work, such as bridges, dams, water supply, and marine works. By way of introduction, two chapters deal with methods of preliminary and subsurface exploration by conventional and by geophysical methods. Since there may be some civil engineers who have not had the opportunity to study geology, a summary outline of this great branch of natural science is given at the outset. This is followed by chapters dealing with the geology of soils (since they are of special importance in civil engineering), with the interrelation of geology and soil mechanics, and with ground water. Appendixes supply guides to the geological surveys of the world and to sources of geological information; they also provide a small glossary of some of the more common geological terms that the civil engineer may encounter.

It will be noted, possibly with some surprise, that the treatment of the subject is purely descriptive; no formulas or mathematics are introduced into the discussion. This is a natural course to follow; it is also one deliberately chosen. Lord Kelvin's famous and oft-quoted dictum to the effect that "when you can measure what you are speaking about, and express it in numbers, you know something about it," with its subsequent denigration of the reverse situation, is one of the writer's main guideposts in his scientific work. But civil engineering is essentially an art—certainly in all its practical aspects—and it depends in large measure for its success upon the exercise of sound judgment. And sound judgment comes from long and tried experience, based on acute observation. Of nothing is this more true than the study of the natural ground conditions upon which, or in which, civil engineering works have to be constructed. Here is where the judgment of the engineer, aided immeasurably by the skilled observations and studies of the geologist, can make such great contributions—in solving difficult construction problems that must be solved in the field and without any delay, in deciding upon the selection of a final site from various alternatives with great economic issues dependent upon the correct decision, in determining when the excavation of a deep foundation may safely be stopped despite possible imperfections in the material to be used as a foundation bed for a great structure. Mathematics is of little assistance on occasions such as these, vital as is its role in the background in relation to designs and computations. Here there is no substitute for good judgment and sound observation.

The ability to observe quickly and accurately is a most desirable attribute in all civil engineers; they can benefit from the training that Boy Scouts get with Kim's game. Field geology is based entirely upon such powers of observation, coupled with the ability to deduce three-dimensional structures from surface features. The civil engineer is trained to think in terms of three dimensions in relation to his structural designs; equally important, if not more so, is the corresponding ability to visualize the spatial character of underground conditions. The geologist visualizes these conditions automatically; the frequently used block diagrams in geological papers are an indication of this. It may not be easy for the civil engineer to gain such ability quickly, but he can do so, and he will find that this ability is of unusual service in field engineering work. Study of simple block diagrams is a first step. Books with colored block diagrams can be of even greater assistance. A particularly notable example is now available from Great Britain, a book that is profusely illustrated with colored block cutaway geological diagrams that vividly illustrate quite complex geological structures.[1.19] It is in the field, and under the tuition of a master teacher, that the art of developing this three-dimensional appreciation of ground structure can most effectively be gained.

Equally important is a full appreciation of the importance of water in geological study. Most engineers will have occasion to observe the remarkable effects of water in many solid materials and especially in soils. Dry soils cause little trouble; wet soils can cause havoc on a job. So is it in many geological formations. Not only, therefore, must the civil engineer learn to visualize subsurface conditions in spatial terms, but he must realize always the added complications that the presence of varying amounts of ground water may cause. That ground water may vary in just the same way as surface water should become a commonplace in his thinking. The relation of both to the weather must always be remembered, especially when field studies are carried out in fine dry weather. One of the basic tools of the engineer in his study of any construction site should be a simple summary of local weather conditions.

These concepts are basic to a full appreciation of the role that geology can and must play in the design and construction of civil engineering works. All are relatively straightforward and simple, calling for no special skills such as may be the privilege of only the gifted few. The ability to "look below the surface," to realize that surface conditions may be vastly different from those only a few feet below ground level, to keep in mind the ever-present possibility of ground-water movement, to visualize the significance of unusual surface topographical features, and to be able to relate these to geological processes of the past—all these are characteristics of observation in which every civil engineer can be trained, in which to a large extent he can train himself. For they can be exercised not only on the construction job but in all travel outside of cities; their application can add greatly to the joys of travel and to the enjoyment of scenery. In this book, however, they are shown in their application to the successful prosecution of civil engineering work in all its variety and with its continuing challenge.

The work to be described is carried out by men for the benefit of their fellows. It may well be remembered, therefore, that behind all impersonal discussions of scientific applications and engineering endeavor lie the relations of man to man and the cooperation of many men working toward a common goal in rendering useful service to their community. This book would not be complete without at least a passing reference to this human background. It is in keeping with this thought that Chap. 1 has been titled "The Civil Engineer and Geology" and that as a frontispiece a portrait has been reproduced—a portrait of a man who epitomized all that has been suggested as the attitude that a civil engineer should entertain toward geology. For his geological work alone, William Smith will always be remembered with honor; but to civil engineers, his fame rests also on the way in which he applied his geological knowledge to his civil engineering work, work of no little importance a century ago. He indeed allowed his "faith" as a geologist to benefit his "works" as an engineer.

Suggestions for Further Reading

In the first edition of this book there was included a list of all the publications in English then known to the author, which dealt with the application of geology in civil engineering (pp. 81–84). In the intervening years, the number of books and papers dealing with this subject has increased so that it is now impracticable to include the same type of list. For those interested in the historical aspects of this branch of applied geology, reference may be made to the earlier edition.

Possibly the most significant development in the field since the first edition appeared was the establishment in 1947, by the Geological Society of America, of its Engineering Geology Division. It is believed that this is the only national organization, certainly it is the only one in the English-speaking world, which deals with the subject matter considered in this volume. The division holds regular meetings as a part of the annual meetings of its parent society; papers then presented appear in various publications, including the *Bulletin of the Geological Society of America*. The division has been active in providing useful printed material in its field. Especially useful is the Engineering Geology Reference List, *Bull. Geol. Soc. Am.*, **66**: 993–1030 (1955), also issued in pamphlet form, which is a concise and well-organized guide to the extensive literature that now exists. A brochure issued by the society, entitled "Teaching Aids and Allied Materials in Engineering Geology" (36 pp., 1957), contains much general information on material available for aid in teaching, but is also of value to practicing engineers.

Through the society, the offices of which are at 419 West 117th Street, New York 27, the Division is publishing a series of "Case Histories" containing brief records of significant examples of the application of geology in civil engineering works. Most notable of the GSA publications in the field, however, is the Berkey volume, "Application of Geology to Engineering Practice," S. Paige (ed.), 327 pp., 1950, published in honor of Dr. Charles P. Berkey.

Of the other recent volumes in English, two may be mentioned:

Schultz, J. R., and A. B. Cleaves, "Geology in Engineering," 592 pp., John Wiley & Sons, Inc., New York, 1955.

Krynine, D. P., and W. R. Judd, "Principles of Engineering Geology and Geotechnics," 699 pp., McGraw-Hill Book Company, Inc., New York, 1957.

The former is well described by its name; the latter is a useful reference book, containing much factual information of relevance to applications of geology in engineering.

From among the many books on geology and engineering now available in languages other than English, the following text is especially noted because of its excellent coverage and because it will soon be available also in German:

Zaruba Q., and V. Mencl, "Inženýrská Geologie" 486 pp., Nakladatelství Cesko-slovenské Akademie Věd, Prague, 1957.

Chapter 2

GEOLOGY: AN OUTLINE OF THE SCIENCE

I have no other book than the sky and the earth, which is known to all, and it is given to all to know and read in this beautiful book. . . . That is why a man who works in the art of the earth is always learning because of unknown natures, and diversity of earths.

Bernard Palissy[2.1]
(A.D. 1510–1590)

THE GEOLOGIST is concerned with every aspect of the composition and structure of the earth's crust. His sphere of work is, therefore, world-wide; his main laboratory is the great out of doors wherein he examines rocks as they actually occur in nature. His considerations range to the beginning of time and far into the future. He studies all that composes the crust of the earth and especially those materials of use to his fellow men. Yet geologists have sometimes been regarded as unduly academic persons, engaged in an unceasing hunt for fossils. This paradox arises perhaps because of the extent of the field covered by the science of geology and because of its relative remoteness from the things of every day, that is, when considered from the purely scientific standpoint.

2.2. Early History. This strange paradox—the contrast between the wide extent and importance of all that is now studied in the field of geology and the generally restricted appreciation of its significance—is found to exist from the earliest days of scientific endeavor. The idea of devoting a special branch of science to the study of the earth itself was not then contemplated, and even the references in early writings to "Earth" as one of the four elements bear little relation to the modern concept of geology. Nicolaus Steno (1631–1686), at one time bishop of Hamburg and vicar apostolic of Denmark, is generally regarded as the founder of geology as an independent branch of science. Of special interest to engineers is the fact that Robert Hooke (1635–1703), who was professor of geometry at Gresham College when he was thirty and whose name is now associated with the law relating stress and strain, was the first man to suggest that fossils could be used to construct a chronology of the

37

earth. The name *geology* does not appear to have been used until the end of the eighteenth century. It is derived from the Greek *ge*, the earth, and *logos*, a speech or discourse; the name is thus truly descriptive. As soon as geology was recognized as a branch of scientific inquiry, it developed rapidly, and before too many years had passed, the true extent of its scope was appreciated. The wide field thus made available for study encouraged, rather than discouraged, interested investigators so that geology, despite its late start, now ranks as a leading branch of natural science.

The first workers were mainly English and Italian, but other Europeans soon made their special contributions to the advance. J. G. Lehmann, a German who died in 1767, was the first, for example, to record the possibility of *order* in the arrangement of the rocks of the earth's crust. De Saussure (1740–1799), a Swiss who studied the Alps carefully, was the first to give the generic name to the science; previously it had been regarded as a part of mineralogy, a position that today is almost reversed. James Hutton (1726–1797), a Scotsman of Edinburgh, was perhaps the first great name in the annals of the science; his "Theory of the Earth," published in 1785, republished in 1795, and finally popularized by Playfair (1748–1819) in 1802, provided the basis for much of the great advance made during the nineteenth century. Hutton first distinguished the three main types of rock which provide the basis for modern theories of earth sculpture. A. G. Werner (1749–1817), a German, was also a most potent influence in geology during these same years, drawing pupils from all over the world to his classes at Freiburg Mining Academy.

William Maclure (1763–1840) is known today as the "Father of American Geology," and Sir William Edmund Logan (1798–1875) will long be remembered for his pioneer work in Canada. Louis Agassiz (1807–1873) is yet another name associated with the North American continent; he was a Swiss who emigrated to the United States of America when he was forty-two years old and there established his fame with his work on fossil fishes. He is generally regarded as the founder of the modern school of glacial geology. William Nicol, a lecturer at the University of Edinburgh, by his invention of the Nicol prism and the method of preparing thin rock sections for examination through a microscope (later to be developed by Sorby), placed the whole science in his debt and laid the basis for much of the laboratory work of today. The names of Sir Charles Lyell (1797–1875) and Charles Darwin (1809–1882) cannot be omitted from this review, brief as it is; both were distinguished geologists, although Darwin is perhaps better known as a biologist. Their publications, notably "The Antiquity of Man" and the "Origin of Species," achieved fame far beyond the confines of the scientific world.[2.2]

2.3. William Smith. One distinguished name was omitted from the foregoing list in order that it might be given special attention—that of the remarkable man whose portrait is the frontispiece of this volume. William Smith is now generally acknowledged as the "Father of British Geology." Born on March 23, 1769, of humble origin, he spent an appreciable part of his life of fifty years as a canal engineer in Somerset, England, and became later a land agent near Scarborough. The science was well founded when he first became interested in the structure of the earth on his journeys along the post roads of England. He was one of the first to introduce the concept of quantitative study and regular stratigraphical succession and so helped to establish the science on its foundation of today. The work for which he will ever be remembered is the preparation of the first real geological map of England and Wales. The "Map of the Strata," as it was first called, was constantly in his mind for a period of over twenty years, but it was not until the year 1813 that the work was definitely put in hand; William Cary was the engraver. The finished map, colored not unlike a modern geological map, was presented to the Society of Arts in April, 1815, and was awarded a premium of £50, designated for the first such map to be produced.[2.3]

Throughout his life, William Smith practiced extensively as a consultant on geological matters, often with special reference to their application to engineering work. Before his death, he was honored by the Geological Society of London by being awarded in 1831 its first Wollaston Medal. The society had been founded in 1807, proof indeed that the comparatively new science was already active and virile. It is of interest to note that the society was thus founded some years before the Institution of Civil Engineers and almost fifty years before the American Society of Civil Engineers. Even more significant, however, is the fact that between the years 1799 and 1825, the period that saw the birth of geology as an organized branch of science, Laplace published his monumental work on astronomy, "Celestial Mechanics"; his earlier "Essay on the System of the World" (published in 1796) contains much that can be read with interest today. Geology had, therefore, a long way to make up, but the years between have seen the gap closed.

2.4. The Science Today. Geology was originally a descriptive science. The geologist studied rocks in the field, recorded his results, assessed these for the region he was investigating, and deduced from his observations the structural arrangement of the rocks he had seen. Detailed study of the composition of rocks eventually led him into the laboratory, first for microscopic investigations and later for chemical and mechanical analyses. Examination of fossil forms inevitably led him to biological studies and, eventually, to that close affinity with biology that has resulted in the joint approaches found today in such disciplines as *paleozoology* and *paleobotany*. Thus began the association of geology with other scientific disciplines that is so significant a feature of modern geological studies. There can today be few branches of natural science that demand a working appreciation of so many sister sciences as does geology.

It will assist the engineer in his applications of geology if he is at least familiar with the way in which the science has branched out into many subdivisions and become associated with other sciences in developing new branches of inquiry. Even though this can here be but a listing of names, the names will at least serve to guide the interested engineer to further study of any subject of special interest. Many of the names are self-descriptive even to those not acquainted with classical languages. *Mineralogy*, for example, is the study of minerals, and has long been recognized as a scientific discipline in its own right, even though it is closely associated with geology. *Crystallography* is, correspondingly, the more detailed study of crystal forms, a discipline not now limited to geological studies but also widely studied in chemistry and physics. *Vulcanology* is a term less frequently encountered; it is used to describe the special study of volcanoes and volcanic action.

The prefix *geo-* is a sure indication of study closely allied with geology. *Geochemistry*, a relative newcomer to the field, is clearly the study of the chemistry of the natural materials found in the earth's crust. *Geography* may not be regarded by geographers as a subdivision of geology (the reverse is a far more questionable view), but there is a close link between the two disciplines. *Geotechnique* is an old term now gaining new usage to describe, generally, the scientific study of the soils in the earth's crust; its close association with geology is discussed in Chap. 4. *Geomorphology* is perhaps the most puzzling of this group of terms: derived first from German usage, it is used more by geographers than by geologists to describe what some still prefer to call *physiography* or even *physical geology*—the sculpture of the earth's surface.

Such qualified segments of geology are readily identifiable; *physical geology*, for example, is the study of the present form of the earth's surface, its structure, manner of origin, and the nature of the modifying processes at work upon it. *Glacial geology* is, correspondingly, the study of glaciers, glacial action, and especially, glacial deposits found in the earth's crust. *Historical geology* involves the synthesis of all those branches of inquiry which point the way to the historical evolution of the earth's crust as it is seen today; the detailed geological succession is one of the main results. *Stratigraphical geology* (or stratigraphy) is the closely allied investigation of existing structural arrangements in the earth's crust and the relation of these to earth forms of the past. *Submarine geology*, a relatively recent branch of the science, is related to one particular part of the earth's surface; its development has been greatly aided by modern underwater techniques. *Pleistocene geology* is a special branch, related not to an area but to a period in geological history.

Of the disciplines with somewhat more unusual names, generally derived from Latin or Greek, *paleontology* has already been mentioned as the study of fossils and fossil life. *Petrology* is a companion study to mineralogy; it is the study of rocks in the widest sense, their mineral constitution, texture, and origin. As an indication of the extent to which detailed scientific study in the geological field has proceeded, one may note that even petrology now has its own subdivisions, such as *sedimentary petrology*. *Cosmogony* is the study of the relation of the earth to the solar system and to the universe, with special reference to the composition of the universe and its members. More frequently encountered in engineering work, however, will be the name *seismology*, the study of earthquakes, earthquake action, and associated vibrations, as well as of all vibrations in the crust of the earth from any other cause.

There may be some who would expect to see seismology listed as a branch of *geophysics* rather than of geology. Geophysics has been left for reference at the end of this summary because of its importance. It is, clearly, the study of the physics of the earth; in recent years, it has probably advanced at a faster rate, and upon a wider front, than any other scientific discipline outside the nuclear field. Among the various factors responsible for this phenomenal advance is the modern progress in scientific instrumentation. One cannot imagine geophysical studies except against a background of geology; correspondingly, one cannot think of geological study today without an appreciation of all that geophysical methods can do to supplement older forms of investigation. Here, then, are two complementary scientific disciplines, the joint progress of which is pushing back the frontiers of knowledge of the earth and of its constitution in a manner and at a rate undreamed of a few decades ago.

2.5. The Earth's Crust. Detailed knowledge of the nature and composition of the earth sphere is confined to an exceedingly thin crust—much thinner than is generally realized. The diameter of the earth is slightly less than 8,000 miles. Geological investigation by means of bore-holes has at present extended to about 25,000 ft below the surface—no more than 0.05 per cent of the total thickness. One may infer, utilizing stratigraphical relationships, that investigations may have extended in some places to a depth of 200,000 ft, but this is relatively little below the surface. Even the irregularities on the earth's surface—mountain ranges and ocean depths—are of small moment when compared with the whole globe. For the highest mountain, Mount Everest, is 29,141 ft above sea level; the greatest depth to the ocean bed so far discovered is in the Pacific Ocean, a distance of about 35,780 ft below sea level. The total of these extremes amounts only to 64,921 ft, or 0.15 per cent of the total diameter; and if average land heights and ocean depth be taken (1,400 and 12,000 ft, respectively), the figure is only 0.03 per cent.

Since about three-quarters of the surface of the terrestrial globe is covered with water, only one-quarter is exposed ground. The great land masses are made up of rocks of many different types and conditions, structurally arranged in an often surprising but always systematic manner.

2.6. Rocks and Minerals. In its widest sense, the term "rock" includes all the solid constituents of the earth's surface, whether solid (such as granite), granular (such as sand and gravel), or earthy (such as clay). To the civil engineer, on the other hand, rock is a term used to signify solid rock masses that cannot normally be excavated by manual methods alone. All rocks are composed of minerals. Minerals therefore are the unit constituents of the earth's crust, and as such they are of great interest and importance to the geologist. The mineral composition of rocks is also of importance to the engineer; it enters to some degree into all applications of the science to engineering work. The study of minerals cannot therefore be neglected by the civil engineer. Minerals are of many kinds; about a thousand separate and distinct kinds are known. Each has its own chemical composition and atomic structure and tends to form crystals whose shapes are determined by this structure. The detailed study and investigation of minerals in the laboratory is a fascinating occupation, but the civil engineer, unless engaged in some special task, will not have recourse to such a refinement in geological work. It may, however, be mentioned that the laboratory work involves the use of sections of rocks and minerals, ground so thin that they can be mounted on glass slides and examined through a microscope. Using ordinary light and also polarized light, the geologist can thus determine the optical and physical properties of a specimen.

Minerals have long been classified on the basis of chemical composition and crystal form. The larger divisions are determined by chemical similarities; the smaller groups and series within these divisions rest on similarities of crystal form. The more important chemical divisions are given in Table 2.1.

All rocks can be divided into three main groups: (1) igneous, (2) sedimentary, (3) metamorphic. The third group is a derivative from either of the other two. The names of these three great classes are descriptive. *Igneous* rocks (from the Latin *igne*, of fire or fiery) were formed by the cooling of parts of the bodies of molten material, which is called, in general, *magma*, erupted from or trapped beneath the earth's crust; *sedimentary*, or *derivative*, rocks were deposited in some geological age mechanically (through the agency of water, wind, or ice action), chemically, or organically; and *metamorphic* rocks (from the Greek *meta*, between, as denoting change, and *morphe*, form or shape) are rocks changed in some way from either an original igneous or sedimentary form.

Since all sands, gravels, clays, and shales are classed as sedimentary rocks, one can readily appreciate that such rocks cover about three-quarters of the earth's land surface; however, one must not indiscriminately interpret this monopoly in area in terms of relative importance. Nor is it a guide to the relative significance of the main rock groups for the geologist, for many of the most complicated geological structures requiring investigation are those presented by

Table 2.1. Some Chemical Divisions in Mineralogy*

Division	Typical example	Chemical composition
Elements............	Graphite	Carbon
Sulphides...........	Pyrite	Iron sulphide
Chlorides...........	Rock salt	Sodium chloride
Oxides..............	Quartz	Silicon dioxide
Sulphates...........	Gypsum	Hydrous calcium sulphate
Phosphates..........	Apatite	Calcium phosphate
Carbonates..........	Calcite	Calcium carbonate
Silicates............	Feldspar:	
	Orthoclase	Potassium-aluminum silicate
	Plagioclase	Sodium-calcium-aluminum silicate
	Hornblende	
	Augite	Complex metallic silicates, containing sodium, potassium, magnesium, iron, etc.
	Mica:	
	Muscovite	
	Biotite	
	Olivine	Magnesium-iron silicate
	Chlorite	Complex hydrous magnesium-aluminum silicate
	Serpentine	Hydrous magnesium silicate

* Distinguishing features cannot usefully be summarized in tabular form; reference may be made to standard books on mineralogy.

igneous formations. For the civil engineer, however, the significance of the main rock groups is to some degree comparable with their relative occurrence, because of the general nature of civil engineering work. Construction operations are generally confined to the proximity of the surface of the earth, and consequently sedimentary rocks are more frequently encountered by the engineer than igneous and metamorphic rocks.

2.7. Igneous Rocks. These rocks are of two main classes: *extrusive* (poured out at surface) and *intrusive* (large rock masses which have not formed in contact with the atmosphere).

Initially, both classes were molten rock. Their present state results directly from the way in which they solidified. If a violent volcanic eruption took place, some material would be emitted, with gaseous extrusions, into the atmosphere, where it would cool quickly and eventually fall to the earth's surface as volcanic ash and dust. This type of action continues even today: dust on the dome of St. Paul's Cathedral in London is of volcanic and possibly cosmic origin. The main product of volcanic action is a lava flow, emitted from the earth as a molten stream which flows over the surface of the existing ground until it solidifies. Extrusive rocks are generally distinguished by their usual glass-like texture and by the "baking" of whatever rock stratum happens to underlie them.

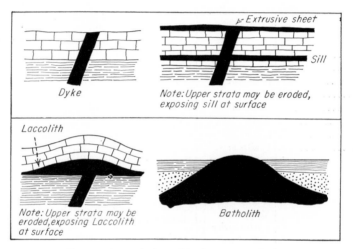

Fig. 2.1. Some forms taken by igneous rock.

Intrusive rocks, which cool and solidify at great depths and under pressure and which contain entrapped gases, are usually wholly crystal-line (*holo-crystalline*) in texture, since the conditions of cooling are con-ducive to crystal formation. Such rocks occur in masses of great extent, often going to unknown depths. Although always originally formed deep underground, intrusive rocks are now widely exposed because of earth movement and erosion processes, explained later in this chapter.

Hypabyssal rocks are intermediate in position between extrusive and major intrusive rocks. Thus, in general, they are partially crystalline in texture. They occur in many forms, the main types of which are in-dicated in Fig. 2.1. *Dikes* are large wall-like fillings in the earth's crust cutting across normal bedding planes. *Sills* are large horizontal sheets intruded into other formations. Common to all these occurrences is the baking of adjacent rock strata on *both* sides of the intrusion, as distinct from baking on the underside only as in the case of extrusive rocks.

Chemical analyses of igneous rocks show that they are essentially composed of the following nine elements: silicon, aluminum, iron, calcium, magnesium, sodium, potassium, hydrogen, and oxygen. These are, of course, in combination, generally as silicates, oxides, and hydroxides. Although the proportion of the oxides varies considerably, the chemical composition of rocks, considered as a whole, varies within quite narrow limits. Within these limits, despite the steady gradation from one composition to another and the varying and quite distinct mineral constitution of different rocks, certain groups can be distinguished. Chemical and mineral composition, in association with the mode of origin of the rock, has therefore been adopted as a basis for a general classification of

Table 2.2. Classification of Igneous Rocks*

	Acid	Intermediate		Basic
	Quartz	Little or no quartz		No quartz
Commonest minerals	Orthoclase⎱ Oligoclase⎰ Mica Hornblende Augite	Orthoclase Biotite Hornblende Augite	Plagioclase Biotite Hornblende Augite	Plagioclase Olivine Hypersthene Augite
Plutonic..........	Granite	Syenite	Diorite	Gabbro
Hypabyssal.......	Quartz porphyry	Orthoclase porphyry	Porphyrite	Dolerite
Volcanic..........	Rhyolite	Trachyte	Andesite	Basalt

* Reference should be made to the text for comment on the indefinite nature of the divisions noted.

crystalline igneous rocks. Silicon dioxide (silica), often crystallized as quartz, is one of the main mineral constituents of igneous rocks, and by the silica content a broad dividing line is fixed. Table 2.2 gives a list of the main types of igneous rocks and suggests broad lines of classification.

2.8. Sedimentary Rocks. This great group of rocks may fitly be regarded as secondary rocks, because they generally result from the weathering and disintegration of existing rock masses. These rocks are somewhat loosely named, since *sedimentary* is truly descriptive of but one section. *Aqueous rocks* is another name sometimes used, but it is not strictly correct, as water is not a depositing agent in the case of all these secondary rocks, nor are they always found *stratified*, another title which has been suggested. In view of the common use of the word "sedimentary," it has been retained here and elsewhere in this book to denote this whole group of secondary rocks.

The distribution of sedimentary rocks over a wide area throughout the world is a result of the great land movements that have taken place in past geological eras. These movements are often vividly demonstrated by the existence of marine deposits, including fossil seashell remains, in places now elevated considerably above the nearest lake or seacoast. Marine deposits are found in the upper regions of the Himalayas and in many other parts of the world thousands of feet above sea level. The top of Mount Everest, the highest point of land in the world, is of limestone, a sedimentary rock.

Sedimentary rocks are generally found in quite definitely arranged beds, or strata, which were horizontal at one time, but are today sometimes displaced through angles up to 90°. This bedding, or stratification, is a direct result of the method of formation; the material was deposited evenly over a lake or sea bottom or in some tropical jungle swamp. Similarly, sedimentary rocks are being formed today by the silt and mud washed down by rivers into lakes and seas and by such marine organisms as the coral of the tropical seas. Measured by human standards of time, the building-up process is almost infinitesimally slow; geological time periods must be used as a basis for comparison.

Sedimentary rocks can conveniently be classified in three general groups. Briefly, the divisions include those rocks which are: (1) mechanically formed, (2) chemically formed (evaporites), (3) organically formed.

The so-called "mechanical processes" leading to rock formation are the action of wind, frost, rain, snow, and daily temperature changes; all these can be classed as weathering influences, which lead to the formation of surface soil, rock scree (or scree breccia), and fine deposits of rain-washed material and blown dust such as brick earth and loess, as well as some special types of clay. The action of running water is a second type of mechanical action, which leads to the formation of rocks that are true sediments such as conglomerate, grit and sandstone, and some types of clay. Finally, glacial action has been and still is a potent factor in rock formation, having given rise to extensive glacial deposits over wide areas of the world. Evaporites, their mode of origin indicated by their name, are chemically formed rocks; typical examples include rock salt, gypsum, anhydrite, and the various types of potash rocks found in some areas. Limestone is perhaps the best known of the organically formed rocks, being generally the accumulation of the remains of marine organisms; it occurs in many different forms. Coal and phosphate rock (coprolites and guano) are other rocks that are obviously of organic origin.

2.9. Metamorphic Rocks. Agencies that have helped to change sedimentary and igneous rocks into metamorphic rock types are many. The principal ones are the intense stresses and strains set up in rocks by severe earth movements and by excessive heat from the cooling of intrusive rocks or from permeating vapors and liquids. The action of permeating liquids appears to have been particularly important. The results of these actions are varied, and the metamorphosed rocks so produced may display features varying from complete and distinct foliation of a crystalline structure to a fine fragmentary partially crystalline state caused by direct compressive stress, including also the cementation of sediment particles by siliceous matter. Foliation is characteristic of the main group of metamorphic rocks; the word means that the minerals of which the rock is formed are arranged in felted fashion. Each layer is lenticular and composed of one or more minerals, but the various layers are not always readily separated from one another. It will be appreciated that these characteristics are different from the flow structure of lava and also from the deposition bedding which occurs in unaltered sedimentary rocks. *Schist* is the name commonly applied to such a foliated rock, and the various types of schistose rock are among the best-known metamorphic rocks.

The nature of the original rocks from which metamorphic rocks were formed has been and still is a matter of keen discussion and the subject of much inquiry. Briefly, it may be said that some metamorphic rocks are definitely sedimentary in origin, some were originally igneous rocks, and some are of indeterminate origin. The presence of fossil remains in certain crystalline metamorphic rocks is proof enough of their sedimentary origin; and, on the other hand, uninterrupted gradation from granite and other igneous rock masses to well-defined schistose rocks is equal proof of the igneous origin of some metamorphic rock types. Of the former types, sedimentary in origin, marble (altered limestone) is a notable example; its appearance frequently demonstrates the organic remains of which it was originally formed. Schistose conglomerate is another well-defined sedimentary type. Quartzite can often be seen to have been formed from sand grains, and the great variety of slates are all obviously of clay or mudstone origin. The rocks classed generally as schists are of varying compositions; mica schist is a crystalline aggregate of mica and quartz and occasionally other minor minerals. *Gneiss* is a term somewhat loosely applied; it is generally used to distinguish a group of rocks similar to the schists but coarsely grained and with alternate bands of minerals of different composition.

2.10. Distinguishing Rock Types. The civil engineer has a natural interest in the study of rocks because he uses them not only as materials of construction but also as foundation beds for many of the structures that he designs and erects. He should therefore be able to distinguish at least the main rock types that he sees in the field. For all the practical purposes of the civil engineer, field tests and simple microscopic examinations will suffice for identification of most of the common rock types. More detailed petrographical investigation will be called for only in exceptional cases; it will clearly be the work of an expert.

Simple equipment is all that is needed for the field investigations mentioned—a geologist's hammer, a tool that will accompany the civil engineer interested in geology on all his out-of-door excursions; a pocket magnifying lens for examination of the smaller crystal structures; a steel pocketknife for hardness tests; and a small phial of hydrochloric acid for the determination of mineral carbonates. A small magnet is often useful, since the mineral magnetite can be separated from other associated minerals (when crushed) by running a magnet through the mixture. The hardness test mentioned is based on a hardness table for minerals, a selected scale based on relative hardnesses, and is of great use in preliminary testing. The selected order is:

Hardness*	Mineral	Test characteristic
1	Talc	Can be scratched with a fingernail.
2	Gypsum	
3	Calcite	Can be cut very easily with a penknife.
4	Fluorspar	Can be scratched easily with a penknife.
5	Apatite	
6	Feldspar	Can be scratched with a penknife but with difficulty.
7	Quartz	Cannot be scratched with any ordinary implement. Quartz will scratch glass; topaz will scratch quartz; corundum, topaz; and a diamond, corundum.
8	Topaz	
9	Corundum	
10	Diamond	

* The numbers given are used as relative hardness numbers, relative only since the actual hardness value of talc is about 0.02, whereas that for a diamond runs into the thousands.

Silt, clays, sand, and gravels can readily be distinguished by superficial examination; they are generally described in terms of their appearance, especially their color and the coarseness of particle sizes. Investigation of the consolidated rocks necessitates closer examination of a hand specimen which may be obtained from the outcrop by a sharp blow from the hammer. It must be emphasized that a clean, fresh rock surface must be used for all examinations. The word "fresh" is used to indicate that the rock surface must have been freshly broken, since most rocks weather on their exposed surfaces to some extent, and thus do not show their true character unless newly broken. From an examination of such a surface, one can usually see whether the rock is crystalline or not.

Of the noncrystalline rocks, *shales*, which are consolidated fine sediments, are usually hardened clay or mud and have a characteristic fracture. Generally dull in appearance, shale can be scratched with a fingernail. If it breaks into irregular laminae, the shale is argillaceous; if gritty, arenaceous; if black, it may be bituminous; if it is gray and if it effervesces on the application of acids, it is calcareous. Slate can easily be recognized by its characteristic fracture or cleavage and its fine uniform grain; in color it may vary from black to purple or even green. All these rocks demonstrate their argillaceous nature by emitting a peculiar earthy smell when breathed upon.

Limestone is one of the most widely known rocks; it can often be distinguished by its obvious organic origin, but a surer mark of distinction is that it effervesces briskly when dilute hydrochloric acid is applied to it. Marble is a crystalline (metamorphic) form of limestone, generally distinguished by its crystalline texture but always effervescent when treated with dilute acid. *Dolomitic limestone* is generally dark in color; it effervesces slowly when treated with cold hydrochloric acid, but more quickly when the acid is warm. *Flint* and *chert*, compact siliceous rocks of uncertain chemical or organic sedimentary origin, occur often as nodules in limestone beds.

Conglomerates and *sandstones* form another interesting group of sedimentary rocks; their granular structure suggests their sedimentary origin. Conglomerates are, as their name implies, masses of gravel and sand, water-borne, as denoted by rounded shapes, and cemented together in one of several ways into a hard and compact mass. Sandstone is the general term used to describe such sedimentary cementation of sand alone. *Quartzite* is a metamorphosed type of sandstone in which the grains of rock have been cemented together with silica so strongly that fracture takes place through the grains and not merely around them. *Grit* is a term sometimes used to denote a coarse-grained hard sandstone containing angular fragments.

The identification of igneous and some of the metamorphic rocks not yet mentioned is not quite so straightforward as the determinations so far described. These rocks are usually crystalline, but the crystals may vary in size from those of coarse-grained granite to those so minute that they must be examined under a microscope. Of the remaining metamorphic rocks, *serpentine*, a rock composed wholly of the mineral of the same name, is generally green to black, fairly soft, and greasy or talclike to the touch; the color may not be uniform. Serpentine is important to the civil engineer, since it is a potent cause of instability in rock excavation. *Gneiss* may be recognized by its rough cleavage and typical banded structure, which shows quartz, feldspar, and mica with a coarse structure. *Schists* may be distinguished from gneiss by their essentially fissile character; in all schists, there is at least one mineral that crystallizes in platy forms (mica, talc, or chlorite) or in long oblong blades of fibers and gives the rock a cleavage parallel to the flat surface.

Granite is a typical example of igneous rocks; it is widely distributed and constitutes an important igneous rock type. It must, however, be noted that the origin of some granites is today a matter of keen debate in geological circles. Granite is composed mainly of quartz (clear), ortho-clase feldspar (white or pink), some mica, and possibly hornblende. All the crystals are about the same size, or even-granular, and the quartz (the last mineral to separate) occupies the angular spaces between the other crystals; this latter characteristic marks a *granitic* structure. Color may vary from pale gray to deep red, depending on the mineral content; an average composition, however, is 60 per cent feldspar, 30 per cent quartz, and 10 per cent dark minor minerals. The texture of igneous rocks varies from a coarse even-granular structure to an aphanitic structure in which crystallization cannot be seen with the unaided eye. In a porphyritic structure, the constituent minerals occur as much larger crystals than the remainder (the large crystals are called *phenocrysts*); the other minerals may appear as a crystalline groundmass, or alter-natively, they may be aphanitic. Finally, there are a few rare igneous rocks found in glasslike form which have not crystallized at all.

As a general rule, the acid igneous rocks tend to be lighter in color than the basic rocks; granite, therefore, is pale because of the pre-dominance of feldspar, a light-colored mineral. *Diorite* has a texture similar to that of granite, but it contains no free quartz. In *gabbro* (the corresponding basic rock), feldspar is subordinated but is still an im-portant constituent; hornblende, pyroxene, and olivine are dark minerals which make the rock dark and give it a high specific gravity. *Dolerite* is a similar basic rock with a smaller grain size; *basalt* is the corresponding aphanitic rock, although occasionally phenocrysts will be found in it.

Granite porphyry and *diorite porphyry* are similar to granite and diorite in composition, but they have a porphyritic structure, feldspar being the most usual phenocryst. The porphyries are a common group of rocks; they are hypabyssal and occur as sills, dikes, laccoliths, and also in lava flows. *Rhyolite*, an extrusive rock, corresponds to granite (an intru-sive rock); it contains phenocrysts in varying quantities. *Andesite* bears a similar relationship to diorite; it contains no quartz. The aphanitic type of both rhyolites and andesites is known as *felsite*, a name that includes most of the large group of light-colored aphanitic igneous rocks; the corresponding dark rocks are classed as *basalts*. Glasslike rocks are found only in the vicinity of cooled lava flows; *obsidian*, a lustrous, dark rock, is the commonest variety. *Pumice* is simply a frothed type of glassy rock.

The foregoing list includes the main common varieties of igneous rock; it must again be emphasized that there is no hard and fast dividing line between a given variety and the adjacent one in scale. It cannot be too strongly urged that study of rock structures *in situ* is the only truly reliable method of becoming familiar with the rock types described. As a preliminary to outside work, one may profitably study hand specimens of rock which are available in the geological departments of universities and in natural history museums. Color, feel, surface appearance, and the nature of fracture are all so important in distinguishing rock types that only through contact with actual specimens can one begin to accumulate that practical experience which is the essence of true geological study.

2.11. The Geological Cycle. The study of the processes that have led to the existing structural arrangement of the earth's crust may be approached by considering the similar processes at work in the world today. These are described generally as the *geological cycle* and may be presented as in Fig. 2.2. Denudation of existing rocks, or earth sculpture, is carried out by agencies such as severe temperature changes (especially

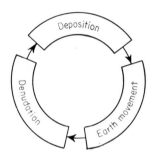

Fig. 2.2. The geological cycle.

the freezing and thawing of ice in cracks), wind action (especially in desert regions), the action of rain water on exposed soluble minerals and on rocks decomposed by water, the action of running water in eroding rock surfaces, the disintegrating and transporting power of the slow-moving ice of glaciers, and finally the erosive action of the sea on almost all coast lines.

Sedimentation is due to either wind or water action, principally the latter, since the action of wind is generally confined to desert regions. Deltas, at river mouths, and the deposits that accumulate behind artificially constructed dams are an obvious result of sedimentation. Other material is carried by rivers into the beds of oceans or lakes, although not all the material derived from earth sculpture reaches this resting place. But in this way a slow change is wrought in the configuration of the earth, and eventually, modifications lead to uneven pressures on the sub-crustal portions of the earth; some movement is certain to result as these pressures disturb the equilibrium of the local crustal structure.

These two parts of the general cycle can be observed to a limited extent today. A true appreciation of the third part of the cycle requires more imagination and an excursion into the realm of geological time. It is true that there are some evidences of minor earth movement occurring now. One example which may be mentioned is the appreciable sinking of large areas of the Mississippi flood plain near New Madrid, Missouri, in 1811. Another is the subsidence of the shores of Lake Maracaibo in Venezuela and at other locations, which will be referred to later. Coal- and salt-mining subsidences are generally familiar examples.

Within recent years, there have also been some violent manifestations of volcanic action, notably the complete disintegration of the volcano Katmai in Alaska, last seen in 1912 and assumed to have been blown up by a severe volcanic explosion. Such effects are small when compared with the great earth movements of the past, which have given rise to the complicated structures known today. They are significant, however, since they indicate that the solid earth is not a conglomeration of unusual structural materials but rather a body that is just as susceptible to stresses and their strain effects as any other structural material. The daily recording of definite load and relief obtained on seismographs that are situated near tidal water is another telling reminder of the elastic properties of the earth's crust. Even the activities of the civil engineer can lead to such earth movement, as will be shown later by examples such as the troubles encountered during major excavation work on the Panama Canal.

Having the foregoing in mind, one may without too much difficulty imagine how great sections of the rock strata at surface level are distorted, strained, and crushed when subjected to stresses which they cannot resist. The movement can be divided roughly into general raising or lowering of large sections of the earth's crust and general bending and crumpling of sections of the crust. After such disturbing action, natural physical conditions readjust themselves to the changed configuration of the earth's surface, and denudation starts again. This will affect the most exposed strata first, and they may be quickly worn away. An underlying stratum will then appear at the surface, and the cycle will continue. By imagining the results of several such cycles, one may appreciate the main reasons for the present complicated structure of the earth's crust.

2.12. Special Structural Features. It will be useful to describe briefly the main structural features which are encountered in normal civil engineering work and which, by their variation from what may be called *standard stratification*, warrant being described as special. It must be emphasized that the unusual features to be described are no more than a few of the more general examples of special structural arrangements; each type described can be subdivided into many detailed classifications, and other more unusual features may be encountered.

Two generally accepted terms, *dip* and *strike*, are used to describe the present position of beds of rock with reference to the existing ground surface. The strike of a rock stratum is the direction of a line considered to be drawn along an exposed bedding plane of the rock so that it is horizontal; obviously, there will be only one such direction for any particular rock layer. The dip of the bed is the angle made by a line considered to be drawn on the exposed bedding plane at right angles to the line of strike, and thus is a measure of the inclination of the bed to the horizontal plane. These two particulars, together with the usual topographical information, definitely locate a rock surface in space; as such, they are invaluable to the civil engineer as they are also to the geologist.

Fig. 2.3. Well-stratified limestone near Port St. Mary, Isle of Man.*

Sedimentary-rock Bedding. The method of formation of sedimentary rocks leads in many cases to an uneven disposition of material and to an uneven distribution of pressure on deposits. Thus, a distinct variation in the physical qualities of a sedimentary bed at different levels, as well as changes in the thickness of a bed, may result. Sedimentary strata often thin out completely, which can cause confusion in geological mapping. Surface markings constitute another special feature of sedimentary rocks; one example is ripple marking—similar to that seen on a flat sandy beach after the recession of the tide. These variations are of minor importance, but another subsidiary feature is worthy of special note: It is what is called *apparent*, or *false*, *bedding*, caused by a special process of deposition—by currents from varying directions.

* All photographs without acknowledgments are by the author.

Igneous-rock Features. These have already been explained, in so far as the principal types of formation are concerned. They are mentioned here again to emphasize the fact that these several types of igneous formation may be encountered in structural geological investigations either in a perfect form (as shown in Fig. 2.1) or in an imperfect form caused by subsequent distortion or denudation.

Jointing. If any typical rock mass—igneous or sedimentary—is studied, it will soon be seen that in addition to bedding planes that may be visible (in a sedimentary rock), fractures also occur in other planes

Fig. 2.4. Cross-bedded Wingate sandstone, Johnson Canyon, Kane County, Utah. (*Photograph by H. E. Gregory. Reproduced by permission of the Director, U.S. Geological Survey.*)

roughly at right angles to bedding planes and give rise to a blocklike structure, though the blocks may not be separated one from another. Such fractures are generally known as *joints,* or *joint planes;* they result from internal stresses either during the cooling of the rock or during structural displacement. They are not unconnected with the cleavage planes of the constituent minerals. Joints are sometimes filled with newer igneous rock, which has penetrated into the cracks while still liquid, or with mineral that has crystallized out from solution, e.g., quartz and calcite. Some remarkably intricate formations of this type may be found in which the filled joints are so small that they are barely visible. In sedimentary rocks, jointing is generally regular; in granite, it is often

irregular; in basalt, it leads to the peculiar polygonal column formation
that is a striking feature of such locations as the island of Staffa off the
west coast of Scotland. There are many examples in North America,
although they may not be quite so generally known as the famous Scottish example. Joints are of great importance to the civil engineer, and
numerous references to them will be found in the main part of this book.

Fig. 2.5. Jointing in white granite, south of Tule Well, Pima County, Arizona,
U.S.A. (*Photograph by J. Gilluly. Reproduced by permission of the Director, U.S.
Geological Survey.*)

Folding. When the variable distortion of rock strata that can take place
is considered, folding is perhaps the simplest structural feature apart from
a general raising or lowering of the whole of one part of the earth's
crust. Basically, folding consists in the formation of simple regular folds,
as shown in Fig. 2.6; the portions are termed *anticlines* and *synclines*,
respectively, according to the type of bend. An anticline and a syncline constitute a fold. This essentially simple type is not always found
in practice. The first, and most general, variation is the inclination of the
axis of the fold with the result shown. In certain special cases, the folding
may not be confined to the one direction; if a rock mass is subjected to

bending stresses all around, a domelike structure may occur. If the simplest basic type is extended, many variations can be obtained, such as *double folds, reversed folds,* and even recumbent and fanlike structures such as are indicated. At first sight, the last might appear to be a purely hypothetical case, but several outstanding examples of this type of structure could be given, including the European mountain group of which Mont Blanc is a leading member. Photographs show something of the appearance of these folds in actual practice. It will be realized that

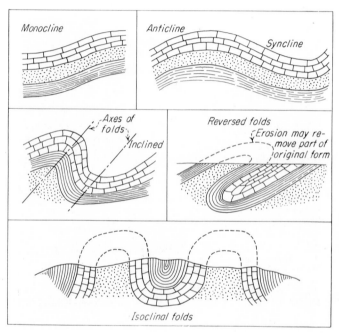

Fig. 2.6. Simple diagrammatic illustrations of some types of geological folds.

if the angle through which rock is folded is at all appreciable, unequal stresses will be set up in the rock mass. Normally, this is of no consequence, but to the civil engineer it can mean a great deal. If such distorted material is underground where the unequal stresses cannot normally be released, underground civil engineering operations may interfere with this condition and bring about unexpected happenings when the previously restricted stresses are released.

Faulting. When subjected to great pressure, the earth's crust may have to withstand shear forces in addition to direct compression. If the shear stresses so induced become excessive, failure will result; movement will take place along the plane of failure until the unbalanced forces are equalized; and a *fault* will be the result. Figure 2.8 shows in simple diagrammatic form the types of fault most generally encountered; the relative displacement of the various strata is clearly shown. In the simple fault, the terms most commonly used are indicated: the first fault shown is a normal fault in which the *hade* (or inclination with the vertical) is always in the direction of the *downthrow;* the *throw* of the fault is the vertical displacement; and the *heave*, the lateral displacement. In the diagram, the fault is shown as a plane surface; in practice, this is not always found. Frequently the rock on one or both sides of the fault is badly shattered

Fig. 2.7. Folded limestone, much contorted, on the foreshore at Scremerston, Northumberland, England. (*Geological Survey of Great Britain photograph; Crown Copyright; reproduced by permission of the Controller of H. M. Stationery Office, London.*)

into what is termed *fault breccia,* finely fractured fragments of rock, often retained in such close contact that they appear at first sight to be a solid mass. The direction of the main line of a fault is dependent on so many factors that it may bear no relation to the dip or strike. Thus, for convenience, faults are characterized by their general direction as *dip faults* and *strike faults. Step faults* and *trough faults* are terms that will readily be understood by reference to the diagram. *Reversed faults* are the opposite of normal faults, having the hade away from the direction of the downthrow.

A cursory consideration of these simple diagrams will suggest the complicated structures that can and do result from faulting, especially where the fault plane cuts across several rather thin strata. All these will be displaced, relatively to one another, at the fault; after denudation has taken place, their surface outcrops will be confusing. In the study of such structural results, the basically simple nature of faults must be kept in mind, coupled with the three-dimensional nature of the faulted section. The civil engineer's usually clear appreciation of three-dimensional drawings, based on solid geometry, will here be of great service. The study of solid geometry leads in particular to considerable simplification in the quantitative (as distinct from the qualitative) investigation of faulting, together with all allied calculations.

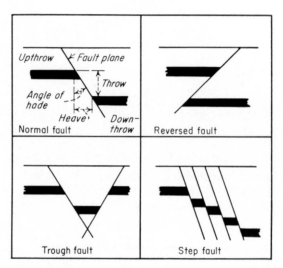

Fig. 2.8. Diagrammatic representation of some types of geological faults.

Faults may vary greatly in size. In length, they may range from a few feet to hundreds of miles; whereas in throw, they may include movements of a few inches or less (even pebbles have been found with perfect fault sections in them) to thousands of feet, as in the case of those in the plateau region of Arizona and Utah, some of which cross the Grand Canyon. Such dislocations may cause no unusual disturbance of topographical detail, although in some cases they may be the main factor affecting the physical character of large areas. In Canada, there are many notable conspicuous faults; for example, Lake Temiskaming, which separates Ontario from Quebec in the north, lies in a fault depression.

Denudation. Denudation listed under special structural features will appear to be almost a contradiction in terms. Yet the direct effects of the erosive action of wind, water, and ice are so markedly a characteristic of almost all geological structures that the use of the term to include these several effects may properly be permitted. On all approximately horizontal beds, the effect of such action will not, as a rule, be unusual; it will, in fact, be generally uniform except where watercourses have cut their way somewhat deeply into the upper strata. Inclined strata, however, may be worn down unevenly, which will result in exposures of varying thicknesses. Erosive action will vary in the intensity of its results, according to the hardness of the strata encountered. The resulting differential action may give rise to unusual structural features such as that indicated in Fig. 2.3 (page 53). Other notable results of erosive action

FIG. 2.9. A normal fault in beds of sandstone and fakes exposed in excavation at Clydesdale Iron and Steel Works, Mossend, Lanarkshire, Scotland. (*Geological Survey of Great Britain photograph; Crown Copyright; reproduced by permission of the Controller of H. M. Stationery Office, London.*)

are found in the history of river systems; this study is of special interest to civil engineers in view of the difficulty always caused by a buried river valley, a feature that will be repeatedly mentioned later in this book. The deposition of material so eroded need only be mentioned, since delta formation and other sedimentary effects have already been considered. Apart from the erosive action thus generally described, glaciation produces special topographical effects which may almost be classed as unusual structural features. These are considered in some detail in Chap. 3 because of their importance to civil engineers.

Unconformity. This is an important effect of the deposition of sedimentary strata on previously deposited sedimentary beds, which is most clearly demonstrated by a diagram (Fig. 2.10). *Unconformity* is the term used to designate the unusual juxtaposition of several newer beds on the older, and it will be seen that an exposure of this contact would not reveal a regular stratigraphical succession. Another term used in this connection is *disconformity*, which describes a juxtaposition of two series of beds with parallel bedding planes; the upper surface of the lower group has been eroded prior to the deposition of the upper group.

2.13. The Geological Succession. Despite all the earth movements briefly indicated in the foregoing pages, the original relation of the various rock strata and groups of strata, not only in one particular area but throughout the world, can usually be determined. Although the complete correlation is still unfinished, much has been done toward solving the many problems involved, and work toward this end is perhaps the supreme task of all

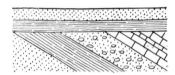

Fig. 2.10. Unconformity of geological strata.

geologists. In countries such as Great Britain, the general correlation can be regarded as complete, and the work now proceeding is generally on detailed local problems. In other parts of the world, however, no final results can yet be reported, and there is still much to do in linking the respective local systems, now studied as a whole. In the working out of all problems associated with stratigraphical succession, the study of the several special geological structures already described plays its part as one of the methods of the geologist. When the local succession of beds has been elucidated, it must be compared with similar arrangements of rock strata elsewhere in order to determine its place in the general geological timetable. This correlation is assisted by comparison of the detailed nature of the various rock types, their specific mineral composition, their general characteristics, and their fossil contents. As early an investigator as William Smith found that similar geological horizons have similar fossilized remains, a discovery that has withstood the test of time and forms one of the main foundations for the stratigraphical work of today.

Long years of intense study led gradually to the construction of a general table of rock groups, called the *geological succession;* it may usefully be likened also to a geological timetable. A summary of this table, which is generally applicable, is given on page 61. Naturally, the main geological measures are subdivided into many different rock groups, each of which is capable of further local subdivision; the table, however, shows what are now regarded as the standard divisions.

The importance of *paleontology*, the study of fossils, will be evident from its vital contact with and use in stratigraphy. Even a slight knowledge of the nature of common fossil forms will demonstrate the variety of types of life now entombed in rock strata, so that it will readily be

Table 2.3. The Geological Succession

Group	Per cent of total	System		Character	Derivation of system name
Recent	...		Present day	Age of reason	Fourth advance in animal life
		Quaternary	Pleistocene	Glacial; man developed	
Cenozoic	4	Tertiary	Pliocene Miocene Oligocene Eocene	Age of birds and mammals	Third advance in animal life
Mesozoic	4	Cretaceous		Age of reptiles and ammonites	The chalk, of Europe, is of this age
	2	Jurassic			From the Jura Mountains, where well developed
	2	Triassic			System has three divisions in Europe
Paleozoic	3	Permian		Age of amphibians	From Perm, U.S.S.R., where well developed
	5	Carboniferous			From presence of coal, in Europe
	3	Devonian		Age of fishes and invertebrates	From Devonshire, England, where first studied
	2	Silurian			From name of race in Wales, where first studied
	4	Ordovician			From name of race in Wales, where first studied
	7	Cambrian			From Cambria or Wales
	64	Precambrian		Beginning of life	Before the Cambrian

appreciated that the zoological aspects of fossil study constitute a further wide and complete field of investigation. Paleontologists themselves now concentrate in many cases on certain sections of their general subject. To these specialists, the civil engineer will always have recourse in connection with inquiries relating to fossils. Such inquiries are by no means so remote from normal civil engineering practice as might be supposed, although they may bear only indirectly on the immediate work in hand. Civil engineers may on occasion use fossils to determine the exact nature of certain strata with special reference to other beds. More generally, however, the works of the engineer will reveal sections of fossiliferous strata that would otherwise remain forever hidden to the geologist. Although not strictly a fossil remain, the skull of the now famous Rhodesian man may be mentioned in this connection. This was discovered, quite by chance, during extensive excavation work of the Broken Hill Mining Company in South Africa. In searching for lead, zinc, and vanadium, the engineer in charge of the work noticed the skull and saved it from destruction.[2.4] The discovery was of the greatest importance to all anthropological study. During excavation work for a new graving dock at Southampton, England, engineers uncovered a heavily fossiliferous section of the Eocene Lutetian beds. Apparently, the unusual fossils present were not noticed on the job; but through the cooperation of the engineers in charge of the work, geologists were able to examine the records of the strata, and scientific knowledge was thereby enriched. Other examples could be quoted, but all would have the same intent: to emphasize the scientific importance of civil engineers' realizing something of the nature of and not a little of the value of fossiliferous remains so that they will bring any such evidence that they may encounter in the course of their work to the attention of geological authorities.

Fossil remains may be of either animal or vegetable origin, and they may vary in size from minute organisms which must be examined microscopically to the great skeletons sometimes seen in museums. They consist of a mold, the petrified remains, or the chemically transformed body of a once-living creature of some sort—animal, insect, fish, bird, flower, or tree—preserved through the long annals of time in the surrounding rock stratum. Their preservation can generally be understood, and the details of the processes involved need not be discussed here. Naturally, only certain types of life have been preserved. All rock strata are not fossiliferous; fossils are therefore found only in some sedimentary and in some metamorphic rocks. Since the span of geological time is commensurate with the span of life on the earth, some demonstration of the evolution of living types might be expected in rocks of different ages, and this is found to be the case.

No attempt can be made here to describe even the leading typical fossils: one plate must suffice to demonstrate a few types as an introduction to fossil forms and possibly to serve as an incentive to further study in standard reference books. It may also be pointed out that the nature and type of fossils found in rock provide an accurate guide to both the cli-

FIG. 2.11. Some typical invertebrate fossils. (*Photographs by Dr. L. S. Russell. Specimens kindly loaned by the Royal Ontario Museum*).

matic and the geographical conditions obtaining on the earth sphere at the time that the bodies now fossilized were alive. Arctic and tropical climates have alternated (broadly speaking) throughout certain stretches of geological time; such changes naturally affected the type of life extant. The fossil types are likewise a sure guide to the nature of the deposition of the rock in which they are found; coal beds (the most generally appreciated repository of fossil life), beds containing fossil snails, and amber are three clear indications of the existence of some type of land surface. Other fossils are just as typical of lacustrine conditions, whereas others equally well denote marine conditions. Earth movements that have taken place since the original deposition during which the fossils were formed have resulted in wide and varied displacements of even marine deposits; for example, fishbeds have been found far inland and often at great heights above sea level. A word may be added finally to explain, if not to defend, the nomenclature adopted for the naming of fossils. Although so strange-looking to the newcomer, this nomenclature is nothing more or less than a simple type of scientific shorthand adapted to give a flexible system of classification, invoking as an aid to this task the classical languages. If this is remembered, *Strongylocentrotus drobachiensis* will become a term of some meaning.

2.14. Geologicial Maps. The main, and often the only, aim of geological field work is the determination of the present structure of the section of the earth's crust being examined and its relation to neighboring and similar structures. Thus it is that maps are used to record the results of these studies. By a logical extension of the principles of topographic mapping, it is possible to indicate clearly and unmistakably the geological structure determined by observation. The production of geological maps in this way is the ultimate goal of every geological surveyor. It is this geological mapping that is of vital importance in civil engineering. An important distinction is to be carefully noted. For the geologist, the geological map —when suitably correlated—is an end in itself. For the civil engineer, it is merely a means to the end represented by his major work. There is thus a distinct difference in emphasis according to the point from which the mapping work is viewed, and it is a difference that must be recognized and cheerfully tolerated in any cooperative work between geologists and civil engineers.

In most leading countries of the world, a geological survey is now an established scientific branch of central governmental activity. The publication of national geological maps and complementary memoirs is one of the main functions of official geological survey departments. Somewhat naturally, it is only in such highly developed small countries as Belgium, Germany, Switzerland, and England that national geological mapping has approached completion. In all leading countries, however, some official geological maps are available. These will often prove useful in civil engineering work, although necessarily in a general way only, since even the most widespread construction projects will call for some detailed geological investigation. Appendix B of this book is a guide to the geological surveys of the world; this will be of assistance in leading those interested to the best sources of published maps.

2.15. Conclusion. If independent geological investigations can be made without undue delay during field work undertaken specifically to assist some construction operations, the civil engineer should appreciate its value and encourage the saving of effort thus achieved. Similarly, it behooves geologists engaged on engineering work to realize that what the civil engineer wants is not a complete geological survey of an entire area but sufficient information to assure him of the conditions to be expected in those parts of the earth's crust likely to be affected by his operations. Mutual regard for the necessarily divergent viewpoints of the geologist and the engineer will lead to finer results from all joint effort. To this may be added the important suggestion that throughout many civil engineering construction operations, sections will be uncovered that may provide records of inestimable value to geologists, in some cases information that can be obtained only at that particular time. The courtesy of bringing these to the attention of geologists (the director of the local geological survey and the geological staff of the nearest university) cannot be too strongly commended.

So important can be this appreciation of the geological potentialities of excavation work, and correspondingly, so unfortunate can be its neglect, that this alone is warrant for the suggestion that all civil engineers should know at least the rudiments of geology. Unfortunately, the time has not yet come when all undergraduate civil engineering programs include a course in introductory geology. This gap in engineering education, slowly but steadily being closed, is one reason for the inclusion in this book of a summary chapter. The chapter also provides a brief refresher course for those readers who have not had occasion to study geology since their undergraduate days. It is, therefore, a chapter for civil engineers and not for geologists. Nobody can realize more fully than the writer the inadequacy of such a brief review of so great a science. It is intended, however, to be no more than an introduction, or a reminder, but it may (and this is the author's hope) act as an incentive to further study in some of the many fine books on all aspects of geology now available. For convenience, a selection of these as guides to further study follows. The attention of all engineer readers of this volume is directed to them; not only can they assist such readers in the field of engineering but they can also provide a background of geological knowledge which will add much to the pleasure of travel and to the appreciation of all that the beauty of nature can mean.

And if there should be any readers who consider it passing strange that engineers should be asked to consider scientific matters, even in connection with such natural features as rocks, while engaged upon their engineering work, they may reflect upon the fact, well recorded, that Alexander the Great (who died in the year 323 B.C.) attempted to survey his vast empire by organizing a special force whose task it was to maintain the condition of the major roads then existing. The services of these earliest of engineers were made available by Alexander for scientific purposes also, such as the collection of information regarding the "natural history" (including the geology) of the districts in which they were at work.[2.5] The association of geology with engineering has, therefore, a long tradition.

Suggestions for Further Reading

The literature of geology, even in English, is now so extensive that it would be invidious to attempt any selective list. Fortunately useful guides are available. At regular intervals the journal *Economic Geology* publishes a full listing of currently available books on geology; the books come mainly from American publishers, but the list also includes some British titles. For a world-wide survey, reference may be made to a small book published by the Museum of Natural History in New York: B. Mason's "The Literature of Geology," 155 pp., 1953. The general guides noted at the outset of Appendix B will also be found useful.

Typical of the many excellent modern textbooks on the subject now available are:

Emmons, W. H., G. A. Thiel, C. R. Stauffer, and I. S. Allison, "Geology: Principles and Processes," 638 pp., McGraw-Hill Book Company, Inc., 1955.

Longwell, C. R., and R. F. Flint, "Introduction to Physical Geology," 432 pp., John Wiley & Sons, Inc., 1955.

Since paperbacks are now so popular and yet do not normally appear in such guides as have been mentioned, please note the following three examples of this type of book; they are of special value to engineers interested in geology:

Zim, H. S., P. R. Shaffer, and R. Perlman, "Rocks and Minerals," 160 pp., Golden Nature Guide, Golden Press, New York. 1957. This is quite the best "pocket guide" known to the author. Convenient in size and unusually well-illustrated, it provides an excellent introduction to the science for quick perusal.

Dury, G. H., "The Face of the Earth," 223 pp., Pelican Books (A447), Penguin Books, Ltd., Harmondsworth, Middlesex, England, 1959. A good review of the essentials of physical geology.

Adams, F. D., "The Birth and Development of the Geological Sciences," 506 pp., Dover Publications, New York, 1954. Fortunately, this justly famous book is now available in this convenient form.

Chapter 3

SOILS: THEIR ORIGIN AND DEPOSITION

Again, do you not see that stones even are conquered by time, that tall turrets do fall and rocks do crumble. . . . Do we not see lumps of rock roll down torn from the lofty mountains, too weak to bear and endure the mighty forces of time finite? For they could not thus suddenly be torn off, if they had endured all through time indefinite all the wrenching of the ages without breaking up.

Lucretius[3.1]
(99–55 B.C.)

THERE IS one branch of geological study that is of special importance to civil engineers—the geology of soils. It is safe to say that the problems and difficulties encountered in engineering work, in both design and construction, are many times more frequent and more serious when structures have to be founded upon soil than upon bedrock. In spite of this fact, geologists as a whole have not devoted anything like the attention that been given to "hard-rock geology" to the corresponding study of the geology of soils. There are many excellent reasons for this relative past neglect, but perhaps the main one is the economic unimportance of soils. Even this is a relative statement, since it is naturally based on the fact that so much officially conducted geological work has necessarily had to be concerned with mining; and in ordinary mining work, soils are at best regarded merely as a nuisance. The picture is slowly changing. The increasing emphasis placed upon geological investigations in connection with ground-water surveys and inventories has inevitably directed more attention to soils. The decreasing amount of sand and gravel in many developed areas is having a similar effect. The recognition that geology is steadily gaining as an essential aid in civil engineering is itself assisting in the same direction. It is now not uncommon for geological surveys to have sections devoted to Pleistocene geology. Corresponding ground-water sections are making their own contributions to a better understanding of the geology of soils. A review of geological literature leaves no doubt of the recent general increase of interest in this somewhat neglected aspect of geology.

67

One very real stumbling block in the last few decades has been the matter of terminology. The word "soil" is popularly used by the man in the street to denote the loose material constituting that part of the immediate surface of the earth in which vegetation grows. As used in this sense, the word describes a layer no more than a few inches thick, usually containing some humus. In scientific agriculture, the word has been adopted to describe something more than this, but still a somewhat limited zone measured from the surface down—that intensively studied by the pedologist. It is this restricted use of the word within a scientific discipline much younger than geology that appears to have led to most of the confusion. The records of geology show that the early geologists used the term in exactly the same way as engineers of today to denote all the loose fragmented material in the earth's crust, no matter how far below the surface it might be. William Smith, for example, used the word in this sense as early as 1815 in his description of his famous "Map of the Strata." The unfortunate duplication in the use of the word appears to have arisen by the translation from the Russian, by way of a German translation, of the two Russian words for topsoil and soil, respectively, as one word in English. With the mutual understanding that exists within the scientific world, the joint use of the word is gradually being accepted without much question; the context usually shows in which sense the word is used. To avoid any possible misunderstanding, however, it may be well to observe that "soil" is used throughout this book to denote all the fragmented material in the surface of the earth, excluding only the top few inches with its organic content, to which the term "topsoil" is applied. This practice follows the general pattern of writing in geology and civil engineering in both North America and Great Britain, as instanced, for example, by the British Code of Practice for subsurface investigation (CP 2001, 1957) wherein the distinction is illustrated in diagrammatic form.

All engineers, therefore, and most geologists use the word "soil" to distinguish loose fragmented material in the crust of the earth from solid rock. Soil mechanics is, correspondingly, the world-accepted English title for the engineering study of such material. It is, admittedly, impossible to draw a hard and fast line of demarcation between soil and rock; some of the softer shales, for example, grade imperceptibly into the stiffer clays. On such a borderline of terminology, however, there is little need for argument. It is with soils, as herein defined, that the engineer has his difficulties, meets his problems, and undertakes his vast earth-moving operations. The word "earth" is a synonym for soil, but it is generally confined to the construction job. The engineer should therefore know something of the origin of soils and how transported soils have reached their present position. This knowledge will improve his understanding of the characteristics of soils, and it is an essential prerequisite to the full appreciation of the potential contribution of soil mechanics to civil engineering practice.

3.2. The Origin of Soils—Rock Weathering. Examination of almost any rock surface that has been exposed to the atmosphere for an appreciable period will show that it has been noticeably affected by this exposure; in many cases, disintegration of the surface layer will be apparent. As a result of the complex action caused by atmospheric factors, soils and, similarly, the mechanically formed sedimentary rocks have been created.

Fig. 3.1. "Nature's architecture"; unusual scenery on the Makran Coast, Iran, attributed to the action of sand-laden winds and to erosion of jointed and stratified rocks by torrential rains. (*Photograph by The Times. Copyright, The Times, London; reproduced by special permission.*)

The process of change resulting from exposure of rocks to the influence of the atmosphere is known as *weathering*. Dr. G. P. Merrill has suggested that the word should be "applied only to those superficial changes in a rock mass brought about through atmospheric agencies, and resulting in a more or less complete disintegration of the rock as a geological body . . . it does not include those deeper-seated changes . . . during which the rock mass as a whole maintains its individuality and geological identity."[3.2] The term *alteration* is used to describe these internal rock changes which are often of the nature of hydration and lead to the formation of new minerals in the rock mass.

So variable and uncertain are atmospheric influences that the process of rock weathering is always most complex; it naturally varies at different localities, at different elevations above the sea, at different times of the year, and with different rock types. It is possible, however, to classify generally the several agencies responsible for weathering, although the

FIG. 3.2. Exfoliating granite on lower Quarter Dome, Yosemite National Park, California. (*Photograph by F. E. Matthes. Reproduced by permission of the Director, U.S. Geological Survey.*)

relative significance of each varies according to local circumstances. It is often difficult to separate weathering from erosion, the process by which the products of weathering are removed from their natural location, since the two are often simultaneous. For convenience, and in accord with the distinct identities of the two processes, they will be considered separately.

The action of the atmosphere itself, i.e., of the mixture of gases that constitute the air, is practically negligible as a cause of weathering; only when water (or moisture) is present are the constituents of the air significant. Movement of the atmosphere, in the form of strong wind, is an important agency in arid parts of the world, and is, in addition, a leading means of erosion. In dry areas, where winds can pick up and carry along in suspension solid particles such as sand grains, the grinding, or "sand-blasting," effect of this solid matter on exposed rock faces can be a very effective mechanical agent of rock weathering. Figure 3.1 shows an ex-

Fig. 3.3. Exfoliation of granite boulder caused by a forest fire, Northern Quebec, Canada.

treme example of the type of scenery resulting from this action, examples of which on a smaller scale will be familiar. Variations in the temperature of the atmosphere are another cause of weathering attributable to the atmosphere itself; if the changes occur suddenly and cover an appreciable range of temperature, the internal stresses set up in an exposed rock mass may be sufficient to cause flaking off of surface layers. *Exfoliation* is a name frequently applied to this particular phenomenon, which is not at all uncommon. Temperature changes are usually of more effect in the case of igneous rocks than in that of sedimentary rocks, especially with the coarser-grained igneous rocks, the several minerals in which may have coefficients of expansion that are sensibly different from one another.

Temperature plays an important part in one of the mechanical processes of weathering caused by water—the effect of freezing water. Rain falling on rock surfaces will naturally fill up any exposed cavities, open cracks, and joints in the rock mass and will tend to fill up the empty pore spaces of the rock. If freezing takes place, this entrapped water will exert a powerful disrupting force on the surrounding rock; the corresponding disintegration will often be considerable even in a short period of time.

Fig. 3.4. Exfoliation of coarse-grained gneiss north of Kidd River, Labrador, Canada. Slabs are wedge-shaped, 2 to 3 in. thick, and are moving downslope. Frost action is probably the responsible agency. (*Photograph by E. P. Henderson, Reproduced by permission of the Director, Geological Survey of Canada.*)

Running water, in addition to being an important factor in erosion, will also act as a weathering agent if it is carrying solid matter in suspension and as a bed load. The removal of solid material from a river bed is primarily a process of weathering, although it becomes immediately a feature of transportation. The corresponding action of moving ice, as in a glacier, is equally important over large areas, and the quantity of soil formed in this way has been appreciable.

Water plays another part in the general process of weathering, because of the fact that in nature it is practically never found in its pure state. The impurities in water give to it certain chemical properties which result in some of the most important weathering processes. Oxidation is one chemical reaction that may take place when rocks are in contact with rain water; it is especially notable in rocks containing iron, as the brown staining of weathered surfaces often shows. The detailed reactions are complex; but hydrated iron oxides, carbonates, and sulfates are some of the products. All these reactions are accompanied by an increase in volume and a subsequent disintegration of the original rock mass. Finally, there is the action of rain water as a solvent to be considered; in some localities this is the most potent of all aspects of weathering. The action is usually thought of in connection with limestones, but many other rock types are also affected to a lesser degree. Although pure water is a poor solvent of the more common minerals, rain water contains an appreciable carbonic-acid content which will in time decompose nearly all the rock-forming minerals.

There are a few other minor weathering agencies. Possibly the most interesting of these are living creatures and plants. It is believed by some that the action of bacteria is of real significance in connection with rock weathering, but the matter is still awaiting full investigation. Ants and similar insects may assist the weathering process by carrying grains of soil and soil moisture underground; in this way the chemical action of water may begin to affect a rock mass. Finally, the effect that plant growth, especially the spreading of tree roots, can have in splitting up solid rock masses and thus allowing other weathering agencies access to the interior of the rock is a phenomenon frequently observed.

The possible complexity of the combined action of all or some of these agencies of weathering will now be clear. When the general process is considered in relation to the measure of geological time, the immensity of this great part of the natural cycle will be apparent. Speculations as to rates of weathering are interesting but of little practical significance; what is of value to the engineer is the evidence of weathering that he encounters in his work and the variety of soils resulting from weathering in the immediate geological past. Wind-cut topography may not be within the purview of every engineer, but evidence of the erosive power of running water will be familiar to all who work out of doors. Glacial action can be traced only in areas that have been ice-covered in the past; in these regions, a variety of typical topographical features may be noted. The chemical action of water is usually seen by more detailed observation; the weathered appearance of most exposed rock faces in temperate regions is due to this agency. Observations of rock outcrops in the field will show how weathering conforms to features of rock masses such as joints and bedding planes, how the extent of weathering may vary with the nature of the rock, how weathering may cause the original rock form to be retained until the decomposed rock is disturbed, and how in other cases the weathering may cause the decomposed or disrupted rock automatically to separate from the parent rock mass.

Observations also show how the nature and rate of weathering are directly dependent on the type of rock exposed. Thus, to take extreme cases, a limestone may be partially dissolved away, leaving a cavity (such as many a famous cavern) and a residue of tough ferruginous clay, whereas a granite may weather only for a thin surface layer into "rotten rock," ultimately yielding sand and clay. Among the general rock types, many of the sedimentary rocks are themselves composed of weathered products (sandstone is a good example), so that it is to be expected that further weathering will be due merely to mechanical action. The other great group of sedimentary rocks, the limestones, are liable to be decomposed chemically. In the case of pure limestones, decomposition can be complete. With impure limestone, many records exist of a loss of weight of no more than 60 per cent; the residue frequently is a tough clay.

Table 3.1. Some Leading Rock-forming Minerals*

Mineral	Main products of alteration
Quartz................	Retains identity
Micas................	Variable; clay minerals and hydrous silicates
Feldspars.............	Soluble matter and clay minerals
Hornblende ⎫ Augite ⎭	Hydrous silicates
Olivine...............	Serpentine and iron oxide

* Arranged in order of resistance to weathering.

The weathering of igneous rocks is not so simple; the precise process of weathering varies with the mineralogical content of the rock and also to some extent with the grain size. The processes are complex, but fortunately, because of the recurrence of a few main mineral types in the more common igneous rocks, a broad outline of the process of weathering can be obtained. Naturally, hard minerals will offer more resistance to mechanical weathering agencies than some of the soft ones. Similarly, the more stable the mineral in a chemical sense the greater will be its resistance to chemical change. In consequence, free quartz, being at once hard and chemically stable, is the most refractory of all common minerals to the action of weathering. Some silicates are but little affected, notably the harder types such as tourmaline and zircon. The weathering of mica depends on the form in which it occurs and the rock of which it is a constituent. Of the feldspars, the potash varieties are generally more refractory than the soda-lime types.

Table 3.1 lists representative minerals and notes on the products resulting from their weathering. From an examination of even such a simplified statement as this, one can readily appreciate that the chemical reactions causing the changes noted are involved and in many cases of long duration. Essentially, the combined effect on rock masses is a breaking down of the mineral contents into relatively stable products of decomposition. The weathering process does not stop at this point. Even the most stable minerals are in time affected by contact with rain water; and if this has leached through an upper layer of humus, carrying with it a small percentage of organic acids, its effect as a weathering agent will be increased. By the prolonged action of this moisture on silicate minerals, certain secondary products of weathering are gradually formed; these range down to colloidal material and consist of what may generally be termed the *clay minerals*. These secondary minerals may be generally classed into three main groups: (1) montmorillonite—beidellite minerals, (2) halloysite—kaolinite minerals, (3) hydrated ferric oxide and alumina.

Many of the peculiar physical properties of clay are due to the properties of these minerals, especially those relative to moisture content. They are chemically reactive (particularly groups 1 and 3), being acidic in nature, and they possess the important absorptive property of ion exchange. This property may eventually prove to be of great importance in the treatment of clays responsible for difficulties in engineering construction. Research on these minerals is widespread, and much notable work has already been done. G. E. Ekblaw and Ralph E. Grim were able to state some years ago:[3.3]

(1) . . . that the concept that all clays contain a mysterious universal clay substance, sometimes called clayite, to which they owe their properties, is fallacious; (2) that the concept that all clay materials are composed essentially of the mineral kaolinite is erroneous; (3) that an alternative concept that these materials are simply heterogeneous assemblages of almost any species of minerals existing in very small particles and that therefore their properties are entirely dependent upon the size-grade distribution of the component particles is also erroneous; and (4) that they contain little or no amorphous material.

On the contrary, this work has shown that clays actually are composed of crystalline constituents throughout—even the colloidal fraction is composed of crystalline particles, the colloidal properties depending on smallness of particle size and also on the shape of the individual particles.

Soils are thus seen to be the aggregation of the products of rock weathering; their formation is due to the simultaneous operation over long periods of time of one or more of several weathering agencies, the general nature of which is known. The coarser particles found in natural soil formations above about 0.05 mm in diameter consist generally of the more stable primary products of weathering—minerals relatively hard and chemically stable. The finer particles consist mainly of the secondary products of the weathering of silicate minerals, called clay minerals, the properties of which are under active investigation.

3.3. Residual Soils. The erosion and transportation of the products of rock weathering, phenomena which are so frequently associated with the weathering process, are not universal. Over many parts of the surface of the earth where the natural rock surface is approximately horizontal, weathering of the rock surface has proceeded without the soils so produced being moved from their original position. Soils of this nature are known as *residual soils*. The name is accurately descriptive, since the soils are actual residues of the original rock; all soluble materials have been leached out by the long-continued seepage of ground water. This chemical disintegration naturally becomes less active as depth increases; the alteration of the original rock gradually becomes less until finally the natural unaltered rock is reached. This gradual downward change from

Fig. 3.5. Brown clayey loam and residual soil over weathered Galena limestone, as exposed in a cut on the Illinois Central Railway east of Monroe station, Wisconsin. (*Photograph by W. C. Alden. Reproduced by permission of the Director, U.S. Geological Survey.*)

the soil to original rock is a distinctive feature of residual soils and one by which they can readily be distinguished. Another characteristic is that the soils contain no minerals foreign to the locality; the entire mineral content is directly related to that of the underlying rock. Particles are sharp-edged and not rounded; fragments of the original rock may be found unaltered in the disintegrated stratum.

In other respects, residual soils may vary. They may retain the structure and even the appearance of the original rock until disturbed in some way; on the other hand, some residual clays show no evidence at all of their origin. Some residual soils are sandy, but residual clays are more common than sands. Others possess peculiar characteristics and have been given special local or regional names. Only one of these—*laterite*—warrants mention in this discussion. This name is generally applied to soils of tropical countries, notably of India; because of the absence of organic material in the topsoil and the consequent lack of humic acid to act as a leaching agent, such soils have a high alumina and iron-oxide content. Clays of this nature are soft when naturally moist but harden on exposure to the atmosphere. The name is sometimes applied in more temperate countries, such as the United States, to clays which have a high silica content, but its use in this way is largely governed by local practice. Residual soils are found only in regions that have not been greatly disturbed during recent geological time. They are not generally found in areas that have been subject, for instance, to glaciation. Some of the more recent soil deposits which are, in a sense, residual soils are not subject to this restriction. They are the deposits of organic and inorganic material accumulated by vegetation; they usually occur in the presence of water, especially in peat bogs and marshes.

3.4. Transported Soils. Erosion has been repeatedly mentioned as one of the great modifying influences at work today on the surface of the earth. It has been responsible for the formation of most of the sedimentary rocks covering three-quarters of the earth's surface; and, similarly, it is today ceaselessly at work removing the products of rock weathering and depositing them elsewhere. Thus it is now forming soils, some of which will in time become consolidated into the sedimentary rocks of the future. It has been estimated that 78 million cu miles of the earth's crust have been eroded in this way; the resulting sediments give 80 per cent shale, 15 per cent sandstone, 5 per cent limestone, and the corresponding unconsolidated materials.[3.4] Chapter 19 includes a discussion of present-day erosive processes and silting. Although gravity is usually thought of as the agency ultimately responsible for the movement of disintegrated rock by erosive processes, the action of the wind is an additional agency of consequence. Deposits of soil formed by the wind are known as *aeolian* deposits. Sand dunes are an obvious and notable example of materials so deposited; the extent of some suggests their age. Their frequent existence near seacoasts shows that arid conditions are not imperative for the formation of aeolian deposits, although wind action is most potent in dry regions. Wind-deposited sand may show traces of stratification; its mineral contents will usually be fresh, since it has been formed by a mechanical weathering agency. The shape of the grains—well rounded and in some cases almost spherical—is the most notable characteristic of aeolian deposits.

A special type of aeolian deposit widely distributed throughout the world is that known as *loess*. It is very fine-grained and is often yellow. It exhibits no stratification but occurs in great massive beds which may be hundreds of feet thick. The material is largely composed of silt-sized particles which under microscopic examination can be seen to consist of sharp-edged fresh particles of minerals, such as quartz, feldspar, calcite, and mica; it also has some clay content. It can fitly be described as an accumulation of wind-blown dust; its dustlike nature when in the air is evidenced in those areas in which it forms the surface of the ground—notably in China where ancient roads have cut themselves into the loess as deep trenches, where caves are excavated in it for human habitations, and where its characteristic color is used in names such as the Yellow

Fig. 3.6. Cut in loess adjacent to the railway station, Timoru, South Island, New Zealand.

River. A somewhat similar deposit found in the southwestern United States is known as *adobe;* it is used for making bricks and other molded articles by sun drying.

The most obvious type of gravitational erosive action is that which leads to the accumulation of rock fragments at the foot of exposed faces of rock, generally classed as *talus;* in extreme cases it may lead to the occurrence of rock avalanches. Here the force of gravity acts directly on the products of mechanical weathering. These accumulate until disturbed in some way, often by erosion of the toe of the talus slope by running water. In extensive accumulations of talus, the mass of disintegrated rock may eventually reach a state of unstable equilibrium, and itself start to move. If the movement is sudden, an avalanche will result, but if it is exceedingly slow, it will be noticed only by long-term observations. The term *rock glacier* is sometimes applied to such phenomena.[3.5] Clearly, they are of importance in civil engineering work; if they are unrecognized and covered by a mantle of topsoil, they may be utilized as a foundation bed, with possibly disastrous results. Study of the local geology in association with test borings and drilling should disclose the true nature of the material. A gradation from disintegrated rock near the surface to fragments of fresh rock at greater depths will be a main distinguishing

Fig. 3.7. Rock-talus slopes on basalt cliffs at Dark Harbor on the west coast of Grand Manan Island, Bay of Fundy, New Brunswick, Canada.

feature; all minerals encountered should be correlated with the adjacent natural rock formations.

Although aeolian deposits and talus are important types of deposits, the most important and most widely distributed types of transported soil are those which have been moved by water and by the slow movement of ancient glaciers. *Glacial deposits,* as the latter are called, are so important and so closely related to topography that they will be treated separately in the next section. *Aqueous deposits* are also important and constitute probably the largest group of transported soils. Aqueous deposits may properly be called sediments, as they have been formed by deposition from either standing or moving water in a manner entirely similar to that in which silting takes place at the present time. They are generally grouped into two main divisions: *marine* sediments and *continental* sediments. The former were deposited in the sea and the latter in fresh water, but in a variety of ways: some by river flow, some as deposits in fresh-water lakes, some as deltaic and detrital cone formations. All the processes of sedimentation can be observed today in some form or another, so that although there are many aspects of sedimentation as yet imperfectly understood, it is possible to classify the main ways in which material is deposited from moving water.

Fɪɢ. 3.8. A "model" alluvial cone; the early stage of the erosion of a soil bank on the ice cover of the Kaministikwia River, Ontario, Canada. (*Photograph by H. B. R. Craig. Reproduced by permission of the Ontario Dept. of Mines from 45th Annual Report, pt. VII, 1936.*)

Continental or terrestrial sediments may, in the first place, be transported by the headwaters of a running stream; disintegrated rock or eroded soil will be carried along by the stream flow, since the bed gradient will be steep. As the stream changes slope on entering a level area, its velocity will decrease, and a great deal of its load will be deposited as an alluvial cone, or alluvial fan. Material has been deposited in this way, probably, at all stages of the earth's history. Such deposits are to be distinguished in the vicinity of most important mountain ranges, and they are often of surprising depth and extent. Much of the sedimentary material found in the coastal plain of the United States of America is thought to have been formed in this way. The deposits show stratification, as would be expected from the nature of their formation;

and because of the change in the volume of flow of all steeply graded streams, adjacent strata may vary greatly. Alluvial cone deposits usually show a major variation from the coarse sediment (possibly including boulders) at the apex to fine clays at the outer reaches. If the process of erosion continues without serious earth movement, the materials in an alluvial cone may themselves be eroded as the life history of the responsible stream develops.

The final stage of river development is also a notable factor in sedimentation. After a stream has reached maturity, any increase in the

Fig. 3.9. River terraces at the junction of the Nicola River with the Thomson River in British Columbia, Canada. (*Reproduced by permission of the Director, Geological Survey of Canada.*)

volume of sediment brought down from its higher reaches will result in an *aggrading* of the river—a steady building up of the river bed. Several notable examples of this process may be seen today. Corresponding *natural levees* are built up at the sides of the normal river channel, and in times of flood the river water will extend beyond these, covering a large area on either side (if in flat country) on which material is slowly deposited; this area is known as the *flood*, or *alluvial*, *plain*. Material deposited in this way will also be stratified, but all of it will be fine-grained. Ancient deltaic deposits exhibit the same structural arrangement of beds; stratification is regular and grain size is uniform. River terraces, or *alluvial terraces*, often assist in the location of deposits of fine-grained sediments. They may be old flood plains below which the river has scoured out a deeper bed, possibly because of interference with the head-waters of the river. Alternatively, they may be evidence of earth movement that has led to a major alteration in the regime of the stream.

In desert regions, rivers may flow (often intermittently) into inland basins that are either dry or covered with only shallow water. The sedimentation that takes place in such regions when the rivers in flood bring down large quantities of material with them is obvious. If earth movement accompanies sedimentation, the depth of the deposits may become considerable, and this has happened in the past. The material will be stratified, and as none can escape, it will be varied, often including layers of common salt and gypsum. Rivers flowing into lakes will tend to form deltaic deposits similar to those at outfalls into the sea or to those of marine deltas.

Marine deposits are usually considered as having been formed in one of three regions: the shore zone; the shelf, or shallow-water, zone; and the deep-sea zone (extending beyond the edge of the continental shelf). It is helpful to recall that all marine sediments are derived from the material transported by rivers and that eroded from seacoasts. Except in the shore zone, therefore, fine-grained sediments are to be expected. The material in the shore zone, although often of considerable local importance, is really of a temporary nature, since it varies with changes in shore line and is itself constantly being changed. It is predominantly coarse and is usually classed as sand and gravel; its observed irregularity is characteristic.

Deposits in the shelf, or shallow-water, zone, often considered as extending to the 100-fathom line, are of great importance. The region is one of ceaseless change; the movement of the sea gradually sorts out the material deposited on the sea beds and the finer material gradually works down into the deeper water. Interesting as are present-day deposits in this zone, the corresponding deposits of previous eras are of greater importance. Upward crustal movements involving parts of previous shallow-water zones have converted many of these sediments to land formations which cover surprisingly large areas and are often of considerable depth (because of repeated earth movement).

They are usually flat and display stratification; they may show gradation from gravel to finer materials, but clays will sometimes be found close to original shore lines. Although usually inorganic, many shallow-water deposits contain lime-secreting organisms which have been responsible for the formation of limestones. Ripple marks are a frequent occurrence in these deposits; and when they are of clay, "mud cracks" may still be seen, caused originally by the action of the sun on the wet clay. Shallow-water sediments sometimes display the tracks of land animals, and their fossil contents are often appreciable. The nature of the fossils can often serve as a basis for distinguishing between a marine shallow-water sediment and one laid down in fresh water; the general characteristics of the two groups are markedly similar.

There remain for consideration the deposits of the ocean depths. Characteristic sediments are muds, organic oozes, and clays of varying color but remarkable uniformity of texture. Of great present-day interest, they are of little significance in the study of soils, since the existence of materials from the ocean depths now forming part of the surface of the earth has been traced in the case of a few islands only. Marine deposits when spoken of geologically are therefore generally to be regarded as shallow-water sediments.

3.5. Glacial Action and Glacial Deposits. Just over 100 years ago, Swiss naturalist Louis Agassiz first reported the existence of boulders so far removed from their natural bedrock that he decided they could have been transported only by glacial action. It was many years before his revolutionary idea was generally accepted; the persistence of the word *diluvial*, suggesting the great flood as the origin of deposits now known to be glacial, is an interesting reminder of this conservative attitude. Today, the importance of glacial action in the geological cycle is generally appreciated. The large erratic blocks so often preserved in public places when discovered in urban areas are significant indications of the power of this great natural process. There are some blocks of this kind that weigh well over 1,000 tons, and some—even of this magnitude—are now at great heights *above*, as well as great distances away from, their original positions. Many readers will be familiar with boulders of this kind and so will appreciate the significance of glaciation as a factor in erosion. At one time this was probably the most influential of all erosional processes, since it is estimated that one-fifth of the land area of the world was covered by ice. This "Ice Age," as it is often called, is of great importance in connection with present-day soils and also with many civil engineering operations.

The existence of glaciers today in several parts of the world, notably in the European Alps and in North America, and the covering of Greenland and the Antarctic Continent with ice sheets have made these phenomena generally familiar. Without such contemporary examples, the state of the world during glacial epochs would indeed be difficult to imagine. Even with these examples available, it is still far from easy to imagine practically the whole of Canada and a large part of the northern United States, most of northern Europe (including the British Isles), Asia, and much of South America covered with ice sheets varying in thickness up to several thousand feet. This is now known to have been the case during the recent Ice Age which occurred during the Pleistocene era. The proof of this has been a fascinating accumulation of carefully observed facts linked to an outline of the effects of glaciation which are about to be described. It is known also that the ice receded at least three times; the interglacial periods were to some extent warmer than present-day climates in, for example, the Toronto district, Canada, where some of the most important *interglacial deposits* yet to be examined have been found.

Fig. 3.10. Sketch map showing area of North America covered by Pleistocene ice. For more complete information see R. F. Flint, "Glacial and Pleistocene Geology," John Wiley & Sons, Inc., New York, 1957. (*After Chamberlin and Salisbury.*)

Why these incursions of ice took place is still a matter of conjecture. The engineer has to accept the accredited fact that glaciation did occur over a large part of the earth's surface, and recognizing this, he must avail himself of all that a study of glacial geology can suggest of the possible effect of glacial features on his work. Figures 3.10 and 3.11 show in broad outline the areas in North America and Europe that were covered with ice and in which, therefore, glacial geology is of practical importance.

In considering glacial action, the reader should make a distinction between the two main types of glacier: the *mountain,* or *valley, glacier,* slowly moving down the valley that it fills; and the *continental glacier,* or *ice sheet,* overriding mountains and valleys and of considerable extent and

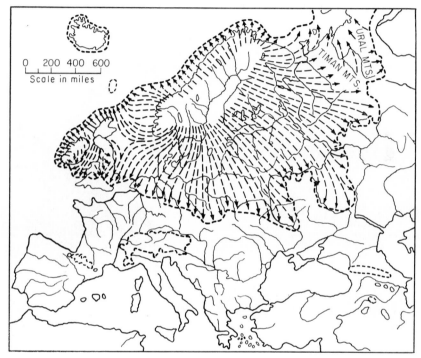

Fɪɢ. 3.11. Sketch map showing area of Europe covered by Pleistocene ice. For more complete information see R. F. Flint, "Glacial and Pleistocene Geology," John Wiley & Sons, Inc., New York, 1957. (*Based, by permission, on a plate in "The Quaternary Ice Age" by W. B. Wright, 2d ed., 1937, Macmillan & Co., Ltd., London.*)

thickness (the ice sheet over Greenland today, for example, is over 5,000 ft thick). Movement of the ice is similar in both cases, although rates of travel may vary considerably; some ice sheets remain stationary for long periods. Many interesting observations of the rate of travel of existing glaciers have been made.[3.6]

The action of glaciers in eroding and transporting material off the surface of the earth is well defined; the effects of the two types of action on topography are naturally different. As the mass of ice passes over the earth's surface, it may pick up loose and unconsolidated material directly, incorporating this into the lowest part of the ice mass. If some of the material is in the form of rock fragments and boulders and is pressed against solid bedrock as the ice passes over it, an abrasive action will result; the bedrock will be eroded, and thus more loose material (*rock flour*) will be picked up by the moving ice. Finally, it is known that thick ice sheets exercise a "plucking," or "quarrying," action; the lower part of the ice formation adheres to large blocks of rock, tears them away from their natural position, and carries them along.

Fig. 3.12. Glacial valley in the Flint Creek Mountains, near Anaconda, Montana, showing typical U shape. (*Photograph by W. C. Alden. Reproduced by permission of the Director, U.S. Geological Survey.*)

This erosive action has a definite effect on the topography of the land covered by the glacier. Continental glaciers level off the surface, eroding high points of land to a greater extent than low-lying ground. The ice sheet will follow the contour of the ground that it covers and erode constantly throughout the whole course of its movement. Thus it is estimated that glaciation removed on the average probably as much as 100 ft from the top of that great area of Precambrian rock now known as the Canadian shield. Much of this area is today bare rock, for weathering since the last glacial period has been insignificant. On exposed rock surfaces, the characteristic polishing and markings caused by rocks embedded in the bottom of the moving ice sheet are to be seen. The polishing is often remarkably smooth and uniform, broken only by the grooves and scratches (striae) made by projecting rock points; these markings are also found on some rock fragments encountered in glacial deposits. The polishing and markings provide good clues to glaciation, should this be in doubt. By studying these marks and by tracing the rocks found in glacial deposits back to their origins, geologists have discovered the positions of the centers from which radiated the ice movements indicated in Figs. 3.10 and 3.11.

Fig. 3.13. *Roche moutonnée* of Leven schist, with evidence of plucking, near Achriabhach, Glen Nevis Inverness-shire, Scotland. (*Geological Survey of Great Britain photograph. Crown Copyright; reproduced by permission of the Controller of H. M. Stationery Office, London.*)

The main erosive effect of mountain glaciers is to smooth out the valleys through which they pass, often deepening them considerably and almost always giving to them a characteristic U-shaped cross section in distinction to the V shape of a young valley being eroded by a running stream. A corresponding result is that valleys are straightened; the projecting hillsides between the valleys of side streams are removed. Frequently, if the side-stream valleys do not have glaciers in them, they will remain at their original elevation while the main valley will be deepened. After the glacier has melted, this will give rise to *hanging valleys*, a topographical feature responsible for many waterfalls and so for potential water-power development sites. The deepening of valleys by glaciation has led to many beautiful fiords and similar inlets from the sea when a general depression of the land surface has followed the glacial period. Another topographical feature caused by erosion is the *cirque*, or steep-sided rounded end of a valley that has been glaciated; this differs considerably from the typical valley formation caused by running water. Cirques result from the initial stages of glaciation; snow and ice collect in the head of the valley and gradually accumulate debris eroded from

Fɪɢ. 3.14. The Hugh Miller Glacier, Alaska, as it was in 1929, showing typical moraines. Mount Fairweather on the right; Mount Crillon on the left. (*Official U.S. Navy photograph from the U.S. Navy Alaskan Survey Expedition; reproduced by permission.*)

the adjacent valley slopes. *Roches moutonnées* are outcrops of rock that, having been passed over by a glacier, exhibit a striking and characteristic form, smoothed and rounded on the side opposed to the glacial movement and in a natural state on the opposite face.

The effect of glaciation on topography cannot be considered in relation to erosion alone; simultaneous deposition of the products of erosion has occurred and is frequently related to some of the erosive features already mentioned. Rock debris is carried in three ways by moving ice: at the bottom of the ice sheet; on its surface; and within the ice sheet, this material having worked its way in from the surface of the ground. While moving, ice deposits little of its load; but during the process of melting, it lays down *glacial deposits* which are of great importance.

Melting at the ends of glaciers can be observed today, but melting has not always been so confined and must be thought of as a much more extensive process, owing to climatic changes of unusual degree.

Material deposited by glaciers is generally divided into two classes: glacial deposits proper; and glaciofluvial deposits, which are laid down by water issuing from the glacier. Glaciolacustrine and glaciomarine deposits are those laid down in lakes and the sea bed adjacent to glaciers. Among the deposits from the glacier itself, moraines will immediately come to mind, as they are often so striking a feature of modern glaciers.

FIG. 3.15. The first stages of soil formation: rock screes and morainal deposits at the foot of the Taweche Glacier in the Himalayas near Mount Everest. (*Photograph by Erwin Schneider. Reproduced by courtesy of Fritz Muller and by permission of the Swiss Foundation for Alpine Research.*)

A *terminal moraine* is the deposit formed by wastage of the end of a glacier; the moving glacier may have pushed forward the material deposited as its front face melted away, or the melting of the glacier may have just equaled in speed its forward movement. Terminal moraines are therefore found as ridges across valleys, often of considerable height and in plan usually convex down the valley. *Lateral moraines* and *medial moraines* are the deposits formed by the material carried on the surface of the glacier at the sides and in its center, often in ridges parallel to its movement. They are frequently of considerable height, especially lateral moraines, some of which are over 1,000 ft high; in plan, they follow the direction of ice movement. Finally, the term *ground moraine* is applied to what is probably the most important of all types of glacial deposits— that deposited from the bottom of the glacier itself and consisting of material previously carried within the ice sheet at its lower surface. In thickness, this type of deposit may vary from 500 ft to almost nothing; it produces a fairly level, gently undulating surface. Occasionally, the surface of the ground moraine will be interrupted by small oval-shaped hills of unstratified clayey material which have their long axes in the direction of ice movement. They are called *drumlins* and are thought to be due to deposition through crevasses in the ice.

Fɪɢ. 3.16. Rough sandy morainal topography near Uxbridge, Ontario, Canada. (*Photograph by L. J. Chapman. Reproduced by permission of the Ontario Research Foundation.*)

Melting of glaciers produces streams of water which, in the course of running away, carry with them at least some of the debris previously carried by the ice from which they flow. Restricted in channel and swift-flowing at first, these streams gradually decrease in velocity and deposit their loads and so give rise to stratified deposits of the debris from the glacier. In a manner comparable to that which causes alluvial fans at points of change in river flow, *valley trains* are formed by the outwash waters from mountain glaciers as they leave the cover of the ice and start their flow down the valley. In the case of continental glaciers, *outwash plains* are the corresponding formation, although they are naturally on a larger scale. Some glacial streams may flow under the ice sheet in tunnels, and the debris they carry with them will tend to be deposited in long winding ridges along the path of the hidden streams. As the ice melts, these ridges will be exposed; they are called *eskers,* and some of them are several miles long. Similar deposits sometimes formed at the mouths of such hidden glacial streams are called *kames;* they are roughly conical hills composed of poorly stratified glacial deposits. If a glacier had its end located in the waters of a lake, depositional features already

Fig. 3.17. Excavation proceeding in glacial outwash deposits (close to dense glacial till) in the Lake St. John district, Quebec, Canada.

described would be somewhat modified, and a deltaic formation would result; *glacial deltas* are a recognized although infrequent type of glacio-fluvial deposit.

Since the different types of glacial deposit are associated with the results of the erosive action of the corresponding glaciers, the modification of topography made possible as a result of glaciation is surprising. Many major modifications have been detected and studied. Thus it is now known that in North America Lake Algonquin, a glacial lake which occupied the present basins of Lakes Huron, Michigan, and Superior, had outlets successively (or simultaneously) past the site of Chicago into the Mississippi, through the St. Clair River and Niagara, and through Georgian Bay. Similar examples from other regions can be found in publications dealing with local glacial features. Of far more importance to the civil engineer are the minor changes that glaciation effected, and these are particularly related to the deposition of glacial deposits in valleys that have been subject to glacial erosion.

"Buried river valleys" will be frequently mentioned in later chapters; their formation is due to glacial or subglacial erosion of a deep valley in solid rock which is afterward partially filled in by a ground moraine or other type of deposit. After the ice has gone, the ordinary river flow will have to carve out a new channel in the surface of the drift, and it is entirely possible that the new course will have no relation to the buried valley. A typical example is shown in Fig. 3.18. Terminal moraines often form natural barriers across the ends of eroded rock valleys. If impervious, they may be the cause of lakes in the valleys; and similarly, they

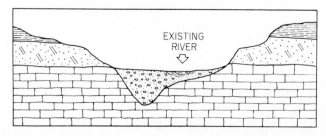

Fig. 3.18. A geological section illustrating a typical "buried valley."

may sometimes be relied upon to form a part of the impervious structure needed for the formation of a reservoir. In all such cases, owing to the unstratified and variable nature of terminal moraines, detailed subsurface examination must be made to obviate all possibility of leakage. In addition to covering up buried valleys, glacial drift will hide from sight all other irregularities of the bedrock surface; in some regions, these may be frequent and of appreciable magnitude, and they may account for some of the strange results obtained when putting down test borings or well shafts in glaciated areas. The latter is not a frequent operation, since the nature of the drift does not, as a rule, promote the accumulation of ground water. Glaciofluvial deposits, on the other hand, particularly outwash plains and valley trains, are frequently good aquifers.

The detailed nature of glacial deposits must finally be considered. The material transported by glaciers varies from the largest type of boulder to clays, including all gradations from one to the other; it is known generally as the *drift*. Prof. W. O. Crosby in a very early investigation found that the drift around the Boston area in the United States, on the average and excluding all large stones, contained 25 per cent gravel, 20 per cent sand, 40 to 45 per cent fine sand, and less than 12 per cent clay. The material either was picked up by the glacier from the natural surface of the ground or was eroded by the glacial action and then transported. If this eroded material is that which is ground off the surface of bedrock, it will usually be rock flour, finely ground fresh rock particles (its mechanical analysis generally places it in the class of silt) with no plastic properties. As deposited directly from the glacier, all gradations of transported material will be thoroughly mixed together; the resulting unstratified, unsorted mixture of unconsolidated material is known as *till*. The term *boulder clay* is often used to describe this unsorted deposit,

Fig. 3.19. Close-up view of glacial till near Wroxeter, Ontario, Canada. (*Photograph by L. J. Chapman. Reproduced by permission of the Ontario Research Foundation.*)

because of its usual boulder content, but the name is not strictly correct, since frequently the till contains no clay at all. A large percentage of the rock fragments will be angular in shape rather than rounded; many will exhibit scratches similar to the striae on polished bedrock surfaces; and the rock types encountered in the till will vary, often bearing no relation at all to any of the local rocks near the deposit.

This same material constitutes the load carried away by outwash streams from the glacier and thus forms the glaciofluvial deposits already described. During transportation by the running water, and through the mechanical nature of its deposition, the material will be sorted according to size, at least to some degree. The coarsest material will be deposited first, and the finest last. Glaciofluvial deposits are consequently stratified to some extent and consist of materials approximating the different soil groups. The exact nature of the deposits depends on the process of deposition. Thus kames, because of their irregular mode of formation and although stratified, will usually consist of materials that vary so much between strata as to make the deposit useless as a source of one particular type of soil, such as sand or gravel. Eskers are not commonly encountered, but because of their formation from running water, they generally consist of coarser materials (sands and gravels). Valley trains, outwash plains,

FIG. 3.20. A kame near Glen Ross, Ontario, Canada, showing structure of the deposit. (*Photograph by A. P. Coleman. Reproduced by permission of the Ontario Department of Mines.*)

and glacial deltas all provide fairly regular deposits of gravels, sands, silts, and possibly clays; the type of soil will depend on the location selected for trial relative to the formation of the deposit.

It will be seen that glacial deposits will not generally exhibit uniformity as a leading feature. This necessitates the exercise of the greatest possible care in investigating them before use. Attention must be devoted not only to the extent of the deposits but also, if one plans to use the soils, to their mineralogical nature. Because of the nature of their formation, glacial deposits will often consist of disintegrated rock that has weathered in a mechanical sense only; the constituent minerals will often be fresh. If, therefore, any of these minerals are liable to weather chemically on exposure to the atmosphere, one must exercise discretion in deciding to use the deposit as, say, concrete aggregate. Similarly, with respect to the finer deposits, one must guard against mistaking rock flour for clay; but with modern methods of soil testing, this distinction is easy to make.

Finally, brief mention must be made of glacial boulders. Erratic blocks were mentioned in a general reference at the outset of this section; they typify the boulders that *may* be met in glacial drift. Examples from construction practice will be cited to show what trouble undetected

Fig. 3.21. A "boulder pavement" at Sunnyside, Toronto, Ontario, Canada. The effect of such a glacial deposit, if not penetrated, on the interpretation of test-boring results can be readily imagined. (*Photograph by A. P. Coleman. Reproduced by permission of the Ontario Department of Mines.*)

boulders can cause. One of those encountered during the construction of the cutoff trench for the Silent Valley Dam for the Belfast water supply, Northern Ireland (page 501), was described as being "as big as a cottage." Although this case is unusual, it illustrates vividly the dangerous possibilities of inadequate subsurface exploration in glacial drift.

If an engineer once recognizes the fact that he is working in drift-covered country, he should obtain diamond-drill cores to a depth of at least 10 ft when "rock" is struck. By a careful examination of such cores, he should be able to tell whether the drilling is actually in bedrock or in a boulder. He will almost certainly gain valuable information if he appreciates the leading features of the main rock types; if he is in doubt, he should consult a geologist. There are few other ways in which geology can be of such direct assistance in the elucidation of an engineering problem.

3.6. Soil Characteristics. In the study of soils, the geologist and the civil engineer take two extreme positions: the geologist is interested primarily in the origin of soils, and the civil engineer, having less interest in origins, is vitally interested in types of soils and the properties peculiar to each type. Such extreme positions are tenable only in theory. In practice, the geologist has to differentiate among gravels, sands, and clays, at least in general terms; and the engineer, if he is to be able properly to appreciate soil properties, must give some consideration to the origin of the particular soils with which he has to deal. Thus, a common meeting ground for the geologist and engineer is the consideration that both have to give to soil characteristics. Note may well be taken, therefore, of certain geological features affecting soil characteristics, and this will be done without venturing further into more detailed aspects of modern soil-testing work.

In general, residual soils and many sediments will vary in character from the surface downward. If the latter are stratified, this fact may assist sampling operations, as the respective strata are identified. River deposits, especially those from swift-flowing streams, will probably be variable in content, as are also several types of glacial deposits. Marine deposits and flood plain sediments from mature stream flow tend to be more uniform. Whatever the origin of the soil, however, a general study of the local geology prior to taking soil samples will be of great value. When once the subsurface survey operations have been carried out, accurate records will be plotted to reasonable scales. In conformity with general engineering practice, one would quite naturally describe cross-sectional drawings of soil conditions as *soil profiles*. This is an expression to be avoided by engineers in their normal work, however, since it has been adopted by pedologists for a rather specific use. In order to avoid any further confusion in soil terminology, engineers should restrict their use of the term "soil profile" to the pedological use. Accordingly, all references to the graphical plots of cross sections of soil conditions, as derived from subsurface investigation, should be couched in terms such as "soil cross sections." Careful study of such sectional records will be invaluable, particularly in showing where additional soil samples should be procured. Especially is this the case with river and glacial deposits. Only when this study of the record has been made can the sampling be regarded as complete.

Special note must be made of the terminology presently employed for soil classification. Each of the main group terms used—gravel, sand, silt, and clay—is based on the *size* of particles composing the soil, generally without respect to their mineralogical nature. This is in contrast to earlier practice in geological terminology. Occasionally, compound names, such as *quartz sand* or *limestone gravel*, are used to describe materials more accurately, but such usage is still infrequent. The more usual compound names have relation to the physical properties of the soil, e.g., *fine sand* and *tough clay*. It is probable that a more frequent use of geological compound names will develop as soil studies progress.

Terminology in the field, as in the recording of test-boring results, provides another problem, since the selection of the names used to describe the soils encountered is still a matter of individual judgment. Experienced boring operators can usually be relied upon to differentiate correctly between different soil mixtures, but they use their own individual standard of comparison. Consequently, if a uniform and recognized standard is to be adhered to throughout the work it is advisable, in all soil exploratory work, to correlate the soil names used by those responsible for taking field notes with the results of laboratory analysis and test (see Chap. 6).

In this respect, as in others, laboratory work on soils can be of assistance to the geologist as well as to the engineer. In the laboratory, for example, the shape of sand grains can be determined, and their mineralogical nature can be ascertained; this information can often be of real assistance to purely geological studies of sedimentary origins. In some cases, it can be obtained by geological study in the field without the aid of laboratory facilities.

Gravels. Gravels are accumulations of unconsolidated rock fragments which result from the natural disintegration of rock and which are at least 2 mm in diameter. From this minimum size, gravel may range up to the largest pieces of rock normally encountered. Names commonly given to larger fragments are *pebbles* (from 4 to 64 mm), *cobbles* (64 to 256 mm), and *boulders* (having a diameter greater than 256 mm, or about 10 in.).

Gravels are widely distributed but rarely found without some proportion of sand, and possibly silt, unless these finer constituents have been washed out subsequent to the deposition of the gravel. They are characteristic shallow-water or river deposits (including the river flows from glaciers); they may also be beach formed, and some gravels are found in kames. The shape of the individual rock fragments and their relative mineralogical freshness will depend on the history of the gravel, but variations from rounded gravel to angular fragments may be met. Gravel that has been transported to such an extent that the individual fragments are rounded will consist of the more resistant rock types, often a mixed collection; but angular gravels, being comparatively new, may consist of fragments of even so relatively soft a rock as limestone.

Sands. Sand is the name applied to fine granular materials derived from either the natural weathering or the artificial crushing of rocks; sand ranges from 0.053 to 2.0 mm in diameter. Various subdivisions are used by different authorities to denote the gradations of sand-particle sizes; the most usual of these is to fix a diameter of 0.42 mm as the dividing line between fine and coarse sand. As it occurs naturally, a sandy soil mixture will frequently have some clay and silt mixed with the sand-sized grains. If the clay and silt content does not exceed 20 per cent, the mixture is called a sand.

The origin and therefore the occurrence of sands are similar to those of gravels; the two are often found together in one deposit. Beach sands, which may today be found far inland as a result of earth movements, are the most uniform type of deposit; river sand often contains relatively large amounts of gravel, silt, and clay. Glacial deposits may contain good sand beds, but they are likely to be uncertain. Residual sands are sometimes found. As sands are often derived from the continued disintegration of gravel, it follows that they will generally be composed of the harder and more stable minerals. The popular conception that all sands consist of quartz particles is, however, far from true. Although some sands consist of almost pure quartz, most of them contain at least a small percentage of other minerals. Some consist primarily of minerals other than quartz; calcareous sands are sometimes encountered in limestone districts. As a rule, their mineral content is fairly stable, but glacial sands may contain fresh minerals liable to weather on exposure.

The shape of sand particles may vary from completely rounded grains to angular fragments. The former are rare and are found generally in desert regions. The age of a sand deposit is no criterion of the shape of the grains; shape depends principally on the rock from which the sand was formed and the history of the sand during transportation. Thus, quartz grains from a granite rock will retain an irregular shape; from felsite they will be more truly crystalline; and from gneiss and schists they may be flat scalelike particles. Long travel in water will tend to round the grains, but this is a slow process, as is shown by the fact that sand at the mouth of the Mississippi is composed of angular grains. As a rule, river sands are more angular than those found in lake and marine deposits.

Silts. Silt is the name now given to soils with particle sizes intermediate between those of sands and clays, i.e., from 0.053 to 0.002 mm in diameter. Most inorganic silts have little or no plasticity, and many glacial silts consist of such fresh minerals that they may properly be referred to as rock flour. Silts that exhibit some plasticity will contain flake-shaped particles, usually one or more of the clay minerals, possibly partially formed. Silts may readily be mistaken for clays; they frequently have the "typical" gray color of clay and the same apparent consistency when wet. Simple hand tests, such as shaking a pat of the wet soil in the hand, will usually distinguish the two; a sample of silt will lose water, and its surface will thus appear glossy. Dry silts will crumble much more easily than any clay; correspondingly, they will create dust easily on light rubbing. In a natural position, and especially when damp, silts will be readily impervious. When disturbed, they will flow easily if an excess of water is present. Local variations sometimes carry expressive names, such as *bull's liver*, a term often heard on construction jobs.

Clays. Soil particles smaller than 0.002 mm in diameter and displaying plasticity when wet are known as clay. The name is correspondingly

Fig. 3.22. Typical section through varved clay at Steep Rock Lake, Ontario, Canada. (*Photograph by R. F. Legget; reproduced by permission of Steep Rock Iron Mines, Ltd.*)

applied to a soil mixture containing clay-sized particles of sand and silt, even up to as much as 70 per cent by weight, although the clay and silt content combined must exceed 50 per cent. Such a mixture will still display the characteristic properties of a pure clay. The essential qualification of plasticity shown by the soil mixture when wet is particularly to be noted; quartz may be so finely ground that it conforms to the size requirements of a clay, and yet it will have no characteristic clayey properties. It may also be noted that clay solids include particles of colloidal size; the colloidal content of clays is of great importance. Clays are now known to be crystalline and not amorphous, as was previously supposed; their particle shape is related to their peculiar physical properties.

As will be noted from a study of soil origins and deposition, clays may be formed by all the main processes associated with rock weathering. They may be residual or transported. Transported clays may be flood-plain river deposits of varying thickness and probably mixed with sand; lake deposits now elevated as a result of land movement; or estuarine or marine clays similarly raised from their original positions. The last are a particularly important group and occur in many parts of the world as large deposits. Finally, glacial clays (often called boulder clays) constitute a widespread series of deposits. The name is correctly applied, however, to many glacial deposits, although the mixture of sand, gravel, and boulders usually present in such deposits often renders them useless as a commercial source of clay.

Unlike other soil types, clays are susceptible to pressure and so may vary from quite soft to extremely hard. It used to be thought that shales resulted when clays were subjected to large pressures for considerable periods, but this view is now extremely questionable. The pressure may have been due to the presence of great depths of other deposits, subsequently eroded, or to that of an ice sheet possibly several thousand feet thick. Pressure of this magnitude cannot easily be duplicated in the ordinary laboratory; still less can the range of geological time be even remotely simulated in experimental work. Thus it is that when once a sample of such *consolidated* clay has been thoroughly disturbed (by remolding), it will lose its original properties, and these cannot be regained. Although consolidated clays can be detected in a laboratory by means of suitable tests, it is clearly of great assistance if this can be foretold from study of the local geology, and this is usually possible.

3.7. Organic Soils. Although organic soils are not frequently encountered in the normal course of civil engineering work, they can cause real problems when they are met. They consist essentially of dead organic matter derived from former vegetation, and they often have a surface layer of living vegetal matter, deteriorated to differing degrees and holding amounts of water that may vary up to well over 1,000 per cent by weight. The origin of these soils is obvious from their composition. They go by various names: *marsh, peat, bogs,* and *swamps* are the most general terms used in settled country, while *muskeg* is used in northern Canada. It is in the North that by far the most widespread occurrences of organic soil are found, for quite contrary to popular impression, the prevalence of organic soils decreases as tropical areas are approached. The rate of organic disintegration in tropical climates is so rapid that there is, to use an oversimplified expression, no time for organic soils to form. Organic soils are rarely of great depth; muskeg deeper than 30 ft, for example, is unusual in Canada. The character of the underlying soil is important in dealing with such soils in engineering work. They occur frequently in depressions in the former land surface, and this assists the accumulation of water. Their structure tends to make them spongelike, so that drainage of the water held by organic soils can be among the most troublesome of associated problems. They can be regarded as assemblages of fossil vegetation; accordingly, their age (if less than about 37,000 years) can be accurately determined by the carbon-14 method, and their original status by means of the corresponding modern technique of pollen analysis. The interesting term *paleovegetography* has been coined to describe this relatively new branch of terrain study,

Fig. 3.23. Typical muskeg country; road construction in northwest Ontario, Canada, showing draining of muskeg with preliminary roadbed construction on brushwood placed on the surface of the muskeg. (*Photograph by I. C. MacFarlane, D.B.R., N.R.C., Ottawa, Canada.*)

which has already a system of classification in reasonably wide use for such types of organic soil as Canadian muskeg.[3.7]

3.8. Permafrost. Permafrost is met with in the practice of civil engnieering even more rarely than organic soils, but it seems to have a degree of popular, and even of technical, interest quite incompatible with its very limited distribution in the far northern and far southern portions of the globe. The top of Mount Washington in New Hampshire is probably the only extensive example of permafrost in the mainland area of the United States, but most of the state of Alaska, about one-half of the land area of Canada, and about one-third of the U.S.S.R. are underlain by ground that is perennially frozen. It is to describe this condition that the word "permafrost" is correctly used, even though Prof. Kirk Bryan made a valiant but abortive effort to have semantically accurate terminology adopted for this new branch of geological study when it came to the forefront following the Second World War.[3.8] Regrettable, perhaps, from the scientific point of view but fortunately for the sake of euphony, *cryopedology* has not come into general use to replace permafrost. Terminological inexactitude has, however, gone even further in this field, since the word permafrost is today all too frequently used to describe

FIG. 3.24. Typical permafrost terrain; a view in the MacKenzie River Delta, Northwest Territories, Canada, showing frost hummocks, water standing in depressions forming ground polygons (due to ice wedges), and, in the right background, three pingoes, or "ice volcanos." (*Photograph by G. H. Johnston, D.B.R., N.R.C., Ottawa, Canada.*)

merely saturated soil that is perennially frozen instead of all such material. Strictly speaking, permafrost describes a condition rather than a material. It can be fully appreciated only in the light of a basic understanding of soil-temperature variation.

If the temperature of undisturbed soil be carefully measured throughout the year, a regular pattern of variation will be observed. Close to the surface, a daily cycle of temperature change corresponds to daily changes of air temperature. This diurnal variation is soon damped out, however, and the variation below 1 or 2 ft is annual only. At increasing depths, this annual variation is also damped out and retarded because of the laws of thermal transfer. In Ottawa, for example, a 6-month time lag exists at a depth of about 12 ft; the annual temperature variation is only 2 or 3°F at about 20 ft, since the temperature has reached the mean value about which the ground temperature above this depth is found to vary. It was originally thought that this mean ground temperature was always the same as the local mean annual air temperature, but this has been found not always to be true. Some carefully observed values suggest that the mean ground temperature is as much as 6°F greater.[3.9] The agreement is close, however, so that as one travels northward (in the Northern Hemisphere) one can expect the mean ground temperature to decrease, consistent with the decreasing mean annual air temperature. Eventually, the mean ground temperature near the ground surface will be 32°F and will go below this as one proceeds still northward. Permafrost is used to describe the ground condition thus created, i.e., to describe all that part of the earth's crust which is at a perennial temperature of 32°F or lower. In general terms, the temperature of the ground, below the lowest level of influence by annual air-temperature variation, increases steadily at a rate of about 1°F for every 150 ft. When this increase is sufficient to offset the low temperature of the ground near the surface, the zone of permafrost has been passed. The depth of permafrost, therefore, varies from zero at its southern edge to well over 1,000 ft in the Queen Elizabeth Islands of the Canadian Arctic Archipelago.

Permafrost describes, therefore, this condition of perennially frozen ground. If the ground consists of solid rock—as so much of the Far North does—the fact that its temperature is below the freezing point of water is of little moment to the engineer, interesting though it may be to the scientist. If the ground consists of well-drained soils such as sands and gravels, normally in a dry condition, the temperature will again make little difference in the use of such ground for human activity. If, however, the ground consists of soils saturated with water, then one is immediately faced with a combination of ice and soil solid. And if, as is so frequently the case with northern soils, the frozen soil is a saturated silt or an unconsolidated clay, then the fact that it is frozen can lead to very serious consequences indeed if its natural state is interfered with in the course of engineering or building work. It is this aspect of permafrost which has attracted such wide attention, since the interest of the public has been diverted by pictures of drunken-looking buildings and of roads and airfields which have failed spectacularly. Today, however, as a result of research that is still being actively pursued by Soviet, American, and Canadian engineers and scientists, means for satisfactory design in areas of permafrost have been developed, as will be mentioned in later chapters. Many problems still remain to be solved, particularly in the scientific field, before an understanding of the thermal regime of the ground in northern regions is achieved; the exact nature of the protective action of muskeg upon permafrost is, for example, still imperfectly understood. From the simple standpoint of geological occurrence, however, permafrost presents no problem, once it is realized that a condition of the ground is being described and not some new and mysterious material.[3.10]

3.9. Conclusion. The condition of permafrost, as it is seen today, and the formation of organic soils are naturally relatively recent developments. The process of soil formation, however, is as old as most of the rocks now found in the crust of the earth. Sandstone is clearly derived from the products of the weathering of older rocks, and some sandstones are among the oldest rocks known. Slates provide similar evidence of early rock weathering; and shales are intermediate between the slates and the clays. Although most of these soil-formed rocks are now unquestionably solid rock, there are other examples of ancient soils that have not been greatly changed from their original form. These are usually clays, but sands and gravels of great geological age are also encountered. Typical are the Triassic clays of England, Cambrian clays near Leningrad, Ordovician clays in Estonia, and the clays usually associated with coal measures in many countries. An unusual combination of circumstances, however, was necessary to preserve these ancient soils; therefore, a relatively small percentage of the soil presently in the crust of the earth antedates the Pleistocene period. As Table 2.3 (page 61) shows, this means that most soils are less than a million years old, quite juvenile by geological time standards.

It is for this reason that Pleistocene geology is of such great importance to civil engineers. To those engineers who have entered upon its study, Pleistocene geology usually and very quickly becomes a matter of genuine interest. It is a great common meeting ground for geologists and engineers, for the work of the Pleistocene geologist is often temporarily suspended until new soil exposures are revealed by the excavation work of the engineer. Many strange and perplexing variations in soil conditions can be explained, and can sometimes be foreseen, only by the geologist who is well versed in the Pleistocene history of the locality being investigated. Correspondingly, it is naturally in the study of soils that the engineer will have an opportunity to cooperate with the pedologist. There is much to be gained, and nothing to be lost, from the closest possible collaboration in this field of mutual interest. Pedologists are well aware of the dependence of their detailed soil studies upon the geological origin of the soils with which they deal; it is implicit in most pedological literature. Geomorphologists, and all who are interested in the physical geology of the present surface of the earth, whatever title they may use to describe themselves, share this interest in the geology of soils, since so much of the earth's surface is now covered with a mantle of soil of recent geological origin.

The geology of soils is therefore a meeting place for several scientific disciplines. Long neglected, it is at last gaining full recognition. This is reflected in the growing volume of geological literature dealing with soils, so remarkably summarized in Charlesworth's encyclopedic two-volume work, "The Quaternary Era."[3,11] The use of this term, and the perhaps more frequent use of the name *Pleistocene*, may possibly prevent engineers from realizing fully the wide interest that does now exist in the geology of soils—an interest in which they can share. Geological societies regularly hold meetings to discuss Pleistocene geology; although some discussions in this field may approach the academic, especially with regard to glacial chronology, there are few that will not have some interest for the engineer concerned with soils. There is even an international organization which holds regular conferences to discuss the interrelation of national Pleistocene studies—the International Association for Quaternary Research (INQUA). In North America there are a number of local groups with the unusual title "Friends of the Pleistocene": they conduct annual excursions for the best type of soil study, that in the field. And in all this work, the soils engineer has his own contribution to make, since the detailed scientific study of the mechanical and physical properties of soils, now called soil mechanics, has already contributed much to an understanding of soil characteristics and gives promise of an increasing potential in this field. To the interrelation of geology and soil mechanics, attention may therefore next be directed.

Suggestions for Further Reading

Two early books dealing with soils are still of real value and interest:

Merrill, G. P., "Rocks, Rock Weathering and Soils," rev. ed., The Macmillan Company, New York, 1911.
Woodward, H. B., "The Geology of Soils and Sub-strata," Edward Arnold & Co., London, 1912.

The following book is a masterly review of all aspects of recent soil formation and transportation. It contains an exhaustive bibliography.

Charlesworth, J. K., "The Quaternary Era," 2 vols., Edward Arnold & Co., London, 1957.

Of great value in all Pleistocene studies is:

Flint, R. F., "Glacial and Pleistocene Geology," John Wiley & Sons, Inc., New York, 1957.

A more popular treatment, the final work of a great Canadian geologist, is:

Coleman, A. P., "The Last Million Years," University of Toronto Press, Toronto, 1941; it presents a broad review of the Pleistocene in North America.

For a comprehensive treatment of soils in the agricultural sense, reference may be made to:

"Soils," Yearbook for 1957 of the U.S. Department of Agriculture, U.S. Government Printing Office.

Chapter 4

SOIL MECHANICS AND GEOLOGY

> The satisfactory solution [to the problem of the stability of clay soils] will one day be recompense for the work of those who, without separating mechanics from natural philosophy, will best know how to adapt to the spirit of the first the material facts which it is the essential object of the second to discover and coordinate.
>
> Alexandre Collin (1846)[4.1]

THE UNCONSOLIDATED materials found in the earth's crust, generally described as soil, constitute so large a part of the actual surface of the earth that few civil engineering operations, apart from rock tunneling, can be conducted without an encounter with soil of some type. Since foundations cannot always be carried to solid rock, the founding of structures on unconsolidated material is probably the most important part of foundation engineering. Troubles met during the construction of civil engineering works, and after their completion, are frequently due to failure of unconsolidated strata. Despite their significance in all phases of civil engineering work, soils were not studied and investigated by civil engineers in any general way until relatively recent years. The contrast between this neglect and the past century and a half of progress in the study and investigation of practically all other materials used by civil engineers is so marked as to be indeed a paradox. Nobody sells soils, however; they are generally a part of the natural order which the civil engineer has to accept as the basis of his operations. It may be that the absence of commercial incentive is linked in some way with this past neglect; the development of testing and research laboratories under public control for public benefit was probably necessary to effect the surprising progress in scientific soil study of the last three decades.

4.2. Historical Note. In the earliest days of modern civil engineering, the characteristics of soils appear to have received some attention, notably with reference to the pressure exerted on retaining walls. The theoretical work of Coulomb (1773) and of Rankine (1856) is fairly well known and appreciated. In France, remarkable pioneer experimental

106

work was performed by Alexandre Collin as early as 1846 in connection with slides occurring during the construction of French canals. Not only did Collin investigate the curved sliding surface which he had noted in clay slips, but he experimented on the changes in the properties of clay caused by changes in moisture content.[4.2] Throughout the remainder of the nineteenth century, attention to the properties of soils appears to have been spasmodic. A paper by Sir Benjamin Baker ("The Actual Lateral Pressure of Earthwork") presented to the Institution of Civil Engineers in London on April 5, 1881, is a notable exception; the importance of geological structure in all such studies was stressed in the ensuing discussion.[4.3]

Not, apparently, until after the turn of the century were anything more than isolated soil investigations carried out, although notable individual contributions were made in the United States by Dr. Milton Whitney and Dr. George E. Ladd. Three major investigations undertaken in the early part of the present century directed the attention of civil engineers to soil problems and may rightly be regarded as the start of modern soil studies. These were the studies made in Sweden of the landslides that had occurred on the State Railway system; the investigation of difficulties encountered during the construction of the Kiel Canal in Germany; and the intensive analysis made of the great landslides that interfered so seriously with the completion of the Panama Canal.

These investigations did not stand alone. In England, a paper was read by A. L. Bell at the Institution of Civil Engineers on January 19, 1915 ("The Lateral Pressure and Resistance of Clay, and the Supporting Power of Clay Foundations"), which, together with the long discussion that it provoked, contained much suggestive material on the mechanics of soils. The necessity of obtaining undisturbed samples—a practice that has been developed in subsequent years—was stressed by this author.[4.4] The paper was the precursor of a notable group of British publications on earth pressure and soil properties. In the United States of America, Dr. C. M. Strahan had begun his investigations of natural-soil roads which led to the presentation of his first paper in 1914; this may rightly be regarded as the start of modern stabilized soil-road practice (although some isolated papers had been published previously). In 1913, the American Society of Civil Engineers set up its first committee on the codification of bearing values for soils, and the work of this and of subsequent similar committees has been of great value.

These few references indicate the awakening of interest in the potentialities of scientific soil study that occurred during the early years of the present century and led eventually to the general recognition of soil mechanics as an important scientific aid to many branches of civil engineering. Soil mechanics was not used as a title to denote an entirely new branch of scientific study but rather as a convenient name for the recognition of the coordinated group of soil studies that were found to be necessary in the application of soil analyses and investigations to the several branches of civil engineering work. The acknowledged leader in this pioneer work has been Dr. Karl Terzaghi. By his classic papers in *Engineering News-Record* and his work for the U.S. Bureau of Public Roads, at Massachusetts Institute of Technology, and particularly at Harvard University, Dr. Terzaghi gave an impetus to scientific soil study in North America that has had most fruitful results; his European publications and activities have been similarly effective for engineers of the Old World. To the great joy of all who are privileged to know him, Dr. Terzaghi has been able to see his own efforts develop fruitfully into a scientific discipline well recognized throughout the world. There are established courses of instruction in soil mechanics at leading universities and a steadily expanding volume of sound literature. The International Society of Soil Mechanics and Foundation Engineering, through its national committees, brings together workers in the field in almost forty countries. Dr. Terzaghi was the president of the society from its formation in 1936 until 1957 and is now its honorary president. The society has held conferences in Cambridge, Mass. (1936), Rotterdam (1948), Zurich (1953), London (1957), and Paris (1961). The published proceedings of these international gatherings form a notable part of modern civil engineering literature. The writings have a strong geological overtone, as might be expected, for Dr. Terzaghi's studies were based upon a background of geology. In his own words:[4.5] "I came to the United States and hoped to discover the philosopher's stone by accumulating and coordinating geological information. . . . It took me two years of strenuous work to discover that geological information must be supplemented by numerical data which can only be obtained by physical tests carried out in a laboratory." The science of soil mechanics is now the medium through which this essential supplementary information is obtained, coordinated, and made available for use.

4.3. Soil Mechanics Today. One of the main features of modern soil mechanics is the impressive body of theory that has been developed dealing with all aspects of the states of stress in soils and with the deformation resulting from such stress conditions. Methods of calculation are now available for determining, theoretically, the stress which an imposed load will cause at any point below a foundation slab, the total pressure upon retaining walls and the pattern of its distribution down the wall, and the earth pressures to be expected upon buried structures such as large culverts. In a corresponding way, it is now possible to determine with accuracy (and with the aid of computers, if desired) the factor of safety against failure of a slope excavated in soil or constructed of soil. Possibly the greatest contribution to theoretical soil mechanics has been the theory of consolidation developed by Dr. Terzaghi. Using this theory, and given certain basic physical properties of the clay in question, one can calculate the total settlement to be anticipated and the rate at which settlement will occur for any clay soil under load at its surface.

These examples are typical of the many theoretical approaches now possible to structural problems involving the use of soil. The qualification noted in the final example is, however, all-important. Excellent though the many theories are, they all depend upon certain basic assumptions with regard to the properties of the soil being used. The accuracy of the application of theoretical calculations therefore depends upon the accuracy of the assumptions made or upon the values for the soil properties provided. This leads to the second major branch of study in soil mechanics: the investigation of soils in the laboratory in order to determine experimentally the values that are required for use in calculations. Still in an active stage of development, the design and use of special equipment for soil testing has made rapid strides in the last two decades. In any modern soils laboratory there are *consolidometers*, rather simple devices for determining the consolidation characteristics of small soil samples under increasing increments of load; *permeameters* for the determination of soil permeability; and of greatest importance, shear-testing machines of two main types. For simple tests, and for shear determinations upon certain special types of soil, *direct shear boxes* are used; these are relatively simple machines in which the soil sample is placed in a split box so that it can be loaded vertically, and while under load, the sample can be sheared along the break in the box by a horizontal force that can be measured. Of far more importance, however, are the *triaxial compression machines* that are now widely used, in which a cylindrical soil sample, sealed in a flexible membrane, is fitted into a larger transparent cylinder and held between top and bottom supports. The large cylinder is filled with an appropriate liquid to which pressure can be applied. With the restraining liquid under pressure and with loads applied vertically to the specimen through the top and bottom supports, the cylinder of soil can be subjected to a combination of three-dimensional stress, and loading can continue until the sample fails, usually on a definite shear plane.

Thus described in simple terms, soil testing might appear to be a simple business. So it often appears to be to the uninitiated. In practice, however, it requires much skill and delicacy of operation; it is the work of the expert and not of the amateur. Not only must the individual tests be conducted meticulously, since the small size of the usual specimen and the relatively light loads call for refinements in technique not needed in most civil engineering laboratory techniques, but also the soil samples must be handled expertly prior to the tests. And just as the accuracy of theoretical calculations depends on the accuracy of the soil properties assumed or determined, so will the accuracy of the results of the soil tests themselves depend upon the accuracy of soil sampling. Therefore, soil samples provided for laboratory experiments must, at the time of test, represent fairly the soil *in situ* from which they came and to which the results of theoretical calculations are to be applied.

Thus becomes obvious the third great division of soil mechanics: the procurement of good soil samples, their accurate description, and the necessary determination of general soil conditions at the site in order to demonstrate the validity of samples obtained. This leads in turn to the relatively new field of *in situ* soil testing. At this point modern soil studies grade imperceptibly into the normal practice of civil engineering, for test boring and sampling (of a sort) were a regular feature of construction work long before soil mechanics had even been thought of as a separate discipline. The refinements that modern soil studies have introduced into subsurface exploration, however, have transformed what was at best a rough and ready sort of procedure into a highly skilled, reliable, and thoroughly scientific operation. Most notable has been the absolute insistence upon so-called "undisturbed samples." The expression is another of those semantic inexactitudes of which civil engineers are so often guilty, since the removal of a soil sample from the ground naturally "disturbs" it. The word is used, however, to connote no disturbance whatsoever of the sample itself, and the retention in the sample of the exact moisture content that the soil has when in place. This last result is achieved by the immediate waxing of soil samples upon removal from a borehole or by the use of special sampling tools, or shields, in which samples can be left, waxed at the open ends, until they reach the laboratory.

The actual techniques of soil sampling and of field soil testing are matters that do not require detailed treatment here; some notes by way of introduction to current methods will be found in Chap. 6 (see page 195). Suffice it to say that soil sampling methods have been developed, even for cohesionless soils, such as sands, that will give to the laboratory worker a specimen of soil upon which to conduct his tests that is as close to the natural condition of the soil in the ground as it is humanly possible to obtain. The first tests will usually be so-called "indicator tests" to determine generally the type of soil. These are used as a basis for consideration of the more elaborate mechanical tests and for purposes of accurate description. Usually the first such test will be made to determine the natural moisture content; this is done by drying a small sample in an oven under controlled and standard conditions. Moisture contents are always expressed as the ratio of the weight of the water contained to the weight of dry solid soil matter, expressed as a percentage. Another introductory test will be made to determine the distribution of soil particles of different sizes, the mechanical analysis of the soil. This is performed by sieving down as low as the standard No. 200 mesh, and determining smaller particles, with some degree of overlap, by means of a sedimentation method, naturally standardized, dependent upon an application of Stokes' law. The results are plotted to a semilogarithmic scale; Fig. 4.1 shows a few particle-size distribution curves for typical soils. It should be noted that, although it is especially useful for coarser soil mixtures such as glacial till, the record of mechanical analysis is not an infallible guide to soil properties for fine-grained soils. The subdivisions shown in Fig. 4.1 for the particles of sand, silt, and clay size are those most generally used in North America.

In normal laboratory procedure, soil samples will next be subjected to so-called "plasticity tests" in order to determine their Atterberg

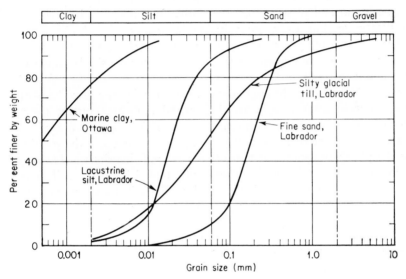

Fig. 4.1. Standard chart showing the mechanical analysis of particle-size distribution for four typical soils.

limits, limits of consistency named after the Swedish agricultural soil scientist who first suggested them. These limits are expressed as percentages of the weight of water, at the points shortly to be noted, compared with the weight of dry soil solid in the sample. If water is slowly added to a perfectly dry sample of soil and uniformly mixed with it, the soil will gradually assume some cohesion, probably first forming lumps. It will eventually reach a plastic stage at which it can be rolled out in a long unbroken thread upon a solid surface. A simple test has been standardized to indicate the limit of water content at which this plastic stage is reached; this test is called the *lower plastic limit*, or more briefly the *plastic limit*. If more water is added and the mixing continued, the soil will gradually achieve the state of a viscous liquid. Another simple test, based on the flowage together of two parts of a pat of the soil-water mixture in a standard cup under standard tapping, has been accepted for general use to indicate this limit of consistency, the (lower) *liquid limit*. The difference between the liquid and the plastic limits is naturally a measure of the range of plasticity of the soil. It is, therefore, called the *plasticity index*, and is expressed also as the usual percentage of moisture content. The third of these "limits" is a much lower value— that percentage of moisture content at which the soil sample stops shrinking as it dries. When this point is passed, the sample will usually grow lighter in color as the drying process continues. This is known as the *shrinkage limit*, but since its physical significance is not so great as that of the other two limits, it is not referred to so frequently.

The liquid and plastic limits are simple in concept and relatively easy to determine, but they are valuable indicators of soil characteristics. They are useful for comparative purposes, since soil samples from similar locations and horizons will have reasonably similar limit values. When plotted, as will be mentioned in a later section, they form well-recognizable patterns. In combination, not only do they give the plasticity index, but in association with the natural moisture content they give another factor called the *liquidity index*. This is obtained by dividing the difference between the natural moisture content and the plastic limit by the plasticity index. All these terms are self-descriptive. They appear almost universally in engineering reports of laboratory soil tests. As indicators of the general characteristics of a soil, they are most useful. When considered in combination with the appearance of a soil, and its mechanical analysis, they assist in the determination of an accurate description of the soils in terms now well accepted, such as "silty clay," "sandy silt," or "highly plastic clay." A guide to the terminology of soils is noted in Chap. 6.[4.6]

Two comments must precede consideration of the place of geology in this over-all picture of soil mechanics. First, it will be noted that no symbols or formulas have had to be used to describe the simple tests now standard in soil testing. This is in contrast with the practice of some writers on soil mechanics who seem to consider their papers incomplete unless they use mathematical symbols, preferably formulas, even to indicate the subtraction of one term from another. Symbols and formulas are, after all, merely a kind of scientific shorthand, with no intrinsic meaning. It seems desirable to use "longhand" here, since the concepts described are so basic and simple that their significance can actually be shrouded by the veil of mathematical symbolism. In the second place, it may be noted that all the simple tests described relate to the quantity of water present in a soil sample at different stages in its wetting or drying. This will not be the last time that the importance of water in relation to soils has to be mentioned. It will gradually be seen that most of the subsurface problems that have to be faced by civil engineers in the conduct of their construction operations are caused by water and not by solid material as such, whether it be soil or rock. The basic importance attached to water in soil mechanics, therefore, is symptomatic of the importance of water in all soil problems.

4.4 Links with Geology. Soil mechanics has become a vital part of the scientific core of civil engineering despite the fact that it deals with a major constituent of the earth's crust. So also does the practice of civil engineering; the close association of the two is therefore quite natural. At the same time, the scientific study of soils must have contact with geology; this, also, is natural and logical. From the outline given above, it can be seen that soil mechanics approaches closely to a geological study when field investigations are involved. It can be said that soil mechanics gradually merges into geology at this one extreme and into structural engineering at the other. Therefore, to regard soil mechanics as a branch of geological study that has unfortunately strayed into civil engineering is just about as foolish a concept as to regard it as a subject of strictly engineering character with no necessary contact whatever with geology.

Reverting to the general outline of soil mechanics given in the preceding section, one can appreciate that geology has few links with the theoretical side of engineering soil studies. Analysis of slope-stability problems may sometimes come up for consideration in geological studies, but the geologist usually has to accept the facts that nature puts before him without being concerned about whether a certain slope is potentially unstable or why some other slope has failed. At the same time, the mathematical concepts embodied in the theories of soil mechanics provide the geologist with a powerful analytical tool for those investigations of major phenomena that now supplement the older, but still invaluable, geological field studies. A masterly example of the direct application of these concepts to theoretical geological work is given by the joint papers of Hubbard and Rubey on the "Mechanics of Fluid-filled Porous Solids and Its Application to Overthrust Faulting."[4.7] At the outset of their papers, these authors state that their attention was focused "upon the newly evolving science of soil mechanics with particular attention being paid to the treatises on this subject by Karl Terzaghi and associates, since it appeared that the phenomena of soil mechanics represented in many respects very good scale models of the larger diastrophic phenomena of geology." The way in which the authors demonstrate how, given sufficiently high fluid pressures (pore-water pressures), very much larger blocks can be pushed over almost horizontal surfaces than would be possible under any other circumstances is a fine example of the application of soil mechanics to a geological problem. The fact that the authors do not agree with all of Dr. Terzaghi's views and that they arranged for some large-scale shear tests in order to check some of their own views, following discussion of their paper, adds further interest to their work, which constitutes a real challenge to all workers in the field of soil mechanics. To geologists, it provides an attractive explanation of such famous geological features as the great overthrust belt of western Wyoming and the adjacent states, while demonstrating how geology can be assisted by the use of techniques, both theoretical and experimental, from soil mechanics.

There are doubtless many other similar problems in geology whose solution may one day be greatly assisted by contributions from soil mechanics. When studies of soil in the field from the engineering point of view are considered, however, one may well ask how they can possibly be conducted without due reference to the local geology. One would imagine that it would be impossible to neglect geology, even if not called by that name. All too often, however, soil studies have been conducted in the field without benefit from contact with geology in any form, recognized or unrecognized. Sometimes no harm has resulted, but this has been by good luck rather than good management. Often, poor results have been obtained through patent neglect of geological features; in all too many cases, money has been uselessly expended because subsurface explorations were not coordinated with the local geology; and occasionally the neglect of geology has had disastrous results. Some of these will be recorded later in this book, always with constructive intent, since the proper study of failures can assist so greatly in obviating similar troubles under similar circumstances on future works. It can therefore be stated without qualification that soil studies in the field, no matter how carefully conducted, are incomplete without some consideration of the appropriate local geology. Herein lies perhaps the chief contact between geology and soil mechanics.

The remarkable increase in the amount of attention that has been given to subsurface exploration on civil engineering projects during the last two decades has naturally had the fortunate by-product of providing for the geologist much useful information in the form of borehole logs. This is not unusual; in a similar way, borings for oil and gas exploration and for the development of new coal mining projects are also constantly yielding new information. In the testing of soil samples in the laboratory, however, an even closer link is developing between geology and soil mechanics. On the other hand, knowledge of the geological origin of a soil greatly assists the laboratory worker by suggesting the range of soil properties to be expected and by indicating special features that should be watched for during the progress of soil tests. In the reverse direction, the detailed study of soil properties that is now possible with advanced soil-testing techniques is disclosing new information that is of value when considered in relation to the generally known pattern of the geological origin of the soil, sometimes filling in gaps in geological knowledge or refining generalized deductions drawn from field observations. Examples will be cited. In this way, perhaps more than in any other, the twin disciplines are being drawn closer together. It is not without significance that the name *Geotechnique* has been adopted as the title of the leading journal in the field of soil mechanics in the English-speaking world.[4.8] *Geotechnical studies* have become a favored description for soil testing in its more general aspects even though it is carried out for engineering purposes. Some well-known national soil-testing laboratories are happily known as *geotechnical institutes*. There is, therefore, steadily developing liaison between the scientific approach to the geology of soils and the engineering investigation of their properties. It is inevitable that this interrelation should progress to the mutual benefit of both and the continued advance of human understanding of the most common of all solid materials.

4.5. Transported Soils. In the preceding chapter, a major distinction was made between residual and transported soils. Aerolian soils, those transported by wind action, are easily recognizable when their geological origin is appreciated. The unusual characteristics of some types of loess, owing to its open structure, will affect soil sampling and result in unusual soil properties frequently calling for soil testing *in situ*, especially with regard to the action of water on such soil. A well-accepted practice today is to saturate loess in advance of placing loads upon it, and then to consolidate the wetted material by external means. This increases its density, and when consolidation has proceeded far enough, shear strength will increase. The serious nature of this peculiar characteristic is shown by the fact that even the watering of a garden lawn has resulted in settlement of an adjacent house because of the unconsolidated underlying loess. Geological recognition of the presence of loess, therefore, can be a vital contribution to engineering soil studies.[4.9]

Alluvial soil, transported down rivers and streams, is usually readily recognizable if the watercourses are those of today. Soil of this type, however, may be found on what were the banks of rivers of the past, now superseded because of recent geological events. These may not be at all obvious to the untrained eye, particularly if the area has been developed in any way for special uses. Knowledge of local geology will be a helpful guide in such cases since the existence of buried watercourses can frequently be foretold from a general appreciation of the sequence of geological events in the area. Once their characteristics are recognized, then the extremely variable and probably unconsolidated alluvial soils can be anticipated in soil sampling and testing.

One of the most important contributions that geology can make to soil studies is at the same time one of the simplest—an indication of whether the site of a projected engineering work has been subjected to glacial action or not. If it has—and this will be the case for almost all the northern section of the Northern Hemisphere, and very small corresponding areas in the Southern Hemisphere—then the civil engineer must be on the alert for the great variation in glacial soils that may be found in relatively short distances, the distinct possibility of encountering in many areas buried preglacial river valleys subsequently filled with glacial deposits that may themselves differ from the overlying soil, and the possible effects of ice pressure upon soils if the area has been glaciated more than once, as is so frequently the case. Glacial till is then a soil type to be expected. If a mixture of dense clay, sand, and gravel is found in boreholes, it need not be characterized just as "hardpan" but should be most carefully studied, if necessary by means of block samples, in order to determine its characteristics under the conditions to be imposed by the engineering use to which it is to be put. If the direction of subsequent ice movement is known, for example, then high till densities and consequent toughness of the material, especially when dry, may be expected. If the material has to be used as a foundation bed, this feature will be desirable; if the material has to be excavated, it may be ruinous if it is not recognized before contract arrangements are made. If the till is of recent origin and if it was deposited in morainal form, then the reverse may be expected, and relatively low densities may be found with corresponding open structure. Till of this kind was encountered in northern Quebec during railway construction; its perfect particle-size grading made it almost impermeable, but the addition of water filled its open voids, and after heavy rains it quickly acquired the consistency of the justly famous local *"soupe aux pois"* with results that can be imagined.[4.10] At least one case is known in which landslide movement shortly after till deposition had the effect of maintaining the till at an unusually high moisture content, detected only by careful soil sampling and testing, a condition that, when recognized, called for special construction methods when the till was used as fill.

It might be thought that there could be no such variations with sands, but many engineers know otherwise, sometimes to their cost. The density of sand can vary appreciably, depending on how the individual sand grains are packed together. It is a normal condition for sands to be close to their maximum density, but for reasons not yet fully understood but almost certainly dependent upon the way in which the material was deposited, sands of low relative density are encountered. The relative density of sands, therefore, is an important soil characteristic that can best be measured indirectly in the field by means of penetration tests; it may also be tested by unusally careful sampling. Geology cannot here be a certain guide, but if sand of low relative density is encountered at a site, geological comparisons between its location and other local sand deposits can usually be helpful in further exploration. When sand of low relative density has been found, it can be consolidated to a greater and more desirable density by a variety of engineering methods, such as pile driving, the use of explosives, and the combined use of water and vibration.

Since glacial silts grade into glacial clays, they may be considered together. At one extreme, a coarse silt may consist of particles of fresh minerals that fully justify the name rock flour, essentially a very finely ground sand. When wet, such materials may appear at first glance to be

Fig. 4.2. Transportation troubles on glacial till in northern Quebec, Canada. The unusual character of this till, causing the trouble shown, is explained in the text. (*Photograph by G. D. Creelman. Reproduced by permission of M. A. Hanna Company.*)

identical with clays. Their true character may easily be detected when they are dry, but the use of simple soil tests will readily display the difference even in the wet condition. The Atterberg tests, for example, will give low values for the plasticity indices of silts. Once recognized, the rather difficult properties of glacial silts can be anticipated, and design and construction measures may be taken accordingly. In some glaciated areas (along the north shore of Lake Superior, for example), it is possible to trace a gradual change in such glacial deposits, all of which look alike, from silts (as described) to true glacial clays. Mechanical analyses of these soils will be almost identical, but the soil particles gradually change from fresh minerals to the clay minerals, and the properties change correspondingly. Here is a case in which the simple tests of soil mechanics not only give the engineer the information that he needs but, at the same time, reveal information of considerable geological significance.

In all such fine-grained glacial sediments, a check upon the natural moisture content and its relation to the lower liquid limit is a first requirement in soil testing. In many areas, especially on and near the Precambrian shield in Canada, the natural moisture content is appreciably higher than the lower liquid limit. When this phenomenon is first de-

Fig. 4.3. Distortions in varved clays located in the center of the drained lake bed of Steep Rock Lake, Ontario, Canada, illustrating potential local variation in subsurface conditions. (*Photograph by N. Vincennes. Reproduced by permission of Steep Rock Iron Mines, Ltd.*)

tected by those who have not encountered it previously, they immediately suspect that the test results are wrong.[4.11] But they may be right. This unusual condition is again explained by the process of deposition. During the settling of the fine particles in the fresh water of glacial lakes, the particles came together in such a way that interparticle attraction led to what can best be described as a "honeycomb structure" of the solid particles. Excess water is therefore held between the particles and gives the resulting soil an artificially high moisture content. When the soil is in its natural position, this unusual condition is of no moment and may be unsuspected. When such soils are disturbed, however (as they can be by engineering operations), the excess water may be released, thus quickly converting what had previously been a solid-looking material into a viscous liquid that will flow readily on low slopes until the excess moisture is lost and the soil "solidifies" and has a new, more natural, moisture content. The manner in which soil of this type was successfully controlled in a vast mining operation is described on page 357. Geological information about the glacial origin of these clays can clearly be a most useful guide, pointing the way to the necessity of careful soil testing before the soil is moved at all. When such soil is detected, geological information can act as a constant reminder of the care that must be exercised in all engineering work not only with soil to be moved but with natural slopes that may be disturbed. The phenomenon of *varving*, the deposition of such soils in thin alternating light and dark layers, is of great geological interest, even though the varving will not usually have any significant effect upon engineering uses of the soil. Tests upon such soils, carried out for engineering purposes, have raised some interesting questions about the classical geological explanation of this widespread feature of glacial lake deposits.[4.12]

Other glacial clays may have been deposited in sea water instead of fresh. Fortunately, the areas in which this has taken place are now fairly well recognized; the most extensive are in southern Scandinavia and in the valleys of the St. Lawrence and Ottawa Rivers, with small extensions into connecting valleys. Clays so deposited are unusually sensitive; they, too, have abnormally high moisture contents. Accordingly, they are quite unstable when disturbed and have been the cause of many disastrous landslides in both the districts mentioned.[4.13]

Repeated references have been made to the indications that the Atterberg limits give of the character of fine-grained soils. This can be illustrated in a general way by a simple graphical record of the relationship of the lower liquid limit and the plasticity index for a group of typical glacial soils. This is shown in Fig. 4.4. Admittedly, the chart is no more than an indicator of soil type, but it is a useful guide, especially when samples of unfamiliar soils are undergoing test. Mention has already been made of another soil test that has considerable geological significance. This is the test upon enclosed soil samples that relates their consolidation under load with time. The graphical record of this interrelation has a well-defined pattern which clearly reveals, for some soils, that the soil has been subjected to a previous long-term load that has already partially consolidated it. This value is known as the "preconsolidation load." The load may have been caused by overlying soil removed for some reason long before the sample was obtained. Commonly, the load will be an indication of the weight of ice that has at some time in the past stood upon the soil in question. The preconsolidation load is an essential factor in the determination of probable settlements when the soil under test is actually loaded by a structure, but the geological significance of the test will be at once apparent.

Another result of ancient ice action must be briefly mentioned; although not often encountered, it is of unusual importance where it does exist. Just as permafrost (perennially frozen ground) exists in northern latitudes today, so is it almost certain that permafrost conditions must have existed at times of glacial advance in areas even to the south of the southern limits of glaciation. Many unusual results of ground movement due to freezing may be observed in northern regions, known generally as "periglacial phenomena." The same types of ground movement must have

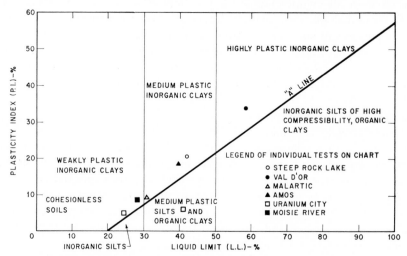

FIG. 4.4. Relation between the plasticity index and the liquid limit for a group of typical Canadian soils, showing also Casagrande's "A" line.

taken place in glacial times in more southern regions when they too were perennially frozen. Naturally buried throughout all the intervening centuries, these distortions of the ground come to light only as a result of engineering excavation work. A puzzle until recently, these "fossil periglacial phenomena" have now been recognized and so are understood. In regions where they are known to occur, they may be anticipated; but they may usefully be kept in mind in all subsurface exploration, since when they are encountered, they can be the cause of otherwise quite inexplicable variations in subsurface conditions. Subsurface exploration in areas of existing permafrost is difficult, but it is so specialized that it calls for only brief mention here and an indication that useful information is available for reference.[4.14]

4.6. Residual Soils. The origin of soils that have been formed by the direct *in situ* weathering of bedrock would appear to call for but little mention since the origin of such soils is usually obvious. There are, however, many areas in the warmer parts of the world where bedrock is far below the surface; the observable soils are of great age and their origin is not immediately recognized. Soil formation under tropical conditions is still only imperfectly understood; the origin of laterites, for example, is still a matter of debate. Laterites have accumulations of iron and aluminum oxides at the surface, with silica content generally leached out to a lower horizon. Black cotton soils constitute another major and important group in tropical areas, but they are well recognized, and their properties are being gradually codified.[4.15]

The physical and mechanical properties of residual soils naturally vary greatly, but they are determined in exactly the same way as those of glacial soils. The simple soil tests will sometimes be found to give clear indication of varying origins of residual soils that may have the same appearance. Results of tests upon two soils encountered during field studies carried out for the Konkouré development in French Guiana are

Table 4.1. Comparison of Properties of Soils Derived from Dolirite and Schist*

Soil property	Doleritic material	Schistic material
Natural moisture content.........	37–43	13.5–37.5
Specific gravity of solids.........	2.80–2.98	2.73–2.85
Dry density, *in situ*.............	1.20–1.35	1.30–1.80
Liquid limit....................	56–74	30–67
Plastic limit....................	21–32.5	5–28.5

* All percentages of dry weight.

SOURCE: Reproduced by permission, from P. Simon and J. Vallee, The Souapiti Fael: The Kon Kouré Development, *Travaux*, no. 282, pp. 193–202 (1958).

typical. Table 4.1 shows distinct differences between two soils found in the same location, which to all appearances were almost identical.[4.16]

Some residual soils, including the black cotton soils so common in India and the Far East generally, have rather unusual properties when considered for engineering use. Among the most difficult of all these soils to deal with are those derived from the weathering of volcanic rocks such as lava flows and volcanic ash. Material of this kind had to be used for the construction of the Sasamua Dam in Kenya, which was built to form a reservoir as part of the water-supply system for the city of Nairobi, located only 50 miles south of the equator. Among the unusual properties of the local clay used for this project are a somewhat high plastic limit, but a much lower plasticity index than would normally be expected; low density at optimum moisture content; considerable variation in the values obtained for the Atterberg limits, depending on the chemical used as a dispersing agent; and higher permeability but also higher shearing strength than would be expected for normal clays with similar liquid limits. This material was difficult to handle and caused many problems during construction. After the properties of the clay were fully appreciated, it was necessary to redesign several times the cross section of the earth dam, which has a maximum height of about 110 ft, and a length (curved in plan) of rather more than 1,000 ft. A fine record of the problems with the dam and its construction has been prepared by Dr. Terzaghi, whose paper also shows the reason for the unusual properties of the Sasamua clay.[4.17] When the mineralogical content of the material was analyzed, it was found that the material consisted of almost 60 per cent halloysite, above 16 per cent "goethite," and much smaller percentages of kaolinite, gibbsite, quartz, and mica. All the unusual properties of the clay could be explained by the assumption (applicable to a clay with a high halloysite content) that "most of the clay fraction of the soil occurs in the form of clusters or hard porous grains with rough surfaces, each of which consists of a great number of firmly interconnected clay mineral particles." Electron-microscopic photographs confirmed this type of internal structure. Experiences with similar clays encountered at four other dams were compared with what was found at Sasamua; not only were the construction experiences similar, but analyses of the other clays also showed the presence of halloysite and goethite. Once the character of the unusual clay was understood, suitable test and construction methods were used, and the dam was completed and placed in service.

4.7. Clay Minerals. The last two examples cited, typical of many cases of the use of residual soils that could be mentioned, show that possibly the most important basic characteristic of fine-grained soils is the dominant type of mineral present. That all clays do consist of minerals —they are known generally as the "clay minerals"—is now well recognized, even though the minute size of the clay particles and the fact that they cannot be observed with the unaided eye make this strange to the uninitiated. Modern methods of mineralogical study, including the use of differential thermal analysis, the electron microscope, and the powerful tool provided by X-ray diffraction techniques, have made possible detailed analysis of individual clays and the study of different types of clay minerals.

Prior to the introduction of X-ray diffraction studies in 1923, it was known that clays consisted of aluminum, silicon, water, and often iron. Such chemical analyses, although interesting, were of little assistance in understanding the properties of different kinds of clay. It is now known that the clay minerals consist of silicates of aluminum and/or iron and magnesium. Some contain alkaline materials as essential components. Some argillaceous material may be amorphous, but this is not a significant component of normal clays. Most of the clay minerals have layered or sheetlike structures. The characteristic properties of these crystalline forms go far in determining the physical properties of a clay. The main

clay minerals can be grouped together as kaolinite, halloysite, montmorillonite, illite, and chlorite; a few others are occasionally encountered, but
those listed most commonly come to the attention of the worker in the
field of soil mechanics. Of special significance is the fact that there is little
bonding force between the successive layers in montmorillonite; there-

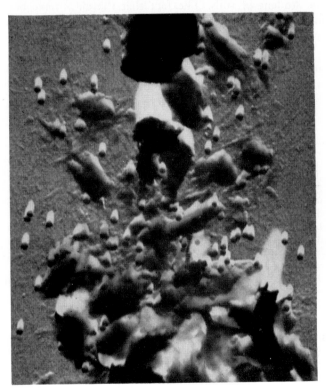

Fig. 4.5. The clay fraction of a sample of Bearpaw shale taken from the site of
the South Saskatchewan Dam, Saskatchewan, Canada; the predominant mineral is
montmorillonite. This electron microphotograph has its scale indicated by the
polystyrene balls of 0.088-micron diameter; the specimen is "shadow case" with
palladium at an angle of 22 to 24°. (*Photograph by S. A. Forman, Mineralogical
Laboratory, Soil Research Institute, Dept. of Agriculture, Canada; reproduced by
permission of the Department.*)

fore, water can readily enter between the individual sheets and cause
swelling, which can lead to trouble.[4.18]

The formation of clay minerals is the direct result of weathering,
which was discussed briefly in Chap. 2. Weathering is an extremely
complex process and is still not fully understood. Climate plays an important role: if a given kind of climate persists in one area for a very
long time, the same products of weathering may result despite differences in the parent, or fresh, material. Vegetation may also have a pro-

found effect: the pH value of the water that percolates down from the surface, and so acts as an important element in breaking down fresh minerals, will be affected by the character of vegetation in combination with local weather, especially rainfall. Interesting though the weathering process undoubtedly is, it is the results of weathering that are of concern to the student of soils. The fact that the clays have been derived from solid rocks, however, by a variety of processes prior to, during, and since transportation from their place of origin will naturally help to explain the otherwise strange variations in materials such as the Sasamua clay already mentioned. This material, for example, showed the following variations in its "limits," depending upon the treatment the clay received before the Atterberg tests were carried out:[4.19]

Table 4.2. Atterberg Limits for Sasamua Clay*

Treatment before test	Liquid limit	Plastic limit
Natural state...	87	54
Dried at 105°C and powdered in mortar................	58	39
As above, but treated with tetrasodium pyrophosphate....	47	37
Dried, powdered, and rehydrated 1 month...............	63	39

* All percentages of dry weight.

SOURCE: Reproduced by permission from K. Terzaghi, Design and Performance of the Sasamua Dam, *Proc. Inst. Civil Eng.*, **9**: 369–394 (1958).

The sensitivity of clay with high halloysite content to the action of chemicals used for deflocculating in the standard sedimentation procedure for mechanical analysis will suggest that, although clays have long been generally regarded as "inert" materials by those engineers who were not chemically minded, they are not so at all. Of special importance is the way in which the small electrical charges carried by soil colloids, and particularly by the particles of clay minerals, will react. The well-accepted limiting size for clay-sized particles, 2 microns or 2μ, was not just a fortuitous choice, but a useful limiting point below which the surface properties of particles begin to dominate the chemistry of the material. Below this size, the electrical charges on individual particles tend to increase with decreasing size. It may seem that this discussion is getting too far away from soil mechanics and from geology, but the very important soil property of cation-exchange capacity can only be fully appreciated against this background. Under certain suitable conditions, some of the ions in clays will exchange; the most common exchangeable ions are calcium, magnesium, potassium, and sodium. As the ions change, properties may also change. If a change can be predicted and controlled, a useful method of altering clay soils is available.

One of the earliest applications of this method is still of interest. At the San Francisco World's Fair in 1939, a 7-acre lagoon was a prominent landscape feature. The inside of the lagoon was lined with a 10-in. layer of calcium clay of loamy texture. Tests with fresh water showed high leakage losses almost immediately. Because of the intended purpose of the lagoon and the time schedule, this was a serious defect. Laboratory studies showed that base exchange would result from contact between the clay and sea water, with its high sodium content, and would increase the watertightness of the clay. The lagoon was therefore flooded with sea water for 45 days, after which fresh water was readmitted. Remarkably little leakage then took place, and the lagoon performed satisfactorily for the duration of the fair.[4.20]

A more practical example of the application of a complex surface chemical reaction, involving full appreciation of the character of clay minerals, could scarcely be imagined. It will serve well to emphasize the importance of clay minerals in even the most practical aspects of soil mechanics, in addition to their significance in connection with all laboratory tests upon fine-grained soils. It will now be clear that the geological origin of clays is of considerable, but indirect, significance in the engineering study of clay soils. The process of weathering is of equal importance, but again indirectly through the influence it has played in producing the clay minerals actually present in the samples being used. Differences in clay mineral content will readily explain differences in soil properties, even those demonstrated so simply by the Atterberg limit tests. In most cases, such indirect evidence will naturally suffice for engineering purposes, as mineralogical analyses are necessary only in unusual cases such as with the clay at the Sasamua Dam. Knowledge of the significance that clay minerals may have, however, is invaluable to the student of soils, for if unusual characteristics are encountered, or suspected, a check on the clay minerals present—such as montmorillonite in relation to swelling clays—may prove of great utility.

4.8. Some Contributions to Geology. It will have already become obvious that the interrelation of soil mechanics and geology is not a one-way street, even though this discussion has considered the matter generally from the point of view of the civil engineer. There is a steadily growing mutual respect and understanding between workers in the two fields; each is contributing to the other. Throughout this book there will be found frequent references to the contributions that the civil engineer can make, and has made, to advance geological knowledge. The use that Hubbard and Rubey made of the theory and test procedures of soil mechanics has already been cited (see page 113). It may be helpful, and of interest to both geologists and engineers, to mention briefly a few other cases in which soil studies that were carried out primarily for engineering purposes have led to significant geological results.

In a study of 163 undisturbed soil samples and 185 disturbed samples from test pits and boreholes in the part of the bed of glacial Lake

Agassiz that lies south of the Canadian border in the Red River Valley, Rominger and Rutledge established five stratigraphic units within the lacustrine sediments.[4.21] Correlation of these units between three localities was aided by the application of statistical methods for study of the soil test results. Profiles worked out on the basis of the results of consolidation tests, indicating preconsolidation stresses as determined by laboratory tests, revealed a period of surface drying of the lake sediments that had not previously been detected; this was an important contribution to the knowledge of the geology of this greatest of the glacial lakes of North

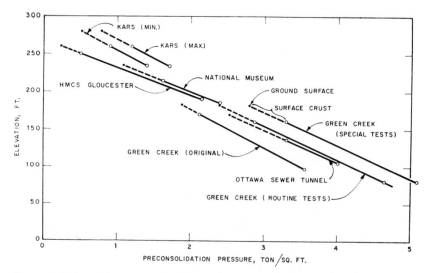

FIG. 4.6. Relation between preconsolidation pressure on the Leda clay and elevation above sea level in the Ottawa Valley, Canada. (*Reproduced by permission of the Royal Society of Canada and the University of Toronto Press.*)

America. The authors stressed the valuable contribution that the "geological study" of the results of soil mechanics tests can give. Rominger carried on the work described in the joint paper by a detailed study of the relationship of the plasticity and grain size of sediments from the bed of Lake Agassiz. He established a definite correlation between the Atterberg limits, as an expression of plasticity, and grain-size distribution and suggested that his results might be applicable on a much wider scale.[4.22] These two contributions present challenging suggestions regarding the valuable geological results which a large collection of simple soil tests from the same geological unit, in this case the bed of a well-defined glacial lake, can produce.

Study of glacial tills in southern Ontario has been greatly aided by the application of the simple techniques of soil mechanics. Dreimanis has recorded in a series of papers the way in which he has used soil-analysis methods common in soil mechanics to assist in his elucidation of the somewhat complex history of successive till deposits in this area.[4.23] Comparative study of the results of consolidation tests upon many samples of the Leda marine clay, of the Champlain Sea area in the St. Lawrence and the Ottawa River valleys, has enabled Crawford to show graphically the close interrelation between preconsolidation loading and elevation above sea level of the respective samples.[4.24] This is illustrated in Fig. 4.6. A glance at this record of the results of engineering soil tests will show clearly its geological significance These two examples are quoted to show, on the one hand, that geologists can use the methods of soil mechanics directly in their own investigations, and on the other, that engineers can aid in the development of new geological information if they will remember the geological origins of the soils they are testing for their utilitarian purposes.

Finally a different kind of example, but one of equal significance, may be mentioned. The delta of the Mississippi River is one of the most interesting recent geological phenomena in North America. Intense activity off the coast of Louisiana in the search for petroleum has led to much offshore engineering. There are now over 1,200 wells in operation on the shelf offshore from this coast. More than 100 test drilling rigs (more than 25 per cent of all the offshore drilling rigs in the world) have been in operation at one time in this area. Supports for these very large drilling installations are in themselves engineering structures of some magnitude. The studies made for their foundation in the sea have included some deep borings and associated undisturbed sampling to great depths beneath the sea bed. Fortunately, the geological significance of the results of these soil engineering investigations has been recognized. An unusually valuable paper has been published summarizing some results, written jointly by one of the leaders in the geological study of the delta sediments and one of the engineers concerned with the drill-rig foundation studies.[4.25] Fisk and McClelland show that the results of soil tests upon the samples obtained for foundation investigation confirmed and extended important correlations between the shear strength of clay deposits and the type and abundance of clay minerals present. At a depth of 164 ft below sea level, a sharp increase in strength was detected in one location, which clearly marked the top of the weathered surface of the late Pleistocene formation known to underlie the more recent deltaic deposits (see page 127). Other changes in soil properties were noted at the same depth, leaving no doubt of the validity of the significant geological change thus detected so far from sight and normal observation.

4.9. Conclusion. The temptation to quote further from this paper by Fisk and McClelland is great, but this brief reference indicates clearly the great mutual benefit of such close cooperation between geologist and engineer in an area of unusual geological complexity. The full paper is worthy of close study. It is a challenging reminder of the value of advance geological information to the engineer in planning his subsurface exploration work and the reciprocal value to the geologist of a careful study of the results of the boring and the soil-testing work of the engineer, when carefully correlated with known geological information. In this way, it vividly illustrates the dual character of the connection between geology and soil mechanics, to which this chapter has been, necessarily, an introduction only. The interrelation is still not fully realized by many geologists, possibly not appreciated by even more engineers. There is, however, a steadily growing recognition of the benefit that can accrue from breaking down the barrier between the two disciplines. This is indicated by the growing number of papers that demonstrate the value of the links that have been sketched in general terms in this chapter. One outstanding paper of this kind, notable for two reasons—that it appeared in the Fiftieth Anniversary volume of *Economic Geology* and that it was written by Dr. Terzaghi—is entitled "Influence of Geological Factors on the Engineering Properties of Sediments." It is a masterly treatment of this one major aspect of the general interrelation that has been discussed.[4.26] Dr. Terzaghi's concluding words, based as they are upon his lifetime of world-wide experience, may well serve to bring this chapter also to a close: "The knowledge of the relation between physical properties and geological history is [therefore] of outstanding practical importance. On the other hand the results of the detailed subsoil investigations performed in connection with engineering operations provide the geologist with a new source of significant information in the realm of physical geology."

Suggestions for Further Reading

There is no book that deals with the geological aspects of soil mechanics, but many papers and books in the field of soil mechanics proper contain incidental references to geology. It may usefully be noted, therefore, that a "Bibliography of Soil Mechanics" is published regularly by the Institution of Civil Engineers (Great George St., London, S.W. 1). The Institution also publishes the quarterly journal *Geotechnique*. Proceedings of the successive International Conferences on Soil Mechanics and Foundation Engineering (Cambridge, Mass., 1936; Rotterdam, 1948; Zurich, 1953; London, 1957; Paris, 1961) contain many papers of interest and value in relation to geology.

For readers who wish to be introduced to soil mechanics, the following book is recommended:

Terzaghi, K., and R. B. Peck, "Soil Mechanics in Engineering Practice," John Wiley & Sons, Inc., New York, 1948.

Chapter 5

GROUND WATER

Just as above the earth, small drops form and these join others, till finally water descends in a body as rain, so too we must suppose that in the earth the water at first trickles together little by little and that the sources of rivers drip, as it were, out of the earth and then unite. . . . Again most springs are in the neighborhood of mountains and of high ground. For mountains and high ground, suspended over the country like a saturated sponge, make the water ooze out and trickle together in minute quantities but in many places.

Aristotle[5.1]
(384–323 B.C.)

IN CERTAIN mines of the Pittsburgh district of America, 20 tons of ground water have to be pumped out of the mines for every ton of coal that is won. In India, 20 million acres of land are irrigated by ground water obtained from wells, an area equal to the total expanse irrigated in North America. Two-thirds of the waterworks in the United States, supplying at least 20 million people, are solely dependent on ground water for their supplies. And although the metropolis of London is popularly supposed to obtain all its supplies from the rivers Thames and Lea, it actually obtains about one-sixth of its public supply (or about 60 million gal daily) from wells, and probably a considerably larger percentage of its total supply, since many industrial concerns in London have their own private well systems.

Ground water now supplies about 15 per cent of all requirements for water in the United States. Since daily consumption of water in the United States increased from about 40 billion gal in 1900 to over 260 billion gal in 1959 and since the percentage of ground water used increased correspondingly, the economic importance of this neglected natural resource will be readily apparent. There are, for example, about 9,000 well-drilling contractors in the United States, employing at least 50,000 men and responsible for drilling probably 500,000 wells every year. In 1953 this work represented an actual investment of $475 million.[5.2]

These figures demonstrate clearly how important a place ground water occupies in the life of the world today. This importance will be appreciated even more when it is considered that the quantity of water within that part of the earth's crust relatively close to the surface is believed to be equal to one-third of the total volume of water in the sea. It is further estimated that water can exist to a depth of 6 miles below surface level. Although water exists almost invariably under all parts of the earth's surface, it may often be located at such depths that it is of no possible use to man. To those who have to work in the earth's crust, therefore, this vast reservoir of water is of great importance whatever their work may be. The miner comes first to mind; for him ground water may be a matter of life or death, and it may be all that swings a venture from success to disaster. Water below ground surface is also of vital importance to the civil engineer not only as a source of water supply but also as the controlling factor in all drainage operations; it is a hazard to be countered in tunnel driving and other underground operations and a feature of foundation work of unusual complexity and occasionally of unique significance.

Despite this importance, there is probably no natural feature still so neglected in the practice of civil engineering as is ground water. At one time this could have been said about soils, but the phenomenal advance of soil mechanics within the last two or three decades has corrected this situation. Water beneath the surface of the ground, however, is all too often regarded merely as a nuisance in the prosecution of construction projects, and it is given due regard only when the troubles to which it can lead have become serious. Important, therefore, as is the study of soils for the civil engineer, his appreciation of soils will not be fully effective unless he has an equal appreciation of the significance of ground water and a basic understanding of its characteristics. It is for this reason that a chapter on ground water is particularly appropriate here. This chapter presents merely an introduction to the study of the water to be found in the earth's crust; the full study of the subject is a well-established scientific discipline of wide extent. To many, ground-water hydrology is of absorbing interest. It should at least have the recognition of every civil engineer and more than the passing acquaintance of all who are to be concerned with the execution of engineering works in the field. In particular, all who are responsible for carrying out subsurface exploration, prior to the design and construction of any civil engineering project, must have a lively appreciation of ground-water hydrology. Possibly the everyday familiarity of water has led to the widespread neglect of its significance when seen at the bottom of a hole in the ground. Examples shortly to be cited should remove any such impression for all time from the mind of the interested reader.

5.2. Historical Note. The existence of ground water has probably been realized by man from the dawn of history. The coyote and possibly other animals will dig down to water if it is close enough to the surface to be reached by an animal's scratchings. One of the earliest documents known to man, the twenty-sixth chapter of the Book of Genesis, discloses that Biblical man had a thorough familiarity with ground-water conditions; other references can be traced throughout the Bible. It is well known that the Romans were familiar with the use of wells; in England they had one well 188 ft deep, and they supplemented their well supplies by means of adits driven in the chalk, a method which some have considered a modern development.[5.3]

Throughout the Middle Ages, ground water continued to be widely used without being understood. Almost until the end of the seventeenth century, men generally conceded that spring water, as observed on hillsides, could not possibly be derived from rain. Many explanations were advanced to explain its origin; one of the most interesting was that, owing to the curvature of the earth, the water in the middle of the ocean was actually at a higher altitude than the springs, and thus furnished the necessary head. The idea that springs had their origin in the sea was often based on passages from the Bible, such as Ecclesiastes 1:7—"All rivers run into the sea, yet the sea is not full; unto the place from whence the rivers come thither they return again."

Not until the sixteenth century were these views questioned. Bernard Palissy (1510–1590) played an important role in developing the theory of the infiltration of ground water. Pierre Perrault (1608–1680), one of the first to put hydrology on a quantitative basis, related the total rainfall and runoff for the basin of the river Seine in France. This work was roughly done, but it may be regarded as the starting point of modern hydrology, especially as it was just about this time that Edmund Halley (1656–1742) conducted the first known quantitative experiments on evaporation, and thus proved definitely the origin of rainfall. Thereafter, hydrological work developed steadily into the scientific study of today, although it was hampered to some extent by strange ideas that persisted with regard to water witching, or divining.

A scientific approach to ground-water problems was thus established when modern engineering began in the early years of the last century. This approach was adopted and developed by several early civil engineers, at least two of whom made notable contributions to the subject. One of them was William Smith; the second was Robert Stephenson, whose name is well known in connection with the early development of British and other railways. William Smith was one of the first to relate the study of ground water to the study of geology; going further than this, however, he applied the results of such combined studies to the solution of engineering problems. The works that he carried out show clearly that he had a very vivid conception of the main principles of ground-water location and movement. Two examples which may be mentioned are the water-supply system that he developed for Scarborough and the drainage of ground at Combegrove, near Bath, in the south of England[5.4]

5.3. Characteristics of Ground Water. That part of the rainfall which is absorbed into the ground is important in many ways. In some areas this absorption accounts for almost the entire rainfall, as in the drier sections of Australia where there are many rivers that disappear and others that flow only for certain limited portions of the year. Even more striking is the elevated area of 2 million acres to the north of Casterton and Colerdine in the state of Victoria, which acts as the "intake" for the great Murray River artesian basin; it has an average rainfall of 25 in. and no runoff.[5.5] This is an extreme case. If an average case is considered, that part of the rainfall which does seep into the ground may be subdivided as follows:

1. That absorbed directly by plants
2. That drawn by capillary action to the surface and there evaporated
3. That which unites with molecules of mineral substances and so becomes chemically fixed
4. That which flows directly into the sea (in coastal districts) through springs and underground channels
5. That which escapes at the surface of the earth through springs or by feeding rivers
6. That which is retained in the earth

The first two divisions are important in agriculture, the last two in engineering, both civil and mining; the fourth is sometimes important in engineering work.[5.6]

Civil engineering considerations of ground water refer almost wholly to that part of the water which is retained in the ground; Fig. 5.1 is here included in order to make clear the general relationship of all subsurface waters. The term *vadose water* has been used in more than one way, but the diagram indicates its correct use; it describes that water which is still in the zone of aeration, i.e., in the part of the crust which is not saturated with water. General vadose water affects the drainage of shallow excavations and is naturally related to surface drainage and irrigation. Below the zone of saturation, what is termed *internal water* is indicated; it is located in that deep part of the earth's crust (estimated by some as a depth of 6 miles) where rock pressure is so great that no interstices occur in which free water can exist. This water and that associated with rock magma are primarily of geological interest.

They are mentioned since, in connection with certain artesian basins and the drainage of some mines, water from plutonic sources, i.e., water that has not previously existed as atmospheric or surface water is undoubtedly encountered. It is known as juvenile, or plutonic, water and may be of two kinds: (1) that which has been imprisoned in the earth's interior since its formation, or (2) that which has been created by chemical combination of primitive hydrogen with oxygen of external origin.

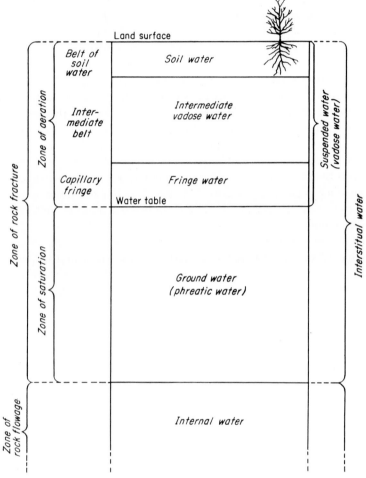

FIG. 5.1. Diagram showing the subdivisions of underground water. (*Reproduced by permission of the Director, U.S. Geological Survey from USGS. Water Supply Paper no. 494 by Dr. O. E. Meinzer.*)

One of the most striking examples of plutonic water was met during the driving of the Simplon Tunnel. Water was encountered that was so hot that workmen were scalded to death. It was found to contain no chlorine, whereas all surface waters contain at least a small percentage of this element.[5.7] During the construction of the foundations for the Harlem Hospital on the Upper East Side of New York City, a daily flow of several million gallons of ground water was encountered. Its temperature was a steady 68°F. It was effectively sealed off but since there was no obvious source of the heat it contained, it may have been of plutonic origin.[5.8]

There are many notable hot springs, such as those near Kivu in central Africa, at Karlovy Vary in Czechoslovakia, and at Bath in England, which are thought to be of internal origin. Similarly, there are the *fumaroles suffaroli* of northern Italy, the steam of which must have a similar origin. Some students of the matter have suggested that probably the sea is fed by plutonic water emerging in the sea bed. At Bendigo, Australia, there are mines that have a zone of workings in which meteoric (surface)water occurs; below this zone is a perfectly dry one; below that, at a depth of 4,500 ft from the ground, springs appear.[5.9] Controversy regarding plutonic water has centered chiefly on the Great Australian Artesian Basin. In this basin, there are wells from which water is obtained so hot that it can be used for making tea or cooking. The origin of this water is an interesting topic and is mentioned here in order to emphasize the fact that in the construction of very long tunnels an unusual factor of considerable importance may arise.

Connate, or fossil, water is water trapped between impervious beds which have been raised and distorted at some time in the past. Such trapped water may also be encountered in subsurface engineering work. As can be seen in Fig. 5.1, the zone of saturation is topped by a "water table." The concept of a water table is a most useful one, apart from the fact that the use of the word "table" suggests a level surface, and a water table is rarely if ever level. One can readily imagine that the distance to a water table varies; it may be great or small, depending on local geological conditions. Seepage has been actually observed through depths of 90 ft of glacial drift into a tunnel on the Pietermaritzburg Railway in South Africa.[5.10]

If the earth's crust were of uniform composition, all that is essential for a summary would have now been said; but underground conditions are far from uniform, and so the disposition of ground water is one of the most complicated problems in geology. Essentially, the disposition of water below the saturation level depends on two main factors: (1) the texture of the local rocks, their composition and relative stability; and (2) their structural arrangement and relationship to neighboring rocks. ("Rock" is here used in its widest sense to include *all* material in the earth's crust.) The variations possible in both these factors will make clear the complexity of the distribution of ground water. Although the conditions underground are variable, the water retained there is still governed by the natural laws governing surface water. Its movement is in accordance with the law of gravity, apart only from the minor motion which is due to capillary action.

It may be well to emphasize the fact that ground water does move. The vertical oscillations of the upper surface of saturation, or water table, will be readily appreciated since so many direct results of this movement are observed, such as the alteration of well-water levels and the intermittent flow of springs. That ground water is often moving in a horizontal direction corresponding to the slope of the water table is perhaps not quite so clear. No more vivid explanation of this underground travel has been given, perhaps, than in this statement of Dr. Herbert Lapworth:[5.11]

It was well recognized that underground water could travel for vast distances. For instance, it was known that in the artesian basins of Australia underground water traveled for hundreds of miles; and there were cases in the United States where it traveled 200 miles, with pressures which ran up to 500 feet head at the surface and something like 2,000 feet head at the bottom. In Algerian Sahara it was known, from borings, that water came a distance of 300 miles from the Atlas Mountains, passing along definite channels, some of which had actually been traced for a length of 70 miles.

The cases quoted by Dr. Lapworth are admittedly extreme, but they indicate clearly how extensive underground travel can be. A more utilitarian example is the water supply of the city of Leipzig, Germany, obtained from an underground source that is almost a "stream," as it is 2 miles wide and 40 ft deep. Another example is a 1,798-ft well at Grenelle, Paris, which draws water from Champagne, 100 miles away.

The usual means of directly observing the position of ground water, relative to the ground surface, is to measure the water level in wells or boreholes; this measurement is indicative of the local water table. Care must always be exercised after the sinking of a borehole to allow sufficient time for equilibrium to be restored in the local ground water, so that the observed level will not be a transitory value. In most areas, ground-water levels vary throughout the year in response to local rainfall and water use. This annual variation is of great importance in excavation work, both surface and subsurface, and also in foundation design, road performance, frost action in soils, etc. In deep boreholes, other factors may influence water levels. These include the effect of tides, atmospheric pressure, winds, earthquakes, and even such transient loads as passing trains where the ground water is held in a compressible aquifer.[5.12] The effect of tides upon ground-water levels near the sea is regularly observed as a rhythmic variation in many wells. Other effects are of relatively minor extent, although they can be appreciable in some areas, such as southern Florida. In a well at Miami, for example, a variation in water level of 4.5 ft was once observed; it was caused by an earthquake in the Dominican Republic 750 miles away.[5.13] Even though variations in water level such as these will not normally be encountered in civil engineering work, they are worthy of this brief record, as they indicate clearly the dynamic character of ground water and its conformity with the laws of physics.

5.4. Influence of the Nature of Rocks. The variation between the distribution of water in ground consisting in one case of uniform coarse sand and in another of solid igneous rock is an obvious illustration of the effect of the composition and texture of rocks on ground-water distribution. Between these extreme cases occurs a wide range of conditions of varying complexity. The influence that the nature of rocks can have on ground water will now be considered, but first, some definitions are necessary. *Perviousness* and *permeability* are words commonly used in this connection; they may be defined as the capacity of a rock to allow water to pass through it. A pervious rock has communicating interstices of capillary or supracapillary size. Its degree of permeability cannot be correlated with any standard scale, but is usually expressed as a volume of flow per unit of cross-sectional area per unit of time (such as gallons per square foot per day). *Porosity*, on the other hand, is a measure of the interstices contained in any particular volume of the rock; it is generally expressed as a percentage and indicates the aggregate volume of interstices to total volume. Strange as it may appear at first sight, a high degree of porosity is no assurance of perviousness. Clay, for example, has a high porosity; examples have been found of newly deposited Mississippi clay with a porosity of between 80 and 90 per cent. When it is saturated, however, it becomes impervious; the water it contains is held firmly by molecular attraction.

Despite the fact that porosity and permeability are not always synonymous, the convenience of the property of porosity as an index to the water-bearing capacity of solid rocks and as one that can easily be investigated in the laboratory has resulted in much attention being devoted to it. Table 5.1 presents some typical values for well-known types of rock.

It must be emphasized that these figures are approximate only. For example, the porosity of the chalk found in southern England varies from 26 to 43 per cent; that of the chalk found in Yorkshire is about 18 per cent; and that of the chalk of Antrim, Ireland, is sometimes less than 10 per cent. Typical of possible variations in porosity are the following figures: Seven sample cores of Bunter sandstone (usually permeable and without joints and fissures) taken from depths varying from 300 to 750 ft gave porosity values from 13.2 to 30.2 per cent and proved to have a permeability ranging from 0.05 to 17.4 gal (Imp) per sq ft per 24 hr.[5.14] These figures serve to demonstrate the wide variation possible in a fairly regular type of rock. The variation is more strongly emphasized by samples taken from a 40-ft bed of this same rock at approximately 100-ft centers; the porosity even under these circumstances varied from 3.58 to 20.3 per cent. Despite this appreciable porosity, the permeability in the direction of bedding, i.e., perpendicular to the cores, was very small indeed, and checks showed that leakage through this rock was practically all taking place along joints and fissures. That this should occur in such a relatively good "water-bearing rock" as sandstone is indeed surprising; the fact that the same feature has been demonstrated to be the explanation of the water-bearing properties of some chalk deposits and even some blocky and fissured clays will thus more easily be appreciated.

It is sometimes observed that, in addition to flowing along joints and fissures, water traverses chalk along the bands of flints and rubble that frequently distinguish chalk strata. Another feature to be noted in connection with both sandstones and limestones is the significance of the

Table 5.1. The Porosity of Rocks*

Type of rock	Maximum porosity, per cent
Soil and loam	Up to 60
Chalk	Up to 50
Sand and gravel	25 to 30
Sandstone	10 to 15
Oölitic limestone	10
Limestone and marble	5
Slate and shale	4
Granite	1.5
Crystalline rocks generally	Up to 0.5

* These figures are presented as illustrative only of the general trend of porosity in relation to various rock types. Tests on actual samples should be performed if a value for porosity has to be used.

material that acts as a natural cement joining the individual grains to form the solid rock. An unusual but striking example of this is given by Monk's park and Ketton stones.[5.15] Both are British oölitic limestones in which the oölitic grains are microporous and similar in size and structure. In the Monk's Park stone, however, the intergranular spaces are filled with a nonporous matrix of crystalline calcite; whereas in the Ketton stone, they form interconnected pores. The Ketton stone is therefore pervious and yields water freely, whereas the Monk's Park stone is impervious. It is sometimes thought that porosity decreases with increase of depth as a result of the pressure of the superincumbent rock. It is suggested that the Chalk of England, usually regarded as the most porous British rock, gives a very small yield, because of the pressure of overlying rock on this relatively soft material; a good example is found under Crystal Palace hill in south London. Few determinations of porosity at great depths have been made.

Confirmation of the importance of fissures and joints in connection with the movement and storage of ground water is available from many sources. In all but pervious rocks such as sandstone and some limestones, fissures are usually the leading factor in determining the water-bearing capacity of a rock. The distribution of joints is a matter of some complexity. It seems clear that beyond a certain depth the distribution and the size of joints diminish appreciably. The critical depth may be about 500 ft. Below this, a regular diminution of supply from joints may be expected, and therefore an economic pumping limit will soon be reached. In any case, pumping is not normally economic below depths of 700 or 800 ft. Although water may be normally available below these levels, it cannot usually be regarded as "commercially" available unless under artesian pressure, a special feature to be considered later.

Distribution rather than the mere location of ground water is therefore the prime question in underground water surveys; for this reason, some general notes on the water-bearing properties of the more common rock groups will next be presented.

Sands and Gravels. Since these materials are both porous and pervious, they may be classed as almost ideal water-bearing strata. Their wide use as artificial filtering and drainage media renders unnecessary any detailed comments. Extremely fine sands, however, are of little use.

Clays and Shales. As a general rule, these will be useless as sources of ground water. Although clays are often wet, the water present is not readily available. Hard shales may yield water at joints.

Sandstones. Sandstones are variable in texture and composition; some may be almost impermeable and others may be so pervious that water actually squirts out from them when under pressure, as from some of the Bunter sandstone of England. In these cases, the diameters of boreholes are of importance, some being made as large as 36 in. Pervious sandstones form an admirable source of ground water, since in addition to giving a high yield, they constitute an effective filtering medium. For example, water from deep wells in New Red sandstone is almost invariably clear, sparkling, and palatable.

Limestones. This extensive group of rocks is second only to sandstones as a source of ground water. Its importance is well indicated by the existence of underground solution channels and associated caverns and other familiar features, and also by the wide dependence on chalk strata as underground reservoirs. The water-bearing characteristics of chalk have already been noted. It may be further observed that as water in contact with limestones dissolves a small quantity of the rock, the use of limestones as sources of water tends always to increase the yield obtained from them. It is calculated that with every million gallons of water pumped out of the Chalk of the south of England, about 3,300 lb of chalk is also removed; thus pore spaces and any existing underground channels are correspondingly enlarged. The idea has been advanced in France that the effective rock volume available at any well or borehole in limestone might be increased by the judicious injection of hydrochloric acid. No records have yet been noted of a practical trial of this idea (except in oil-field work), but it suggests interesting possibilities.

Crystalline Rocks. In general, these rocks are not classed as water bearing, although few are absolutely dry when encountered in excavation. When decomposed, as the result of weathering or some other cause, and also when fractured and fissured, they may yield appreciable quantities of good potable water. Fresh crystalline rocks in massive formation will not generally yield any useful quantity. Granites, when decomposed, may have a relatively fair yield; quartzites, slates, and marbles may yield a useful supply because of jointing; gneisses and schists, unless they have decomposed badly, cannot be relied upon for any appreciable quantity. In Cornwall, England, several important towns obtain their water from wells in granite; it is probable that the water collects in the blanket of disintegrated rock at the surface. In Maine, there are many wells in other igneous rocks, but their yield is usually small unless jointing is very marked.

5.5. Quality of Ground Water. The quality of ground water is a matter of vital importance whether the water is to be used for industrial or for domestic purposes. In general, ground water is free from bacteria, since the passage of the water through the ground strata constitutes a natural filtering process. This possibility does not remove the vital necessity of the bacteriological examination of all ground water that is to be used for domestic purposes, especially when the arrangement and nature of the strata would permit contamination of the water stored in them from surface sources.

Ground water is usually found at a fairly constant temperature. Since the temperature is usually moderate (between 40 and 60°F), the water is cool in summer and warm in winter—one feature that commends it as a source of domestic water. The even temperature of ground water has taken on an added significance in connection with its use as cooling water. The development of air-conditioning systems in many large buildings in cities calls for steady supplies of cooling water, not in themselves large but appreciable when many buildings are dependent on the same source of supply. Consequently, in New York, for example, several large theaters are permitted to use well water for cooling air-conditioning systems provided that (1) a closed circuit is used for the water to obviate any possibility of contamination, and (2) all water used is returned to the ground by means of wells. The rise in temperature averages about 10°F. In some American cities, the extensive use of ground water for this purpose has resulted in serious problems.[5.16]

There was at least one location at which ground water was used for domestic supply in which the reverse process had to be used. Riverside, California, obtained a supply of 2,000 gpm from an artesian well 965 ft deep installed in 1931. The temperature of the water was 110°F, and in consequence a special and elaborate cooling system had to be installed by the water authority in 1936. Two adjacent wells, each 1,100 ft deep, provided cool water. Clearly, some peculiar underground structural arrangement must be held responsible for this unusual condition.[5.17] Unfortunately this unique plant was destroyed in March, 1938, by severe floods on the Santa Anna River, which changed its course and now flows over the site of the plant.

Ground water will almost certainly contain dissolved solids and gases. Of the gaseous impurities, methane may occasionally be encountered in

Fig. 5.2. Cooling plant for ground-water supply to the city of Riverside, California, U.S.A. Unfortunately, this unique plant was destroyed in March, 1938, by severe floods on the Santa Anna River, which changed its course and now flows over the site of the plant. (*Reproduced by permission of the Superintendent, Municipal Water Dept., City of Riverside.*)

water that has not traveled far from surface deposits or that has been in contact with deep-buried strata of organic origin. The gas is usually caused by the decomposition of organic matter in the absence of free oxygen. It is dangerous; and therefore if it is present in such quantities that it is liberated from the water on reaching atmospheric pressure, it can be a source of trouble. Hydrogen bisulfide is occasionally met and is easily detectable if present in any appreciable quantity; its origin may vary, but a possible source is the interaction of organic acids from surface deposits with underground sulfates. The gas is easily removed by aeration; its presence is often the chief feature of medicinal spring waters. Carbon dioxide is the most important gaseous impurity of ground water; its origin is generally the atmosphere. It gives to water a sparkle which is not unpleasant, and it is not therefore objectionable. But in water, the gas makes a weak solution of hydrocarbonic acid. This acts as a solvent for several different rock constituents, and for this reason the presence of the gas is often significant.

Free carbon dioxide gas is occasionally encountered in civil engineering work in sufficient quantities to be troublesome. On the great aqueduct that conveys water from Owens Valley to the Los Angeles area in California, severe corrosion was discovered in the steel pipelines; tubercles formed very quickly, and constant cleaning and painting were necessary for adequate maintenance. Careful tests were made of the water at the entrance to the aqueduct, but no peculiarities were found. Further checks were made; and it was eventually found that between the two ends of a 7,000-ft tunnel the carbon dioxide content increased from a negligible amount to 4.2 ppm. The tunnel was therefore unwatered and examined; the gas could actually be heard hissing as it escaped through cracks in the concrete lining. The tunnel penetrates what is locally known as Soda Hill, a granitic rock formation containing many badly fractured fault zones; hot limestone beds are thought to exist nearby. The consequent acidity of the water was clearly the cause of the corrosion troubles. The remedy adopted was to lead the gas through special chases into a pipe beneath the tunnel invert which, in turn, was connected with a new adit, 2,000 ft long, through which the accumulated gas could escape.[5.18]

Pure water will dissolve only 20 ppm of calcium carbonate and 28 ppm of magnesium carbonate, but water containing carbon dioxide will dissolve many hundreds of parts per million of the solids. These and similar solid impurities in ground water may give rise to the main purification problems of the waterworks engineer. It follows that water obtained from limestone strata is always suspect, even without test. The dissolved carbonates give to the water what is termed *temporary hardness*, since the dissolved solids can be removed by simple chemical processes. If the dissolved solids are the corresponding sulfates, the corresponding hardness of the water is termed *permanent*, since it cannot be removed by simple processes used for eliminating the carbonates. Chemical analyses are necessary to determine the degree of hardness of the water; if this exceeds about 200 ppm of calcium carbonate the water requires *softening*. Clark's lime process, a chemical method, is often used to remove temporary hardness. For permanent or mineral hardness, various processes exist, but zeolites are generally used in all of them. Zeolites have the property of exchanging nonhardening constituents for the hardening constituents present in water; when exhausted, they can be regenerated by treatment with a brine solution. Artificial zeolites formed of complex silicates are now available, but the original zeolites from a natural source were formed from glauconite (a complex silicate of alumina, iron, and potassium).

Iron salts are another impurity in ground water that can be of serious consequence in industrial work, e.g., dyeing; and they are a nuisance in connection with domestic supplies. Soft water is likely to contain less iron in solution than hard water; the maximum iron content for hard water is generally about 1 ppm, but it depends on the other salts present. Manganese salts may also be present; they are often associated with iron salts, though always in small quantities. They affect the taste of water and give black stains, whereas iron salts produce red or brown stains. Deferrization of such water is a simple matter in principle but difficult in actual practice. It is essentially a chemical process, aiming at the production of ferrous hydroxide as a coagulant which can be precipitated or removed by filtration. One of the most unusual construction accidents caused by ground water ever to be recorded was related to iron deposits. During the construction of a tunnel in Milwaukee five workmen were killed in the access shaft to the tunnel; it was found that their deaths were due to carbon dioxide poisoning. Pumping operations had reduced the ground-water level so that the excavated rock was exposed to air for the first time. This caused a change in its ferric content to the ferrous state, and thus liberated carbon dioxide. When compressed air was applied to the tunnel, it forced some of the liberated gas into the shaft; quite unsuspected, the gas soon proved fatal to the five men who were working in the shaft.[5.19]

"Trace elements," a term now familiar to the informed reader, describes those minute quantities of the rare elements which are essential for healthful living: the absence of the necessary minute quantity of fluorine in water, for example, causes dental decay. Correspondingly, there are other elements, minute traces of which can be fatal. They are not unrelated to ground water, as the records can demonstrate. There were, for example, several cases of arsenic poisoning some years ago north of Kingston, Ontario; poisoning of this kind is a most unusual medical occurrence, apart from poisoning due to obvious sources of arsenic.[5.20] The presence of arsenic was finally detected in the farm well water used by the victims. This, in turn, was traced to minute quantities of ferrous arsenate existing naturally in the limestone stratum through which the well had been excavated.

In Los Angeles, just before the Second World War, it was found that citrus leaves were turned yellow by the presence of minute quantities of boron in the water used for irrigation. This water came from the Owens Valley Aqueduct supplying Los Angeles; it had been safely used for 15 years previously with no ill effects. Careful investigation showed that the quantity of boron detected was not injurious to human beings but was dangerous to some of the crops grown in the Los Angeles area. Years were spent in tracking down the source of the sudden occurrence of boron, and the investigation is an example of "engineering detective work" at its best. It was finally determined that 75 per cent of the troublesome boron content was being contributed by the Hot Lake area in Long Valley. The boron concentration was found to increase at points where hot gases and hot water bubbled up through lakes and springs which fed into the aqueduct. By taking the aqueduct out of service for its usual maintenance period at times when boron concentrations were highest, much of the boron could be deposited in Owens Lake (a temporary reservoir). Later, as a further expedient, water containing boron was spread over land, formerly irrigated but since abandoned, and allowed to seep to discharge points at lower elevations, whence it could be pumped back into the aqueduct; this natural filtration was sufficient to remove almost all traces of the troublesome element.[5.21]

The presence of high concentrations of calcium and magnesium sulfates in ground water can cause very serious trouble with concrete work in contact with the ground. Occurring chiefly in heavy clay soils, high-sulfate ground water is common in western Canada; it is so widespread in Great Britain that the Institution of Civil Engineers began an investigation of the effect of sulfates in soil upon cement products in the years immediately preceding the Second World War. A summary of the initial findings of this research project has been published by the Institution.[5.22] It was found that the sulfates of calcium, magnesium, and the alkali metals occur widely in the Mesozoic and Tertiary clays of Great Britain, including such widely known formations as the Keuper marl, the Lias, and the Oxford, Kimmeridge, Weald, Gault, and London clays. Superficial deposits, generally glacial, were substantially free of sulfates; thus, it is only where the geological structure is such that the older formations come to the surface that trouble with sulfates is encountered on any appreciable scale.

Sodium chloride remains for mention as the final important mineral impurity liable to be encountered in underground water. It may have its origin in the sea, as explained later in this chapter, but may also be of mineral origin. Rock-salt deposits are an obvious source of supply; some are "mined" by means of brine solutions. Although this system of mining is of great interest from the point of view of utilizing ground water for mining purposes, it can have unusually serious consequences if the workings are so close to the surface that settlement can result. This will be a matter for discussion in Chap. 11.

The quality of ground water has so far been treated by considering the nature of possible impurities; it may be useful to add a brief summary of what may be expected from typical water-bearing strata. The only type of clay from which water supplies are regularly obtained is boulder clay, which may sometimes have a pervious structure. Water thus obtained may be quite hard; traces of hydrogen sulfide are often found. Sands usually give a fairly pure water, but occasionally they yield water with a small ferruginous content. The same may be said of water from sandstones; if the cementing material is calcium sulfate or calcite, the water can be quite hard. Water from limestone, chalk, or similar rocks will almost certainly be hard, but occasionally other impurities will also be present. Water from some of the East Anglian chalk in England, for example, contains so much ferrous carbonate that it must be treated.

To deal with the possible impurities in ground water in this brief space necessarily means that only a sketch of the subject can be presented. This is done with one main purpose in view—to demonstrate the relation of such impurities to the geological conditions of the ground from which the water is being obtained. This correlation is useful for two reasons. First, preliminary study of the local geology will at least suggest the possible impurities to be expected in any prospective ground-water supply; and, second, accurate knowledge of the relevant geology will demonstrate the course of any known impurities and indicate the probability of any increase or decrease of the amount of contamination. All civil engineers should be able to gain at least a general idea of the geology of the source area of the water supply of a town they may be visiting merely by noting the relative hardness of the local water when they first wash their hands.

5.6. Influence of Geological Structure. Underground conditions affecting ground water differ from the ideal case not only because of the wide variation of materials in contact with the water but also because of the way in which the various rock strata are arranged, in general and in relation to one another. In the following discussion, the concept of a level ground surface will be maintained merely for convenience. The first variation from the ideal that may be considered is the alternation of pervious and impervious beds. If the impervious stratum constitutes the surface layer, no water would normally penetrate to the potential underground reservoir provided by the pervious bed. Possibly a more usual case is that in which the pervious bed is at the surface; rain will soak through until it reaches the main body of ground water retained above the impervious stratum from which supplies can be drawn by means of boreholes or wells. The arrangement is capable of duplication, and a "sandwich" structure can be imagined. Such structures actually occur; the middle Lias formation in Northampton, England, only 93 ft thick, contains no less than five water-bearing horizons separated by impervious clays, any four of which may be present at one location. The condition illustrated in sketch *A* of Fig. 5.3 will be interfered with only if the impervious stratum is pierced. This would seem hard to imagine, but cases have occurred in which wells have been drilled too deep. At Kissingland, near Lowestoft in England, the bottom of an old well penetrating 50 ft of gravel was pierced, and all the water tapped by the well ran down to the lower stratum. A similar instance happened in the drilling of a 70-ft well at Nipigon in Ontario, Canada.

A further variation will be obtained when the strata are inclined instead of level, as indicated in sketch *B*. In this case, the inclined impervious stratum will constitute a barrier between the two pervious beds, so that the elevations of the respective water tables need not and probably

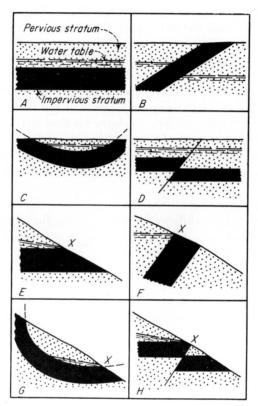

Fig. 5.3. Diagrams illustrating the effect of geological structure on ground-water distribution.

will not be the same. A similar effect is noted when alternating layers constitute part of a fold; many arrangements are naturally possible, but only one general case is illustrated. Sketch *C* shows how water will collect in such a distorted stratum. It may be noted that the geological structure underlying the city of London is of this type. Finally, sketch *D* demonstrates the effect that a fault may have on the distribution of ground water in alternating strata. The variations possible in this simple case are dependent on the relative thickness of the strata, the nature of the fault, and the throw of the fault. In the case illustrated, the barrier provided by the impervious stratum remains, but a slight increase in the throw of the fault would leave a gap in the barrier, with consequent alteration of the ground-water conditions. The shatter zone generally found in rock bordering a fault plane may also alter the water-bearing character of a rock by providing water passage along the planes of fracture.

The four simple cases already considered are illustrated in sketches E, F, G, and H, with the surafce of the ground inclined; the altered ground-water conditions are indicated diagrammatically and need no elaboration. It will be seen that two peculiarities are immediately introduced. At the points marked X, bodies of ground water will come into contact with the atmosphere. This leads directly to the second feature, viz., that the surface of the ground water will not be level but will be inclined at the hydraulic gradient necessary for flow to take place through the material of the stratum. This is a general condition, as has already been explained. An important consequence is that, as a rule, the "water table follows the ground surface"—a broad statement, but useful as a guide.

Of particular significance is the variation in the yield of water obtained from the same rock at different positions along the range of a fold in which the rock has been distorted. If the folding has been anticlinal and is of relatively short radius, there will be a distinct tendency for fissures to develop. Similarly, if the folding has been synclinal, there will be a tendency for the rock to "tighten up" and have its usual perviousness reduced; this tendency is most marked in the softer rocks. This has been demonstrated in connection with the water supply of the municipality of Richmond, London, where the construction of a well and over 10,000 ft of adits in the chalk failed to develop an appreciable supply because the location was on a syncline in the chalk formation.[5.23]

5.7. Springs. Springs sometimes provide a useful and pure water supply, but often an engineer will have to investigate their capacity to provide a continuous supply. Alternatively, an engineer may be called upon to study the source of springs in connection with possible water-lowering operations, such as pumping for water adjacent to springs already in use. Again, as springs often accompany instability of ground and especially of steep natural slopes, their course may have to be traced in drainage operations. Sketch E (Fig. 5.3) represents in simple fashion the geological arrangement necessary for the existence of steadily flowing springs; if the principle therein presented is applied to local conditions, one can readily see the nature of many springs. The flow may vary; but because of the relatively slow movement of ground water, a spring will not dry up except in very dry spells. This slow movement when related to rainfall explains the lag between major movements of the water table and

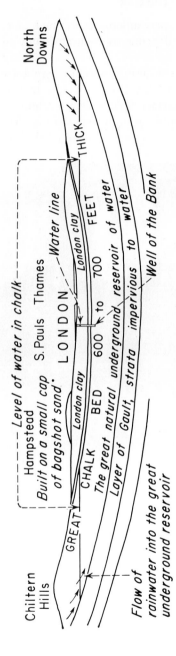

FIG. 5.4. Simplified geological section through the London Basin, London, England.

Chiltern Hills

Flow of rainwater into the great underground reservoir

Level of water in chalk

Hampstead
Built on a small cap of bagshot sand

S. Pauls   Thames   Water line

LONDON

London clay

GREAT   CHALK   BED   600 to 700 FEET   THICK
London clay

The great natural underground reservoir of water

Layer of Gault, strata impervious to water

Well of the Bank

North Downs

heavy rainfall, a lag that may amount to as much as 6 months in temperate climates and on which depends the real efficiency of ground-water supplies.

Although springs that flow intermittently are not numerous, they have an interest all their own. Sketch *F* shows the basis of one type of intermittent spring. If the surface level of the ground water drops below *X*, as it might through depletion elsewhere during dry weather, the spring previously existing will disappear, returning only when the ground water

Fig. 5.5. The "Thousand Springs" on the north side of Snake River Canyon in Idaho, U.S.A. The water issues from the open-textured basal portion of a lava sheet and flows over compact clay and volcanic lapilli. (*Photograph by I. C. Russell. Reproduced by permission of the Director, U.S. Geological Survey.*)

has been so replenished that the level again rises above *X*. The principle illustrated may again be applied to local geological conditions and thus explain natural phenomena such as the "breaking out of the bournes" in England after the early spring rains (*bourne* is a name applied in southern England to this type of spring). They are a feature of the chalk uplands and also of the oölitic limestones of the Cotswold hills in England; they occur frequently in northern France. Names of villages in England betray the existence of such springs; Winterbourne Zelston and Waterbourne Whitchurch are two delightful examples from the county of Dorset. Many springs discharge into the sea because of local geological conditions; this could well happen in the situation given in sketch *G*. In the Persian Gulf, natives dive to the sea bottom with leather bags which they fill with drinking water from spring discharges.[5.24]

5.8. Artesian Water. Water is said to be *artesian* when the ground water rises either up to or above ground level as soon as the water-bearing bed is pierced; local geological structure, in which the water is stored

Fig. 5.6. Water under artesian pressure flowing out of the casing pipe of a test borehole in the bed of the Grand River, Ontario, Canada, at the site of the Shand Dam.

in the bed under hydrostatic pressure, accounts for this phenomenon. Its name is one of the few in connection with subsurface conditions that is not self-descriptive; it originated from that of the province of Artois, France. The term *subartesian* is used to denote wells in which the ground water is under hydrostatic pressure but not to such an extent that it is forced to ground level; as soon as it is freed it comes to rest at some point below ground level but above the top level of the water-bearing bed. The usual cause of artesian pressure is the hydrostatic head of that part of the body of ground water which is confined by impervious strata above the level at which it is tapped. This condition may arise in a synclinal structure of alternating pervious and impervious beds, as illustrated in Fig. 5.7; two alternative structural arrangements are illustrated in the same figure, and other similar conditions can be imagined.

Artesian water may quite possibly exist beneath impermeable strata which form a river bed, with results such as the rather unusual occurrence shown in Fig. 5.6. The author took this photograph after a test borehole at the site of the Shand Dam in Ontario had penetrated glacial till and entered the underlying Guelph dolomite beneath the waters of the Grand River.[5.25]

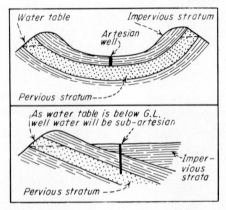

FIG. 5.7. Simplified geological sections illustrating artesian ground-water conditions.

There are many examples of artesian waters, but naturally the water encountered in Artois may be said to be the leading example. The ground water in the well-known chalk deposits there does not find its natural level until the overlying Tertiary clay is pierced. Despite the general adoption of the name, the use of artesian water was revived rather than initiated at Artois, since it had been extensively used in much earlier periods, particularly in northern Africa. At Thebes, for example, shafts were sunk, and excavation was continued as bores 6 to 8 in. in diameter to water-bearing sands, in many cases 400 ft from the surface.[5.26]

Artesian conditions may exist in the form of artesian slopes or artesian basins. In both, but especially in the former, artesian water may be present at depths to which it is uneconomical to drill. Local conditions and demands will determine the relative economy of using such supplies, and the inevitable variation of conditions will explain the great variation in the depths to which artesian wells have been sunk. In Berlin, Germany, and in St. Louis, Missouri, depths of 4,000 ft have been necessary and have actually been drilled; in England, a well 1,585 ft deep at Ottershaw appears to be about the maximum depth utilized in that country; in Australia, a well at Boronga, New South Wales, is 4,338 ft deep; whereas along the Atlantic seaboard of the United States, artesian supplies at depths of a few hundred feet are relatively common. One famous well on this coast is the 12-in. well at St. Augustine, Florida, which originally supplied 10 million gal a day from a depth of 1,400 ft.

Although the areas in which artesian water can be tapped are often relatively small, there are, on the other hand, some extensive areas under which ground water is stored under pressure. One of the best known of these is the Great Dakota Artesian Basin in North and South Dakota, which has an area of about 15,000 sq miles. It is widely used as a source of water supply; the water-bearing bed is Dakota sandstone, and it has been the subject of detailed ground-water investigation. Particular attention has been paid to the possibility that some if not all of the artesian pressure may be due to the weight of the superincumbent rock strata. Pressure due to the weight of rock is still a subject of debate in geological circles, but it is of interest to note that the subject was discussed by Thales about 650 B.C., and also by Pliny, and was suggested as the agent responsible for elevating sea water to the level of springs.

Australia is a continent in which artesian water is of major importance; the Great Australian Artesian Basin is almost worthy of classification as one of the wonders of the world. Having an area of more than 590,000 sq miles, it is located in the states of South Australia, Queensland, and New South Wales. Over 3,000 artesian wells draw on the supply that it provides—a daily flow of over 500 million gal (Imp). In form, the basin approximates the ideal complete artesian basin; the eastern rim is tilted up to a greater altitude than the western. The main aquifer extends as a practically continuous body under the whole of the basin and consists, in general, of Jurassic sands, occurring as very soft sandstones. Artesian conditions proper extend over the greater part of the basin; but in the western section, the head is sufficient to give rise only to sub-artesian conditions. The water obtained is of good quality, but its temperature is high, extremely so in the parts which reach a depth of 5,000 to 6,000 ft. Experiments in New South Wales have shown that the temperature varies almost directly with depth; records range from a temperature of 86°F at 700 ft to 122°F at 3,000 ft. From among the many notable records obtained from this great basin may be mentioned the drilling of an experimental well at Careunga, near Moree, New South Wales, to a depth of 4,014 ft. In this depth, three separate artesian flows were encountered at different pressures, with different compositions, and with different emissions of methane gas; records of the three flows were kept separately. There are several other large and important artesian basins in Australia; the most notable one is the Murray River Basin, lying in the states of South Australia, New South Wales, and Victoria; it has an area of 107,250 sq miles. It is of special interest to engineers to note that the conservation of these great natural reservoirs of ground water has been recognized in Australia as overriding ordinary state boundaries. In consequence, since 1912 a series of regular interstate conferences has been held, attended by geology and engineering delegates from most of the states concerned; records have been exchanged, experiences discussed, and general conclusions arrived at with regard to the many problems involved. The printed records of the conferences, together with

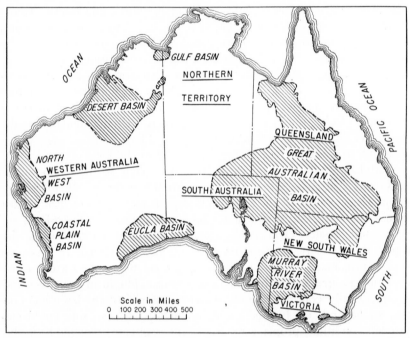

Fig. 5.8. Sketch map of Australia, showing the extent of known artesian basins.

the relevant state geological bulletins, constitute a most valuable part of ground water literature.[5.27]

One might expect that civil engineers, with their basic training in hydraulics, would have no difficulty in appreciating the fundamentals of artesian pressure and that they would be ever mindful of its potential. Unfortunately, the records prove otherwise, for there are many cases in which the movement of structures has been attributed to artesian pressure beneath foundations, particularly when construction pumping has temporarily lowered the water table and thus temporarily concealed the final head of water that will be effective. The matter can be illustrated by brief reference to experience during the construction of the Conchas Dam in New Mexico. The main section of this dam is a concrete gravity structure, placed in separate monoliths which reach a height of 200 ft and which are founded upon a porous sandstone where ground water is under artesian pressure. This extends 40 ft below the base of the dam and is underlain by 30 ft of a dense shale which overlies another stratum of porous sandstone where ground water is also under artesian pressure. Pumping operations during construction lowered the effective pressure; high pressure grouting was carried out under the monoliths. When pumping was stopped, movement of some of the monoliths up to a maximum lift of 1 in. (despite their immense size) was noted. The matter was most carefully studied and it was determined by laboratory tests that the elastic properties of the sandstone alone could not account for the rise observed; this led to the conclusion that the movement was associated with the swelling characteristics of the shale stratum.[5.28]

5.9. Ground Water near the Sea. The presence of sodium chloride in ground water has already been mentioned as one of the impurities that can develop through contact of ground water with rocks having some degree of soluble content. There is, however, another possible source of sodium chloride and allied salts: encroaching sea water in coastal areas. Although originally a phenomenon of almost academic interest, the matter has now assumed most serious proportions in several parts of the world where increasing sea-water encroachment is interfering with the purity of ground water used for domestic supply. Basically, the matter is one of simple hydrostatics. Since the specific gravity of sea water is slightly greater than that of fresh water, a state of equilibrium will exist when the two are in contact in a porous medium, as illustrated in Fig. 5.9. This superimposing of a lens of fresh water over sea water is called the *Ghyben-Herzberg* effect after two of those who have investigated the matter in theory. The whole of the Florida peninsula and such islands as Oahu on which Honolulu is situated are most certainly completely underlain, at depth, by sea water. The state of equilibrium illustrated in the simple diagram is, however, a delicate one. It can very easily be disturbed, and once disturbed, it cannot readily be restored. Overpumping the fresh water will permit an advance of the boundary between fresh water and salt and will be one sure way of interfering with the natural state of balance.

This has happened in many parts of the world. Wells along the shores of the Thames Estuary and in the Liverpool district of England, wells along much of the California coast line,[5.29] wells tapping the remarkable ground-water reserves under Long Island, New York,[5.30] all have been made brackish when salt water became mixed to varying degrees with fresh water because of excessive drawdown of the latter. The matter is one of almost world-wide importance, having been investigated intensively in England, Holland, Japan, and North America. Some of these investigations will be mentioned in Chap. 15, but the matter is directly related to civil engineering operations in coastal areas and is so clearly illustrative of the geological implications of ground-water movement that some further reference to it here seems warranted.

The presence of brackish water in wells is indicative of the existence of water-bearing, i.e., pervious strata. If the wells are adjacent to the sea, it will normally follow that at some point the fresh water will be in contact with the infiltrated sea water. The zone of diffusion between the two is relatively small, and thus any appreciable change from the normal position of the ground water (such as can be caused by excessive pumping) will result in a corresponding change in the position of the salt water. As the average salt content of sea water is about 35,000 ppm, and

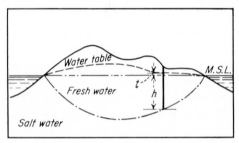

Fɪɢ. 5.9. Diagrammatic section illustrating the elements of the Herzberg effect when fresh water overlies salt water. (*Based, by permission of the Director of the U.S. Geological Survey, on fig. 2 of USGS Water Supply Paper no. 537.*)

the normal maximum salt content for water for domestic use is about 3,000 ppm, it will be clear that it takes but a small contamination of fresh water by sea water to make the former unfit for human use. Rainfall onto the exposed land surface is the means whereby loss of fresh water due to evaporation and transpiration is balanced.

Herzberg's original investigation of the interrelation of sea water and fresh water was carried out in Germany about 1900. His results and those of other investigators have been fully confirmed by field studies in the coastal lands of Holland and in other areas. They apply generally to all geological conditions in coastal areas and so should be kept in mind not only with regard to pumping ground water in coastal areas but also with regard to any civil engineering works which may interfere with natural ground-water conditions. The case of Angaur Island, one of the Palau Islands of the Pacific, about 800 miles southwest from Guam, is an illustration of the serious results that simple excavation can have under such circumstances. Angaur Island, roughly triangular in shape, has an area of only 3.2 sq miles. Valuable phosphate deposits on the island have been mined steadily since 1908, although the commercially available deposits are now just about exhausted. In 1938, the Japanese introduced power-operated equipment in order to speed up the mining operations. With the availability of such improved methods, large excavations were soon completed. Some of these large "holes" went appreciably below sea level. Water from the fresh-water lens overlying the main body of sea water formed pools in the excavations. However, because of the increased volume of water required to fill the "holes," as compared with that previously required to fill merely the voids in the coral, movement of the ground water took place, flow of sea water was induced, and the previously fresh and usable ground-water supply on the island was contaminated. Remedial measures carried out by American forces after the war included sealing off artificial lakes and reducing their size, using coral rock as rubble, with as much fine material included as possible.[5.31] Admittedly this is a small and rather isolated case. It is, however, a vivid reminder of the delicate equilibrium that exists wherever sea water and fresh water are in contact beneath the ground, a situation that should never be forgotten when civil engineering works, especially pumping operations, have to be carried out near the seacoast.

5.10. Movement of Ground Water. Some of the examples given have illustrated the fact that ground water does move. Surprising though it may seem, this concept is not so widely appreciated as might be imagined. In general, the movement follows D'Arcy's law, amended to allow for the pervious medium through which flow takes place. Much work has been done in developing the necessary theory, and correspondingly, much experimental work in both laboratory and field has been carried out in checking upon theory. Well established as is the subject of ground-water hydrology, it can never be forgotten that the theory assumes certain specified subsurface conditions and that the practical application of the theory demands accurate information about subsurface conditions —in other words an appreciation of local geology. Despite the fact, therefore, that this volume is concerned with geology and not with hydrology, some further reference to the movement of ground water is desirable in order that readers may have a well-rounded picture of this vital aspect of subsurface conditions.

Reference may usefully be made to the movement that will take place when pumping is started in an open well that has been successfully completed to below the water table. The water level in the well will naturally fall when pumping begins and will continue to do so until the hydraulic gradient in the material surrounding the well is such that flow into the well will occur at a rate equal to that at which water is being removed by pumping. It can be shown theoretically that, for uniform material, the curve that the hydraulic gradient will assume between the water level in the well, under equilibrium conditions, and the unchanged natural level of the water table will be a parabola. As this condition will obtain all around the well, a *cone of depression* will result; the apex of the inverted conical form of the ground-water surface will be the water level in the well. The intersection of the cone of depression with the natural water table will, theoretically, be a circle which will mark the limit of the range of interference of the pumping operation. Any other well located within this circle will be interfered with to some degree; its effective yield of water will be reduced. Such interference can be a critical matter in built-up areas where it is desired to have wells close together so that ground-water resources will be used to maximum extent. It is surprising to note how wide these ranges of influence may be in very pervious strata. In Liverpool, England, for example, the effect of pumping has been noticed as far as 2 miles away from a pumped well; in this instance, the intervening ground was, in general, a pervious red sandstone.

Since ground water is always hidden from sight, the effect of pumping and the extent of the range of interference can only be checked by means of observation wells or boreholes sunk at varying distances from the pumped well and so arranged that the water level in each can be readily measured. In later chapters, as the effect of ground water upon various types of civil engineering operation is described, examples will be given which show actual installations of such observation wells and thus illustrate from engineering practice the effects of ground-water movement. One general example may be cited here. Nine miles east of Harrisburg, Pennsylvania, is the Hershey Valley, a pleasant area underlain generally by an Ordovician limestone of the Beekmantown formation. For many years, the Annville Stone Company had been mining the high-calcium Annville limestone at a location $1\frac{1}{2}$ miles northeast of the factory of the Hershey Chocolate Company. The stone company had pumped 3,500 gpm out of its workings without serious effect. In May, 1949, the company suddenly increased its pumping rate in its lower workings to 6,500 gpm. Within a short time, ground-water levels were affected to varying degree throughout an area of 10 sq miles. Over 100 sink holes developed, some with serious effect. Since the Hershey Company was affected, it started recharging ground water from the surface in December, 1949, in order to restore ground-water levels at its plant. It began with 3,500 gpm, but soon increased this to 10,000 gpm. Ground-water levels immediately started to rise again, but the pumping rate of the stone company also increased from 6,500 to 8,000 gpm. After attempting to have the recharging operation stopped by the courts, without success, the stone company adopted a program of grouting around their operations. With the recharging continuing, ground-water conditions in the area around the mine were thus effectively restored by May, 1950. The field investigations carried out in connection with this case constitute a splendid example of a good ground-water survey.[5.32]

5.11. Underground Cavities and Ground Water. Impurities in ground water have already been mentioned; these result from the solution of matter with which the ground water comes into contact. The process of solution will naturally be greatly accelerated if the water is moving. This simple fact has such important consequences that it calls for attention next. Moving water is utilized, on quite a large scale, for the extraction of common salt when underground circumstances favor this method of mining. Sodium chloride is not, however, a mineral commonly encountered, whereas limestone is one of the most widespread of all sedimentary rocks, and it is soluble to varying degrees in water. Therefore, in limestone country, subsurface "erosion" caused by the solution of calicum carbonate in flowing ground water becomes a problem. It is a phenomenon encountered all over the world. Sinkholes are a minor evidence of such solution processes. In other locations, lakes are becoming deeper because water seeps from them into underlying limestone. In Florida, for example, the vicinity of Ocala is noteworthy in this respect. A spring at Silver Springs has a steady flow of 545 cfs and carries 274 ppm of solids, which represents about 400 tons of dissolved rock per day.

A figure such as this makes it readily understandable that such transfer of solid material will, in the course of many years, result in major cavities beneath the ground. The civil engineer, therefore, always has to be on guard when working in limestone country; later chapters will present examples showing the troubles that can arise when such solution cavities are encountered in excavation or beneath structures. They have a wider interest, however, since it is this same action that has caused most of the large "natural caves" which are such interesting natural features in some parts of the world. There are many good examples in North America; the Carlsbad Caverns in New Mexico are but one example. The most noteworthy are those found in France.

Many of the caves in northern France have been known and used since the earliest days of human settlement. Those bordering the river Seine are notable in this respect. Near Vetheuil, hills of chalk are almost honeycombed with caves, many of which have been used for the shelter of men and beasts for hundreds of years. In more recent years, they have proved to be admirable (and natural) bomb shelters. One of the greatest of Norman chiefs made his home in a group of caves known as Le Grand Comombier (the great dovecote), which includes one cave forming a room over 100 m long. Of more interest to some readers will be the great caves at Pommeroy Park. These are known to have been used by the Romans as a convenient quarry for building stone, but their fame today arises from the fact that they provide almost perfect storage for the maturing of champagne.[5.33] Millions of bottles can be seen by the visitor to the caves, all naturally under careful guard and constant attention. In the south of France, close to the valley of the Rhone, is the greatest of all these underground wonders, the Bramabian, with its underground river and 6 miles of galleries. The underground river of Labouiche is said to be the longest in the world, more than 2 miles. Visitors can sail more than 1 mile by boat. The underground torrent of the Cigalière with its waterfalls 60 ft high is in the same area. Then there

Fig. 5.10. Wine storage in the Cave de Vouvray, typical of the way in which limestone caverns are used in France for this significant purpose. (*Reproduced by permission of the Editor, La Revue Vinicole, Paris.*)

are chasms such as the *gouffre* Martel which goes down 1,400 ft, 900 ft of which has been explored.[5.34]

Possibly even better known are the extensive caves in the Pyrenees between France and Spain. Here some of the world's most extensive underground networks of interconnecting caves and tunnels have made the area a mecca for spelaeologists (*spelaeology* is recognized as the name for this rather unusual outdoor sport). Norbert Casteret, one of the most intrepid underground explorers, has written an exciting book about this area and his travels in it, or rather under it.[5.35] Of special interest is an incident he relates regarding a famous hole, Le Trou du Toro, high among the peaks of the Pyrenees, down which disappear the rushing waters of one of the mountain streams. There had long been speculation about where the water reappeared, and the general belief was that it came out lower down the same valley, which is on the Spanish side of the border. When a hydroelectric development was being planned for this valley, Spanish engineers had to find out exactly what did happen. Speculation had to give way to fact, especially since there was also a rumor that the water penetrated beneath the mountain ridge through an underground passage, which the spelaeologists had not been able to explore, and reappeared in France. Under the leadership of Casteret, therefore, engineers introduced a suitable quantity of dye into Le Trou du Toro. Older inhabitants of the lovely upper Garonne countryside still talk of their amazement when, on the morning of July 20, 1931, they saw their beloved river running a vivid green. Only the Spanish engineers failed to share in the general excitement since they now had no claim to the water they had planned to use.

Whenever, therefore, an engineer hears of a "disappearing stream," when he sees sinkholes or visits famous underground caves, he may well be reminded that here is evidence of the long-term power of ground water in contact with limestone, and he should make careful mental note of such possibilities in case he should ever be called upon to undertake construction work in limestone country.

5.12. Subsurface Drainage. The existence of large underground caverns and their possible use as convenient depositories of waste has naturally not been lost sight of by those responsible for the ever-growing problem of urban waste disposal. An interesting example is Bellevue, Ohio, where caverns in the limestone which underlies the town are used for the disposal of all the town's sewage. An estimated 1,500 sinkholes are used for the direct discharge of household sewage and all drainage into the partially water-filled network of caves many feet beneath the surface. In 1946, however, the Ohio Water Resources Board ruled that the use of any well for disposal of sewage "or other material considered deleterious to the potable underground water" was to be prohibited in Ohio, and the State Health Department considered that the Bellevue procedure was a potential menace. Plans have therefore been prepared for a sewage-treatment plant, but legal difficulties with regard to the necessary financing have prevented the actual start of construction; septic tanks are now used, however, before the sewage is discharged into the ground.[5.36]

Prior to this, however, the town had had its own warning, which again illustrates one of the fundamentals of ground-water hydrology. On June 26, 1937, rain so heavy as to constitute a cloudburst fell in the area to the south of the town, reaching its greatest intensity close to the town itself. It was estimated that between 7 and 8 in. of rain fell on the town in 9 hours. Ordinary surface drainage facilities were naturally taxed beyond their capacity, and surface flooding occurred. The underground caverns into which the town had been discharging its surface drainage were very quickly filled, because the normal underground flow from the caverns was susceptible to exactly the same laws of hydraulics as surface waters. The underground system therefore overflowed, and geysers 15 to 20 ft high broke through into the streets in the lower parts of the town. Since the overflow was not all rain water, but included sewage that had previously been discharged in the usual way, the distress of the town can well be imagined. Time took care of the emergency, and Bellevue drainage soon returned to normal.[5.37] This incident, which the local residents have long since forgotten, is not recalled in any critical way, but as a most revealing example of the simple fact that water poured into a hole in the ground does not just "disappear."

The expression just used is almost an accurate description of an unusual arrangement used for the taking care of the surface drainage from a new bypass road built around the ancient city of Winchester, England, just before the Second World War. Most of the new road lies in the valley of the river Itchin, one of the famous trout-fishing streams of England, whose waters are inviolate from such possible pollution as road drainage. Fortunately it was possible to collect all surface runoff from the road into ditches and to discharge these through "soakways" into the local chalk. Although actual cavities can rarely be used for the disposal of surface drainage, exactly the same procedure is being followed when water is allowed to penetrate from the surface of the ground into underground permeable strata; the "cavities" are the voids in the structure of the permeable material. This has long been a well-accepted method of drainage. When the pervious stratum is at the surface, drainage into it is an obvious procedure. When, however, the pervious material is some distance below the surface, overlain by less-permeable material, then drainage has to be conducted to it down specially excavated bores.

These have long been called *dumb wells,* a singularly lucid name since the bores do act as wells in reverse. Throughout the world, there are many well-known examples of this type of drainage. In South Australia, the famous Dismal Swamp was drained, with partial success, by boring dumb wells from the surface into the underlying limestone. Dumb wells have long been used in Lincolnshire, England, for draining the upper estuarine clays into the Lincolnshire limestone. During the construction of the London tube railways through the London clay, at least one contractor saved himself a lot of money by boring a dumb well from his excavation, deep as it was below the surface, into the underlying Chalk, through which he drained his workings, having previously determined the exact position of the Chalk and the fact that the normal water table was below the level of the tunnel he was excavating. The use of dumb wells for both surface and subsurface drainage has been described; it will be appreciated that only rarely are circumstances such that these wells can be used for drainage of underground works. More often, the only recourse in such cases is to pump the water which accumulates in the workings to the surface and to drain it away in surface watercourses. There are, however, occasions when a careful study of local topography and ground-water conditions will show that gravity can be made to take the place of such pumping with resultant economy. An example of this is provided by the lead and zinc mines of northeastern Wales, bordering on the estuary of the river Dee; these mines have been worked for many years, always with difficulty because of the presence of excessive water in the surrounding strata. This is a "block and checkerboard" arrangement of limestone, with many cross veins that provide for a free flow of ground water.

As early as the year 1818, the mines were drained by a tunnel known as the Halkyn (deep-level) Tunnel, which started in a hillside at Nant

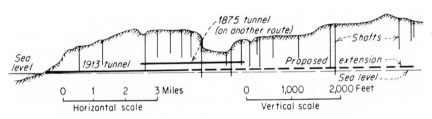

Fig. 5.11. Section through the drainage tunnels from the Halkyn Mines, North Wales. (*Based, by permission of the Institute of Mining and Metallurgy, London, on a drawing in reference 5.38.*)

Flint at an elevation of 200 ft above Ordnance Datum; it was driven thence in a southerly direction, eventually for a distance of 5 miles. After most of the accessible ore had been removed from the space thus drained, the Milwr, or Holywell-Halkyn, Tunnel was started in 1896 from the banks of the Dee, 190 ft below the level of the older tunnel. In a similar way, it drained a large volume of limestone, and thus permitted a great extension of mining operations. Figure 5.11 illustrates this extensive drainage operation diagrammatically.[5.38]

The removal of the water from the mines raised no difficulties, since the water drained directly to the river Dee. It has to be remembered, however, that underground drainage is usually a reciprocal operation, for the water drained from one area must be disposed of elsewhere. If the water is contaminated, this may give rise to serious problems. It may create drainage problems elsewhere. In some cases, water drained from underground for one purpose can be put to use as a water supply. Thus, what is believed to be meteoric water, which appears as flows from coal seams in the Rishton Colliery, Lancashire, England, is pumped out of the mine and by means of a suitable connecting system augments the public water supply of the town of Accrington.[5.39] Less constructive, perhaps, but undoubtedly effective was the work of the Royal Engineers in the First World War in directing a supply of water into an abandoned mine gallery under Messines Ridge whence it percolated through to one of the lower German counter headings from which it had to be laboriously pumped out.

The other side of this interdependence is well illustrated by the widely quoted "Montebello incident" in California. The wastes from a plant making a weed killer commonly called 2-4-D were discharged into the sewers of the city of Alhambra. After passing through the city's sewage-treatment plant, the wastes were discharged as a small part of the effluent into the Rio Hondo River about a mile upstream from an interconnection with a subterranean ground-water basin. Within a short time, 11 wells serving 25,000 people were so seriously affected that even after cutting off the source of contamination, large expenditures were necessary to treat the water in order to make it safe again for public use.[5.40]

With the great increase in oil drilling, oil refining, and chemical manufacturing, the danger of such contamination of ground water is continually increasing. Already, the Los Angeles area has had to face serious problems because of the contamination of its ground-water resources by the wastes from oil wells. Trouble started when sumps were excavated along the east bank of the Los Angeles Flood Control Channel for the purpose of reclaiming the oil which remained in the waste waters from oil-well drilling. These sumps handled more than 2.5 million gpd of waste water, containing 9,000 ppm of chlorine or 13,000 ppm of sodium chloride. Adjacent wells penetrating the local sands and gravels soon showed contamination; some had to be abandoned and others deepened and cemented in to seal off the source of contamination. Tests showed conclusively that the bottom and sides of unlined ditches and sumps were not sealed off by the drilling mud and oil emulsions carried by the waste waters.[5.41] This example is typical of the kind of problem that must be faced whenever ground water is being used that may have contact with possible sources of industrial waste contamination. In the past, a major source of such pollution has been the waste water from coal mines, especially that from disused mines which are not being actively maintained. Some states have had to take very strong legal action in order to eradicate the grave danger which arises from the interaction of air and water upon the sulfur-bearing compounds exposed in coal-mining operations. The problem has been aggressively tackled, and the results have been highly satisfactory.[5.42]

As this problem is minimized, however, another arises the full extent of which cannot yet be foreseen. This is the disposal of radioactive waste material. So serious is this aspect of the utilization of radioactive material for civilian purposes that it has already attracted much attention in the public press. It is certainly a major factor in the selection of the site of any plant that is going to discharge radioactive waste material. Serious consideration has been given to depositing this material in the ocean, at such locations that it would accumulate in ocean "deeps"; but disposal underground, i.e., in ground-water basins, has been the principal means of waste disposal for plants already built. The extent of the problem is indicated by the fact that the total volume of all effluents from the various chemical processing plants at the Hanford Works, Washington, from January, 1944, to June, 1957, has amounted to 29.6 billion gal of which 26.7 billion gal were process cooling water and 2.9 billion gal were low-level radioactive wastes.[5.43] These have been discharged into the underlying ground-water basin, the water table of which is as much as 350 ft below ground level. The considerable ion-exchange capacity of the formation through which the wastes percolate results in the removal of measurable radioactivity before the wastes reach the ground water. One of the most extensive ground-water surveys (see page 169) yet undertaken constantly checks the effects of the Hanford waste-disposal procedure on ground-water conditions throughout the surrounding area of over 600 sq miles. At Oak Ridge, pits have been constructed in a shale formation to serve as storage basins for the wastes, with some concentration of the waste by evaporation. Investigations of the possibility of injecting radioactive wastes into salt domes, abandoned salt mines, and other salt formations are being carried out at the University of Texas. It is already clear that a major problem in the field of subsurface drainage and associated contamination of ground water has been created.[5.44]

5.13. Ground Water near the Surface. The examples that have been used to illustrate the foregoing discussion of the geological aspects of ground water have necessarily been taken from major engineering undertakings. It may be thought that all this has little to do with the day-to-day problems of the civil engineer in ordinary practice, concerned as he usually is with works on a much smaller scale where the ground water is relatively close to the surface. The principles to be applied, however, do not vary whether the works be large or small, deep underground, or close to the surface. The dependence of all subsurface drainage upon geological conditions cannot be overstressed. Clearly, if ground is to be effectively drained at the surface, the water table must be at such a level that gravitational flow will automatically lead excess water away from the ground surface. Where this is not the case, artificial measures to achieve the same result may have to be adopted. A useful example is on record from Arizona. In the Salt River valley of that state, 203,000 acres of improved farm land were threatened with serious waterlogging due to excessive irrigation. The surface materials consisted of sandy clay, loam, and loess, underlain by clay and *caliche* which sloped gently toward a river channel. Drainage by means of open channels proved to be ineffective because of the nature of the surface materials, and the water table rose 1.4 ft per year after irrigation started. Soon 64,000 acres had ground water within 10 ft of the surface. After all the local conditions were studied, especially the local geological formation, pumping was decided upon; this was an economic possibility in view of available cheap off-peak power. Pumping was started in 1923, and the waterlogged area was quickly reduced.[5.45]

Rarely will such an extreme method as pumping have to be adopted for lowering a water table, but the basic principle is that which underlies all successful drainage, i.e., getting the water table to such an elevation that normal ground-water flow will result in the removal of unwanted water either from the ground surface or to the depth at which construction operations are to take place. The principle will be well illustrated when the use of well points for open excavation is discussed in Chap. 9. One of the first "modern" applications of the idea will be described in Chap. 10 when the construction of the Kilsby Tunnel by Robert Stephenson is mentioned and some of Stephenson's own words are quoted as a singularly clear exposition of the principle he was using. But the Romans knew the concept too, even though the expression "cone of depression" may not be encountered in classical writing. In some of their remarkable tunneling operations, Roman builders used drainage tunnels which show clearly that they knew that control of ground water was a prime requisite of successful underground work.

Exactly the same idea is used in a modified form in the application of drainage tile for shallow surface drainage. Long used in European farming, tile underdrainage was introduced into North America in 1835 by a Scottish farmer, John Johnson, with an installation near Geneva, New York, that is still in use. His pioneer contribution to good farming is memorialized by a bronze plaque at his farm, sponsored by the American Society of Agricultural Engineers.[5.46] Civil engineers might well have shared in this recognition, for the use of tile drains around building foundations, at the rear of retaining walls, etc., is in the same tradition; its effect is to induce gravitational flow of ground water away from soil in which water is not desired.

Brief mention must finally be made of that part of ground water which is close to the surface but which cannot be drained gravitationally. Long neglected by civil engineers, although of obvious importance to the agriculturist, "soil water" is now appreciated as being important in many branches of engineering work, particularly in connection with the stability of foundations on clay soils. Again, the relevance of geology will be clear, since if it is known that buildings are to be founded upon a clay soil susceptible to shrinkage when drying, then special study must be given to local rainfall records in order to determine the potentiality of trouble. In such investigations, once the local geology is known, Thornthwaite's evaluation of local soil-water balance through consideration of rainfall and evapo-transpiration, will be of great value.[5.47]

5.14. Ground-water Surveys. Not only for the purpose of discovering whether ground water will provide a satisfactory supply of potable water at a new site, but also for discovering whether ground water will be encountered in underground construction operations, determination of ground-water conditions becomes a vital part of preliminary site investigations. When water supply is involved, the quality of water must also be known with some certainty in advance of its actual use. Obtaining this information is the objective of ground-water surveys. These cannot be considered directly comparable to topographical surveys since they are most complex and generally call for trained and expert hydrological advice. Local geological conditions are always involved, and so a working knowledge of local geology is a prerequisite for any ground-water investigation. In addition, familiarity with the hydrological characteristics of the rocks met is essential before even general principles can be applied to the particular problem. Thus it is that the services of an expert are always desirable and often essential in a complete ground-water survey. The following note is only an outline of what is involved in this survey work; it is presented so that engineers engaged in ground-water problems may know how to regard them and may appreciate the advisability of expert assistance when the necessity arises.

The problem is not merely that of "finding water," as is often and popularly imagined, for there are probably few parts of the earth's surface under which water cannot be found at some depth. The engineer's problem usually is to find water at such a depth, in such quantities, and of such quality that it can be utilized economically in the public service. Despite this economic limitation, finding water is an important part of ground-water investigations. It seems probable that plants and other vegetation were the first indicators of ground water to be used regularly; they still constitute a fairly reliable guide. Vitruvius listed plants known to him that indicated the presence of ground water near the surface of the ground and even endeavored to suggest when they were reliable guides. The subject has received little concerted attention until comparatively recent years. Scattered references to water-indicating plants, shrubs, and trees occur in geological and botanical literature, but it has been left to the United States Geological Survey to publish a general review of existing knowledge. This survey was prepared by Dr. O. E. Meinzer, who suggested the term *phreatophytes* to denote those plants that habitually grow in arid regions only when they can send their roots down to the water table.[5.48] This publication shows that the vegetation encountered will be some indication of the depth to the water table, and it shows that there is at least some basis for the idea that plants indicate the quality of the ground-water. In other parts of the world, information with regard to plants that may serve as good guides can generally be obtained from observant local inhabitants.

The search for water can be likened to prospecting for minerals; water is, in a sense, a mineral, although of a special kind. The two branches of investigation have sometimes been closely related, as when Vogt in his water investigations discovered one of the world's richest potassium salt deposits at Mulhouse, Alsace. They have also been associated throughout a long period of time, since both have been the object of attention by "diviners," those gifted individuals who are said to be influenced by a divining rod when they carry it over a deposit of mineral or ground water. Divining rods have been used not only for the alleged locating of water and minerals but also for attempting to find hidden treasure and even lost children, criminals, and corpses. They appear to have been used by the Scythians, the Medes, and the Persians; Marco Polo found them in use in the Orient; and there are people who believe that the rod of Moses was a divining rod. Originally, incantations were used in conjunction with the rods, and it is said that in Cornwall, England, the belief still exists that the rod is guided to the deposit by pixies. For about a century (1669–1760), religious authorities debated whether water divining was an invention of the devil or not.[5.49]

Despite these mystical associations, the use of the *virgula divina*, as it was known to the ancients, has been treated more realistically for some considerable time. Probably the first scientific account was that in "De Re Metallica" by Georgius Agricola (1490–1555). Since then, a constant stream of literature has emerged from those who feel strongly about the matter; almost 600 relevant works were published between 1532 and 1916. There have been a special journal and a society in Germany devoted to the study and encouragement of the *Wünschelruthe* (wishing rod). In 1946, however, the official use of dowsers in West Germany was prohibited by order of the inspector general for water and energy. There is a British Society of Dowsers, and international conferences on *rhabdomancy*, the modern name for the ancient belief, have been held. One delegate at the first such conference in 1932 is reported to have suggested that divining could aid in climatology and in "hydromineral therapeutics." This conference agreed that the principles of rhabdomancy are established but that there is some charlatanism; it proposed that a union be formed in order to keep out the charlatans.[5.50]

Few will deny that water diviners sometimes find water, but engineers generally will need much to convince them that this has not been a combination of the ordinary laws of chance coupled with a good working knowledge of the principles of hydrology. To both engineer and geologist, actual field tests alone are of value; the evidence that they supply seems to be conclusive. In 1920, the Commission for Water Conservation and Irrigation of New South Wales, Australia, reported that in

an official test of 56 bores at sites selected by diviners, only 70 per cent
were successful; the tests then were stopped, as the divining rod was held
to be discredited. Tests conducted at Sunbury, England, in 1925 by the
(then) Anglo-Persian Oil Company with regard to "oil divining" were
even more conclusive. In a sports field, where no oil had been buried,
eight definite locations of oil were divined. When taken to within a few

A—Twig. B—Trench.

Fig. 5.12. An early illustration of the divining rod in use; a woodcut from "De Re
Metallica" by Georgius Agricola, first published in 1556.

feet of the company's oil store, the divining rod gave no indication at all
of the presence of the several hundred gallons of light oils in the store.[5.51]

If it is remembered that, whether ground water is located by a diviner
or in some other way, its presence is due to the local geological structure
in association with surface-water conditions and the character of the
local strata, all of which may be determined in a scientific manner, the
attraction of rhabdomancy will be reduced. This possibility is mentioned
quite seriously; even today, one may meet senior engineers who, caring

little for all that geology can do for them, will employ water diviners. It cannot be denied that some people are influenced physically by the presence of water. The writer, as also probably many readers, has good friends who are dowsers but who, fortunately, have such respect for geology that they do not presume to place dowsing in the same category. There is not, however, any agreement on the cause of this effect. The subject is discussed in an illuminating manner by the great scientist, Sir J. J. Thomson, who relates in his autobiography that in the early years of the present century he examined many samples of water from wells and found that "all contained the radio-active emanation from radium. This only retains its activity for four days so that if the water was stagnant it would soon lose its radio-activity."[5.52] This suggests a possible link with dowsing. The distinguished author goes on to relate that the most active water he tested came from a brewery, a fact he was forbidden to publicize at the time. (An American friend suggested to him that, if such a thing had happened in the United States, the whole country would have been quickly plastered with advertisements for "Dick Smith's Radio Beer.") He relates also that he once met a dowser who could tell whether a bottle of medicine would do him any good or not merely by passing his dowsing rod over it. Following the lead of Sir J. J. Thomson, one may readily admit that the observed movement of divining rods or forked sticks in the hands of some individuals is not charlatanry, but that it is no guarantee of finding water; the existence of ground water is completely dependent upon local geological and hydrological conditions and is therefore capable of being determined scientifically. As a distinguished and sympathetic French writer on the subject of dowsing has said, "It is no good looking for water where geology tells us there is none."[5.53]

It is not, therefore, suggested that a divining rod is not affected in some way at some time when carried by some persons, but it is suggested that, since nobody can find water where the geological conditions are not favorable, recourse should always be had to the use of geology for finding it and not to a method that, in 1883, was described by R. W. Raymond as follows:[5.54]

Its claims to virtues derived from Deity, from Satan, from affinities and sympathies, from corpuscular effluvia, from electrical currents, from passive perturbatory qualities of organo-electric force are hopelessly collapsed and discarded. A whole library of learned rubbish about it which remains to us furnishes jargon for charlatans, marvellous tales for fools, and amusement for antiquarians; otherwise it is only fit to constitute part of Mr. Caxton's "History of human error."

To enumerate the geological studies by which ground water may be investigated would be but to repeat much of what is to be said in Chap. 6 with regard to geological mapping in general, because when ground water is being investigated, accurate knowledge of the geological structure is first necessary. In addition to the usual investigations, however, close attention must be paid to all evidences of ground water. Records of all existing wells and boreholes must be examined and correlated. By this means, when records are available, it is possible to prepare contour maps for ground-water levels over large areas of country.

Contour maps provide one means of estimating the quantity of ground water available; this quantitative work is the other main branch of ground-water survey work. Various methods may be used; their relative suitability is dependent on local conditions and the data available. One method is to attempt to prepare a water balance sheet for the area considered, measuring the total runoff and rain, estimating the losses due to evaporation and absorption by plants, and determining the remaining balance which may normally be assumed to be the addition to the ground-water supply. Measurements may also be made with regard to actual discharge of ground water into watercourses from areas in which the water table is known to be reasonably steady. A time lag will always be found between the falling of rain and increase in ground-water flow; but with this determined, estimates can be made of the percentage of the rainfall available as ground water. A good example of a survey somewhat on these lines is available in connection with the valley of the Pomperaug River, Connecticut, United States, which has a catchment area of 89 sq miles.[5.55] The most reliable method and that most widely employed is to determine and use the *specific-yield* factor for the rock in question; the one serious obstacle to the application of this method is the possible variation in the nature of the local rocks, which may invalidate the calculations to some extent.

Specific yield means the "interstitial space that is emptied when the water table declines, expressed as a percentage of the total volume of material that is unwatered."[5.56] For the measurement of specific yield, various methods have been suggested, some of which can be utilized in a laboratory on samples of the materials encountered in the area under investigation; others necessitate field observations. Laboratory methods are convenient and interesting, but the possible variations not only of the materials tested but also of their structural arrangement in the area being studied make these methods of doubtful value unless unusual precautions are taken. On the other hand, they can often provide a useful guide to probable yield of ground water before major operations can be undertaken in the field, since the most effective field methods for estimating specific yield depend on the recording of water levels underground during pumping or recharging. These observations can be made only after boreholes have been sunk to required levels. Ground-water levels will always be the most useful guide to ground-water supplies, since inevitably they take into consideration all the subsurface variations that may possibly be disregarded in the application of any experimental test results. Even in the use of recorded water levels, however, observations from adjoining boreholes and wells should be carefully correlated with one another and with what is known of geological conditions in the vicinity so that any underground irregularity may be detected if this is possible from the data available.

To select any one example to illustrate the wide field covered by this branch of ground-water study involves a difficult choice. Possibly a record of one of William Smith's many engineering activities in England may be cited in view of its historic interest and of its intrinsic illustrative value. In a letter dated February 24, 1808, from John Farey to Sir Joseph Banks, the following descriptive note has been found:[5.57]

We met the Reverend Mr. Le Mesurer, Rector of Newton-Longville near Fenny-Stratford, who related his having undertook to sink a well, at his parsonage house, within a mile or two of which, no good and plentiful springs of water were known, but finding clay only at the depth of more than 100 feet, was about to abandon the design: Mr. Smith, on looking into his map of the strata, pointed out to us, that Newton-Longville stood upon some part of the clunch clay strata, and that the Bedford limestone appeared in the Ouse river below Buckingham, distant about eight miles in a north-west direction, and he assured Mr. L. that if he would but persevere, to which no serious obstacles would present themselves, because all his sinkings would be in dry clay, he would certainly reach this limestone, and have plenty of good water, rising very near to the surface; Mr. L. accordingly did persevere in sinking and bricking his well, and at 235 feet beneath the surface (the first 80 feet of which were in alluvial clay with chalk and flints, etc. similar exactly to what I have uniformly found on your estate at Revesby, and in the bottoms of many of your fen drains) the upper limestone rock (8 feet thick) was reached and found to be so closely enveloped in strong blue clay as to produce not more than 9 feet of water in the well in the course of a night; from hence, an augur hole was bored in blue clay, for some distance, to the second limestone rock, which produced a plentiful jet of water, which filled and has ever since maintained the water, I believe almost up to the surface of the ground.

5.15. Conclusion. Among the subsurface conditions with which the civil engineer may have to deal in carrying out his projects, ground water must be considered an integral part of the relevant geology. This must be done whether the works be large or small. In his own limited experience the writer has become increasingly impressed with the over-all importance of ground water in civil engineering work, its relative simplicity (at least in principle), and its widespread comparative neglect, very often just because of its inherent simplicity and the fact that water is so "common" a substance. On the largest project with which he has been associated, control of ground water was the key to the solution of a major problem; on one of the very smallest jobs with which he has assisted, exactly the same condition prevailed. In both cases, and in many others, it could be pointed out that if there had been no ground water present, there would have been no problem. It was water, in association with soils that would have been quite stable if dry, that was the cause of the trouble; if the water could be removed, or controlled, the troubles would be quickly minimized. This was found to be a telling argument, simple though it is. It will perhaps explain why this chapter has been placed where it is in order to emphasize the importance of ground water in civil engineering work before necessary preliminary site investigations are discussed, since adequate subsurface investigation *must* include as much study as is possible of local ground-water conditions in addition to the study of local geology which, in all too many cases, is thought of as the geology of rocks alone.

Suggestions for Further Reading

An excellent general introduction to the many phases of water in relation to its use by man is provided by:

"Water," Yearbook for 1955 of the U.S. Department of Agriculture, U.S. Government Printing Office; it contains many useful references that will serve as a guide to other publications in the field of ground water.

Publications of the United States Geological Survey, especially the "Water Supply Papers," contain much information of value on various aspects of ground water.

A comprehensive review of the ground-water situation in the United States is presented in:

McGuinness, C. L., "The Water Situation in the United States with Special Reference to Ground Water," United States Geological Survey Circular 114, June, 1951.

A more complete treatment of the general subject will be found in:

Tolman, C. F., "Ground Water," McGraw-Hill Book Company, Inc., New York, 1937.

Chapter 6

PRELIMINARY AND EXPLORATORY WORK

If I wished to find some in some province where it is not yet known,
I would search out all the pits that potters, brick and tile makers use in
their work . . . then I would want a very long auger, which auger
would have a hollow tube at its tip, in which I would house a stick
that would have at the other end a handle through it like an auger,
and this done, I would go through all the ditches of my property,
into which I would plant my auger to the full length of the handle, and
after taking it out of the hole, I would look into the recess to see what
kind of earth it had brought up, and after cleaning it, I would take out
the first handle and put in another much longer one and would put the
auger back into the hole I had made, and deeper into the earth with the
second handle, and thus, with several handles of various lengths, one
could know what the deeper earths were.

Bernard Palissy[6.1]
(A.D. 1510–1590.)

BEFORE A civil engineer can design any projected work, he must know
something about the material on which his structure is to be founded or
in which his work is to be carried out. This will necessitate an examination
of the site of the work before designing is started and a thorough investigation of the site before detailed designs are prepared. Truisms? Admittedly, but truisms that have often been neglected in the past, sometimes
with disastrous results and almost always with consequent monetary loss.
This last statement might be characterized as too sweeping were it not
possible to confirm it indubitably by many examples from engineering
practice. To the civil engineer with even a slight appreciation of geology,
neglect of what is to him the obviously essential course of making
thorough and complete preliminary investigations before embarking on
construction will appear to be utter folly. An engineer who failed to
make such investigations might with propriety be compared to a surgeon
who operated without making a diagnosis or to a lawyer who pleaded
without having any prior discussion with his client.

172

To the engineer who has not studied geology, these analogies might appear far-fetched; in many cases the nature of the surface of the ground and experiences on similar adjacent works might seem to him to be warrant enough for making certain assumptions about subsurface conditions on which designs can be based. It may be that some such reasoning has led to the neglect of preliminary explorations in the past. Similarly, it is probable that unquestioning reliance on the information given by test borings alone, considered without relation to the local geology, may have sometimes resulted in unforseen difficulties in construction and have led engineers to distrust the value of such preliminary work. All too often, however, it has been the difficulty of obtaining the necessary funds before the start of construction that has prevented engineers from carrying out the explorations that they knew to be necessary. This results from a shortsighted policy on the part of some owners which engineers may find hard to understand.

Discussion of this attitude and of other factors that may have furthered the neglect of subsurface explorations on civil engineering works in the past will not be profitable. Most civil engineers today recognize the supreme importance of this preliminary work. Readers who may entertain doubts about its value will not have to read far beyond this chapter before they find evidence that should set all their doubts at rest. But all engineers may have to deal with owners who have not had an opportunity to visualize the necessity of exploratory work. The following section therefore presents argument that may be of use in demonstrating the economic value of such preliminary expenditure.

6.2. Economics of Preliminary Work. "Economics" may be too technical a word to apply to the following brief considerations of preliminary work. It will serve, however, to describe a discussion of the cost of such work relative to the total cost of a project and of the savings that may be effected and the difficulties that may be avoided by such a precautionary measure. Preliminary work, as here intended, is held to include geological surveys, geophysical surveys, test pits, borings, drillings, and any further exploratory measures that may be called for in special cases. Examples of the total expenditure on such work for complete projects are not easy to obtain, because the totals are usually so small that they cannot suitably be featured in the summaries of cost that form most valuable parts of published descriptions of engineering works. It has been possible, however, to assemble some figures for interesting examples of tunnel, dam, bridge, and building construction; these are given in Table 6.1.

Cost records from works of such differing character and in such varied parts of the world show clearly that the cost of preliminary work relative to the total cost of a civil engineering project is small indeed. It is believed that the figures are typical for normal engineering work. If the costs thus presented are compared with other percentages which are usually included in civil engineering estimates, their significance will be appreciated. Special thought might perhaps be given to the comparison of this 1 or 2 per cent for the total cost of underground investigations with the item of "10 per cent for contingencies" which is so frequently calculated in civil engineering estimates. For some types of work, especially marine work, contingencies must be allowed for in any estimates of cost; but in general, this broad item is often used to allow for just those uncertainties which thorough subsurface exploration will assist in eliminating. Viewed in this light, the cost of preliminary work may not appear to be so high as may at first be thought by an owner who is faced

Table 6.1. Some Examples of Costs of Subsurface Exploration

Project	Location	Total cost	Cost of preliminary work	Per cent of total
Pressure tunnel	Bridge River, B.C., Canada	$2,227,000	$7,575	0.3
Pressure tunnel*	Vancouver, B.C., Canada	$1,249,641	$91,540	7.3
Concrete dam	(Hoover) Colorado River	$76,770,396	$826,081	1.1
Steel-arch bridge	Perak, F.M.S.	£175,000	£3,150	1.8
Steam power station†	London, England	£2,141,550	£3,500	0.2
Earth dam	Yeoville, England	£440,140	£4,400	1.0

* A most unusual case in view of the extraordinary difficulties, necessitating much extra investigational work.

† Cost of constructional work only, i.e., not including station equipment.

with the necessity of spending some money in order to find out if he can even build the main project he is planning.

Further argument may be needed, however, to persuade a dubious owner. If cost records are not sufficient, actual examples from engineering practice may be drawn upon to complete the picture that the engineer wishes to present. This book contains many examples that might thus usefully be quoted, but for convenience a few may be summarized here. Consideration will first be given to cases in which adequate preliminary work was *not* carried out. For example, the contract for a tunnel included a large bonus payment for every day gained in completion before a certain fixed date. The engineers based their estimate of construction time on a calculated rate for excavating the tunnel through the quartzite exposed at the two tunnel portals. The tunnel line pierced an anticline, however, and it was found that the quartzite overlay easily excavated shale. The tunnel was driven very quickly and the contractor's bonus was so large that it led to a legal battle.

An even more serious case was that of a dam for water supply which was to be built in a valley as an earth-fill structure with a concrete core wall carried to rock at an assumed maximum depth of about 60 ft below the valley floor. This figure was derived from test borings which were stopped at what was believed to be solid rock but which later proved to be boulders of a glacial deposit. The core wall finally had to be carried to a depth of 196 ft, and the cost of the dam was increased correspondingly by a very large amount.[6.2] Jacoby and Davis mention an example from bridge engineering practice in which a bridge was built upon a surface of "hardpan" in the river bottom, but no examination of this was made because of the difficulty of taking borings in the river current of 5 mph. When constructed, the bridge pier sank out of sight, causing the loss of the two adjacent spans of the bridge and a number of human lives. An examination was made later, and it was found that the "hardpan" was only a thin stratum overlying a deep layer of soft clay.[6.3]

These examples show what trouble can be encountered through neglect of preliminary investigations. What of the constructive contributions that such work can make to civil engineering practice? Many examples could be quoted, although the actual monetary savings effected are usually hard to assess. The successful completion of many notable tunnels, such as those under the river Mersey in England or those constituting the Catskill and Delaware Aqueducts for the water supply of New York, which will be referred to in more detail in Chap. 9, provide striking evidence of the value of preliminary geological studies and underground investigation. Evidence supplied by the Hoover Dam and a vast number of smaller dam structures founded on strata previously investigated is also striking. From the records of bridge construction, there might be mentioned, to similar effect, the San Francisco–Oakland Bay Bridge, the foundations for which are referred to in some detail in Chap. 17; despite their unusual size and the record depths to which they were carried, their construction agreed closely with what was anticipated as a result of the preliminary exploration on which the sum of $135,000 was expended.[6.4]

A somewhat unusual example may be given to illustrate the value of underground exploration for building foundations. The Lochaber water power scheme in Scotland has its powerhouse located at the end of a steel pressure pipeline 3,240 ft long which descends from the slopes of Ben Nevis. The discharge from the Pelton wheels enters a tailrace about 3,000 ft long excavated partially in rock tunnel, partially in open rock cut, and partially in open cut through drift deposits. As originally planned, the powerhouse was to have been much nearer the river Lochy; the tailrace was to have been only 100 ft long, and the length of pipeline 6,200 ft. Further investigations were conducted, however, through an extensive program of shallow test borings all over the available sites for the power-house and along corresponding routes for the tailrace. In all, 1,040 ft of borings was carried out at a total cost of £1,340. Results so obtained were carefully plotted, mainly to locate contours on the rock surface underlying the surface deposits; all borings were carried at least 3 ft into the rock to make sure that boulders had not been encountered. On the basis of this information, 16 complete schemes for the power-house location were prepared and their over-all costs estimated; the final decision was for the arrangement already described, for which the combined cost of tailrace, pipeline, and powerhouse excavation (on the average 40 ft deep) was a minimum. A substantial saving was thus effected over the original plans which amounted to many times the cost of the exploratory work that made the saving possible.[6.5]

6.3. The Pattern of Preliminary Work. When a civil engineering or building project is first contemplated, the site will almost always be examined in a preliminary way, and such topographical maps as are available will be obtained for office study. As plans develop, more detailed and possibly more extensive surveys will be required, and more accurate maps may be made; upon the basis of these, economic studies can proceed and the feasibility of the project can be evaluated. Finally, if the work is to proceed, detailed designs are prepared, the necessary contract documents and drawings are assembled, tenders are called, a contract is awarded, and the job gets under way. This is a familiar pattern, followed with only minor variations for the vast majority of construction jobs, large and small. What is meant, then, by preliminary work supplementary to these well-recognized steps? As has already been indicated, an absolutely essential complement of these preliminary studies of the topography of the construction site is an equally careful study of the geological strata to be encountered in excavation and to be utilized as foundation beds and construction materials. The procedure for this part of the preliminary investigation is equally straightforward, equally simple in its essentials, equally easy to follow.

Even a general reconnaissance of the site can be used to good advantage by a cursory examination of those features that betray something of the local geology. General examination of the physiography of the country around will give at least some idea of the geological history, e.g., whether it is glaciated or not. But more accurate knowledge of the local geology will usually be available (for all but remote sites in unmapped country) through the medium of published geological reports. Real study of the site, therefore, may well begin in a library. The records of the local geological survey will naturally be the starting point; for this reason, a concise list of geological surveys around the world is given in Appendix B. Officers of geological surveys will always be helpful in directing inquiries to sources of geological information most useful for the site in question.

These may include information privately available at other locations, such as universities. Geological reports will usually include geological maps and sections, the careful study of which is an essential preliminary to work in the field; they are described on page 185. The extent of this procedure will vary from cases of wild inaccessible country for which only the most general information is available to city building sites for which complete geological information is readily available in printed form.

Similar study of the records of the geology encountered by adjacent works is a corresponding step. For urban sites, this may be rewarding; for isolated sites, there may be no such records. Assembly of all available information from test borings put down in the area of the proposed work, if not already publicly available (as it now is in some cities, as noted in Chap. 12), can often be most rewarding. A good illustration from the building of the Toronto subway is given in Chap. 10 (see page 345). Examination of well records in the area of the work will often yield information of value.

Further records to be sought out and studied, especially for civil engineering works (such as highways and airports) that do not involve deep excavation are those of agricultural soil studies, frequently summarized conveniently in descriptive memoirs of the soils in counties or similar local regional units. Naturally, these valuable records are available only for the more developed parts of the world, but they are always helpful when they can be used. Often associated with such soil studies are descriptive works dealing with the physiography of regions. Although general in character, such volumes can often provide a useful background to more detailed site investigation. An outstanding example is a volume describing the physiography of southern Ontario, Canada, by Chapman and Putnam, a well-written and interesting book accompanied by a most useful map of the area; it is mentioned as typical of the sources of information available to civil engineers that would not normally come to their notice in their ordinary practice.[6.6]

When all such information has been obtained and studied, examination of the site itself is the next essential. In times past, this meant going to the site, but today a first approach may be made through the medium of aerial photographs. The potential of aerial-photo interpretation is outlined in the next section, so important a part of modern site investigation has it become. When all possible information has been obtained from aerial photographs, with alternative sites possibly greatly reduced in number and limited in area by this ingenious method, site study itself must be undertaken. A geological survey is the first site investigation called for on all but the most restricted sites and those in urban areas. It can often be done in remote locations concurrently with topographical survey work but by different personnel. Although naturally the work of geologists, geological survey work should at least be understood in broad outline by the engineers who are to use the results it gives; it is therefore also outlined in a later section.

Geological survey work may be supplemented by geophysical investigations, depending on the area involved and the local geological features revealed by the earlier studies. Chapter 7 is devoted to a review of geophysical methods of exploration, now so vital a part of many major civil engineering operations. When all possible progress has been made with such methods, and by careful geological surveying, final confirmation of deduced subsurface conditions will always be necessary through actual determination by means of test holes either as test pits or test borings. Frequently, these operations are all that a civil engineer thinks of when he considers preliminary site studies, but it can now be seen that they form only a part, though a vital part, of a much broader operation. Test boring and test drilling are given further treatment in succeeding sections as is also the use of the information they give.

In such field work, not only will rock and soil be studied, but also ground water—its location, its quality and the impurities it contains. In areas suspected of having high sulfate content in their soils, this is a particularly important part of the field study. Soil and rock samples obtained during the course of field work will frequently be subjected to laboratory tests. On large jobs, field testing of soil and rock may also be necessary, either by tests on existing ground surfaces or in specially excavated test shafts, tunnels, or excavations. And in very unusual cases, extraordinary test procedures, such as trial excavations, the placement of trial sections of fill, pumping tests to determine permeability *in situ*, or trials with grouting methods may be necessary.

Actual practice will naturally vary from one job to the next, and the extent of preliminary work will depend on the size and location of the job. The over-all pattern, however, remains the same—first, a search for all available written information; second, a study of the site, first through aerial photographs (if available) and then on the site itself, in which all the techniques of geological surveying and geophysical prospecting are used; third, the development of a test drilling program based on what has been determined of the local geology and checked continually as it progresses with the gradually unfolding picture of the local geological structure so that maximum advantage can be obtained from every test hole sunk; and finally, the prosecution of such special tests and field investigations as the work so far carried out suggests are necessary in relation to the structure to be built.

6.4. Aerial-photo Interpretation. All engineers who have had the opportunity of viewing some geologically interesting country from the air must have been impressed by the value of such bird's-eye views. It is not, therefore, surprising to find that concurrently with the remarkable development of aviation has gone a similarly significant development in the use of aerial photographs for mapping and survey purposes as well as for generalized geological studies. What is surprising, and not perhaps commonly realized by the younger members of the profession, is the relative youth of this now widely accepted technique. It was only in 1919 that a real start was made in taking photographs from the air. Early photographs were made by adapting the rough and ready ex-

FIG. 6.1. "Geology from the air"; drift-covered Paleozoic lowland in southern Victoria Island, Northwest Territories, Canada, showing the well-developed drumlin pattern. Exposed sedimentary rock is in the foreground. (*Photograph by Royal Canadian Air Force; reproduced by permission.*)

perience gained by a few intrepid flyers in the First World War. The first maps to be produced from aerial photographs were issued in 1923. In 1931, the first use of aerial photographs for highway location appears to have been made. Not until 1935 does there seem to have been any widescale use of aerial photography for geological study; a significant application was made by the Dutch in that year in a reconnaissance study of New Guinea.[6.7] It is not to be wondered at, therefore, that in the first edition of this book, the use of aerial photographs as an aid to site exploration called for one paragraph only; an example from South African practice was included in that volume, and it is shown again as Fig. 6.2, if only because of its historical interest.

Great progress has been made in the last two decades. The American Society of Photogrammetry has over 3,000 members, which is an indication of its standing and of the widespread interest in the use of aerial photographs. Photography from the air is now used in 30 states as an aid to route location; it is also used in most of the provinces of Canada and by the government of Canada for road location in the Far North. Despite the fact that Canada is the third largest country in the world, and that its Arctic archipelago is wild and inhospitable in the extreme, the entire

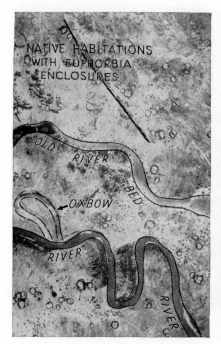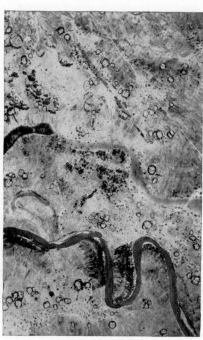

FIG. 6.2. An early example of aerial photography as an aid to geological surveying, showing old and new river beds, an old oxbow, and a dike near the shores of Lake Victoria, East Africa. (*Reproduced by permission from the Transactions AIME, vol. 126, pp. 622–623, 1937.*)

country has now been photographed from the air. So the record can be continued. A new tool of great significance has become available for the civil engineer and geologist; it can be of invaluable assistance in general regional geological studies.

The analysis of the features to be seen on aerial photographs and their interpretation in terms of local geology have now been developed as well-accepted techniques to which there are some excellent printed guides. As with so many other modern technical developments, the services of the expert are advisable in order to derive maximum benefit from aerial photographs of areas to be studied. An increasing number of civil engineers and geologists are now getting training in this field, and aerial-photo interpretation is ceasing to be the novelty and thing of mystery that it appeared to be in its early development. Aerial photographs are especially useful in betraying old earth movements such as landslides; some major slips, undetectable on the ground, have been located in this way. The use of stereophotographs is particularly helpful in work of this sort. It is now possible to recognize many of the surface manifestations of permafrost from aerial photographs, and this is especially

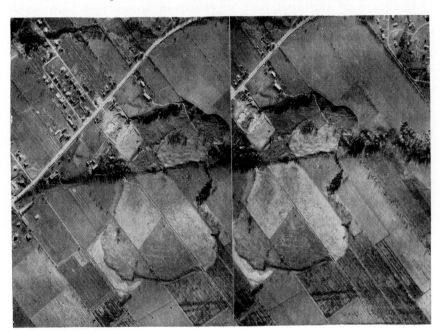

Fig. 6.3. Stereoscopic vertical aerial view of an old flow slide in the Leda clay of the Ottawa River valley, Ontario, Canada, a flow not readily discernible at ground level. (The twin views are arranged for viewing with a standard portable stereoscope.) (*Reproduced by permission of the City of Ottawa and the National Capital Commission, Ottawa, Canada.*)

useful in the region of discontinuous permafrost (i.e., on the southern boundary of perennially frozen ground).[6.8] Muskeg provides its own peculiar patterns when viewed from the air; since these are most revealing when seen in color, the use of strip-color aerial photographs has become a powerful technique in route location through terrain made difficult by extensive muskeg deposits.[6.9]

Location of sand and gravel deposits, always a matter of concern in major civil engineering work, is greatly assisted by aerial-photo interpretation. These deposits may be located by careful study of physiographic features and of local microrelief, of the forms of gullies as indicating the results of erosive processes, and of the examination of soil tones and vegetal pattern in relation to microrelief. Mollard and Dishaw have recorded work in so locating most of the available sand and gravel deposits in the plains of western Canada, a task extending over more than a decade.[6.10] Over 2,000 prospects were mapped in an area of 32,000 sq miles. In one season's work, 340 prospects were mapped and good material was found at 305 of them. In 227 of these locations, there were no pits excavated at the time of their discovery on aerial photographs. Experiences of this kind have suggested an accuracy in such work of at least 75 per cent, which readily suggests the economy possible with the judicious use of aerial photographs.

A similar approach is used for assessing the general geology of an area, including study of photographic tone, ground texture, the pattern of physiographic features, especially of drainage, the shape of unusual features, and the interrelation of all these aspects with existing knowledge of typical geology for the area under review. The information thus derived from the photographs can be indicated on maps that may themselves be prepared from aerial photographs; this is but one interlocking of photogrammetry and photo-interpretation. The result can be a useful guide to further, more detailed site investigation. It will be clear that the larger the area to be investigated, the more useful will be the use of aerial photographs; as the area being studied gets smaller, so will the utility of aerial photographs decrease until they cease to be a necessary or useful aid at all, as in the case of urban building sites. This point directs attention to the overriding fact that, even with optimum use of the best possible photographs and the most expert interpretation, aerial-photo interpretation is not a substitute for investigations on the ground, but only a most useful preliminary. The efficient use of aerial photographs can save considerable time and effort in eliminating obviously unsuitable sites or routes; their proper interpretation can point clearly to features calling for special study on the ground. But in the final analysis, accurate knowledge of the subsurface conditions at the site of engineering works must be obtained by careful subsurface investigation. And this must, in turn, be based upon at least a general knowledge of the geology of the site; thus, even with the aid of aerial-photo interpretation, study of the geology of the site on the ground is almost always a further preliminary to actual subsurface investigation.

6.5. Geological Surveying and Mapping. It should not be difficult for an engineer to appraise the general nature of the local geology at a site, provided that he entertains an appreciation of the importance of the science in his work. He should have little difficulty in obtaining assistance when necessary with regard to his geological problems from the respective geological survey, the staff of a local university, or a consulting geologist who has specialized in engineering work. He will probably be able to assist, either personally or through his staff, with the necessary geological survey work, which is the job of a specialist; his cooperation will certainly be needed in placing before the geologist a succinct account of the work to be carried out and the specific questions relating to subsurface conditions which are consequently of importance.

The initial simplicity of geological field observations is almost dangerous, certainly to a beginner. Although so simple, involving little more than accurate observations with the unaided eye and simple measurements with hand instruments, they call for an unusual concentration of attention and involve a background of experience. After the geologist has made a general reconnaissance of the area to be surveyed, he must carefully examine all exposures of solid rock, noting and recording the nature of each exposure and its dip and strike. These direct observations are, however, but the start of investigation. Although in topographic mapping, record is made only of what can be seen, in geological mapping the contacts of adjacent beds are the main goal of the survey, and these are quite often hidden from sight by surface deposits of drift material. Thus, the direct examination of rock exposures must be followed by a detailed examination of all topographical features that may give a clue to the hidden geological structure beneath.

Escarpments, indicating a relatively hard stratum; unusual deviations of watercourses and waterfalls, also often indicating a hard-rock layer; the elevation and location of springs: these and many other topographical features come within the critical review of the geologist in the field. The natural slope of the ground must always be remembered, especially when consideration is being given to such surface features as are demonstrated by the soil, in which case the upper limit of all special effects is clearly the only one that can be used with certainty. Naturally, a contact of two adjacent beds can only rarely be traced, or even seen, except in isolated places; its general location must be obtained by inference from the accumulated evidence of other observations. In a similar way, the various structural features noted in Chap. 2 will not often be found in anything but minor and infrequent locations. Occasionally complete sections of rock folds are exposed; but generally, folding will be revealed only after the study of numerous dip observations. Faults are sometimes shown a little more clearly, especially if they are of comparatively recent origin and their effect on topographic detail is still unobscured. Glacial structures and effects are sometimes clearly indicated. It cannot be too strongly emphasized that these notes are no more than an introduction to geological field methods; mention is made only of the principal points to be noted. Experience in the field under expert guidance is the only sure training, although much help can be obtained from the writings of experienced geologists.

Perhaps the impression may have been given that geological surveying can be carried out only in country exhibiting noticeable topographical variations and frequent outcrops of solid rock. This is not the case, although it must be admitted that mapping the structure of exposed solid sections of the earth's crust is comparatively easy when compared with mapping a drift-covered area. In addition to solid maps, however, a second complete set of geological maps may exist which show the nature and structural arrangement of the superficial deposits above the solid ground formation. The superficial deposits are sometimes characterized as drift (although they include all recent deposits and not only glacial till), and the maps are described as "drift maps." The importance of this branch of geological surveying to the civil engineer will immediately be obvious. Attention was first given to "maps of drift" by the Geological Survey of England in 1863, and since that time they have gradually come to be regarded on an equal footing with solid maps, especially in countries where the surface has been glaciated and therefore has a soil mantle of glacial deposits.

Mapping methods for soil are similar to those for solid-rock strata, but there is added emphasis on the close examination of the soil constituents. The surveyor may be unwittingly aided by the excavation work of burrowing animals, not only because of the spoil dumps which they accumulate outside their burrows but also because of the well-known habits of the main species, e.g., the habit which rabbits have of choosing dry sand deposits. The hand auger provides a simple and ready means of obtaining actual sections through deposits with the expenditure of little energy or cost—in marked contrast to the use of test drilling in rock strata. Drift maps are naturally complementary to solid maps, covering only those areas of ground over which solid rock is not exposed. The actual structure of any particular area covered by both solid and drift maps may therefore be visualized by imagining the latter superimposed on the former. It is often difficult to locate the exact line of demarcation between solid and drift deposits. Similarly, there are areas in which it is difficult, if not impossible, to map the underlying rock strata; if these strata are situated at a great depth below the surface, the drift map will constitute the only geological map for the area.

Because soils are derived from parent material whose location can usually be readily determined from the over-all geological picture of a region, detailed study of soil constituents is now being developed as an indirect method of "prospecting." *Geochemical prospecting* is already a term of real meaning. Vogt, a pioneer in this work in Norway, noticed many years ago that the health of grazing cattle was affected by changes in the chemical composition of the soils on which they grazed. These changes were due to variations in the underlying bedrock, which he thus mapped. Study of vegetation is therefore also developing as a special aid to geological surveying, and *geobotanical prospecting* is another term that the civil engineer may encounter and with which he should be familiar.

Naturally, such studies of soils are closely linked with the soil survey practice of the agricultural soil specialist; soil surveying is an important part of all pedological work. The field methods employed are identical with those used in geology, but are usually carried out in more detail, since the pedologist is concerned with even minor changes in soil type. Correlation between over-all geology and the general pattern of agricultural soil distribution will usually be noted in the records of pedological soil surveys. Correspondingly, there is a growing volume of information with regard to the interrelation of pedological soil subdivisions and the engineering properties of the soils so classified, especially in highway and airport engineering.[6.11]

Geological maps, as distinct from the field work on which they are based, must be mentioned. The main information to be recorded on field maps is noted carefully in the field on the topographic map in use; for this purpose it is naturally advantageous to adopt a special shorthand which extends the signs used on topographic maps to cover the geological features. Most important of these special signs is that indicating the direction of strike and dip. One sign generally used for this purpose is shown in Fig. 6.4; the cross line is drawn in the direction of the strike, and the arrow in the direction of the dip. The limits of rock outcrops must also be indicated clearly; one method used is to draw a line around the boundary of the outcrop, coloring or shading the side of the line corresponding to the start of the drift coverage of the solid rock. Figure 6.4 illustrates the usual signs in general use; local variations will naturally be introduced by every observer, although it is essential that a rigid system be adhered to in all field work by each observer to avoid possibility of error. Different types of deposits may be indicated either by lettering or by characteristic shading or coloring for each exposure.

At the conclusion of each day's work, all observations must be clearly and accurately inked in either on the map used in the field or on a special copy of the base map retained for office use only, but preferably on both. As such notes gradually accumulate on a map, geological structure will slowly reveal itself. The limits of the surface exposure will first appear in a general way; later the boundary-contact lines will become traceable with some degree of accuracy; structural features such as faults will appear in correlation with the rock strata; and finally the cause of certain topographical features may become plain. Naturally, the progress of this elucidation of geological structure will vary from one locality to another, but usually the surveyor will reach a point at which he can finish off his map with some degree of confidence.

In finished form, the map will have the various strata exposed at the surface differentiated by several wash colors or by special shading, prefer-

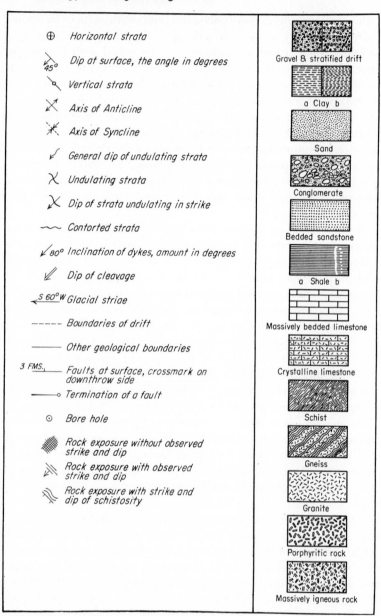

Fig. 6.4. Typical signs and shading used for geological maps, generally according to the practice of the U.S. Geological Survey (see also Data Sheets AGI 1–3 of the American Geological Institute). Legends on maps other than American should always be carefully studied since map conventions of different countries vary slightly.

ably the former, although the latter is often essential for published maps where color printing cannot be adopted. Different surveys have different standard color forms; and whenever possible, the local standard arrangement should be followed. Observed contacts can be marked as full black lines; inferred contacts as broken black lines. Faults are often marked as heavy (full or broken) white lines superimposed on the base colors. Other details noted on the original map will be retained, indicated in a general way by pen and ink markings. Such finished maps should always be accompanied by an index table or legend of the colors used and possibly of the special signs incorporated in the map.

Remembering that geological maps are a two-dimensional representation of an essentially three-dimensional structure, the reader can appreciate that prior to the completion of many geological maps it is necessary to plot a cross section along some special line across the area under investigation in order to study the inferred structure from another angle. Similarly, when a geological map has been completed, one or more sections will almost always be advisable in order to present a more vivid idea of the structure studied than can ever be obtained from a study of the surface map alone. It is not unusual to find one or more such sections printed in the borders of officially published geological maps. Naturally, the vertical scale used is distorted, but to engineers this feature of geological sections will not be strange. The preparation of these sections from the base map obtained is a rather straightforward matter. The dip of the rock strata at the several contact planes plotted will indicate the general direction of the beds; and when these are drawn out, the fundamental structure of the rocks will often become clear immediately. An important point to note when using such sections is that if the section taken does not align exactly with the direction of the dip of the beds, a projected dip will show in the section. The relation of the direction of the section and the dip of the main strata should always be stated.

A completed geological map for country of normal structure will be a fairly simple-looking topographical map, specially colored and marked. It represents, however, far more than the usual topographical map ever indicates and therefore deserves careful and detailed study. A number of publications deal solely with the quantitative interpretation of such maps, a matter that can only be touched upon here. The basis of all interpretative study is a realization of the fact that the topographic signs and, in particular, the contour lines represent the surface of the ground only, whereas the geological markings indicate subsurface structure as well.

The relation of the two leads to certain definite results which will gradually be realized after some study of geological maps. An elementary observation is that the projected distance between contacts shown on the map is no indication whatsoever of the thickness of the stratum in between, since this depends on the inclination of the beds and on the difference in elevation of the ground surface between the two contacts. An appreciation of this is fundamental. Certain characteristics will become evident after study of different types of maps, the most common of which can readily be memorized as four general rules:

1. Lines on the map representing boundaries of strata that are horizontal will be parallel with contour lines.

2. Lines on the map representing boundaries of strata that dip into a hillside will wind less than do the corresponding contours.

3. Lines on the map representing boundaries of strata that dip away from a hillside will wind more than the contours of the hill except when the dip exceeds the average inclination of the hill.

4. In valleys, strata will show up on maps with a V shape leading upstream in all cases except those in which the dip is downstream at a greater angle than the inclination of the valley floor.

The reasons for these rules will become clear from a study of geological maps of different and differing regions; then the interpretation of new maps will be much easier, and some idea of the structural relationship of the various rocks in an area can be obtained from a study of the geological map alone without the aid of drawn-out sections. Since quantitative study is also possible and is often desirable, a small subsidiary branch of specialized study has arisen which may almost be called "geological geometry" or "geological graphics." By measuring boundary locations and elevations on maps, the geologist can make accurate calculations of the actual (not projected) thicknesses of the beds being studied.

A geological map, therefore, through the aid of ingenious graphical devices, presents a great deal of useful information in compact form, readily available if the map be interpreted in the right way. Unfortunately, since color cannot be used for illustrations in this volume, it is impossible to illustrate adequately this most important facet of field geology. Figure 6.5 is included, however, since, even with the limitation of reproduction in black and white, it gives some indication of what can be learned from a good geological map. If the geological section in particular is related to the map itself, some general features readily make themselves clear, such as the appearance on the map of the inlier of Precambrian rocks, the traces of the overlying Cambrian and other formations, and the influence of geology upon the local drainage pattern.

Fortunately, there is available for civil engineers a most unusual but a singularly valuable publication of the United States Geological Survey (through its Engineering Geology and Ground Water Branches) that illustrates as well as can possibly be done the great utility of geological maps in engineering work. This is a folio of maps entitled "Interpreting Geologic Maps for Engineering Purposes."[6.12] It includes six maps of the same area, the Hollidaysburg Quadrangle in south-central Pennsylvania, all printed to the well-known high standards of the USGS. First comes a standard topographical map of the area, followed by the standard geological map. Since the area contains mountainous country, the

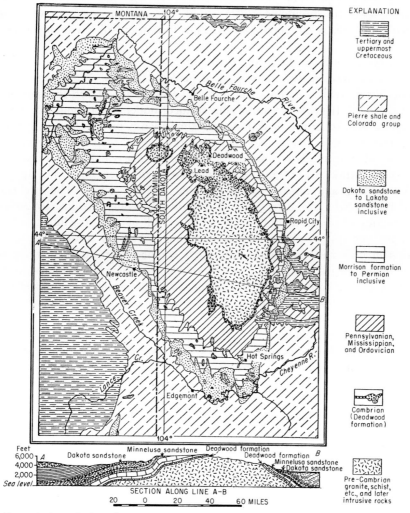

Fɪɢ. 6.5. A typical geological map and section of Black Hills in South Dakota and Wyoming, U.S.A., illustrating a structural dome. (*After N. H. Darton. Reproduced by permission of the Director, U.S. Geological Survey.*)

geological map is a vivid example of the utility of color in representing geological formations. There follow four interpretative maps, prepared after office and field study by the staffs of the two branches. These show how the local geology affects, respectively, foundation and excavation conditions, the availability of construction materials, water supply (both surface and underground), and the selection of sites for engineering works. This list alone again illustrates the vital place that geology can and should occupy in the planning of civil engineering operations. The folio should convince even the most skeptical of the great value of preliminary site study through the medium of good geological maps. It should be a valued item in all civil engineering libraries.

A brief note may be made of the interest to be derived from the field work involved in the preparation of geological maps. As in many other outdoor activities, nothing can quite take the place of actual experience in the field. If geology can be thus studied, under expert guidance, more can be learned in the field in a short time than is possible through many months of book study. Not only will geology become "real" and the sense of the three-dimensional structure of the earth's crust become second nature in the mind of the interested engineer, but a new feeling for scenery and the beauty of the land will be gained. The attention of readers who are attracted to these possibilities may be directed to the activities of local natural history clubs and geological clubs (in the larger centers). Contact with a local university may lead to participation in university geological field work arranged for students. It was in such field work, during the course of some extremely strenuous weeks of geological mapping in the mountains on the borders of England and Wales, and under the tutelage of the distinguished geologist who has written the Foreword to this volume, that the writer gained his first real insight into geology.

6.6. Subsurface Exploratory Work. Rarely will a geological survey alone, no matter how accurate it may be, provide sufficiently reliable information with regard to underground conditions for civil engineering work. Information on ground water, to mention but one feature, cannot always be obtained accurately from surface observations, and in many cases this information is a vital part of that required by the civil engineer. More often, however, the geological survey will be incomplete in respect to detailed matters owing to the existence of superficial deposits of unconsolidated material. As a general rule, therefore, underground exploratory work—test pits or borings—will have to be carried out. It cannot be too strongly emphasized, however, that underground exploratory work must always be considered supplementary to and conditioned by previous considerations of the local geological structure.

Brief consideration of the possibilities of complex structures existing beneath a relatively simple-looking ground surface will confirm the validity of this suggestion. It is unusually important in country that has been subjected to glacial action where glacial drift now covers an original rock surface which may be entirely unrelated to present-day topography. Even without the existence of glacial conditions, however, disastrous results have been known to occur when reliance was placed on the results of test boreholes that had not been correlated with the local geology. Consider as an example (not taken from actual practice but typical of many a river valley) the conditions shown in Fig. 6.6. Cursory surface examination of exposed rock in the immediate vicinity of the proposed dam would disclose outcrops of shale only. Test borings might be put down to confirm what these rock outcrops might appear to suggest; and if they were located as shown—as well they might be if the local geology were not considered—they would give an entirely false picture of the subsurface conditions across the valley, possibly with disastrous results. How could geology assist in such a case? Any geological survey made of this dam site would include at least a general

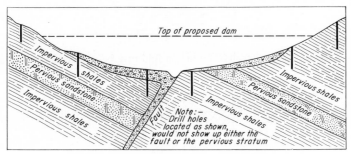

Fig. 6.6. A geological section showing how a fault may be undetected by test drilling.

reconnaissance of the neighborhood, and it is almost certain that, either by observation of the outcrops along the river bed or through some peculiar features of local topography, the fault would be detected. Even if this were not done directly, a detailed examination of the outcrops of shale on the two sides of the valley would almost certainly reveal differences between the two deposits, possibly minute, possibly even of their fossil contents, but enough to show that they were not the same formation, and thus to demonstrate some change in structure between the two sides of the valley.

Figure 6.7 shows a case in which casual surface examinations and the use of the information given by the boreholes shown would be misleading because of the existence of folds in the strata, the outcrops of which are drift covered. Figure 6.8 illustrates the necessity, where the strata involved dip steeply across the site being investigated, of correlating the strata encountered in one drill hole with those pierced by the adjacent hole. If this were not done, and hole 3, for example, had been put down only as far as the point marked *A*, the existence of the fault would have been undetected unless it were discovered through surface geological investigations.

A geological survey, even of a preliminary nature, will usually reveal whether or not an area has been subjected to glacial action. This information will be particularly valuable in the prosecution of underground exploratory work, since it will at once suggest some of the unusual subsurface features that may be encountered. The study of underground conditions in glaciated country is often complicated by boulders and buried river valleys. Those in the valley of the Rhine have already been mentioned; in Chap. 9 the buried valley that complicated the construction of the Mersey Tunnels in England will be described.

These examples are not mentioned to show that test borings and similar investigations are often faulty; such a conclusion would, in fact,

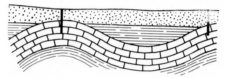

FIG. 6.7. A geological section showing how a fold may be undetected by test drilling.

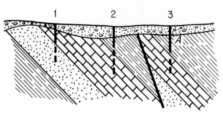

FIG. 6.8. A geological section illustrating the desirability of correlating steeply inclined strata in test drilling.

be incorrect, because in all the cases cited the results from the boreholes may have been correct, but their interpretation might not have been if the results were not correlated with the local geology. From study of the cases described and many other similar instances, the following general rules with regard to underground exploratory work may be suggested. (For convenience, the word "boreholes" will be used to describe all such subsurface work.)

1. No boreholes should be put down before at least a general geological survey of the area has been made.

2. Boreholes should, whenever possible, be located in relation to the local geological structure.

3. Boreholes should, whenever necessary, be carried to such depths that they will definitely correlate the strata encountered in adjacent holes by an "overlap" into at least one bed.

4. In exploring superficial deposits, one borehole at least should, whenever possible, be carried to rock.

5. In all cases of superficial deposits extending to no great depth, test borings should be taken into the rock for some specified distance, never less than 5 ft, but more than this if the nature of the work warrants the extra cost or if large boulders are liable to be encountered.

6. Unusual care must be exercised in putting down test borings in areas known to have been subjected to glacial action, especially with regard to checking all rock encountered during drilling (as in 5) and for the possible existence of buried river valleys.

7. The three-dimensional nature of the work must always be remembered; for example, three boreholes properly located will define exactly the thickness, dip, and strike of any continuous buried stratum.

Discussion of preliminary work would not be complete without at least a brief survey of the methods available. This is presented in the following notes and in Table 6.2, which is a modification of one included in a valuable booklet by H. A. Mohr, a publication of the Graduate School of Engineering of Harvard University, which contains details of most of the generally accepted methods of subsurface investigations.

6.7. Test Borings. Methods adopted for penetrating unconsolidated materials and solid rock are naturally different, even though they may often have to be employed in the same hole. It is convenient to describe the former as test borings and the latter as test drillings; test pits are sometimes used as an additional precaution in superficial deposits. Exploratory work will therefore be considered under these three headings.

The purpose of underground investigations must be clearly appreciated at the outset. Only in special cases is the purpose merely to find out where the hidden surface of rock lies. As a rule, it is also necessary to identify the material penetrated before rock is reached, not only for purposes of construction but also for the preparation of designs, especially when foundations are to be constructed in the unconsolidated material. For important foundations, and when rock has to be excavated, the nature of the rock penetrated by drilling must also be investigated. Usually, therefore, the aim of preliminary work is not only to provide information about underground boundaries between essentially different materials but also to procure samples of the materials for laboratory analysis and testing. In view of the attention now paid to the testing of sands and clays, it is almost always of the utmost importance to obtain relatively undisturbed samples.

The simplest type of exploration in unconsolidated material is done by probing with a steel rod; in shallow ground, depths to rock may sometimes be explored in this way, but the method is extremely limited in its application. The next stage involves the use of a soil auger, a boring tool described by its name, which may be obtained equipped with many special devices for penetrating different kinds of material and for procuring samples that, although not undisturbed, are often satisfactory

Table 6.2. Methods of Subsurface Exploration

Name of method	Materials in which used	Method of advancing hole	Method of sampling	Value for foundation-bed investigations
Test pits and test caissons	All soils: if ground water is encountered, compressed-air caisson or water-lowering process will be necessary	Usually by hand excavation in lined pit or beneath caisson	Samples taken by hand from original position in ground	Most valuable, materials can be inspected *in situ*, and adequate samples of all soils are easily obtained
Pricking	Shallow soils overlying rock	Steel bar forced into ground until rock is reached	. . . .	Limited to locating rock surfaces at shallow depths
Hand-auger boring	Cohesive soils, and some granular soils above water level	Augers rotated until filled with solid material and then withdrawn	Samples obtained from material brought up by auger	Satisfactory for shallow investigations for roads, small building foundations, etc.
Wash borings or wash-sample borings	All soils except the most compact (will not penetrate boulders)	Washing inside a driven casing	Samples recovered as sediment in wash water	Almost valueless and dangerous because of possibility of misleading results
Dry-sample or core-sample borings	All soils except the most compact (will not penetrate boulders)	Washing inside a driven casing	Open end of pipe or special spoon forced into soil at bottom of hole	Most reliable of inexpensive methods; permits accurate soil classification and penetration tests, if necessary
Shelby tube sampling	All soils except the most compact (will not penetrate boulders)	Forcing Shelby (steel) tubing into the ground by suitable means	Samples obtained in steel tubes	Best available method for soil sampling
Core drilling	All solid materials —rock and boulders	Rotating power-driven coring tools with diamond, shot, or steel-tooth cutters	Cores cut out and recovered from holes	Best method of studying nature of rock and boulders

SOURCE: This table is based upon, but is a modification of, Table I of H. A. Mohr's paper Exploration of Soil Conditions and Sampling Operations, Harvard Univ. *Graduate School Eng. Studies Bull.* 208, 1943.

for preliminary testing in a laboratory. The auger bores the hole, and samples of cohesive material are obtained by withdrawing the tool and cleaning off the material adhering to it. Holes through sand have to be lined with pipes, but special drills and devices with which samples may be obtained are available for this type of work. A soil-auger set, complete with the usual extra fittings and capable of boring to 30 ft, weighs less than 100 lb when packed for carrying and is relatively inexpensive. It is strange that more use is not made of this equipment, at least for small-scale work.

The soil auger could, it seems, be very usefully substituted for a type of boring, generally called *wash boring*, which was widely adopted by engineers in the past. In wash boring, a hole is excavated by washing inside a pipe casing which is forced into the ground as the hole is made; material excavated is trapped in a washtub, where it is examined and identified (if possible). Wash borings may be useful in some cases to show where a hidden rock surface is located; but as a means of exploring unconsolidated material, they are worse than useless, since they can give most misleading information. They reveal the material penetrated only in a thoroughly disturbed state, generally with much of the finer material washed away; they give no clue to underground water conditions and no sample of any use at all for testing.

A simple modification of wash boring provides a much more satisfactory method. A cored hole is sunk by washing, but the washing is stopped at intervals (determined by the nature of the ground) so that a pipe or special sampling device may be lowered into the hole, forced into the undisturbed material at the bottom of the hole, and withdrawn with a sample enclosed. Washing out then continues until another sample is required. This method also has the disadvantage of not immediately disclosing underground water conditions. The boring of holes in the dry with an auger is the only certain way of obtaining this information without waiting for ground-water conditions to reach equilibrium again after disturbance by a wash-boring operation. Correspondingly, the soil at the bottom of the washed-out hole is disturbed to such an extent that the sampler must penetrate the soil amply to make sure that a good proportion of the soil sample will be truly undisturbed. The design of samplers for this purpose has progressed considerably since the need for undisturbed samples was reaffirmed by the advance of studies in soil mechanics. (The word "reaffirmed" is used, since Alexandre Collin stressed as long ago as 1846 the need for samples of clay that were in their "natural state.")[6.13] A variety of excellent tools are now available for obtaining good samples from all the main types of soils. Piston samplers are a common type, but for friable soils the so-called "Dennison sampler" is useful because loss of the sample is prevented by spring guards.[6.14] Freezing, chemical injection, and impregnation with asphalt have all been used in developing methods for procuring undisturbed samples of cohesionless soils such as sands. The necessity of getting undisturbed samples arises from the vital importance that the actual density of such soils in place may have; if in a loose state, they may cause trouble through subsequent compaction as by vibration.

A parallel development has been the design of improved methods for obtaining what are now commonly called "Shelby-tube" samples, taken by forcing thin-walled steel tubing into the undisturbed ground, without

FIG. 6.9. Test drilling on city streets: test boring in progress on Yonge Street, Toronto, Ontario, Canada, as a preliminary to the construction of the city's first subway.

the aid of wash boring; the steel tubing is so arranged that the lower section can be removed for sample retrieval. Soil sampling in this way has now become an accepted practice in soil mechanics. Measurement of the force required to penetrate successive soil strata, if carefully recorded, can itself, in association with sampling, be used as a guide to soil properties. A further development has been the use of vaned tools that may be turned when penetrating buried soil; the torque measured thus gives an *in situ* measurement of soil shear strength. The use of cone penetration devices is a similar technique. These, however, are engineering tests.

Emphasis must again be placed upon the importance, for the proper study of subsurface soil conditions, of obtaining good undisturbed soil samples. Pioneer work in this direction was carried out in the exploratory work that preceded the construction of the San Francisco–Oakland Bridge. Undisturbed samples were obtained along the line of the bridge from depths up to the record maximum of 273 ft below low-water level; thus, the unusually deep foundation for this great structure could be designed with accuracy and confidence. On the east coast of the United States, another pioneering test-boring program was carried out in 1935 and 1936 in connection with the Passamaquoddy tidal-power scheme, then projected by the United States government. This work was all in exposed coastal waters and was hampered by severe winter climatic conditions, tidal currents in excess of 8 knots, and a tidal range of 28 ft—a combination of adverse conditions that could hardly be equaled. Despite this, however, test sampling was conducted and core drilling into the rock over a large area of the sea near the coast was carried out in conjunction with geological investigations; thus foundation-bed conditions for the structures then proposed were accurately investigated. The deepest hole put down during these interesting operations was in 120 ft of water and through 164 ft of unconsolidated material above the rock, which was then core-drilled.[6.15] More than 20 years later, the Passamaquoddy scheme being still under investigation, further exploration was made of the sea bottom from a fully equipped barge that had to be towed 3,000 miles to the site. It was moored with long anchor lines, and a 12-in. casing pipe was lowered through its center, decreasing in size to a 6-in. pipe, ingeniously guyed under water to the ends of the barge to give requisite strength against bending. With this arrangement, 5-in.-diameter undisturbed samples of marine clay were satisfactorily obtained (with a fixed-piston sampler) from depths as great as 326 ft below the surface, despite the high tidal range and swift currents already mentioned. Core drilling, through a 4-in. casing in the sea bed, to a penetration of 15 ft, was also carried out.[6.16]

It is not only in the sea that deep water has to be penetrated in procuring soil samples. For the foundation of the Tappan Zee Bridge across the Hudson River (see page 653), test boring was carried out to depths of 295 ft, and undisturbed soil samples were obtained for laboratory testing. It is, however, somewhat natural that the most difficult test-boring operations are those conducted in the open sea. A significant record of successful work of this kind is gradually being built up; one of the most hazardous examples yet undertaken is the recent investigation of the bed of the English Channel in connection with revived hopes for a channel tunnel (see page 340). Test borings were made to depths of 225 ft, and samples were obtained; the work was done in the open sea in depths of water up to 160 ft, with added hazard caused by the strong currents that sweep through the Straits of Dover on every tide. This work naturally involved the use of specially equipped ships. A variety of craft have been adopted for this kind of work, but wartime landing craft have been found especially suitable.[6.17] If there is any possibility of using fixed stagings, however, even in the open sea, they are to be preferred; the cost of their construction is usually more than repaid by the added security and continuity of the work. In exploring sites for possible oil-well derricks in the deep waters of Lake Maracaibo in Venezuela, up to 10 miles offshore, test boring was carried on from welded tubular-steel platforms that were floated out to location and

Fig. 6.10. Converted landing craft "Ian Salvor III" in the English Channel taking borings in the bed of the Straits of Dover as part of the 1957–1960 studies of the proposed channel tunnel. (*Photograph by Skyphotos. Reproduced by permission of George Wimpey & Co., Ltd.*)

then secured in place by means of steel spuds 120 ft long. From such platforms, soil samples were obtained from depths up to 250 ft.

These were all big jobs; they are mentioned to show that there is no reason why subsurface exploration cannot be carried out anywhere that civil engineering works may be constructed. On small jobs, however, just as much as on the largest jobs, the same attention must be paid to test-boring work in order to ensure accurate records of all soil strata penetrated and the best possible undisturbed soil samples for testing in the laboratory. In this way, preliminary geological studies can be corrected, confirmed, or extended with a view to determining accurately the subsurface conditions that will be encountered when construction commences.

6.8. Test Pits and Shafts. Another means of investigating superficial deposits is the test pit, an excavation large enough for a man to dig in conveniently. In practically all cases, test pits must be lined with timber, the design and placing of which must always be carefully checked. Clearly, there is a limiting depth to which test pits may reasonably be carried, so that their main use is for the investigation of relatively shallow depths of unconsolidated material and particularly for the study of surface deposits of gravel, sand, or clay for use in construction. They have the advantage that the deposits penetrated can be easily examined in place, and undisturbed samples can be obtained, when necessary, from the bottom of the pit. They will disclose underground water conditions in the material penetrated, but clearly, they can be used only on dry land. For extensive exploratory work, test pits are usually more expensive than test borings; but on small jobs for which a drilling outfit would have to be specially procured, they may sometimes prove economical

When test pits are used to investigate surface deposits of construction material, it will be necessary to take regular samples of the materials encountered. Sampling is a matter that does not always receive the attention that it deserves in engineering work; it is not just the haphazard collection of small quantities of material that one might imagine it to be. Two objectives are important in sampling: (1) obtaining samples typical of average conditions for all material to be investigated, and (2) obtaining samples representative of maximum and minimum characteristics of the material.

When investigating material to be used in construction, both objectives must be remembered, although the former will usually be the controlling one unless the material is very variable in composition. Samples must always be taken at regular intervals in materials of the same appearance; and from a large number of these, thoroughly mixed at the site, one or more average samples should be taken. These may then be used for testing, but they must always be accompanied by at least one unmixed sample, selected as typical for the stratum of material being studied, in order to check on the correctness of the average samples obtained. (Naturally, this procedure applies only to materials that can easily be mixed and not, for example, to stiff clay from which a number of individual samples must be selected.) All samples should be most carefully marked with full information about the location from which they have been taken; it is most exasperating to have a good set of samples which cannot be identified.

Simple windlasses can be used in test pits for removal of excavated material and samples, but there is naturally a maximum depth to which pits can be sunk with such simple means. When hand power for such haulage has to be abandoned in favor of mechanical equipment, the exploratory operation becomes an engineering task and must be subject to the usual preliminary economic and design studies. Test shafts of great magnitude have been used on some large civil engineering projects of recent years, one notable example is briefly described on page 366. Tunnels may also be used for exploratory purposes in exceptional cases; test tunnels are almost always so located that they may be later utilized

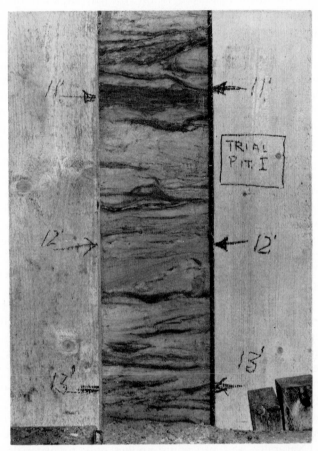

Fig. 6.11. A photograph of undisturbed soil strata as photographed in the side of a test pit. (*Reproduced by permission of Soil Mechanics, Ltd., London, England, and the Midlands Project Group, Central Electricity Generating Board.*)

as pilot tunnels for major excavation or in some other way. In some underground power stations, for example, the essential exploratory tunnels have been used as cable tunnels from the completed plant; this was done in the Snowy Mountains project in Australia (see page 23). The objective, however, is the same as in the simplest test boring or shaft, i.e., to determine by actual examination of the soil or rock in place, or as samples, the accuracy of preliminary geological deductions.

This is one step toward building up a complete picture of subsurface conditions which will give the essential information needed for design and full knowledge of the conditions to be met when construction starts.

6.9 Test Drilling. When rock surface is reached, either in a test pit or in test boring, a change in method is necessary if the rock has to be penetrated. Usually the rock is penetrated, if only to determine its nature and to make sure that it is solid rock and not a boulder. Various methods are available, but reference need here be made only to core drilling in which a cylindrical hole is drilled around a central core which is periodically broken off from the bedrock at its lower end and removed from the hole for examination. The rotary drilling machine used for this purpose is fitted with a special bit equipped with black diamonds (diamond drilling), chilled-steel shot (shot drilling), or removable steel cutting teeth. The choice of equipment will depend to some extent on the nature of the rock; the size of hole will depend on the drilling tool available and on the anticipated depth of the hole. Core drilling is a highly specialized operation, necessitating skilled workmanship and experienced supervision. Percussion drilling is another means of penetrating rock, but it is not widely used for exploratory work.

The idea of diamond drilling originated in Switzerland in 1863. The first machine was hand operated, but a steam-driven machine was used as early as 1864 in the Mont Cenis Tunnel between Italy and France. The bit speed was only 30 rpm, and the penetration was about 12 in. per hr. The first United States patent for a steam-driven diamond drill was issued in 1867; by 1870 a 750-ft hole had been drilled with the first American machine in the search for coal near Pottsville, Pennsylvania.[6.18] Steam continued to provide the motive power for diamond drilling until the First World War, after which gasoline engines took over. With higher speeds possible and with greater flexibility due to the use of lightweight materials, diamond drilling has steadily improved so that today it is an efficient and reliable operation in the hands of expert workmen.

In some types of soft or disintegrated rock, it will sometimes prove difficult to obtain complete sections of core by drilling, and estimates will then have to be made, based on the operator's observations and his experience, with regard to the exact nature of the material. The amount of core recovered will vary with the type of rock penetrated; typical average values are quartzite, 90 per cent; granite, 85 per cent; sandstone, 70 per cent; limestone, 60 per cent; shale, 50 per cent; slate, 40 per cent. These figures are naturally only a guide to what may be expected.

The action of a core drill will not, in general, affect the bedrock through which the hole is drilled; diamond bits, especially, bore a clean, smooth hole. Consequently, it is possible to utilize cored holes for other purposes. When the rock is to be subjected to water pressure (as in a dam foundation), drill holes can be capped and filled with water which is then kept under observation while pressure is applied to it; note can be made of whether the hole "holds water" or not. An interesting investigation can sometimes be carried out in drill holes of relatively large diameter (about 4 in. and over) by the use of a periscope device

Fig. 6.12. Diamond drilling at a prospective dam site in northern Ontario, Canada, showing log cribs and staging from which the work was carried out. (*Photograph by R. F. Legget. Reproduced by permission of the Power Corporation of Canada, Ltd.*)

equipped with an electric light below the inclined mirror. When this is lowered into the hole, the appearance of the rock walls can be examined with a fair degree of certainty. This simple idea has been greatly extended by the development of ingenious "borehole cameras," specially designed instruments that fit into even small-diameter boreholes and secure a photographic record at any required depth and through the

360° exposure around the hole. One of the most notable of such instruments is the NX camera developed by geologists of the United States Corps of Engineers, with special reference to the investigation of a fault condition in foundation rock encountered during the construction of the

FIG. 6.13. NX borehole camera developed by the Corps of Engineers, U.S. Army. (*a*) Camera proper, stainless-steel tube 2¾ in. in diameter, with quartz window enclosing conical mirror near lower end; (*b*) power supply; (*c*) crankshaft for crank (*d*), used for raising and lowering camera; (*e*) cable spool for dummy camera operated by crank (*d*), before using camera; (*f*) cable wheel for camera cable; (*g*) cable guide and depth measuring wheel. (*Reproduced by permission of the Chief of Engineers, U.S. Army.*)

Folsom Dam.[6.19] The instrument is designed as a slim cylinder that fits into a 3-in.-diameter borehole. Through a rotating conical mirror it will photograph throughout the 360° of the borehole onto a flat 35 mm film; the process is reversed when the developed film is viewed by those responsible for the investigation. At the Folsom Dam, not only did a camera of this type reveal details of the critical fault zone, but it showed up delicate changes in rock coloring and fractures as small as 0.01 in. in thickness as well as the surface of the ground-water table.

Further improvements have been made in this field in Europe; an electronic borehole camera has been developed which, in association with the appropriate circuits, will project an image directly onto a television screen above ground. This instrument will also operate in 3-in.-diameter boreholes, giving a reasonable image on a 21- by 7-in. screen.[6.20] Since the idea of combining television and geology may seem strange to some, it may be appropriate to note here that underwater closed-circuit television cameras have been successfully employed for unusually difficult river-bed exploration. A notable example was the study of the bed of the Columbia River before designs and plans could be made for the closure of the Dalles Dam. Preliminary surveys by divers proved to be unsatisfactory because of high velocities, and so television was used for the final investigations carried out in 1953. The camera, suspended by a steel cable, was operated from a strongly moored barge. By this means, the character of the river bed, i.e., whether it was bare rock or covered with gravel, could be distinguished. On the basis of this information, plans for the critical closure operation were successfully developed, and the gap was finally closed after over 3 million cu yd of fill was placed.

Reference has been made only to vertical boreholes, since the great majority of holes are vertical, especially unusual ones such as those necessary for undersea investigations. Diamond drilling had to be carried out, for example, in the Strait of Canso, in eastern Canada in order to prove up the bottom of the strait prior to the placing of a massive rock causeway which joins the island of Cape Breton with the mainland of Nova Scotia. Using a tubular steel frame for supporting casing and drill rods through 186 ft of water, the contractor successfully carried out regular diamond drilling after passing through and casing 50 ft of soil. (Such efforts will pale into insignificance when the projected "Mohole" is successfully drilled off Puerto Rico to penetrate the full crust of the earth, through the "Moho" to the mantle rock.)

All drill holes, however, need not be vertical. It is, in fact, essential that civil engineers in particular remember that holes can be drilled at any desired angle, since for some investigations inclined holes, horizontal holes, or even holes inclined upward may be necessary. A good example of the use of inclined holes was given by the investigation of rock conditions in the bed of the Hudson River, New York, outlined on page 294. Horizontal holes were used extensively in the investigation of rock conditions in the abandoned tunnels utilized for the Pennsylvania Turnpike. In this case, working faces were available, and knowledge of the rock to be penetrated as the tunnels were completed was essential. Accordingly about 3,500 ft of horizontal holes were drilled to supplement the 10,000 ft of vertical holes in the thorough study made of the geology of the turnpike tunnels. One of the horizontal holes was successfully drilled to the almost unprecedented length of 1,450 ft from the east heading of the Tuscarora Tunnel.[6.22] And in the necessary exploration of Ripple Rock, British Columbia, before its demolition

FIG. 6.14. Examining exposed rock formations at Niagara Falls, Ontario, Canada, in connection with the design of the flow remedial works, now complete. (*Reproduced by permission of the Hydro Electric Power Commission of Ontario.*)

appreciable overhead drilling was carried out when the access tunnel had extended out under the two rock mounds that had to be removed by blastng as described on page 729.[6.23]

Entirely novel when first introduced, but now a normal part of rock-drilling technique, was the use of cored holes large enough for a man to be lowered into. Holes of this size had been frequently used in the past in other branches of work, and their value in civil engineering practice was quickly recognized. They are drilled with machines of the "calyx" type, with diameters varying normally up to 42 in. (although holes up to 72 in. in diameter have been drilled). The method of drilling and removal of the cores is similar to that followed for smaller holes, although breaking off the core from the bedrock is sometimes difficult and necessitates the use of special wedging devices or of blasting. The holes are of avail only if leakage of ground water into them can be taken care of by a small pump; special precautions must always be taken to keep a supply of fresh air at the bottom of the holes, particularly if blasting has been used for core removal.

When the holes are drilled to the requisite depth and cleaned out, the geologists and engineers in charge may be lowered down in suitable cradles; with the aid of portable lights, they can carefully inspect the surrounding rock exactly as it occurs in place; they can investigate boundaries between beds, study fissures, and make a thorough and complete exploration of the rock with certainty and convenience. If the holes are drilled after grouting of the foundation beds has been carried out, the efficacy of the grouting operation can thus be checked; this is a most valuable feature in view of the inevitable uncertainty regarding the penetration of grout. The cost of holes of this size may be con-

Fig. 6.15. Drill rig for sinking 48-in.- diameter exploratory holes on Delaware Aqueduct work, New York, (*Photograph by Ingersoll-Rand Company.*)

siderable, but it is commensurate with the great advantages that they present for underground investigation.

The use of these large-diameter holes in civil engineering work appears to have developed initially in the United States of America, although they have been used successfully in several other countries. Early applications were mostly in connection with dam-foundation work, as for the Grand Coulee and Norris Dams. A particularly significant early application was at the site of the Prettyboy Dam, constructed to impound water for supply to the city of Baltimore, Maryland. The site is physically a good one; the valley is quite deep; but geological conditions required unusual precautions in the excavation of the cutoff trench below the base of the main structure. This called for placing about 190,000 cu yd of concrete. The rock formation beneath the dam is mainly mica schist with some limestone, gneiss, and intruded quartz, and it has been twice subjected to earth movement. Faulting was therefore to be expected. The exposed rock had undergone weathering to a considerable degree. It was realized that extreme care would have to be taken in blasting for the excavation of the foundation bed. As a preliminary operation, it was decided to use calyx core drills to drill several deep shafts, 36 in. in diameter, so that the consulting geologist could be lowered into them to study the formation of the schist in place. By this means, the geologists were able to prepare accurate sections showing the position of all faults and large seams as well as the direction of their strike and dip. Disintegration of the schist on the hanging-wall side of a major fault, traced in this way, considerably increased the volume of excavation. Because of the use of wide-diameter holes, it was possible to obtain truly representative samples of the schist, the study of which constituted an interesting investigation in pure geology.[6.24]

Large-diameter drill holes of this type were widely used during

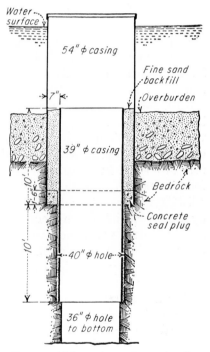

Fig. 6.16. Telescoping casing and cofferdam as used for carrying out 36-in.-diameter test-hole drilling at the site of the Watts Bar Dam, Tennessee River, by the Tennessee Valley Authority. (*Reproduced by permission of The Editor, Engineering News-Record.*)

the great program of dam building that distinguished the early years of the Tennessee Valley Authority. One particularly interesting application of large-diameter drill holes was developed by the engineers of the TVA in exploring the unusually complex underground structure on which the Watts Bar Dam is founded. At various locations across the river at the dam site selected, large holes were drilled by means of the cofferdam arrangement sketched in Fig. 6.16. This worked admirably; the rock was penetrated to depths up to 68 ft, which permitted complete inspection of the sections thus revealed.[6.25] The potential of this drilling technique was well demonstrated in the investigations for the cross-Florida barge canal; a calyx drill was successfully used for sinking a 42-in. casing through 50 ft of soft Ocala limestone underlying sand at the surface, in order to reach underlying dolomite, in which a 36-in.-diameter calyx hole was then drilled in the normal way.[6.26] One of the most extensive jobs ever undertaken with calyx drills was, strangely enough, not for subsurface investigation but for the forming of holes in rock for penstocks. Five 6-ft-diameter calyx holes were successfully sunk 1,435 ft through granite on the Canon del Pato hydroelectric development on the Rio Santa in the Peruvian Andes. The penstocks thus formed connect a 5½-mile pressure tunnel with an underground powerhouse, which houses five 25,000-kw generators.[6.27]

6.10. Supervising Exploratory Work. It will be obvious, even from this brief discussion, not only that the accuracy of underground exploratory work is of supreme importance but also that the conduct of the work often requires exceptional skill and wide experience on the part of the man in charge. In engaging men to undertake exploratory work, therefore, employers should give particular attention to their experience and reliability. It is often advantageous to carry out all exploratory work by direct administration since the ultimate extent of the work is not always known when the work is begun. If this is possible, and if the engineer is able to employ experienced men, it constitutes probably the most satisfactory procedure. Many large engineering organizations, such as highway and public works administrations, maintain special test-boring divisions for conducting all their regular exploratory work. On other civil engineering work, however, carried out by consulting engineers or by engineering offices that are not able to maintain regular boring crews, it will be necessary to engage an outside test-boring contractor for this work. The necessary contract documents must be prepared with special care. Because of variations that may be revealed as the work proceeds, it is most important to ensure a wide degree of flexibility not only in the extent of the work but also in the location of test holes. It will be clear, therefore, that under no circumstances whatsoever should a test-boring contract be awarded on a "lump-sum" basis. Unit prices must be secured, probably with a guaranteed minimum number of holes and total depth of drilling or boring, with modified prices for operations in excess of certain specified limits. Although the usual practice of calling for tenders will probably have to be followed, the award of the contract should not be made on the basis of price alone; due regard should be paid to the experience and reliability of the respective contractors who have tendered and to the test-boring and drilling equipment that they have available, details of which should be required with the tenders.

Exploratory work is of value only if a complete and accurate record of the results is obtained for the use of the engineer in charge and his advisers. This is so obvious that there would seem to be little need to emphasize the necessity of obtaining accurate records. Not infrequently, however, recording is left in charge of the test-boring foreman, supervised by occasional visits of an engineer; this is often done even when a considerable amount of money is being spent on the exploratory work. Even an experienced and conscientious foreman should not be left in charge of the records, not only because he will probably not be well versed in record work but also because it is important that the results of the exploratory work be checked by an independent observer.

As a general rule, therefore, a member of the engineer's staff, himself a qualified engineer, should always be present throughout exploratory work in order to watch its progress and keep the necessary records. If a geologist can undertake this task, so much the better, but this will be possible only when a large field geological staff is available. If a geologist is being consulted about the work for which the testing is being done, he should occasionally visit the site of the exploratory work while the work is in progress so that he may see the results for himself and discuss them with the men in charge. When it is realized that the success or failure of an entire construction project may depend on the accuracy of records of exploratory work, this insistence on their accuracy will be appreciated.

It is clear that an accurate record of the nature of all strata must be kept in order to achieve the second objective of subsurface investigations —study of the materials encountered. This record will be supplemented by samples of each stratum and by the cores obtained in core drilling. The importance of preserving soil samples in their undisturbed state has already been stressed; it cannot be overemphasized. Arrangements must be made for the proper and immediate sealing (with paraffin or other suitable sealant) of all soil-sample tubes right at the drilling site so that the samples, once they are removed from the ground, will lose no moisture. If soil is needed for visual inspection, additional samples should be procured for this purpose, since the samples to be used for laboratory testing must not be handled at all on the job after they are sealed. If this point ever has to be emphasized to field engineering staff, a simple demonstration of the rate at which water will evaporate from a soil sample, carried out by exposing a small sample of moist soil on a delicate chemical balance in an ordinary dry atmosphere, will usually be more effective than any argument.

Rock cores must also be carefully stored; the most convenient way of doing this is to use special core boxes—flat wooden boxes divided into narrow compartments, each wide enough to hold one core and, for convenience, an even number of feet long. Into these compartments, the cores are placed as they are obtained, care being taken to place them in compartments corresponding exactly in position to the location of the core in the holes; thus, gaps will have to be left periodically to allow for the inevitable core losses. Obviously, large-diameter rock cores cannot be kept in storage boxes, but arrangements are usually made to have the various sections of core, as they are secured, laid out in order and in line adjacent to the hole so that they may readily be examined by those interested.

Fig. 6.17. Calyx-drill core (36-in. diameter) from foundation strata beneath the Grand Coulee Dam, laid out for inspection with allowance for core losses. (*Reproduced by permission of the Commissioner, U.S. Bureau of Reclamation.*)

Finally, a prime requirement of all records of exploratory work is that materials encountered should be accurately described. When it is possible to examine samples of all the materials after the hole has been made, accurate descriptive notes as the work proceeds are not imperative, provided that all samples and cores have been properly correlated with the progress records. It will be a distinct advantage, however, if accurate terminology can be used in the day-to-day records. The engineer who is keeping them should therefore be familiar at least with main rock groups and the distinctions between the various grades of unconsolidated material. The latter should always be described by the use of the appropriate geological term—gravel, sand, silt, or clay, or a mixture of two or more of these—together with an accurate notation of the physical condition of the material, e.g., whether it is hard packed or very loose. Terms that are essentially popular, such as "hardpan," or local in application, such as "pug," should be avoided. If an exact measure of the state of the material is desired, this must be obtained by using a penetration device of some type. Naturally, the more uniform such field descriptions are, the more useful they will prove to be. There is no widespread agreement, even in the English-speaking world, on terms to be used for the field description of soils, but there are available a number of printed guides. One of the most useful of these, to the writer's knowledge, is also one of the smallest in physical size, a little pocket-sized pamphlet now widely used throughout Canada.[6.28]

6.11. Utilizing the Results. Underground explorations such as have been described in the preceding sections can be fully effective only if they are correlated, without delay, with the results of geological survey work at the site being investigated. This requirement provides another convincing argument in favor of having an engineer in constant attendance at all exploratory test work, since the correlation can best be carried out while the work is in progress. The obvious, and most useful, means of combining the results of the two methods of investigation is to draw tentative geological sections, based on survey work, along lines on which test holes are to be put down; the records of these holes can then be plotted to scale on the section as work proceeds. It may be necessary to use a distorted scale for this plotting; but provided that this fact is not lost sight of and that a definite scale is used to relate the boreholes and sections with one another, the resulting record can be easily interpreted. By means of this simple device, it will be possible to keep constant check on the progress of holes, to stop them when they have gone far enough, to locate new holes in order to clear up doubtful points revealed by the section, and generally to see that no effort is wasted and no necessary information left unobtained.

The problem, however, is a three-dimensional one. Although a general appreciation of the three-dimensional aspects of many drawings will usually enable the engineer to follow the progress of subsurface exploratory work merely by a study of drawings, those who are not accustomed to "three-dimensional thinking" will be greatly aided by an actual model of the subsurface information gradually revealed by a test-boring and drilling program. The use of models for this purpose, on all but the very smallest jobs, is now well-established practice. In their simplest forms, such models can consist merely of vertical sticks, colored to correspond with the different strata encountered and so located on a plan of the works as to be in correct relation one with another. The steady development of the underground picture, even through such a simple and inexpensive medium, is always revealing. For special jobs, and for complex underground conditions, more elaborate arrangements can be made. One of the most extensive models ever developed for study of subsurface conditions was developed by engineers and geologists of the TVA to illustrate the exploration program carried out at the site of the Kentucky Dam, near Gilbertsville, Kentucky. The bedrock is a siliceous and chert limestone. The dam is a concrete and earth-fill structure 8,650 ft long. The exploratory program extended over 4 years because of the complexity of underground conditions encountered; in all, 817 borings were

Fig. 6.18. Model of the Kentucky Dam site near the mouth of the Tennessee River, Kentucky, U.S.A.; the total length is about 100 ft; every drill hole is represented by a painted steel rod. (*Reproduced by permission of the Chief Engineer, Tennessee Valley Authority.*)

put down, aggregating 100,631 ft; this constituted one of the most extensive of such investigations ever carried out in North America. Progress of the work was followed by means of a peg model constructed of $\frac{3}{16}$-in. steel pins, suitably colored and arranged in plan to a scale 1:100. The resulting model was over 100 ft long, but it proved invaluable not only to those engaged upon the work but also to the consultants on the dam site during their regular visits of inspection.[6.29]

The basic idea of such models cannot be improved upon, but the advent of new materials such as plastics has permitted some variation in the type of model. It is now possible to form transparent models, embedding pegs to illustrate test borings; thus a vivid impression of underground conditions is given by means of a solid model that can be handled and viewed from a variety of angles. And in the case of extensive underground excavation, the process can be carried still further and a model of the excavation itself prepared, marked or colored to correspond with the geological strata that are to be encountered, as determined from test borings, test shafts, and tunnels. With the aid of such models, contractors can readily visualize the character of excavation work and can plan their

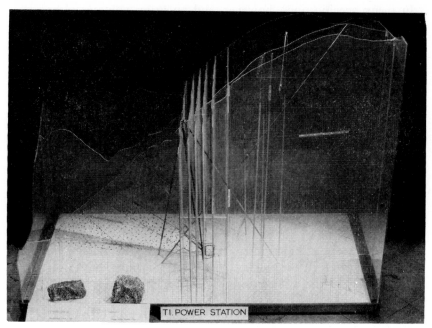

Fig. 6.19. Model of subsurface conditions as revealed by test borings at the site of the Tumut 1 underground power station of the Snowy Mountains project, Australia. (*Reproduced by permission of the Snowy Mountains Hydro-Electric Authority.*)

drilling and blasting operations long in advance of actually encountering the changes in strata with which they have to contend. Figure 6.19 illustrates such a transparent model developed by the Snowy Mountains Authority for use on some of its major underground excavation work in Australia.

Just as the completion of the initial geological survey of a site will usually enable the civil engineer to prepare preliminary plans for a project, on which will depend the program of exploratory work to be carried out, so will the completion of the exploration program enable him to prepare final designs in detail. The combination of the results of the exploratory work and the geological survey, in all but exceptional cases, will enable the engineer to obtain a complete picture of the underground structure at the site in so far as it will affect his plans. He will know to what limitations his design is subject; he will be able to calculate with a fair degree of accuracy the amount of material that will have to be excavated; and he will know what natural construction materials are available within easy reach of the site. Thus will he utilize the findings of his preliminary work, embodying the results in his contract plans and specifications.

In many specifications, however, and on many contract plans something similar to this clause will be found: "Drawing X contains details of borings that have been made at the site of the work, but their accuracy is not guaranteed; and intending contractors are required to take, before they tender, the borings that they may deem necessary to satisfy themselves as to the accuracy of the information regarding local conditions conveyed by the plans and specifications."

If this qualification is considered at all seriously, it will be seen to evidence a surprising paradox, since the engineer has presumably based his entire design upon the information that he suggests the contractor should not use in case it may be wrong. The clause is probably a carry-over from the days when preliminary investigations were not always comprehensive and when the methods available did not permit even the engineer to place great reliance upon the results obtained. Today, however, the clause is an anachronism. If there is any need for each of the contractors who intend to tender on a contract to take individual sets of trial borings, then the engineer's design cannot be assumed to be free from doubt, and the expenditure of all the money necessary to take the borings may be doubly wasted. On the other hand, if the engineer's design is based on accurate exploratory results, there is usually little need to include the clause. A final necessary comment on this strange feature of contract documents is that the courts do not always support the intention of the clause, viz., to put the onus of anticipating satisfactory foundation conditions on the contractor. In this connection, it has been stated editorially in *Engineering-Record*[6.30] that:

The established view of the courts on the matter roughly appears to be this: The owner is responsible for unforeseen costs to the contractor when the engineer's borings are found to contain inaccuracies or fraudulent misrepresentation. The owner also is responsible when the engineer does not reveal to the contractor his complete record of preliminary investigations even when he has reason to doubt their accuracy.

On the other hand, the owner is not responsible for the fact that incomplete borings do not reveal hidden ledges of rock in an earth bank, buried cribs along old waterfronts, and the like. . . . Lower courts have penalized owners when unforeseen difficulties have caused the contractor to sue, but only under exceptional circumstances have higher courts ruled that the risk of such discovery is the owner's rather than the contractor's, provided always that there has been no concealment by the owner.

Some provision, however, must be made for the possibility that underground conditions when opened up during construction may not be found to be exactly as suggested by preliminary exploratory work, despite the care with which this has been carried out. One of the most satisfactory solutions to this difficulty appears to be that contained in the standard form of contract used for construction work carried out for the Federal government of the United States of America.[6.31] This reads:

Changed Conditions. The Contractor shall promptly, and before such conditions are disturbed, notify the Contracting Officer in writing of: (1) subsurface or latent physical conditions at the site differing materially from those indicated in this contract, or (2) unknown physical conditions at the site, of an unusual nature, differing materially from those ordinarily encountered and generally recognized as inhering in work of the character provided for in this contract. The Contracting Officer shall promptly investigate the conditions, and if he finds that such conditions do so materially differ and cause an increase or decrease in the cost of, or the time required for, performance of this contract, an equitable adjustment shall be made and the contract modified in writing accordingly. Any claim of the Contractor for adjustment hereunder shall not be allowed unless he has given notice as above required; provided that the Contracting Officer may, if he determines the facts so justify, consider and adjust any such claim asserted before the date of final settlement of the contract.

This appears to be a reasonable provision and may suggest how the possibility of changed conditions can be dealt with in other specifications. Another solution to this very valid difficulty is that adopted by certain public engineering organizations; e.g., in the case of dam construction, the site of the dam may be cleared and the foundation bed may be prepared by direct administration and then a contract may be awarded for the construction of the dam structure alone, about which there should be few serious disputes. This method, however, is applicable only to certain projects and is by no means free of disadvantages. It may be suggested, therefore, with propriety that the best of all methods for avoiding contractual disputes regarding foundation-bed conditions is to have the preliminary and exploratory work so well carried out that there remains, when construction begins, small chance of encountering serious variations from assumed subsurface conditions.

6.12. Conclusion. This chapter ends as it began, with a renewed suggestion of the great importance in all civil engineering operations of adequate preliminary geological investigations and underground exploratory work. The services of geological advisers of wide experience can be secured without difficulty; methods and equipment of wide scope and great utility can now be utilized; estimates can readily be prepared to show the relatively small cost of this work; and many records can be found in the annals of the art to demonstrate the futility of its neglect and the great value of its correct utilization.

In the succeeding chapters of this book, many examples will be found of extensive and splendidly executed programs of subsurface exploration. Records will also be found of jobs in which this preliminary investigation was poorly executed, and in some extreme cases, actually neglected. Cases will be cited in which quite unexpected conditions were encountered, despite careful subsurface exploration, a reminder that when the engineer is dealing with unseen underground conditions, he can never be *absolutely* certain of the conditions he will encounter until all excavation is complete. The uncertainty is especially great in areas that have been subject to glaciation, but even here, if this fact is known from geological studies, the requisite note of warning can be sounded in the appropriate contract documents which can be so prepared as to protect the contractor from the unexpected. One branch of exploratory work only has not yet been treated: the use of geophysical methods. Because of their special character, they are considered separately in the next chapter, which may be regarded as a subchapter of this treatment of subsurface exploration in general. Against the background thus provided, attention will then be directed to the main branches of civil engineering work in order to see how the interrelation of geology and civil engineering so strongly emphasized throughout this chapter is experienced in the actual practice of the art.

Suggestions for Further Reading

There is a strange lack of published information on subsurface exploration; two of the most useful references that are available are:

Mohr, H. A., "Exploration of Soil Conditions and Sampling Operations," 3d rev. ed., Harvard University, Graduate School of Engineering, Soil Mechanics Series 21, November, 1943.

Hvorslev, M. J., "Subsurface Exploration and Sampling of Soils for Civil Engineering Purposes," United States Corps of Engineers, Waterways Experiment Station, Vicksburg, Miss., 1948.

Although related specifically to mining work, the following publication contains useful information for civil engineering use:

LeRoy, L. W., and H. M. Crain (eds.), "Subsurface Geologic Methods," Colorado School of Mines, Golden, Colo., 1949.

An excellent guide to geological work in the field is provided by:

Lahee, F. H., "Field Geology," 5th ed., McGraw-Hill Book Company, Inc., New York, 1952.

For a useful introduction to the geometry and use of geological maps, the reader may refer to:

Roberts, A., "Geological Structures and Maps," 2d ed., Clever-Hume Press, Ltd., London, 1958.

Eckel, E. B., "Interpreting Geological Maps for Engineers," Special Technical Publication 122 of Am. Soc. Test. Mats. (Philadelphia), 1951, pp. 5–15; this contains a most valuable symposium on "Surface and Subsurface Reconnaissance."

A remarkably full coverage of the subject is now available in this volume from Czechoslovakia:

Pouba, Z., "Geologické Mapování," Nakladatelstvi, Československé Akademie Věd, Prague, 1959, 523 pp.

A comprehensive treatment of the methods used for test drilling and boring is available from France:

Combefort, H., "Forages et Sondages," Editions Eyrolles, Paris, 1955.

A splendid introduction to the use of aerial photographs in geological work is given by:

Roy, R. G., "Aerial Photography in Geologic Interpretation and Mapping," USGS Professional Paper 373, 1960.

The general subject of photo-interpretation is excellently dealt with in:

"Manual of Photographic Interpretation," Am. Soc. of Photogrammetry, Washington, 1960, 868 pp.

Chapter 7

APPLIED GEOPHYSICS AND CIVIL ENGINEERING

Bishop Watson compares a geologist to a gnat mounted on an elephant, and laying down theories as to the whole internal structure of the vast animal from the phenomena of the hide. The comparison is unjust to the geologists. . . .

Lord Macaulay
"Critical Essay on History"

GEOPHYSICAL METHODS of subsurface exploration constitute one further means of determining underground conditions. The fact that this short chapter is devoted to geophysical methods alone is due, however, not so much to any special intrinsic merits of the methods themselves as to the importance of the general implications of geophysical study for all civil engineers. The methods can be a useful and economical supplement to a test-boring program; they are briefly described with some illustrative examples from civil engineering practice. Fully to appreciate the value of the methods, however, demands an awareness of the contributions which physics is now making to the development of geological knowledge. As an introduction, therefore, to a summary account of geophysical methods of subsurface exploration, a note on the broad scope of these contributions may be helpful.

Classical geology was essentially a descriptive science, based on careful observation in the field and in the laboratory, aided by careful reasoning in deducing general principles from individual observations. With the turn of the twentieth century, however, increasing attention was paid in geological studies to the contributions that could be made to geological problems by application of the principles of other sciences. Chemistry proved of such assistance that *geochemistry* is a branch of study now recognized in its own right. Botany has made its contributions also, mainly through paleobotanical studies; the recent development of pollen analysis has placed a new and most useful tool in the hands of the Pleistocene geologist. Statistics, similarly, is receiving steadily increasing attention

218

from geologists; statistical analysis is already an accepted technique in sedimentary petrology.

It is by the application of physics to geology that the greatest transformation in geological study has taken place. *Geophysics* has been recognized now for almost a century as a scientific discipline of major status, linking the two older and more traditional branches of human inquiry. A witty writer has gone so far as to describe geophysics as "geology once removed." Like many a witticism, this happy saying carries with it more than a germ of truth. When one hears geophysics defined as "the science concerned with the constitution, age, and history of the earth, and the movements of the earth's crust," it is difficult to distinguish geophysics from geology, as defined by some workers. There is, however, a real distinction between the two branches of study, for geophysics, as now generally understood, starts with the solar system and considers the earth in relation to this system; its consideration of earth problems is predicated upon an appreciation of the globe as a whole. In a way, it can be thought of as providing the framework within which classical geological studies can helpfully be viewed; the general methods of geophysics when applied to detailed geological problems broaden the limits of human understanding of the world in a rewarding and challenging manner.

Geophysical studies have led to the estimate of $4,500 \times 10^6$ years as the most probable age of the earth. The size of the earth and its distance from the sun are such that in combination they lead to a mean temperature at its surface that, under the influence of the thin protective atmosphere surrounding it, permits the existence of water as a major constituent of the surface covering (water is extremely rare elsewhere in the universe). Concerned as engineers usually are with problems on land, few probably realize that 70 per cent of the earth's surface is covered by the oceans. Eighty-one per cent of the land area lies in one hemisphere, with the "land pole" (as it may be expressed) located in Brittany; the corresponding water pole is near New Zealand. Although 45 per cent of the surface of the globe has sea opposite sea, only a little more than 1 per cent has land opposite land. Most of the small islands that stud the central parts of the oceans are volcanic peaks or coral reefs that in all probability have grown upon volcanic cones. Ocean deeps adjacent to some of the isolated islands give rise to changes in elevation that exceed anything known above sea level. The peak of Mauna Kea in Hawaii, for example, is 4,201 m above sea level and yet is only 74 km southwest of a point on the ocean floor sounded as 5,563 m deep. This range of 9,764 m is probably the greatest sudden change in surface level anywhere in the globe; the ridge that forms the islands of Hawaii rises higher above its base than does Mount Everest.

Great as these distances are, they take on a new proportion when considered in relation to the earth itself. Although spoken of as a sphere, the earth is really an oblate spheroid; its mean radius varies from 6,378 km at the equator to 6,356 km at the poles. The relative significance of these figures can be illustrated by imagining the earth reduced to the size of an 18-in.-diameter globe. The maximum and minimum depths and heights known anywhere on earth could then be represented by no more than $\frac{1}{16}$ in. The highest mountains would be represented by no more than $\frac{1}{75}$ in. and the average elevation of the continents by the thickness of a mere coat of varnish. Since man's observations have to be confined to this extremely thin crust, exploration of the interior of the earth has had to be made by indirect measurements and by careful deductions based upon them. Geophysical studies have thus shown that the average density of the earth is 5.5 gms per cu cm. The significance and interest of this figure becomes apparent when it is realized that the average density of the rocks that form the crust of the earth is no more than 2.8 gms per cu cm. Explanation of the difference leads to detailed study of the constitution of the earth, a matter of great scientific interest but somewhat outside normal engineering thinking. The composition of the crust itself, however, is a starting point for engineering considerations of the earth. It appears almost certain, for example, that the oceans are underlain by a relatively thin crust of basaltic rocks (5 to 6 km thick) and there seems to be abundant evidence to support the idea that this crust is continuous beneath the continents, even though the explored crust is composed, in general, of lighter and more siliceous rocks.

It is a logical development of such studies to explore the temperature conditions within the earth. One of the latest estimates suggests that the temperature at the earth's center is about 5000°C, the corresponding pressure being 3.5×10^6 atmospheres. It is possible to measure directly the heat balance at the surface of the earth, although this is not easy. Such measurements suggest that of the observed heat flow at the surface not more than 20 per cent can come from the original heat of the earth, but that most of it is due to other sources, mainly radioactive. Because of the slow rate at which heat is being lost from the central part of the earth, this source of heat is of little direct significance with regard to the temperature of the ground near the surface. This is a matter of great importance in engineering in relation to such matters as the heat losses from structures, the performance of cold-storage buildings, and the widespread extent of permafrost in northern regions. Here is an important meeting point for engineering and geophysics, with climatology as a singularly important factor in determining the now well-recognized pattern of ground-temperature variation. Long-term studies of climate verge into geophysics and are naturally linked closely with geology.

The existence of glaciers is perhaps the most vivid reminder that climates can change.

Despite the popular interest so frequently displayed in glaciers, it is not generally appreciated that about 10 per cent of the land surface of the earth is still covered by ice (about 6 million sq miles). There are glaciers in every continent except Australia, and geological evidence suggests that glaciers existed even there within recent geological time. They are found not only in the Arctic and Antarctic but also in the tropics; in New Guinea, Tanganyika, and Kenya small glaciers are located almost on the equator at elevations of over 5,000 m. Calculations suggest that if all the existing glaciers were to melt, the general level of the sea would rise about 50 m, with what catastrophic results an engineer can well imagine. Only recently have glaciers been studied on a wide scale in any detail, but *glaciology* is now well recognized as a distinct scientific discipline linked closely with both geology and geophysics. Accurate measurements show clearly that most glaciers, in the Northern Hemisphere at least, are at present receding. This corresponds with the slight but definite recent warming of the atmosphere that careful climatological studies suggest, as does also the average rise in the level of the sea by about 6 cm per century. Both of these facts are a reminder that the earth is in one of its rare transient cold periods. In the geological past, the climate generally has been warmer and more uniform. One is vividly reminded of this when one finds far to the north, in Canada's Arctic, fossils of both animals and plants that could only represent life in semitropical climates, although polar wandering might also have had some influence. Studies of glacially deposited soils have shown conclusively a succession of glacial advances (see page 84), the last of which stopped abruptly about 11,000 years ago. But for at least 100 million years before the Recent Ice Age, there was no similar glacial period on the earth.

Current recession of glaciers is, in some cases, a matter of vital engineering concern. The illustration on page 623 is a graphic reminder of this. The Columbia ice field in the Rocky Mountains is receding relatively rapidly; since it is from this ice field that the great rivers of the Canadian prairies derive much of their low-water flow, the ultimate effect of this phenomenon will be serious. Recession of one glacier in the Alaska panhandle is said to have caused mild diplomatic concern since the retreat of the Taku glacier might yet give Canada a site for another seaport through the Alaska panhandle. When one takes the long view, therefore, as is imperative in much engineering work, such apparent curiosities as the history of glaciers can become significant. To many the concept of changing climates is difficult to appreciate, so accustomed do people get to their local climatic pattern. But all who have had the experience of going relatively rapidly from semitropical surroundings at the base of a great mountain range, up its slopes, and through successive changes of vegetation, then above the tree line and possibly into the range of perpetual snows will need no reminder of the delicate balance of geophysical conditions that has resulted in the world as it is known today.[7.1]

The enduring rocks remain, however, despite all such environmental changes, affected by them only superficially and only through aeons of time. To the physical properties of this great mass of material which makes up the thin crust of the earth, geophysicists have devoted continuing attention from the time of the earliest linking of physics with geology. The residual magnetism of rock masses, the speed with which shock waves move through the crust, the effect of variations in the density of adjacent rock masses, and even the electrical properties of the crust have excited the curiosity of scientists for many decades. As methods were developed for measuring these and associated properties—by the further development of the simple dip needle, the invention of seismic recorders, the precise study of gravity, and the application of electrical techniques to the study of the ground—farsighted men saw the practical potential of such methods for subsurface exploration for the discovery of minerals and oil as well as for the determination of underground conditions for the special purposes of the civil engineer. So arose the widespread activity of today known as "geophysical prospecting" or "geophysical exploration."

It may be useful to emphasize that geophysical methods constitute only another exploratory aid to geological surveying and that, as applied to civil engineering, they must never be regarded as anything more than this. They will not disclose more than will a good set of test bore and drill holes and usually not so much, and they can never be used without specific and constant correlation with geological information. In fact, a preliminary geological survey is necessary before the methods can be applied with any certainty of success, since they necessitate knowledge of certain general conditions of local geology if their interpretation is to be at all effective. The most favorable condition is when rock occurs under a shallow superficial deposit and the physical characteristics of the two are markedly different. This condition, in connection with civil engineering work, occurs most frequently as a deposit of glacial drift overlying a solid rock body, and it is to the study of the geology of such deposits, especially as regards the depth to bedrock, that geophysical methods have generally been applied in civil engineering practice.

7.2. Magnetic Methods. The phenomenon of terrestrial magnetism has been known for a long period, and it is not surprising that magnetic methods of investigation are the oldest of all geophysical methods for studying underground conditions. On the earth's surface, there is a magnetic field which is relatively constant in direction and strength and which can be measured by a magnetic needle. When the needle is freely suspended on a vertical axis, it will come to rest in a direction known as the "magnetic meridian"; when it is suspended on a horizontal axis, it will come to rest at an angle with the horizontal called the "magnetic dip," if the axis is perpendicular to the magnetic meridian. The earth's magnetic field is not absolutely constant; it varies slightly at any locality in a regular manner and has a slow seasonal change and a rapid daily

Fig. 7.1. Airborne electromagnetic surveying instrument in use in northern Manitoba (see text for historical significance of this location). (*Photograph by George Hunter. Reproduced by permission of the International Nickel Company of Canada, Ltd.*)

variation; it may also be affected irregularly by magnetic storms. In addition, the field may vary in an unusual manner between one location and an adjacent point owing to the presence underground of some material possessing the property of a permanent magnet. Minerals of iron most notably possess this property. Magnetite, or lodestone, an oxide of iron, and pyrrhotite, a sulfide of iron, are the minerals most notable for this property. Some other minerals and rocks, however, also have weak magnetic effects and by employing suitably sensitive instruments it is possible to map the distribution of certain types of concealed rock and mineral formations by detecting these effects.

De Castro, in the seventeenth century, appears to have been the first to realize that hidden masses of magnetic material might cause local magnetic anomalies and that these masses might be detected by determining the magnetic changes that they cause. Since that time, instruments, based essentially on the simple magnet, have generally been developed for measuring these anomalies; the more usual types of such instruments are known as "magnetic variometers," and they may be of either the vertical or the horizontal type. In place of a magnet, a rotating coil may be used to measure the vertical or horizontal magnetic force; the induced current is measured by suitable electrical devices.

The modern magnetic variometer is a highly complex instrument, but despite this, magnetic methods of investigation are capable of relatively wide use in their restricted field. One recent development has been the use of specially designed airborne *magnetometers* for mineral exploration over wide areas from low-flying aircraft. Some notable discoveries have been made in Canada by this means. This geophysical method contrasts markedly with the earliest simple magnets, such as those used by William Wales, who was sent to Fort Churchill on Hudson Bay by the Royal Society in 1768 to conduct various scientific experiments, including a series with the dip needle; this isolated location is but 200 miles from the scene shown in Fig. 7.1.[7.2]

7.3. Seismic Methods. Earthquakes have been studied by scientists for a long period, but scientific methods have been applied to their investigation only in the last century and a half. As early in the development of this branch of study as 1846, Robert Mallet suggested that artificial earthquakes (and thus earthquake waves) could usefully be created for experimental purposes by exploding gunpowder on land or on the sea floor. This idea is the basis of geophysical seismic methods; since the vibrations set up by earthquakes, either real or artificial, do not travel at the same speed in different media, the existence of a change of medium may be detected. Although the idea was suggested at so early a date, and some experiments were later conducted along the lines suggested, it was not until the early part of the twentieth century that satisfactory instruments were devised for measuring and recording the vibrations reaching the point of observation. Since then, the original instruments have been improved and new ones have been developed, so that seismic methods of underground investigation are today widely used.

Artificial earthquakes are produced by blasting with powerful explosives. High-strength gelatins and dynamites are most suitable, and the charges should be buried in order to obtain best results. The two types of waves so set up in the ground—elastic earth waves, as they are sometimes known—are due, respectively, to longitudinal and to transverse vibrations. The latter may be principally in a vertical direction or, alternatively, horizontal. Other minor types of waves may be generated, but they are subsidiary to the two main types. Of these, the longitudinal waves travel faster than the transverse waves and so will be the first to reach the point of observation. Both types of waves travel through different kinds of rock with different velocities, and they will be refracted as they pass from one medium to another. This fact is the basis of geophysical seismic methods of investigation; records of observed vibrations are taken at different distances from the location of the explosion, and the results are correlated with known facts about wave travel in different media.

If two rock strata are to be investigated, the upper one allowing waves to pass through it at low velocity and the lower one at high velocity, a charge of explosive will be detonated at some convenient location in the upper stratum. Waves will then be dissipated in all directions through this stratum; some will reach the observation points that had previously been set up at different distances from the explosion point, by thus traveling directly through the low-velocity medium. Some waves will reach the surface of the high-velocity lower bed. It has been found that some of this energy will travel along the boundary surface at velocity equal to that of the waves in the lower stratum. It is being continually diffracted back to the ground surface through the upper layer, and eventually some will reach the observation points already set up for the purposes of the investigation. The relation of the time of travel by this route to that of the waves which proceed directly through the upper stratum will clearly depend on the relative velocities in the two media, the depth of the upper layer, and the relative positions of the observation points. It will be clear that a point can be reached at which the second path of the wave will become the quicker; and if simultaneous readings are taken at all observation points, it should be possible to find the position of this point (or, actually, this circle) within reasonable limits. Determination of this point is the object of this type of seismic investigation.

A reflection method has also been developed in which observations are taken at a convenient distance from the point of explosion of the time required for waves to travel downward to the surface of the lower stratum and then to be reflected therefrom to the point of observation. The practical difficulties of eliminating the recording of the waves reaching the observation point directly, so that the very much weaker reflected waves may be noted, have been overcome, and the method is credited with some remarkable results. It is being widely used, especially in exploration for oil.

The instruments used for recording the vibrations reaching the points of observation are specially designed field-model seismographs. They are of two main types, the mechanical and the electrical. In the former

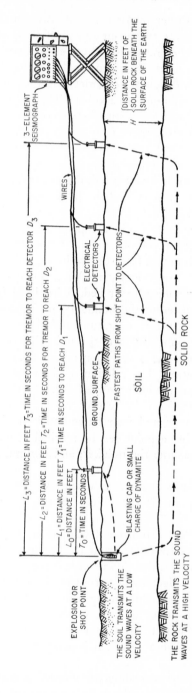

FIG. 7.2. Diagrammatic section illustrating the principle of the seismic-refraction method of subsurface exploration. (*Reproduced by permission of the U. S. Bureau of Public Roads.*)

L_3 = DISTANCE IN FEET T_3 = TIME IN SECONDS FOR TREMOR TO REACH DETECTOR D_3

L_2 = DISTANCE IN FEET T_2 = TIME IN SECONDS FOR TREMOR TO REACH D_2

L_1 = DISTANCE IN FEET T_1 = TIME IN SECONDS TO REACH D_1

L_0 = DISTANCE IN FEET

T_0 = TIME IN SECONDS

3–ELEMENT SEISMOGRAPH

DISTANCE IN FEET OF SOLID ROCK BENEATH THE SURFACE OF THE EARTH

H

WIRES

ELECTRICAL DETECTORS

GROUND SURFACE

FASTEST PATHS FROM SHOT POINT TO DETECTORS

SOIL

SOLID ROCK

BLASTING CAP OR SMALL CHARGE OF DYNAMITE

EXPLOSION OR SHOT POINT

THE SOIL TRANSMITS THE SOUND WAVES AT A LOW VELOCITY

THE ROCK TRANSMITS THE SOUND WAVES AT A HIGH VELOCITY

type (now largely superseded by the latter), the necessary magnification of very small vibrations is achieved by mechanical or optical methods; in the latter, this is done by electrical means. The essential part of both types of seismograph is a heavy mass suitably mounted by a nonrigid suspension in a box or cover. The inertia of the mass will tend to keep it in a state of rest, whereas the cover will tend to move in accordance with vibrations reaching it through the ground; the instrument thus measures its movement relative to that of the mass. Usually, a clockwork

Fig. 7.3. Simple hammer-type seismic-prospecting device, showing apparatus for recording refracted waves. (*Photograph by S. Hiemstra. Reproduced by permission of the Director, Geological Survey of South Africa.*)

mechanism is included that produces a continuous photographic record of the vibrations; time intervals and the instant of firing the explosive charge are also marked on the same record strip. Normally, several seismographs are used, as already indicated; in the electrical instruments, the detector parts can be used at each observation point, and the records can be transmitted electrically to a control instrument on which all the results are photographed simultaneously.

In recent years, steady improvement in instrumentation has been achieved, but the scientific principles involved have naturally remained unchanged. A simplification in technique has been introduced by the commerical production of an easily operated recorder, actuated by the waves created by the fall of a heavy sledge hammer upon a steel plate in contact with the ground. The method presents interesting possibilities, but experience with the equipment is still rather limited.

7.4. Gravitational Methods. The fundamental law of gravitation was announced by Isaac Newton in 1687; it stated that the force of attraction between any two bodies is directly proportional to the product of their masses and inversely proportional to the square of the distance between them. Originally, the law was associated only with large bodies such as those of the solar system. Scientists soon turned their attention, however, to the attraction exerted by large mountain masses. Bouguer appears to have been the first to experiment in this direction; he carried out some experiments at Mount Chimborazo (in South America) between 1737 and 1740 in which he used a pendulum at a height of 9,000 ft and again at sea level. Similar work was done in Scotland by Maskelyne in 1775 and in the following century by various experimenters. The results of these early experiments were not as expected, but they were not explained until many years later after a further series of important observations had been made in India. From the study of these, there was finally formulated the principle of isostasy, which is "the basis of all accurate work on the variation of gravity at the earth's surface. [It] . . . implies that above some depth below the surface neighboring vertical columns of the crust contain the same mass."[7.3]

Determinations of the value of gravity at different locations are still made by means of pendulum-type instruments, although the instruments of today are specially designed and constructed so that they may be used in the field as well as in the laboratory. Many interesting gravity determinations have been carried out from submarines by Dr. Veining Meinesz. Recently they have also been carried out on shipboard by means of long period instruments that are not affected by wave motion. With such instruments, an accuracy of about one part in a million can be attained, but this is not sufficient to measure the variation of gravity between closely adjacent stations. That variations do exist is known from the different values obtained by gravity determinations carried out at different points. The changes that can thus be measured by pendulum instruments are due to extensive buried masses of relatively dense material, some of which have been located in this way.

This method of detecting underground structure was greatly extended by the use of an instrument generally known as the Eötvös torsion balance which would record changes in the horizontal component in gravity with an accuracy of one million millionth part of the total gravitational attraction. Today, however, gravity measurements are more generally made with *gravimeters*, or gravity meters, the basis for the operation of which is shown in the simple sketch on page 229. It is thought that the principle was first suggested by Sir John Herschel; it depends upon the extension of a balanced spring as the instrument is moved from one station to another. Modern models are very compact devices, little larger than a large vacuum flask; it is possible to survey up to 100 stations a day with such modern instruments.

Like other geophysical methods, a torsion balance can be used to detect the existence of two adjacent rock strata of different densities; clearly, the best results will be obtained if the change in density occurs near the ground surface. The instruments will be affected not only by changes in the rock density but also by any change in level of the adjacent ground and by the presence near the point of observation of obstructions such as buildings or trees. In addition, special care has to be taken in areas covered by glacial drift, since any large boulders in the

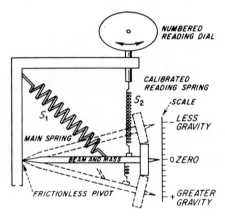

Fig. 7.4. Diagram of the essentials of a gravity meter. (*After a sketch by Sherwin F. Kelly.*)

drift may affect the balance almost as much as the structural feature being investigated. The use of the instruments is consequently a most delicate matter, but it is possible by taking a series of observations to eliminate the effect of any feature other than that which has to be investigated.

7.5. Electrical Methods. The various materials that constitute the earth's crust possess electrical properties of wide variation; the two most commonly used in geophysical work are conductivity and its reciprocal, resistivity. The differences in conductivity of different rock types are so large that the range of variation is much greater than that of any of the other properties so far discussed; this may be a partial explanation of the wide use to which electrical subsurface prospecting methods have been put. Some sulfide minerals, as a result of chemical changes, occasioned possibly by ground water, have set up in them small electrical currents which circulate in the adjoining ground. A good deal of experimental work has been done in investigating such currents, but the method is not generally applicable because of its specialized nature. The more usual methods of investigation depend on passing a current through a section of the earth's crust between two (current) electrodes, placed at a fixed distance apart and exploring the nature of the ground adjacent to or between them by means of two or more (potential) electrodes inserted into the ground at specially selected points.

Fig. 7.5. A Gish-Rooney electrical-resistivity apparatus set up near Swan Lake, British Columbia, Canada, for conducting an underground survey to detect possible drainage paths around the lake. (*Photograph by Sherwin F. Kelly.*)

The basic electrical theory underlying the several developments of this system is not new, but it was not until the beginning of the present century that successful field methods were evolved. Daft and Williams, working in England, appear to have devised the first satisfactory equipotential method, which has since been improved and extended by other investigators.[7.4] By means of suitable equipment, lines of equal potential are traced out on the ground, and the shapes so obtained are compared with the perfectly symmetrical distribution that would be obtained in homogeneous ground; the differences between the shapes are an indication of the presence of buried material having electrical properties different from those of the material at the surface. Alternatively, the resistivity of sections of the ground may be determined in a similar way. Practical difficulties at first prevented the general use of this method, but these were gradually overcome; notable advance was made in 1912 and 1925 by Schlumberger and by Gish and Rooney following the work of Wenner, working independently in different countries. A third group may be classed generally as electromagnetic methods; some of these are related to the reception of Hertzian waves, measured at different points; the variation in intensity is an indication of geological changes in the adjacent ground. Other electromagnetic methods are based on the induction of currents in the ground under the action of alternating magnetic fields and measurement of the distortions from results that should be obtained in homogeneous material, an operation that can now be carried out even from low-flying aircraft.

It will be seen that these methods cover a wide field of electrical theory with which the civil engineer will be generally unfamiliar. He will therefore have to allow specialists in this class of work to apply the methods for him. The methods most usually applied in civil engineering practice, however, are related to resistivity measurement, and so a word or two may be added with regard to them. It may first be noted that if the methods are to be fully effective, a general conception of the local geology must be available before they are applied. Particularly is this true with regard to the possible presence of ground water, since the resistivity of certain types of rock varies appreciably with water content and also with the salinity of the water. A general mode of operation is to measure the average resistivity of a volume of earth by gradually increasing the distance between the potential electrodes and plotting the results so obtained in the form of a curve relating resistivity and electrode spacing. A curve having an upward trend will suggest that resistivity is increasing with depth, whereas an abrupt change in curvature will indicate, if no other complicating features are present, a change in the nature of the material underground at a depth approximately equal to the distance between the electrodes at which the change occurs.

It is of some interest to note that the instrument known as the "megger," which will be familiar to some civil engineers as that used for testing the resistance of buried grounds in power-station construction, can be used for measuring ground resistivity by means of a special adaptation. Results obtained with it compare favorably with those obtained with other methods. Another development of interest and of great utility in special circumstances is the use of resistivity methods in wells or drill holes, known usually as "electrical coring." Three insulated conductors are lowered down the hole, with their ends at different depths; the deepest will be one of the current electrodes, and the other two the potential electrodes. The recording instruments are read at the

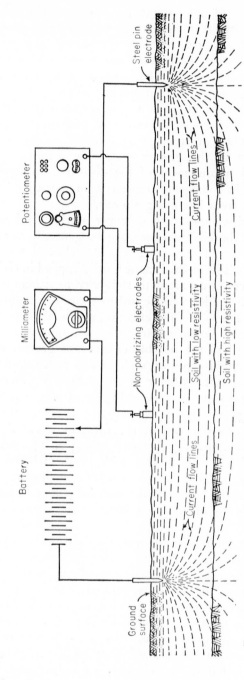

Fig. 7.6. Diagrammatic section illustrating the principle of the electrical-resistivity method of subsurface exploration. (*Reproduced by permission of the U.S. Bureau of Public Roads.*)

surface; by means of special operating devices, great speed can be achieved—up to 1,000 ft of hole can be examined in an hour.[7.5]

7.6. Applications in Civil Engineering. It will be seen that the main methods of geophysical exploration, in their practical form, are developments of the twentieth century; some are of relatively recent invention. Despite this, geophysical methods applied to civil engineering have already achieved notable results. An early example of significance

Fig. 7.7. Electrical-resistivity geophysical apparatus used for the survey of the South African Building Research Institute site survey noted in the text. (*Photograph by S. Hiemstra. Reproduced by permission of the Director, Geological Survey of South Africa.*)

was in British Columbia. The Bridge River Tunnel was completed in 1930 for the British Columbia Electric Railway Company, Ltd. The 13,200-ft tunnel passes through Mission Mountain at a depth of 2,400 ft below the summit; it was constructed in connection with hydroelectric development and is located 110 miles northeast of Vancouver. A geological survey of the surrounding area was made by Dr. V. Dolmage of Vancouver before tenders were called; the structure disclosed is shown in Fig. 7.8. Driving the tunnel started at the two ends, and work at the northern end proceeded without trouble. About 1,200 ft in from the southern portal, however, bad conditions were encountered as a very pronounced fault zone was met. The greenstone was found to be finely crushed and extensively altered to talc and serpentine, and the whole zone was highly water bearing; so much pressure was exerted on the timber supports that a short length of the timbers was completely demolished. The probability of encountering such material had been foretold by Dr. Dolmage and confirmed by test borings, but it was necessary to find out how wide the zone was. This was done by the application of the resistivity method, then used by the Schlumberger

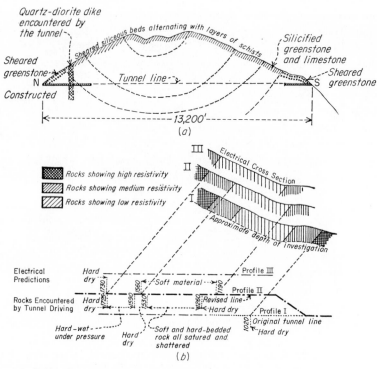

Fɪɢ. 7.8. Bridge River Tunnel, British Columbia, Canada. (*Reproduced by permission of the B. C. Electric Co., Ltd.*)

Electrical Prospecting Methods. It was found that the high-water content of the fault zone had a resistivity much different from that of the surrounding hard greenstone, and it therefore proved possible to determine the width of the zone on three trial locations from the tunnel center line. The second of these was adopted, and the tunnel was diverted by 150 ft from its original location through this fault zone. As a result of the geophysical survey, it was estimated that the troublesome section of tunnel would be 370 ft wide. Excavation proved it to be about 270 ft wide, with another short section of water-bearing rock some 60 ft farther on. The value of this determination to the engineers in charge of the tunnel work will be obvious, since construction methods could be devised for driving through this relatively short stretch of water-bearing material with the knowledge that a return of satisfactory conditions could soon be expected.[7.6]

Geophysical methods applied to dam-foundation problems have been principally concerned with determining the depth to the surface of solid rock through superficial deposits. What is believed to be the first application of geophysical methods to civil engineering work in North America was made in 1928 at the site of the Fifteen Mile Falls water-power station of the New England Power Association on the Connecticut River near Littleton, New Hampshire. Briefly, the local bedrock of Precambrian schist and occasional intrusions of granite was overlain by glacial deposits of boulder clay, gravel, and sand. The presence of boulders made test-boring operations expensive, and so an electrical-resistivity method was employed for investigating the two available sites. A buried valley was known to exist beneath the glacial deposits, and its presence was detected under an overburden of 300 ft. Other positive results were obtained. Test boring and drilling was carried out as a check; and for those holes which were related to the previous electrical prospecting, the depth thus predicted varied generally between 69 and 118 per cent of the true depths.[7.6] Similar work was done in some of the early studies on the international section of the St. Lawrence River; drilling in this case revealed an average error of only 6.6 per cent. The cost of this work has been stated to be $60 per determination, and average progress was slightly less than three per day.[7.8]

In Europe, some pioneer work was done in applying geophysical methods to the detailed study of rock strata used as the foundation beds for dams. Messrs. Lugeon and Schlumberger carried out early experiments at the site of the Sarrans Dam, located on a tributary of the river Lot, La Truyère, in the department of Aveyron, France. The dam is of the gravity type, slightly arched, 345 ft high, and contains 600,000 cu yd of concrete; it is founded throughout on granite. Drill holes and exploratory tunnels were used extensively in the investigation of foundation-bed conditions throughout a period of several months; this work disclosed several zones of weathered granite, transformed into a granular mass by the alteration of the feldspar and mica. A geophysical electrical survey of the ground around the dam site was later carried out, and some interesting results were obtained, notably in a correlation of a decreased value for the resistivity with a known zone of moist crushed granite from which it was concluded that "the resistivities studied from the surface actually bring into evidence the direction of geological features which otherwise could be discovered only by drilling exploration or excavation work."[7.9]

Throughout the world, geophysical methods are now frequently used for preliminary investigations at potential dam sites and at the proposed locations of other types of civil engineering structure; these investigations are almost always carried out in association with a test drilling program, and the combination of the two methods has usually proved to be an economical and speedy means of subsurface investigation. Typical of such work was the study of the White River Dam site in South Africa in an area underlain by continuous granite, considerably weathered at the surface. Moisture content of this decomposed material was low (not more than 5 per cent) because of seepage and other losses, including transpiration of vegetation. Its resistivity was consequently high (40,000 to 200,000 ohm cm). Resistivity of the solid granite was, correspondingly, at least 10^5 ohm cm, so that it was possible to distinguish between fresh

Table 7.1. Example of Correlation of Test Boring and Geophysical Results

Borehole no.	Depth to bedrock (ft)		Percentage difference
	Geophysical	From borings	
36A	16	15.1	6
37A	18	16.4	10
38A	25	21.0	19
39A	10	8.5	18
40A	8	6.9	16
41A	16	13.5	18
42A	6.5	6.5	0
43A	10	8.5	18
44A	26	31.8	−18
45A	25	20.7	21
46A	40	30.8	30
47A	34	31.2	9
48A	78	81	−4

SOURCE: Reproduced by permission from J. F. Englin, Geophysics as an Aid to Foundation Engineering, *Trans S. African Inst. of Civil Engs.*, **3:** 53–54 (1953).

and decomposed granite fairly readily by resistivity methods. A dike of diabase which follows the river bed was traced by the application of magnetic methods.[7.10] Table 7.1 gives actual comparisons of depth to rock as determined by test holes and the corresponding deduced depths from the geophysical work. Resistivity measurements in this investigation were considerably influenced, for some feet below the surface, by an increase in the moisture content of the surface soil and underlying decomposed granite following very heavy rainstorms, a variation indicative of the potential accuracy of the method.

Australian engineering practice also presents interesting and instructive examples of geophysical subsurface investigations; one of the most recent is the use of this procedure for some of the dam sites in the great Snowy

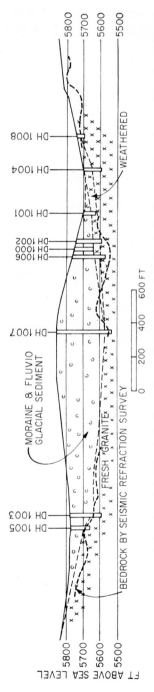

FIG. 7.9. Section through the site of the Kosciusko Dam site on Spencer's Creek, part of the Snowy Mountains project, Australia, showing results of seismic survey. (*Reproduced by permission of The Snowy Mountains Hydro-Electric Authority.*)

Mountains Hydro-Electric scheme. One of these is located near the highest point in Australia, Mount Kosciusko (7,313 ft above sea level), in the vicinity of the only glaciated region in Australia (three stages of Pleistocene glaciation have been recognized). The dam site lies on Spencer's Creek, a tributary of the upper Snowy River, at an elevation of about 5,660 ft; the valley is flat-bottomed due to glacial action, and is underlain generally by slightly weathered granite. A potential dam site was presented by the break through a large terminal moraine created by the natural stream; unusually careful subsurface investigation was called for, since it was planned to use the moraine itself, if possible, as the left abutment for the dam. Geological mapping, test drilling, test pits, and seismic surveys were all employed by the engineering geologists of the Snowy Mountains Hydro-Electric Authority in their thorough study of the site before it was finally adopted for use. Much difficulty was experienced because of the presence of granite boulders, usually considerably weathered; in particular their presence complicated permeability tests in the moraine. The work was successfully completed, and seismic results checked closely with the depths to rock established by test boring.[7.11] The proposed dam has now been constructed and is performing satisfactorily, together with the associated water-power plant. When seen by the writer in 1956, the dam, in its rugged surroundings and under a cover of snow, was more reminiscent of northern Canada than of the popular, and generally correct, impression of the Australian scene.

Probably the most extensive use of geophysical methods in the practice of civil engineering has been in the United States; all the larger Federal engineering organizations, and notably the Bureau of Reclamation, the Bureau of Public Roads, and the Corps of Engineers, have used geophysical methods regularly in their preliminary exploration work. Typical of these uses was the application of the seismic-refraction method for determining the bedrock profile at the site of the Englewood Dam on the Cimarron River in Oklahoma, a project of the Reclamation Bureau. Four test boreholes were available as controls when the first geophysical work was done; fifteen seismic depth points were then determined with good agreement with predictions from the test-hole records. At a later date, twelve additional drill holes were completed on the projected axis of the dam. Eight were in locations that gave further checks upon the geophysical work and showed that the seismic depths to bedrock were accurate within an average error of 3 ft; the average depth to bedrock was 33 ft. The seismic method appeared to give equally reliable results in sand and gravel and in clay overburdens. Direct comparison of the costs of the respective methods was possible, and this suggested a ratio of about 7 to 1 for the cost of test drilling as compared with that for the geophysical work.[7.12] It must be remembered, however, that the two methods are really complementary to each other and not direct alternatives. The wide use made of geophysical methods by the U.S. Bureau of Reclamation has permitted Dart Wantland to prepare and publish a useful comparison of over-all costs for the four main geophysical methods.[7.13] With permission, this is reproduced as Table 7.2; even though the specific costs noted were given in 1953, the ratio of the four sets of figures remains valid, despite changing price levels.

7.7. Investigation of Shallow Deposits. One of the most effective applications of geophysical methods, both seismic and electrical, is in the investigation of shallow surface deposits, as in exploration work for sand and gravel deposits and in the classification of highway excavation before the material is moved. Several states of the United States now include this work as a part of the regular operations of their highway departments,

Table 7.2. Cost of Geophysical Field Operations

Method	Cost of field crew per month (approx.)	Men on crew	Data points per day	Cost per data point (approx.)	Estimated cost of equipment (approx.)
Seismic	$3,500(e)	4–5(a)	4–8(c)	$20–50	$10,000
Resistivity	3,000	4–5(b)	2–4(d)	25–50	2,000
Magnetic	1,500	1–2	20–30	3–6	2,000
Gravity meter	3,000	3–4	30–40	2–5	8,000

(a) 1 geophysicist, 1 electronics technician; (b) 1 geophysicist; (c) seismic depth points; (d) resistivity depth measurements; (e) assume 20 days field work for each month. Costs cover calendar month.

SOURCE: Reproduced by permission from Dart Wantland, The Application of Geophysical Methods to Problems in Civil Engineering, *Bull. Can. Inst. Min. and Met.*, **46**: 288–296 (May, 1953).

and the U.S. Bureau of Public Roads has carried out extensive work in this field. Interesting figures testifying to the success of this work are available.[7.14] Schappler and Farnham report that in 1931, on a selected number of highway projects on which geophysical methods were not used, an error of 12.92 per cent was made in estimating the quantity of solid rock; whereas on a similar number of similar jobs in the following year on which geophysical methods were utilized, the error was reduced to 1.04 per cent. The state of Minnesota was a pioneer in the use of electrical prospecting methods for locating road material (sand and gravel); it is reported that over 100 prospective sites were tested for this purpose in a little more than a year and that 98 per cent of the holes subsequently dug have verified the predictions of the electrical results.[7.15]

In more recent years, although the progress made in the application of geophysical methods to highway engineering in the United States has not yet been so extensive as earlier experiences suggested, there is now available abundant evidence to demonstrate the efficiency and efficacy of the methods in this branch of civil engineering when terrain conditions are suitable. In the state of Massachussets, for example, the United States Geological Survey has been pursuing a steady program of seismic investigation in connection with highway construction; the glacial and therefore varied character of local surface deposits make the method particularly suitable. Well over 200 separate studies have now been completed; where it has been possible to check on results by means of test borings, good agreement has been found. Operating expense for the one crew engaged on the work has been $170 per day; five traverses, with six shot points, can usually be achieved in 1 working day.[7.16]

For those sections of the 123-mile Massachusetts Turnpike (running westward from the vicinity of Boston to the border of New York State) in which an appreciable depth of cut was necessary, with no adjacent exposure of bedrock, seismic investigation was used in the selection of the final location. Again, it was the glacial character of the surface deposits and the corresponding uneven surface of bedrock that dictated the suitablity of geophysical work as a supplement to a test-boring program. Seismic instruments were mounted on four-wheel-drive trucks for ease of movement; three parallel lines were generally run along selected sections of the route, one on the proposed center line and the others parallel to it and between 50 and 65 ft to right and left. In the period August 9, 1954 to May 4, 1955, approximately 4,000 shots were fired, resulting in 45,000 instrument readings; the information thus obtained was used for the preparation of more than 1,400 cross sections which assisted in final route selection. In general, results from the seismic work checked with depths to bedrock obtained by borings within 2 ft. Some difficulty was experienced with the layer of seasonal frost encountered during winter months; the frozen layer constituted, in effect, a separate geological stratum, but despite the difficulty thus introduced, the work was continued successfully throughout the winter. The sites for two major bridges on the turnpike were also investigated in part by seismic methods.[7.17] Geophysical methods were also used with success in the planning and design of the Ohio Turnpike to which further reference is made later in this book (see page 240).

Sweden is another country in which geophysical methods, and the seismic method in particular, have long been used in relation to civil engineering work; a useful summary account of Swedish investigations is available in English.[7.18] Stimulated by some early German experiments, Swedish geophysicists carried out their first seismic-refraction tests in 1922, a year before corresponding work was first done in North America. Thereafter applications developed slowly but steadily, with the commonly experienced rapid increase following the Second World War. Over 8,000 investigations have now been carried out with seismic methods in Sweden, generally, but not exclusively, at water-power sites, and mainly in connection with relatively shallow overburden deposits. Six seismographs are usually employed, spaced at 5 m intervals; investigations generally involve the use of a leapfrogging technique in order to get complete coverage of the area. Experience has shown that one seismic crew, consisting of an observer and six helpers, can profile 150 m per day. This involves up to 900 m of travel, with 25 to 30 shots for either five or six seismograph setups; a maximum rate of 400 m in one day has been reached, although greater speeds than this are usual in North American practice. The method is now regarded by Swedish workers as reasonably

Fig. 7.10. Instrumentation for seismic prospecting; a 12-channel photographic recording system mounted in a 4-wheel-drive station wagon (*Photograph by V. J. Murphy; reproduced by permission of Western Geophysical Engineers, Inc.*)

foolproof for suitable terrain. Repeated checks on the accuracy of seismic work suggest that an error of no more than 10 per cent can now be almost guaranteed, or of no more than 1 m for deposits less than 10 m deep. Swedish workers and those of other countries have also applied the same methods to determinations of the depth of ice in glaciers; this application is greatly extending the knowledge of glacier formation and travel.

South Africa has provided an unusual example of the application of two seismic methods to the study of the subsurface conditions at a building site—that for the new buildings of the Council for Scientific and Industrial Research, including, appropriately, the headquarters of the National Building Research Institute.[7.19] Geologically the site was somewhat unusual; it was underlain in part by quartzite up to the line of a fault which was found to cross the site roughly from east to west; north of the fault there was a considerable depth of decomposed diabase covered by sand of varying composition. A dike intersected the quartzite. A test drilling program, coupled with an electrical-resistivity survey, had given a reasonably accurate picture of the subsurface conditions and had revealed the existence of a large block of quartzite overlying the diabase and located exactly where the National Building Research Institute was to be built. This part of the site was therefore further studied by means of a new seismic method developed by D. I. Gough; work proceeded at night because of the high ambient noise level in the daytime. This further study delineated the quartzite block and also revealed the presence of a smaller block at a depth of about 40 ft under the same building site. Test borings gave a rather puzzling correlation, but this was explained later when excavation for the building showed that four boreholes had all struck smaller fragments of quartzite; the results of the seismic survey were then found to be substantially correct.

The use of geophysical methods for the study of a building site points to the potential that the seismic method in particular holds for the investigation of subsurface conditions in restricted areas when test drilling is either impossible or inconvenient. Investigations in the city of Detroit show what can be achieved with relatively simple equipment and a minimum of interference with municipal services. By means of a six-trace seismograph with a suitable control unit, giving a continuous record on sensitized paper, it was found that in some cases a hard blow from a sledge hammer was sufficient to give useful records for shallow depths. Inserting part of a stick of 40 per cent dynamite in a hole 4 ft deep was effective for rock depths up to 100 ft. Proper precautions naturally have to be taken in carrying out such work in city areas, but with the accurate plans of underground utilities now maintained by almost all modern cities, the placing of such small charges can usually be arranged with safety. In one test case in Detroit, rock was located at a depth between 123 and 142 ft with an error of only 3 per cent. At a midtown site in Detroit, depths of rock up to 100 ft for the purpose of determining pile lengths were successfully determined by work carried out on a Sunday; the results were available for use on Monday morning. Writing of this work, R. H. Wesley states that geophysical exploration "is not a universal tool, but intelligently used in conjunction with drilling and soil testing [it] can clear up many doubts as to what will be encountered when construction begins."[7.20]

7.8. Geophysics and Ground Water. Can geophysical methods be used successfully to determine the existence and position of ground water? The question arises since it relates to what is often the one matter that cannot be foretold in preliminary work from geological investigations alone; test boreholes are often necessary to check only on ground-water conditions. It is reasonably clear that geophysical methods by themselves will not discover ground water, but they can be of considerable assistance in determining subsurface conditions that are favorable to the occurrence of ground water, although a drill hole must always be put down to determine the actual presence of water. It has been established, for example, that the resistivity of a rock depends mainly on two factors, the porosity of the rock and the salinity of the solution held in the pores of the rock, which may be ground water in open-textured rocks. Thus gravel, even when water bearing, sometimes has a very high resistivity; this is explained by the possibility that the water present may be exceptionally pure and free from electrolytes. In general, resistivities are high for dense impervious rocks and low for porous water-bearing rocks. Bruckshaw and Dixey give the following typical values for resistivity (i.e., the electrical resistance of a cubic centimeter of material when the current flows parallel to one edge):[7.21]

Fresh crystalline rocks...................... 20,000 to 1,000,000 ohm cm
Consolidated sedimentary rocks............. 1,000 to 50,000 ohm cm
Recent unconsolidated formations........... 50 to 5,000 ohm cm

This variation in resistivity provides a clue to the possibility of the direct determination of ground water by electrical-prospecting methods. As waterlogging will affect the resistivity of any one material, the upper surface of ground water occurring in a uniform medium will, in effect, be the boundary between two media with different resistivities, the wet and the dry material, respectively. This simple ideal case will rarely occur in practice; but by a development of the idea that it represents and its extension to three- and four-layer conditions, it presents possibilities for direct ground-water determination. On some trials, satisfactory results have been achieved by a careful use of this method correlated with detailed knowledge of the local geology, but on other trials, results have been disappointing.

Expert opinion is still divided on the ultimate possibilities of direct determination of ground water by geophysical methods, but in view of the disappointments experienced in some field trials, it should be noted that there are available records of a number of quite successful determinations. Todd has published a useful review of successful investigations and a bibliography of more than 60 references. Many of these come from Africa; an early example is the work of H. J. R. Way in Uganda.[7.22] In the Eastern Province of that country, at a site underlain by granite, water was to be expected in the deep zone on weathered bedrock, extending in some places to a depth of 400 ft. Lateritic soil forms the surface, and the degree of decomposition of the granite decreases with depth. First, the electrical-resistivity method was used to make a test geophysical survey in the vicinity of an existing well. Studies were then made at selected locations around the village, and by a comparison of the resistivity profiles thus obtained with that obtained from the site where water was known to exist, one location was selected for the drilling of a new well. Water was found, as indicated by the geophysical studies, and the well yielded 764 gph, which was sufficient for the needs of the village.

Despite the uncertainty that still surrounds direct determination of the presence of ground water by geophysical methods, there is an indirect approach that can be used, and has been used, with reasonable confidence. Ths method reveals, at a cost generally lower than that of comparable test holes, the local geological structure, from which the probability of the presence of ground water may be determined. An obvious example is the revelation, by geophysical methods, of a depression or buried valley in the rock surface under porous superficial deposits, in which ground water might be expected to collect. The area that can be covered in a given time by geophysical methods, once the equipment is available in the field, as compared with the test holes which may be bored or the test pits dug, is so great that the resulting economy in water-finding operations will be obvious. This work is no different from the usual geophysical-prospecting work in connection with civil engineering projects; but because of its association with water supply, in which the average man is directly interested, there is a tendency to consider such work of a special nature.

It is the interpretation of results so obtained which is, in a sense, a specialty and which necessitates a fine appreciation of the geology of the entire neighborhood and of hydrological principles governing the local ground-water distribution. Notable work has been done with the aid of geophysical methods in finding ground water in several states of the United States, in South Africa, in the Middle East, and in the U.S.S.R. In South Africa, savings of 66 per cent in the cost of drilling successful water boreholes have been reported, and doubtless, similar economies have been experienced elsewhere.[7.23] Further advances may confidently be anticipated in this branch of applied geophysics, all of which will be of benefit either directly or indirectly to civil engineers in many branches of their own work.

7.9. Conclusion. It is possible to quote almost astronomical figures to illustrate the amount of money and the degree of effort that are today being expended on geophysical investigations, particularly in the United States and Canada, in the search for oil. Excellent publicity coupled with the undoubted fascination of such "scientific" methods used to explore deep beneath the surface of the ground have made the public well aware of the current extent of geophysical exploration.

There is a real danger that this popular enthusiasm for geophysical work will be translated into injudicious appreciation of its place in civil engineering. It is useful therefore, to recall that the requirements of underground investigation in civil engineering and in oil prospecting (for example) are essentially different; the accuracy and certainty demanded in the former are incidental in the latter to the discovery of oil. With this qualification must always be associated the thought that, in civil engineering geophysical methods are no more than a special means of exploring subsurface conditions, generally in association with trial drill and boreholes and always in addition to preliminary geological surveying which, indeed, must be carried out before the methods can be applied. All the methods are subject to definite geological restrictions—rocks of essentially different physical character must be in contact, and the strata encountered must be fairly uniform in respect to their physical character. And finally, all information obtained as a result of geophysical prospecting must be studied and utilized only when properly correlated by a geologist with the maximum available information regarding local geological conditions. Despite these qualifications and necessary restrictions, geophysical methods are a powerful and useful tool available for the use of the civil engineer in his preliminary and exploratory work; they are almost certain to achieve increasing importance in this field. They must naturally always be used by experts: it is for this reason that no details of the methods or instrumentation have been given in this summary account.

Beyond the practical utility of geophysical methods in civil engineering practice, there is the further aspect of their use which was noted at the outset of this chapter as warrant for this special attention to just one means of subsurface exploration. The appreciation by civil engineers that basic physical laws are as relevant to the materials constituting the earth's crust as they are to materials handled in the laboratory is an extremely important "by-product" of the use of geophysical methods for exploration. This awareness, when carried into the field and especially on major civil engineering works, can prove to be invaluable. Engineers may well note the significance of the studies of ground temperatures that have enabled geologists to detect ore anomalies. They can take careful note of the extension of echo sounding (another geophysical method) to the determination of the character of underwater sediments, a study still in its infancy. On a more restricted scale, they can consider the similarity of the vibrations due to pile driving to the effects of shocks induced for purposes of seismic investigation, realizing that the two are identical in character though different in degree. They can understand why the dynamic design of machinery foundations is not a matter of simple "rule of thumb" (such as the classic advice to use 1 cu ft of concrete in a foundation block for every indicated horse power of the power input to air compressors), but a matter that depends for its complete solution upon a detailed study of the physical laws governing the transmission of vibrations in the materials supporting the foundation.

Finally, an appreciation of geophysics may sometimes suggest a solution to the unusual sort of problem that so frequently characterizes construction operations. An example may usefully be cited to support this generalization and to bring this chapter to a close in an appropriate manner. During the construction of a power plant in northern Ontario, an unavoidable accident in a cofferdam caused a clay bank to fail. The clay happened to be one of the sensitive glacial clays found in the vicinity of the Precambrian shield of Canada, with the result that the bank failure led to an extensive clay slide, or more literally, clay flow slide. The accident occurred at night, and the flow slide completely engulfed a large mobile crane that was in the cofferdam area. Workers viewing the site on the following morning could see no sign of the crane, but the magnitude of the slide suggested that it must have been moved from the position in which it was last seen. Test holes dug at random and test drilling over an area of 300 by 70 ft failed to reveal any trace of the crane. It was then that a geophysicist, Dr. Lachlan Gilchrist of the University of Toronto, was called in by the engineers responsible. Since the object being sought was made of steel, the magnetic method provided a possible solution. Using a very sensitive magnetometer, Dr. Gilchrist made a careful survey of the slide area along lines parallel to and at right angles to the magnetic meridian, taking observations at 5-ft intervals. Two anomalies were immediately evident when the results were plotted. Digging was started immediately at the first of these and the crane was located 11½ ft below the surface of the slide material. The second anomaly proved to be caused by large bundles of reinforcing steel that had also been buried by the slide. *The Case of the Missing Steam Crane* might be a very pedestrian title for a thriller, but it may possibly provide a suitable mnemonic for readers of this volume; it may serve to remind them of the remarkable possibilities presented to them in their practice of the art of civil engineering by the judicious combination of physics and geology.

Suggestions for Further Reading

A most helpful introduction to the wide scope of geophysics is provided by:

Jacobs, J. A., R. D. Russell, and J. Tuzo Wilson, "Physics and Geology," McGraw-Hill Book Company, Inc., New York, 1959.

For a concise review of the theoretical basis for the main methods of geophysical exploration, please see:

Eve, A. S., and D. A. Keys, "Applied Geophysics in the Search for Minerals," 4th ed., Cambridge University Press, Cambridge, England, 1957.

The wide use of geophysical methods in the mineral industries, particularly in the search for oil, has resulted in a vast literature which includes many notable texts. These have only indirect value in relation to the use of geophysical methods in civil engineering, but occasional papers contain information of specific use. "Geophysical Abstracts," prepared by the United States Geological Survey and available from the Superintendent of Documents, U.S. Government Printing Office, provides a convenient means of reviewing such current literature.

Chapter 8

MATERIALS OF CONSTRUCTION

> And they said one to another, Go to, let us make brick, and burn
> them thoroughly. And they had brick for stone, and slime had they
> for mortar.
>
> Genesis 11:3[8.1]

MOST OF the materials used by civil engineers in the construction of
the projects they design are obtained directly or indirectly from constituents of the earth's crust. Probably little thought is given to this fact
in connection with the use of steel and other metals, for example, but the
discovery and working of metallic ores are branches of economic geological work of great importance to civil engineering. With such indirect
contacts the civil engineer is rarely concerned, but there are other
materials that he frequently uses, the geology of which is of direct significance. The construction of an earth dam, in which local deposits of unconsolidated materials are used, provides an obvious instance. The use of
clay for the manufacture of bricks, tiles, and similar products is clearly
related to the geology of the clay thus utilized. The peculiar properties
of the natural materials used for the production of limes and plasters are
to a large extent determined by geological features. Finally, the extensive
use of stone for building construction and the steadily growing use of
artificial building "stone"—if concrete may be so described—are intimately connected with the geological history and mineralogical nature
of the rocks thus employed.

All the materials mentioned are regularly utilized in ordinary civil
engineering work. Despite the fact that they may be supplied for use
after having been inspected and approved by independent testing organizations, the civil engineer should be at least generally familiar with their
origin and nature, particularly, as he may one day be faced with the
problem of selecting and approving such materials without aid when engaged on pioneer work. No treatment of geology as applied in civil engineering would therefore be complete without at least an introduction to
the geology of these natural materials of construction. Even a brief sum-

mary of this vast subject, however, will serve to direct attention to the very real importance of geology in relation to materials that can, all too easily, be taken for granted. For convenience, some sources of more detailed information are noted at the end of this chapter. It will be seen that the specialized literature available is of wide scope; in general, this is an indication of the attention that has been devoted to this contact of geology with civil engineering.

The economic importance of natural building materials has, quite naturally, led geological surveys, bureaus of mines, and similar public agencies to take an active interest in the location of deposits of what are frequently called "industrial minerals." There are, therefore, more published papers available for consultation in this part of the application of geology to civil engineering than in any other. A particularly good example, but typical of many such publications, is a bulletin of the United States Geological Survey on the "Geology and Construction Material Resources of Morris County, Kansas."[8.2] It was prepared in cooperation with the State Highway Department of Kansas as a part of the program of the U. S. Department of the Interior for the development of the Missouri Basin; some of the engineering features of this program will be referred to later (see page 742). Of particular value for engineers not versed in geological terminology is a table listing the outcropping stratigraphic units and showing what construction materials may be obtained from each. The table starts with the System, then the Group; it next gives general geological sections with thicknesses noted and the symbols used on the map; then the names of formations and members; and finally, an indication of the construction materials that may be available from each member. The report discusses the availability of aggregate for concrete, mineral fillers, riprap, structural stone, road metal (the old English word is used), and finally subgrade and embankment materials. This bulletin is an excellent example of what such a regional survey should be and can show.

8.2. Soil for Earth Dams. Despite the usually restricted meaning of the word "earth," its use to describe dams constructed of natural unconsolidated materials has now been generally accepted. Earth dams are essentially simple structures. Frequently, they are the most economical of all types possible. They are probably the most common type of small dam; but in recent years, many earth dams have been constructed that may truly be classed as major engineering structures; some are over 400 ft high. Their simplicity has resulted in their use in primitive communities, exemplified by some of the notable ancient dams of India. Their economy is often due to the fact that they can be constructed of material found adjacent to the dam site, a feature well demonstrated by some of the great natural earth dams.

The preliminary investigations at the site of an earth dam must naturally include due attention to the local geology. Studies will not be restricted to the dam site, however, if an earth dam can be considered as a possibility for the final design; subsurface studies must be continued around the site until uniform beds of suitable soils have been located that are sufficiently extensive to serve as sources of material for the dam. This work will ordinarily be conducted along standard lines; test borings, test pits, and possibly geophysical methods will be used to supplement and confirm the results of surface observations. Samples of material in sufficient quantity to permit detailed study will be required; they need not be undisturbed, since the soils sampled will have to be moved if they are to be used for dam construction. If preliminary tests of grain size, permeability, and porosity show that the material is suitable, more detailed investigations of the sources of supply will be necessary. These may be carried out by means of more frequent test borings and sampling; in some cases, test cuts with an excavator are made. Close study of the local geology, especially that relating to the origin of the soils, can obviously be of great service in this work.

Up to relatively recent years, the design of earth dams, involving selection of the material, proportioning of the cross section, and a decision as to the necessity of a concrete or clay core wall, was based to a large extent on previous experience and general engineering judgment. The utilization of scientific design methods initiated a notable change of procedure which the use of the results of soil mechanics studies has developed still further. Today, none but the very smallest earth dams should be designed on any basis other than a complete and detailed analysis of all the factors involved; modern soil-testing methods, scientific stability calculations, and accurate field control should be utilized. There are few types of graded soil mixture containing a reasonable amount of fine material that cannot successfully be used for earth-dam construction, so that once a suitable source of material is located, its geology ceases to have any special significance in relation to design. Construction methods will depend to some extent on the type of soil being used. Dams built in rolled layers are frequently composed of material high in sand and gravel, at least for the downstream side of the core wall, if one is included in the design. The ease with which material can be spread and rolled is a determining factor which automatically eliminates many soils with an appreciable clay content.

Three examples will be briefly noted to illustrate the influence that geology may have upon the design and construction of earth dams. The first major rolled earth-fill dam in eastern Canada was built in 1939 across the Grand River in southwestern Ontario as a pioneer water-conservation structure in this part of the Dominion. Having a maximum height of 75 ft, the dam has a central mass concrete spillway section, typical of the kind of dam commonly used in such locations and for water-control purposes. Study of an alternative design in which glacial till obtainable on the site of the dam itself and from nearby locations would be used demonstrated the undoubted economy of this type of structure. Flanking the central concrete section, therefore, are two massive embankments containing about 500,000 cu yd of compacted glacial till, which was obtained from borrow pits at the dam site and required little even in the way of additional moisture to render it suitable for placing. Compacted densities up to 135 lb per cu ft were readily obtained. The use of this

Fig. 8.1. The Shand Dam on the Grand River, Ontario, Canada. The main embankments consist of glacial till rolled into place, with no core wall.

widely distributed material directed attention to the potential of glacial till as a most useful material of construction.[8.3]

Very different was the use of soil for the construction of a multiple-purpose dam on the Neusa River high in the Andes Mountains of Colombia, 35 miles north of Bogota and almost 10,000 ft above sea level. With a height of 149 ft above river bed and a total length of 1,150 ft, this dam contains just over 1 million cu yd of rolled fill. The original design contemplated a rolled core of compacted clay between two shells of compacted Guadalupe sandstone. Study of the weathered clay from the right abutment, thought to be suitable for the impervious fill, showed it to consist very largely of the mineral halloysite, which possesses low strength when saturated. The design, therefore, had to be changed. It was found that an impervious fill with adequate strength properties could be obtained from the thin-bedded soft shales found also in the Guadalupe formation on the left bank at the dam site. The sandstone could be rolled with heavy rollers in order to break it down effectively and could apparently be used to form the two pervious shells. When work started, inspection of the borrow areas showed that it would be difficult, if not impossible, to separate properly the shales from the sandstone. Therefore, the idea of separate pervious shells was abandoned, and

FIG. 8.2. The Mammoth Pool earth-fill dam under construction in the narrow gorge of the south fork of the San Joaquin River, California, U.S.A. (*Reproduced by permission of the Southern California Edison Company.*)

the entire dam was made of a compacted rolled mixture of the two materials. A satisfactory structure resulted.[8.4]

Another high dam, high in location and in design, is the main dam of the Southern California Edison Company's Mammoth Pool development in the High Sierras. Located in a narrow gorge on the San Joaquin River, the dam is 330 ft high and 830 ft long; it retains water for passage through a pressure tunnel 40,000 ft long and 20 ft in diameter, which leads to a penstock supplying a powerhouse in which there are two 75,000 kva units. Figure 8.2 shows the precipitous sides of the gorge in which the dam was built, seemingly ideal for a concrete dam, either arched or of gravity section. Economic studies, however, showed clearly that a rolled-earth structure would be most economical, by a margin of at least $1 million. It was found that 80 per cent of the required fill was available in borrow pits only 2 miles away from the dam site, and the road from the borrow pits to the dam was on a 6 per cent downgrade, ideal for hauling. The remaining material came from a variety of local sources; filter material was dredged from the river bed below the dam site. In all, about 5 million cu yd of fill was required; a large proportion of it had to be well watered in the borrow pit before it was moved in order to give the necessary moisture content when rolled in place.[8.5]

8.3. Puddle Clay. It was common practice until the thirties to have a core wall in the center of many earth dams constructed of "puddle clay," natural clay mixed with water to form a plastic mass which can easily be handled and which can be "worked" into position to form a continuous wall of material. The puddling was usually done in a pugmill of special design. Puddle clay has also frequently been used to seal leaks in canal banks and similar water-retaining structures. The term is one that is somewhat loosely applied, since many types of clay can successfully be used for the purposes indicated. The three main requirements of the puddle clay used in dam construction are tenacity, imperviousness to water, and the property of drying without seriously cracking or shrinking. These properties have been tested in the past by means of simple field tests. Although these tests have been superseded by the more detailed tests evolved in soil mechanics laboratory practice, they may be given at least this passing attention, since they have been successfully applied to the puddle-clay requirements of many notable earth dams. Tenacity was often tested by making up a roll of the puddle clay about 1 in. in diameter and 12 in. long; this had to remain as one piece when suspended by one end. Permeability was tested by making a bowl of clay, filling it with several gallons of water and comparing the loss therefrom with that from a similarly filled impervious basin. Rough and ready as they may now seem to be, tests such as these have proved of great service in the past.

The design of earth dams is changing the status of puddle clay rapidly, as has just been indicated, and it will not in the future be regarded with the same veneration as in the past. Despite this, it still has its uses, particularly for parts of rolled-fill dams that cannot readily be properly compacted by standard methods. It has also been used for forming a cutoff wall for stopping sea-water intrusion into the subsidence basin of the Wilmington and Long Beach Harbor areas (see page 405). In all, almost 12,000 ft of puddle-clay core wall, 32 in. wide and 25 ft deep, was constructed; a novel aspect of the project was the use of bentonite slurry to maintain the open excavated trench until the clay was placed, an idea more recently applied to other construction operations.[8.6] Since information about material used to form puddle clay is sadly lacking, Table 8.1 is included as a reference that may be useful to any who have to neglect

Table 8.1. Mechanical Analysis of Puddle Clays

Name of reservoir	Proportion of clay, per cent	Proportion of sand, per cent	Proportion of water when pugged to max. plasticity, per cent	Contraction on drying in bar 100 mm long, per cent	Percolation of water through a layer of clay 2 in. thick under a head of 7 ft, cc			Tenacity of molded briquettes 1 sq in. in section when dry, lb
					After 24 hr	Total in 432 hr	During last 24 hr	
1. Pontian Ketchil (Singapore Municipality)	94.6	5.4	29.8	7.2	Nil	Nil	Nil	65
2. Blaen-y-cwm (Ebbw Vale Steel Company)	79.0	21.0	21.0	5.0	0.8	11.6	0.6	67
3. Carno (Ebbw Vale U.D.C.)	71.5	28.5	20.0	8.0	1.4	11.4	0.5	73
4. Taf Fechan (Merthyr Tydfil Corporation)	71.5	28.5	17.4	2.9	0.2	2.2	0.1	
5. Silent Valley (Belfast Water Commissioners)	60.0	40.0	20.9	4.0	Nil	Nil	Nil	156
6. Burnhope (Durham County Water Board)	57.3	42.7	20.1	5.9	Nil	Nil	Nil	107
7. Alwen (Birkenhead Corporation)	50.6	49.4	15.0	2.5	2.3	17.6	0.6	30
Average	69.2	30.8	20.6	5.1	0.7	6.1	0.2	83

SOURCE: Reproduced, by permission, from G. McIldowie, The Construction of the Silent Valley Reservoir, Belfast Water-supply, *Inst. Civil Eng. Min. Proc.*, **239**: 504 (*London*) (1935).

temporarily the scientific achievements of soil mechanics and revert to this old but tried method for some especially difficult piece of work.

8.4. Bricks. Civil engineers are rarely required to become brickmakers; but as in the case of other materials of construction, the source of bricks and the leading features of their manufacture should be familiar to those who have to use them frequently; civil engineers are numbered in this general company. Bricks are of three main kinds: concrete bricks, sand-lime bricks, and fired-clay bricks. The first two have little direct relation to geology. They are manufactured by specialized processes, in the one case from mixtures of portland cement and aggregate and in the other from sand and lime.

The peculiar properties of many clays that make them so useful to man have been known from the very early years of human history, as recent archaeological work has demonstrated. Working rules based on long-established practice had to suffice until comparatively recent years for the guidance of brickmakers. Today a vast amount of scientific information is available, obtained not only in connection with brickmaking but also in connection with the ceramics industry generally, which has made brickmaking a specialized and highly technical industry.

The two properties that have made clays so important a source of useful articles are their plasticity, by reason of which they can be molded into desired shapes when wet, and the way in which they will harden when subjected to the action of heat, thus establishing the molded shape permanently. The term "plasticity" is here used in relation to molding processes; if too plastic, a clay will be hard and sticky to mix; and if deficient in plasticity, it may break up as it is being molded. Mixtures of clay and sand are therefore sometimes used in order to obtain a satisfactory material for the molding process. Shrinkage of clays is another important property in connection with brickmaking; uniformity of shrinkage is desirable. The actions that take place when clays are heated are complicated. Generally, however, two recognizable stages are of importance when bricks are made: that at which the clay vitrifies or becomes hard by a fluxing together of the whole mass which still retains its shape; and that at which the whole mass becomes soft or viscous, as a result of excessive fluxing, and loses its shape. Clearly, in the manufacture of bricks in large kilns, an appreciable temperature interval between the two stages is desirable.

A combination of these properties is what determines the suitability of a clay for brickmaking, provided that the clay is uniform, clean, and free from gravel and boulder intrusions. Thus it will be apparent that although most clays can be baked to give some sort of brick, by no means all will give a brick that can satisfactorily be used in construction. The presence of gravel in clays is an objectionable although not an insuperable difficulty; but if pebbles of limestone are present, or if the clay is calcareous, it will be advisable to continue the search for a suitable brick clay elsewhere. It is in the location of possible sources of clay supplies that the contact between geology and brickmaking is made, since when a uniform clay supply has been located, its suitability for brickmaking depends primarily upon its physical and chemical properties, which have to be determined by suitable laboratory tests.

Fɪɢ. 8.3. Red-burning shale being excavated at Canton, Ohio, for the Belden Brick Company. (*Reproduced by permission of the Structural Clay Products Institute.*)

Adobe clays, which contain sand, are often used for making sun-dried bricks in hot climates. Common bricks are made from a wide variety of suitable clays. Special "engineering," or high-quality pressed bricks are made from especially pure high-quality clays or shales and sometimes from inferior fire clays. The latter are clays that will stand a high degree of heat without fusing; their use for making firebricks is well known. They are frequently found in association with coal deposits, in adjacent strata from 1 to 5 ft thick, but not all clays found with coal are fire clays.

Paving bricks are made from clays that can be accurately machine molded and that vitrify at a moderate temperature.

It is sometimes thought that the color of bricks is an indication of their quality. This is so in the case of the famous Staffordshire blue bricks of England, made from clays and marls of the county of Stafford, which contain from 7 to 10 per cent iron oxide; the bricks are burned at unusually high temperatures. But this is a rare exception, for in general, the conception is erroneous. Pure clay would be white, but the usual color found in most clay deposits is due to oxides and carbonaceous matter. When clays are burned, those which are white usually remain so; but colored bricks result from colored clays, although the tint may change. The effect of iron oxides is generally to give a red or buff color; if lime is present, its effect may counteract that of the iron oxide and produce a cream-colored or yellow brick. Terms such as "red burning" and "buff burning" are used to describe the final color of brick clays after they have been vitrified. In the course of the long-established business of brickmaking there has gradually developed, especially in Europe, a definite correlation between clay deposits of well-defined geological position and their suitability for brickmaking. Information on this correlation and the areal distribution of the clays so described is usually obtainable from local geological surveys.

Finally the fact may be mentioned that in certain parts of the United States in which there are no outcrops of solid rock for use as railway-track ballast, burned-clay ballast has been extensively and successfully used. The same material has been used even for such a purpose as the riprap protection for the slopes of earth dams. Material of this type was specially developed for use on the Keystone (Kingsley) Dam of the Central Nebraska Public Power and Irrigation District, a rolled-earth structure that required 500,000 square yards of riprap for protection. The nearest quarry rock suitable for this purpose was 186 miles away from the dam site and the rail haul rendered it unusually expensive. A type of random ceramic block was developed by fusing together ordinary bricks, giving a weight of over 2,000 lb per cu yd and all the requisite properties for riprap in the way of soundness, absorption, toughness, and wear.[8.7] The ceramic riprap has now been in use for 20 years and has performed well. It is an unusual illustration of the wide use to which clay products are put in the practice of civil engineering.

8.5. Tile and Other Structural-clay Products. An extension of the use of clay for the provision of building materials was the development of structural-clay products (as they are commonly called), such as hollow tile and architectural terra cotta. These products are widely used in connection with buildings constructed as steel or reinforced-concrete frames. Some idea of their economic importance is given by the fact that in 1955 structural and facing tile produced in the United States was equivalent to approximately 13 per cent of the vast total of 7,147 million clay bricks produced.

Common to the manufacture of all these articles are processes similar to those used in brickmaking. Fine-grade clays are used, and because of the finished shapes, they are processed under more rigid control than common brick. All the clays are regularly submitted to detailed testing and analysis in order to guard against an excess of impurities, such as iron,

Fig. 8.4. Starring Potteries, Littleborough, Lincolnshire, England. The fire clay here used for the manufacture of drainpipes, etc., is about 4 ft thick and immediately underlies an extensive coal seam, 1 in. thick (which is worked as "The Inch Mine"). (*Geological Survey of Great Britain photograph. Crown Copyright; reproduced by permission of the Controller of H. M. Stationery Office, London.*)

magnesia, or lime. Stoneware is usually made from refractory clays which burn to a dense mass at relatively low temperatures; clay mixtures, sometimes with sand added, are frequently used. Sewer pipes have to be glazed during manufacture, and this is done with salt or with a special glazing material. It is said that a high iron content is of assistance, but the main requirement of clays for pipe making is that they shall be high in fluxes so that they will vitrify readily. The materials most commonly used for structural tiles are fire clay of first and second grades, high-grade brick clays, and suitable clay shales. Some of the latter have to be blasted; therefore, regular quarrying operations may have to be planned and directed in connection with tile manufacture in addition to the mining that is necessary in connection with the supply of some fire clays.

Manufacturing methods for these varied products are interesting but generally outside the scope of this book. Two details may perhaps be mentioned. In many plants, it is usual to store the clay or shale out of doors for an appreciable period before use. Broken up and exposed to the atmosphere in this way, the clay or shale will disintegrate and soften. This result, although often so unfortunate in civil engineering construction, is here an advantage, since the weathered material can be easily worked. Color is important in connection with some structural-clay products, especially hollow tiles to be used for partition walls. With uniform clays, color can be controlled during manufacture; but it is possible —and the practice is often followed—to introduce iron oxide (and other substances) during manufacture in order to ensure a uniform shade of the desired color.

8.6. Building Stone. "The style of a national architecture" wrote John Ruskin, "may evidently depend, in a great measure, upon the nature of the rocks of the country." Although modern methods of construction have in many instances reduced building stone to a mere facing, this forthright statement remains a telling reminder of the close connection between geology and the successful use of building stone, as specially cut and trimmed rock is generally called. The granite of Egypt and the marble and limestone of many European countries bear this out, as does also such a typically popular description as "The Limestone City" (Kingston, Ontario, Canada) or "The Granite City" (Aberdeen, Scotland). The relationship provides one of the few points of contact between civil engineering and geology that appear to have been generally and continuously recognized, at least to some degree, throughout the past century.

The study of the geology of building stones may, indeed, have sometimes induced too great a regard for geological features and the neglect of other physical characteristics or even of quarrying methods. This was well shown at a very early date in connection with the stone used for the construction of the "new" Houses of Parliament in Westminster, England, about the year 1840. In 1838, a commission was appointed to select a suitable building stone for the work; William Smith and Thomas de la Beche, the first director of the Geological Survey of Great Britain, were members. After an exhaustive examination of many supplies of stone, a dolomitic limestone from Anston, near Mansfield, was selected as the most suitable. In the year 1861, just about 20 years later, another government commission had to be appointed to consider the "Decay of the Stone of the New Palace of Westminster," so serious had the disintegration of the selected stone become. The fault appears not to have been in the geological selection but in the fact that there was no inspection of stone at the quarry before it was shipped. It has been stated that if only 15 per cent of the original stone had been rejected at the quarry (as showing signs of weathering or traversed by vents), trouble would have been obviated. Confirmation of this is given by the use of the same stone, but quarried and used under strict supervision, for the construction of

Fig. 8.5. Doorway of the Jermyn Street Geological Museum, London, England, for many years the headquarters of the Geological Survey of Great Britain, showing the excellent preservation of the stonework referred to in the text. (*Geological Survey of Great Britain photograph; Crown Copyright; reproduced by permission of the Controller of H. M. Stationery Office, London.*)

the Jermyn Street Museum in London within about 1 mile of the Parliament Buildings. After almost a century's exposure to the London atmosphere, the stone still presented a splendid appearance when the building was recently closed. It is, perhaps, of more than passing interest to note that the establishment of the British Museum of Practical Geology (predecessor of the well-known and justly famous South Kensington Museum of Geology), which was for so long the headquarters of the British Geological Survey, was largely due to this investigation; the

Jermyn Street building was provided to accommodate the many specimens of British building stones assembled by the Commission of Enquiry.
It was opened in 1851, superseding a smaller building opened in 1841.[8.8]

Geology, therefore, is only one of the factors on which the suitability
of a building stone depends, but it is one of prime importance. Unless
the geological nature and mineralogical content of a natural rock are
satisfactory, other tests of its suitability as a building stone are useless.
There is, fortunately, an extensive literature on the use of natural building stone (or "dimension stone" as it is sometimes called) to which the
geologist and civil engineer may turn with profit when specific studies
have to be made. Well-recognized standard tests are available. In view of
the decrease in the use of natural stone in building and engineering work
in the Western world, however, a civil engineer rarely has to consider
opening up a new quarry for dimension stone; most of that used today
comes from one or another of the large well-established stone suppliers.
That building stone is far from being an outmoded material of construction is shown by the fact that in 1956 the value of its annual production in the United States exceeded $76 million. In the less developed
parts of the world, however, new stone supplies will still have to be
developed, if only because of variations in national economies. In India,
for example, it is still more economical to build gravity dams of hand-
placed masonry than of mass concrete, even with the aid of the most
efficient of modern construction machinery.

Availability of Suitable Rock. This is an obvious prerequisite for the
use of cut stone as a structural material, and one that can be determined
only by means of a geological survey. In open country, this may be a
simple matter; but in drift-covered areas, the services of a trained geologist may be essential.

Relative Cost of Cut Stone. Cut stone will not ordinarily be used on
civil engineering works, except as decoration, unless it proves to be an
economical alternative to concrete. Delivered cost of the stone will depend on ease of quarrying, extent of handling, length of haul, and cost of
dressing (including wastage). Quarrying and dressing costs will be determined by the nature of the rock to be worked; massive formations of
hard igneous rocks are obviously more expensive to work than blocky
limestone, which can be quarried without the aid of explosives and can
be readily dressed. Geological investigations will assist, therefore, in cost
determination, particularly in securing an estimate of the essential homo-
geneity of the rock mass.

Appearance of Dressed Stone. The final appearance of dressed stone in
a structure will depend on its texture, its mineralogical composition, and
the weathering to which it is exposed. In civil engineering work, a
beautiful appearance is not often the controlling factor in the selection of
a building stone, although a satisfactory appearance will always be desir-

able for any stone that is to be exposed to public view. Uniformity of color and texture will usually be desirable; they can be checked generally by visual examination of the rock mass before quarrying, coupled with an appreciation of its geological nature.

Strength and Weight of Building Stones. These physical properties are of obvious importance in connection with the use of stone in civil engineering work. They depend on the geological nature of the rock, as a glance at any table of weights and strengths of building stones will make

Fig. 8.6. General view of the campus of the University of Saskatchewan, Saskatoon, Saskatchewan, Canada. Most of the buildings are faced with a buff limestone obtained from local boulders and field stone; the nearest bedrock is several hundred miles away. (*Reproduced by permission of the University of Saskatchewan.*)

clear. As one indication of the influence of geological nature on these properties, the fact that fine-grained rocks are usually stronger than coarse-grained rocks, may be noted. The strength of porous rocks (particularly sandstones) depends on the quantity of water present in them; tests should therefore always be made on both wet and dry samples. The variation in strength may amount to 50 per cent of the test results for the dry stone; thus, it is advisable that ample factors of safety be applied if dry stone is to be used.

Durability of Building Stones. Durability is a prime requirement of a building stone that is to be used in civil engineering work. Expressed in simple terms, the durability of a stone is its capacity to retain its original size, strength, and appearance throughout a long period of time while performing the work intended for it in the structure concerned. Essentially, durability is related directly to the normal weathering of rocks. The first and most obvious test of a building stone is therefore to be made by visiting the quarry from which it came and there examining the evidences of weathering on the naturally exposed surfaces of the untouched rock. If this were always possible, and were an invariable practice, some troubles with building stones would be avoided. Conditions of exposure at a quarry may not be comparable with those to which the cut stone is to be subjected. This is especially important if the stone is to be used in city areas where the atmosphere may be charged with soot and the waste gases of industry, which may tend to form weak acids in combination with atmospheric moisture. (The sulfuric-acid content of soot layers resting on building ledges has been found to amount to as much as 5 per cent.) Therefore, a second test of a very general nature is to examine stone obtained from the same working which has been exposed to the same type of atmospheric conditions as those contemplated and to compare the result of such observations with the length of exposure.

The Use of Building Stone. The large number of variable factors influencing the durability of building stone suggest that there may be restrictions to be observed in connection with its use that will assist in its preservation. Some of these may be noted. The advisability of always setting sedimentary building stones parallel to their bedding planes has been mentioned; it is most important. If dressed stone is to be used, this direction should be determined before the stone is dressed. In the case of porous stones, every possible precaution should be taken to facilitate drainage of the stone, particularly as some stones become more pervious the wetter they get. No ledges should be left unprotected on which water can collect, particularly if the exposure is in a city area. The greatest care must be taken in the selection and use of mortar for jointing. Portland cement mortar should not be used with sandstones or with some limestones. Pitting of high-quality limestone (and sandstone) has been observed in buildings in Liverpool, England. Although the exact reason for this is uncertain, the accompanying efflorescence suggests that the portland cement backing to the stone is the cause.[8.9] All mortar for stone should be kept as low in lime and cement content as possible. Some authorities suggest that pointing should be left rough, and not troweled off, in order to be sure that the joint is not sealed tight. Limestones and sandstones should never be used together in alternating positions.

Stone has been a leading building material for a very long time; in all probability, it was first used in ancient Egypt. When the methods developed by the Egyptians for quarrying stone are reviewed, they give a new perspective to modern stonecutting. For quarrying the granite from which so many of their notable monuments were made, they got rid of the surface layers by alternating burning papyrus on them and drenching them with cold water; if no natural fissure could be found, a trench was formed by pounding with balls of dolerite. Wooden wedges were inserted in fissures or in formed trenches, driven tight when dry, and then wetted. Levers, sledges, dragropes, and unlimited slave labor were used to move hewn stone blocks, the handling of which would challenge even an

Fig. 8.7. The Rock of Ages Granite Quarry at Barre, Vermont, U.S.A. The scale of the operations is shown by the size of the workmen on the staging. (*Reproduced by permission of the Rock of Ages Corporation.*)

expert rigger on a modern construction job. The Great Pyramid was built of limestone in this way about 4700 B.C. Recent studies of the way in which it has weathered, since its outer facing of hard white limestone was removed from the ninth century on for providing stone for mosques and other buildings in Giza and Cairo, suggest that it will last at least another 100,000 years.[8.10]

Even today, cut stone is still usually required for those parts of civil engineering structures where resistance to wear is highly important, as for such items as dock sills, lock-gate quoins, and large valve seats. And the real beauty of a carefully designed and well-constructed stone-building exterior is still frequently called for, especially in the Old World, when the finished structures of a civil engineering project must blend as satisfactorily as possible with natural beauty that has had to be temporarily disturbed. The permanence of such buildings is well shown when a stone building has to be demolished to make way for one of more modern design, the permanence of which may perhaps be in keeping with current trends in aesthetic design. It is to be regretted that this short section could not end as it began, with a quotation from John Ruskin. Those who know his writings can well imagine how he would have commented upon some aspects of modern architecture with ringing commentary on the fact that stone will long remain the master building material.

8.7. Lime and Plaster. Although the importance of lime and plaster in civil engineering work has declined with the steady advance in the use of concrete and concrete products, limes are still used in connection with building work and masonry construction and so are of significance for the engineer. Lime and quicklime are calcium oxide and are never found in nature; impure forms are prepared by calcining limestones, the calcium carbonate of which loses its carbon dioxide and yields calcium oxide mixed with whatever impurities were present in the original limestone. The distinguishing property of lime is the slaking that takes place when water is put into contact with it; calcium hydroxide results from the strong chemical reaction of the two. The slaking manifests itself by a general effervescence and disintegration of the usual lumps in which "quicklime" is obtained from a lime kiln. The "slaked lime" has the property of setting when exposed to the atmosphere, and for this reason it is used in building mortars.

The impurities in limestone may vary in quantity from a slight trace to a large percentage of the total volume of rock. They determine in large measure the nature of the lime that will be obtained when the limestone is calcined. The impurities cannot often be distinguished by eye, but they can be roughly determined by solution of the calcium carbonate in hydrochloric acid. When an engineer has to test a limestone as a possible source of lime, his easiest course will usually be to calcine a small quantity of the natural rock and then examine the properties of the resulting lime. The more usual impurities are siliceous and clay materials; they have the effect of slowing up the slaking of the lime and developing its "hydraulic" property, i.e., its ability to set when immersed in water. "Hydraulic limes," as they are called, are commonly yellowish, in contrast to the white of pure quicklime; they set slowly and have little strength unless mixed with sand.

The impurities that cause these variations in the properties of limes naturally depend on the formation of the limestones from which the limes are made. They may therefore vary considerably, even between the top and bottom of a bed of rock. In the quarrying of limestone for lime making, care must therefore be exercised with regard to the exact character of the rock being obtained. For example, in the well-known Lias beds of England, the quantity of aluminum silicates present may vary from 8 to 64 per cent; the corresponding quantity of calcium carbonate may vary from 90 to 34 per cent.[8.11] Limestones that contain

Fig. 8.8 Working face in gypsum quarry. Dingwall, Cape Breton Island, Nova Scotia, Canada. (*Reproduced by permission of National Gypsum (Canada), Ltd.*)

fossils may produce a lime with variable and uncertain slaking properties because of the peculiar calcining of some fossil material. Small particles that will not slake may occur; they subsequently take up water and tend to disintegrate the mass of material surrounding them.

Manufacture of lime is carried out in coal-, gas-, or wood-heated kilns; calcining takes place at about 900°C, or somewhat less if steam is present in the kiln. Higher temperatures will cause clinkering or partial fusion of the rock if clay impurities are present. The resulting quicklime will be obtained in blocks corresponding to the original blocks of rock; it is usually slaked in special boxes before being used. Various names, such as "fat lime," "rich lime," and "poor lime," are used to denote different grades; the rate and nature of slaking are a usual criterion. These descriptive terms should be accepted and used with caution, as they are essentially local in significance. If the lime has an appreciable percentage of magnesium oxide in it, derived from the magnesium compounds present in the original rock, it will be designated as a "magnesian" or "dolomitic" lime.

The plasters that play so important a part in finishing processes in building construction are derived mainly from deposits of gypsum, the hydrous sulfate of calcium. This occurs as natural deposits, usually as a solid rock mass but in some places as unconsolidated sandy material. It is fairly widely distributed; one of the most notable deposits of high-grade gypsum is in the extreme north of Nova Scotia on Cape Breton Island, Canada. It is often quite pure, having probably originated by the evaporation of oceanic waters and the consequent concentration of the dissolved salts. It is often found in association with common salt. Gypsum will frequently change to anhydrite, the anhydrous calcium sulfate, some of which will be found in most gypsum deposits. Unlike gypsum, anhydrite is of limited commercial value and so has to be carefully distinguished and discarded. When pure gypsum is heated to a temperature between 250 and 400°F, it loses most of its combined water and gives an amorphous substance commercially known as "plaster of paris." When this is mixed with water, it takes up by chemical combination as much as was previously lost and sets as a hard and compact mass. Special plasters may be obtained by variation of the calcining process and by the admixture of other materials with plaster of paris.

8.8. Cement. Because of the general availability of modern portland cement, prepared by expert manufacturers to rigid standards of quality, a civil engineer seldom has to give close attention to its origin. So widely is cement used, however, and so far reaching has been its effect on modern construction that a brief note on the geological aspect of its preparation is warranted. Portland cement was patented in 1824 by an Englishman, Joseph Aspdin, and so named because he obtained his limestone from the famous Portland quarries. Since he naturally had no ball mills for grinding his limestone, he gathered powdered stone from the main road; this led to his being arrested and charged with the theft of public property.

Cement is an artificial product, since it is made by partially fusing together a specially prepared mixture of natural materials; the word "artificial" is used in distinction to the natural cements which are available and which are mentioned later. The usual mixture for cement manufacture consists of limestone (to give the necessary lime), clay or shale (to give the necessary silica and alumina), and a small quantity of iron oxide. The clinker obtained by heating this mixture is finely ground to give the gray amorphous powder familiar to all civil engineers. The limestone used can have a wide variation in hardness, texture, and chemical composition; but magnesia, free particles of silica, and sulfur are undesirable constituents. Clays used in cement manufacture are often impure, but they cannot contain gravel or any free solid particles. Relative proportions of the several materials can be determined by calculation when the nature of the constituents is known; this is one of the several phases of cement manufacture that are the work of experts. Portland cement is distinguished by its relatively high strength and its slow and even setting when mixed with water. Its exact chemical composition is complicated; but by means of modern methods of analysis, some knowledge of this has now been obtained.

In addition to standard portland cement, special cements are available for a variety of unusual purposes. Thus, white cement for decoration is obtained by the use of clays that burn to a final white color. Aluminous cement, having an unusually high alumina content, is produced by fusing together a mixture of limestone, bauxite, and coke; it is unusually quick setting and is said to be more resistant to the action of sea water than ordinary portland cement. Tests have shown clearly that it is more resistant to the action of acidic moorland waters.[8.12] In Canada, a special high-silica cement has been developed that is extremely resistant to the peculiar alkaline soil conditions found in some parts of the west of the Dominion.[8.13]

Although artificially prepared cements are now in general use, they represent an ingenious adaptation of natural materials to give an imitation of a natural product. If a limestone has a very high clay content and certain other impurities, it may give a natural cement when calcined at a higher temperature than that used for the production of lime. Although not common, deposits of this kind are used—sometimes with small admixtures—for the manufacture of cement. One of the very early master builders of North America, Lt. Col. John By of the (British) Royal Engineers, found an exposure of argillaceous limestone in 1827 from which he made his own "cement" (described as better than any obtainable from England) for his masonry work in constructing the Rideau Canal, a military defense work linking the fortress of Kingston on Lake Ontario with what is now the site of Ottawa, Canada's capital city. The quarry he started still supplies modern portland cement works.[8.14] Natural cements usually set more rapidly than portland cement and have a somewhat lower strength; they are naturally rather variable in composition. Natural cement is sometimes called "Roman cement"; it appears to have been discovered by a Mr. Parker of London, England, in 1796, who took out a patent in that year for the manufacture of what he called "Roman cement from the septario of clayey limestone found in the London clay formation of the island of Sheppey, England." It was found later that other deposits would yield similar natural cements.

Mention of the name Roman in connection with cement is a reminder of one of the most fascinating aspects of early Roman engineering—the discovery and use of *pozzuolana*. This is a volcanic ash found in great beds near Naples at Puteoli from which was derived the ancient name *pulvis Puteolanus*. Puteoli is now called Pozzuoli, from which the modern name has been derived. The Romans found that if this ash was mixed with lime instead of the sand ordinarily used, a watertight "cement" was obtained which would set under water. This mixture has been found in the lining of the water channel in the Aqua Marcia, dating back as early

Fig. 8.9. Quarry face at the Montreal East plant of the Canada Cement Co., Ltd., somewhat weathered due to no recent working. The limestone quarried here gives a natural cement mixture. (*Reproduced by permission of the Canada Cement Co., Ltd.*)

as 144 B.C. It was subsequently the principal constituent of the "concrete" so boldly used in later Roman structures. Modern Italian builders still use the same material; in other countries, similar deposits of volcanic ash are used to make pozzuolana cement. Smeaton used pozzuolana in the construction of the Eddystone Lighthouse (1757), one of the pioneer structures of modern engineering. The name is often loosely used; a slag cement made up of a mixture of finely ground blast-furnace slag and lime is sometimes thus described. It would seem that the name should rightly be restricted to cement containing natural volcanic ash.[8.15]

8.9. Sand. Sand is used as a material of construction not only as filling and as a porous foundation blanket (as for roads) but also to a wide extent as a filtering medium and as a constituent of mortars and concrete. In view of these important applications, it must be pointed out that the term "sand" is used to describe naturally granular material of a certain grain size irrespective of the shape of the grains, their uniformity, and their mineral composition. The formation of sands during the process of rock weathering and the way in which they are transported before reaching their final position affect all three of these leading characteristics of sand. The mineralogical nature of sand is important, especially in view of the popular belief that all sands are composed of quartz particles. Although quartz is frequently a major constituent, pure silica sand is the exception rather than the rule. Depending on the nature of the rock from which it was formed and on the erosive action to which it has been subjected, many other minerals may be found as constituents. Mica will sometimes be present; feldspar is more common; even particles of shale occasionally occur. The presence of such materials in sand make a detailed examination of many sands imperative before their use as concrete aggregate, for example. Feldspar is not a thoroughly stable mineral, and its presence in some sands seems to be responsible for "hair cracking" in concretes. Shale particles and soluble salts may be equally injurious.

Specifications for sand for concrete usually exclude all sands containing deleterious substances and restrict the clay and silt content of sand to a small amount, often 5 per cent or less. Usually they also exclude sand that is not "clean," a term used to signify freedom from organic matter such as tannic acid derived from surface vegetation. Geology can often assist here by suggesting the mode of origin of sands, the probable extent of deposits, and the probable origin of organic matter; it thus presents a guide to the condemnation of either a whole deposit or just an upper layer. Uniformity of grain size is important in connection with special sands used for standard concrete tests and for filtering media. For the latter purpose, sands should have a high silica content in addition to uniform grain size. The latter property is described by the use of *uniformity coefficients* and *effective size* statistics, definitions of which are to be found in engineering texts; it is determined by the origin and mineral content of the sand. Sands that have been subject to marine action are often fine-grained and fairly uniform. River sand may have similar properties but it is likely to be more variable. Glacial sands frequently are mixed with gravel and are not generally uniform. These several types of sand have fairly characteristic grain shapes, none of which, incidentally, are rounded as a general rule. Rounded grains are generally an indication of a wind-deposited sand.

8.10. Crushed Rock. Crushed rock is used for a variety of purposes in civil engineering; it has the advantage over natural gravel of having angular particle shape, and its limiting size and grading can be controlled as desired. It is widely used as railway ballast and as a base course for roads. It is most useful as a special type of fill material, especially for drainage work. It is also very widely used as coarse aggregate for concrete making; since the resulting concrete is in effect an artificial conglomerate of the aggregate used, the geological significance of this application will be discussed in the next section.

A common practice on construction jobs is to utilize any rock that has to be excavated as a source, when crushed, of concrete aggregate and for other purposes. If the rock is suitable for concrete work, a qualification discussed later, this practice may lead to great economy in construction. It comes within the experience of many civil engineers, and it might therefore be expected that the operation of rock-crushing plants and their correlation with the nature of leading rock types would have received wide attention in civil engineering literature. This does not appear to be the case. Even though the rock-crushing plant can often prove to be the key unit in the construction plant layout for a major undertaking, it is all too often the least appreciated and the least understood because rock crushing is very generally regarded as a rather crude operation. It is far from that; it calls for just as much engineering attention as the most complex machinery on the job, and it requires an appreciation of the geological significance of the types of rock to be crushed.

The effect of different rock types is well shown by a record of crusher jaws lasting only 10 days when crushing granite, whereas a pair of exactly similar jaws lasted 7 years when used for crushing limestone. This surprising difference is best explained by variations in the toughness and hardness of rocks. Hardness is generally measured by testing the abrasive quality of rock in a machine in which a sample is pressed on a revolving steel disk, and toughness is usually measured by impact tests on rock samples. The strength of rock specimens tested to failure in compression can be related to their behavior when being crushed into rock fragments. The shape of the fragments obtained from a crusher is largely influenced by natural planes of weakness in the rock, but in general, particle shape may be influenced also by the nature and direction of the blow struck by the crusher mechanism, i.e., by the type of crusher being used. Grain size is also important; coarse-grained rocks are poorer in quality than corresponding fine-grained rocks. Geological age, in the case of sedimentary rocks, is also significant.

The variable factors are so numerous that no very specific statements can be made with regard to the crushing qualities of individual rock types. The following general statements are a guide. Granites possess variable crushing qualities, although their behavior when crushed is related to their resistance to impact. Porphyries are, in general, very tough and hard. Basalts naturally show a wide variety of results, but crushing strength is found to be related to porosity, possibly produced by partial decomposition. Quartzites are moderately tough, but gneisses are much less so because of their foliated texture. The nature of the cementing material governs the performance of many sedimentary rocks during crushing.

These notes are an indication of the correlation of geological and physical properties of rock types with their performance when being crushed. A careful geological examination of samples of any rock to be crushed should therefore be made before plans for rock crushing are completed. If this examination can be supplemented by physical tests on samples and also by petrological examinations, a good general idea of the probable behavior of the rock during crushing will be obtained. Special attention should always be paid to the natural planes of cleavage. The natural tendency to break along these planes can be offset to some degree by the use of a suitable type of crusher. Variation in particle shape can have an appreciable effect on the workability of concrete and therefore on the amount of cement necessary. A change to a correct type of crusher may sometimes result in a saving of one bag of concrete per cubic yard; the monetary saving that this can mean on a large construction job can readily be imagined.

The economic importance of crushed rock is well shown by the fact that in 1956 it represented an expenditure of over $400 million in the United States. This figure includes the value of construction aggregate, railway ballast, riprap, and rock for highway subgrades. As further evidence of the scale of crushed-rock operations there may be cited the construction of the Fontana Dam of the TVA which necessitated the quarrying and crushing to size of more than 6 million tons of rock for concrete aggregate alone. The rock used was the Fontana quartzite which was exposed in a special quarry giving good access to the deposit between the under- and overlying beds of slate, 900 ft apart. The high silica content of the quartzite made drilling slow and expensive; an average of only 5 ft of hole was obtained with the 9-in.-diameter drill bits before resharpening was necessary. An average of 3.2 lb of explosive was used for each ton of rock excavated.[8.16]

Riprap for the protection of erodible surfaces, such as the slopes of earth-fill dams and embankments, is another widespread use of crushed rock. The long standard "one-man stone" still holds its own as one of the most effective types of slope protection when durable rock is selected for use and the riprap is carefully installed. There is at least one case on record where a carefully designed and placed porous concrete protection apron failed, had to be removed, and was then replaced by "old-fashioned" rock riprap at a cost of over $3 million.[8.17] In the selection of rock for riprap, the greatest care must be taken in studying the character, durability, and quarrying characteristics of any rock available; here, too, geology is of prime importance.

One of the very few uses of crushed rock which has decreased in importance through the years is for providing "road metal," to use again the old English term that is so expressive. It was not too many decades ago that water-bound macadam road surfaces were regarded as the best obtainable. Today, however, they are a rarity; stabilized soil roads have come into their own for even the most secondary of secondary roads, and stabilized soil subgrades are almost universal as the foundation for either concrete or asphalt pavements. This use of soil is a development of the last half century; it appears that investigations initiated in 1906 by Dr. C. M. Strahan, then county engineer of Clark County, Georgia, were among the earliest attempts to apply to road work some of the facts concerning soil behavior that were then just being observed. Dr. Strahan's first public statement was made in 1914. At the first conference of state highway-testing engineers held in Washington in February, 1917, the matter received considered attention, and from that time forward advance can be noted. Water-bound macadam, however, is almost a century older in its "modern" form; some of the highway-building practices of the Romans could be said to have paved the way for the great work of Telford and McAdam, the outstanding British road engineers of the early nineteenth century. In those early days, water-bound macadam (named after McAdam) was the finally perfected type of road construction. If only for its historical interest, the importance that McAdam himself gave to the geology of the rock he used is well shown in these words from his own notes (1823):[8.18]

Flint makes an excellent road, if due attention be paid to the size, but from want of attention, many of the flint roads are rough, loose and expensive. Limestone when properly prepared and applied makes a smooth solid road and becomes consolidated sooner than any other material; but from its nature it is not the most lasting. Whinstone is the most durable of all materials; and wherever it is well and judiciously applied, the roads are comparatively good and cheap.

Among the principles that McAdam laid down were the following: No stone should exceed 1 in. in any major dimension; all stone used should be clean; the foundation should not be solid rock or hard pavement (a matter on which Telford had other opinions); the camber used should not be too great; and the rock when laid should possess a natural water bond. McAdam's ideas were based on his practical experience; his selection of rocks suitable for road use was similarly empirical. Subsequent detailed study and microscopic examination of rocks available for road work generally confirmed his original ideas.

There must finally be mentioned the use of broken, although not crushed, rock as a dam-building material. Rock-fill dams have been increasingly used in recent years, and a number of refinements have been made in their design; notably, sloping impervious cores, or blankets, are a feature that has greatly widened their potential use. As in the case of rolled-fill earth dams, selection of a rock-fill dam will depend jointly on the availability of a supply of suitable material and a study of the economics of alternative designs. Experience with the San Gabriel Flood Control Dam 1 is a useful reminder of the care that must be taken in the selection of durable rock for rock-fill dams (see page 536). With standard tests now accepted and tried by long experience, the suitability of rock proposed for a dam structure can be readily determined well in advance of design. Typical of recent practice is another structure in the High Sierras, the Courtright Dam on the Helms Creek, a tributary of the Kings River, California; this project of the Pacific Gas and Electric Company contains 1½ million cu yd of rock and rises 310 ft high above stream bed. Located also in a narrow canyon that might appear to be more suited to a concrete structure, the Courtright rock-fill dam was shown by detailed studies to be the most economical of all available solutions, since it was almost possible to blast granite down from the canyon walls to form the dam. As no impervious fill was economically available, a reinforced-concrete upstream membrane was constructed to provide the necessary cutoff; the rock-fill structure provided the necessary support. Rock was dumped or blasted directly into place, and high-pressure water sluicing finished the operation; blocks of rock, put into position by cranes, formed a relatively smooth face on which the upstream concrete membrane was placed.[8.19] This example and the typical rolled earth-fill structures noted on pages 251 and 539 show clearly the possibilities presented even when high dams are built with local natural building materials.

8.11. Concrete. Concrete is one of the three main materials of construction utilized in modern civil engineering work. It is, perhaps, that which should be most closely studied by civil engineers. The quality of a given piece of timber cannot be varied, and steel has also definite physical properties when supplied for use. But the quality and strength of concrete are under the control of the engineer in charge of construction. This provides at once an opportunity and a responsibility which are being met by continued study of and instruction in concrete technique.

The use of concrete in modern practice probably dates from about the year 1850; but as in the case of cement, this was a rediscovery rather than an innovation. The fame of the Romans as the master builders of olden days is due in no small measure to their use of a kind of concrete, *structura caementicia*, which they made from the pozzuolana cement, already mentioned, mixed with broken fragments of stone and tile. They placed the material into timber forms, the marks of which can still be seen in places, and they even used pumice as aggregate when lightweight concrete was needed. The great dome of the Pantheon and other vaulted roofs testify to their skill in the use of this early concrete, lacking only reinforcing steel to make it the counterpart of that used today.[8.20]

Despite the number of factors that determine the final character of concrete, the aggregate is always of prime importance. When it is recalled that in an average concrete, 70 per cent by volume and possibly

Fɪɢ. 8.10. Vaulting of Roman "concrete" (*structura caementicia*) with brick facing, in Trojan's Market Hall, Rome, Italy. (*Reproduced by permission of the Society for the Promotion of Hellenic Studies, London.*)

80 per cent by weight, consists of the coarse aggregate used, this importance will be more readily appreciated. The attention usually devoted to the testing of coarse aggregate is not always in accord with its importance in the finished product. Compared with the care exercised in the testing of cement, the checks made on the suitability of aggregates are sometimes insignificant. Although the old saying that "the strength of a concrete is the strength of its aggregate" cannot be upheld as generally accurate, it does give a vivid indication of the general im-

portance of the aggregate in a concrete mix. It must be added that a good aggregate will not ensure good concrete; the possible variations in grading, mixing, placing, and curing (quite apart from climatic conditions during setting) are so great that they may far outweigh the initial advantages presented by an unusually sound and strong aggregate. On the other hand, the use of a poor aggregate is one of the easiest ways of obtaining concrete that will be a source of constant trouble.

A satisfactory aggregate must meet five main requirements: It must be clean; it must be durable; it must be correctly graded in size; it must be uniform both in grading and in quality; and it must not possess any chemical characteristic that will react with portland cement after mixing and placing. Grading can be controlled in the crushing and screening plant in the case of a crushed rock. Uniformity can be similarly controlled by close inspection of the supplies of aggregate. Cleanliness can be obtained if suitable measures are taken, and durability can be determined before an aggregate is selected for use. Both these properties are dependent on the geological history and composition of the rock to be used.[8.21]

The cleanliness required of coarse aggregate is similar to that required of fine aggregate; organic impurities are the most objectionable "dirt." These impurities are usually in the form of weak organic acids or their derivatives, which may seriously impair the setting of the cement. One of the earliest occasions on which the serious effects of organic matter on concrete was noted was during the construction of the Quinze and Kippewa Lake dams in the upper reaches of the Ottawa River, Quebec, by the Department of Public Works, Canada, in 1910 and 1911. The organic matter could not be detected by eye, since it had formed transparent coatings around the particles of the siliceous aggregate used. Eventually it was found that the impurity could be removed by washing the aggregate in a 3 per cent solution of commercial caustic soda. This was therefore done in a special plant. The concrete made with aggregate not so treated distintegrated rapidly.[8.22] A colorimetric test, involving the use of a similar solution of caustic soda, is now almost universally employed as an indicator of the presence of organic matter in aggregate. It is of special interest to note that organic acids will not be encountered in calcareous sands or in limestone or similar calcareous rocks, with the calcium carbonate of which the acids can react. This simple geological fact will often prove a useful guide in locating good aggregate. In "limestone districts," clean aggregates will usually be widespread; this is the case in Ontario, Canada, west of the Niagara escarpment, apart from a small area near Windsor.

Aggregate must often be washed with water not only for removing organic impurities but also for washing out surface dirt and dust. It is also imperative with some types of crushed rock in order to remove the rock dust attached to the rock fragments as they leave the crushing plant, which may be a potential source of trouble. Minute particles of feldspar formed during the crushing of some granites affect the quality of concrete, and other injurious minerals present in rock may have similar serious effects. The detection of these injurious minerals is related to the study of the durability of a proposed aggregate in a way similar to the use of petrology in building-stone investigations. It can therefore be investigated by physical tests on porosity, by freezing and thawing, and by soaking in salt solutions, always coordinated with petrological study of the rock under the microscope. Injurious minerals in building stones will be injurious minerals in aggregate and for the same reasons. Possibly the most serious defect is the presence of any material that will swell when in contact with water.

This last property is of unusual importance in connection with concrete, since many types of rock that would not be considered as building stones will often be used as concrete aggregate. The temptation to use rock that has to be excavated on a construction project as a cheap concrete aggregate has already been mentioned. It has probably been responsible for much of the poor-quality concrete seen today. There are not many jobs so fortunately placed as was the construction of the Denver Hilton Hotel in Denver, Colorado; on the site of the hotel a light-pink pea gravel was found which had to be excavated and was used as concrete aggregate. The gravel was so suitable for the unusual architectural treatment of the hotel building that acid was used to etch the precast concrete frames so that the aggregate would be exposed to view.[8.23] In many cases, engineers may have been forced to use unsuitable rock in this way against their better judgment. Limestone with any clay content, or so-called "argillaceous limestone," looks sound and durable when freshly quarried, but it is unsuitable for use as aggregate. Argillaceous shales and slates are similarly undesirable; Fig. 8.11 shows an extreme case of disintegration arising from the use of shale as aggregate; the rock is shown in place in the foreground. (Other types of shale, if relatively strong, can sometimes be used, although the typically laminated structure is always a source of weakness.) Clay in any form is therefore to be avoided in concrete aggregate; petrological examination will assist in its detection.

Porosity of rock is just as important a factor in aggregate as in building stones. In addition to the usual penetration of rain water into exposed aggregate, it must be remembered that when the concrete is placed in position it has a high water content so that the aggregate will be in a saturated condition. This may lead to strange results, especially if the concrete is subjected to frost before the outer part has had time to set permanently. The freezing of water thus trapped in the aggregate may sometimes lead to the disruption of otherwise sound concrete. This is a reminder that the aggregate used is only one of the variables involved in the preparation of good concrete. Possibly for this reason it is a little difficult to specify exactly the desirable characteristics of a high-grade concrete aggregate. The prohibition of such generally recognized materials as gypsum, anhydrite, and chert is frequently inserted. Some specifications also prohibit any clay content or limit it to a very small percentage. Metamorphic rocks of doubtful value can also be excluded by reference to fragments having a foliated structure. There remain

Fig. 8.11. Disintegration of concrete pedestal supporting a log flume, due (in part) to the use of local shale as aggregate. The shale, *in situ*, can be seen in the foreground. Lower part of pedestal has been patched, but disintegration has continued.)

a number of possible potentially dangerous mineral constituents, but it is impossible to list them all in the usual specification. To overcome this difficulty, a general clause restricting the use of aggregates to those obtained from approved sources of supply may sometimes be possible without hardship to contractors; alternatively, the engineer may himself arrange for the supply of satisfactory aggregate on the job. These are precautions by which close check can be kept on this important constituent of concrete.

Comments on aggregate for concrete thus far have necessarily been general, but it can be seen that study of the petrology of crushed rock and sand, as used for concrete making, is a vast field. There is available an extensive literature to which some guides are given in Appendix D. Three special matters, however, call for brief mention even in this summary. In those parts of the world where the ground water is heavily charged with sulfates, as in the plains of western Canada, special study must be made of the possibility of concrete disintegration due to reaction with such sulfates. If the danger is a real one, and this can readily be tested, then a special sulfate-resistant cement, such as was first developed

FIG. 8.12. Disintegration of concrete in the structure of a university stadium, due (in part) to the use of a local argillaceous limestone as aggregate.

by Dr. T. Thorvaldson for use in Winnipeg after sulfate reaction in concrete had been there detected, must be utilized with all requisite care.

A more modern requirement is the specially dense concrete needed in nuclear plants for shielding purposes. Among the special aggregates used to meet this requirement are limonite and barytes for modest increases in density; magnetite and ilmenite for medium increases; and ferrophosphorus or even steel punchings for extra-heavy concrete. Various mixtures of these several materials are naturally possible. Some difficulties have been experienced with the use of ferrophosphorus, but ilmenite has proved highly satisfactory and is probably the most widely used special aggregate for nuclear installations. Densities of 246 lb per cu ft have been obtained with ilmenite from St. Paul in the province of Quebec.[8.24]

Finally, one of the most complex and troublesome of all problems with concrete, the interaction of some types of aggregate with high-alkali cements, must be mentioned. Concrete is now so widely used as a construction material, and in almost all cases so satisfactory a material, that undue stress must not be placed upon this difficulty. At the same time, alkali-aggregate reactions do take place with some materials, and in certain localities serious trouble has resulted. Naturally, intensive study has been given to the problem which is, essenlially, one in the field of petrography; thus, its solution calls for special scientific investigation. It was first identified in 1940. Tests have now been devised and standardized for detecting most "unsound" aggregates, as they must be called. These include acidic and intermediate volcanic rocks and tuffs, cherts, and siliceous limestones.[8.25] Experience in the Kingston area of Ontario has revealed a dolomitic limestone that is not susceptible to the standard tests for reactive aggregates, and yet which does react with high-alkali cements such as have long been used normally in Quebec and eastern Ontario. The exact cause of this reaction is not yet known with certainty, but a simple bar test provides an infallible guide to the character of limestone aggregates; the major disadvantage of having such a test made is that it takes 3 months to obtain a positive answer. Care should, therefore be exercised in the use of dolomitic limestone as concrete aggregate, especially if the cement to be used has a higher than normal alkali content.[8.26]

Concrete technology, therefore, is still progressing. As it does so, the utility of this most versatile of construction materials will increase still further. Recent developments in the use of concrete made by placing coarse aggregate in forms and then intruding it with special cement grout seem to present great promise. Concrete made in this way is, indeed, artificial conglomerate, and this demonstrates, in a surprisingly vivid way, the absolute dependence of the character of concrete upon the character of its aggregate and so upon geology.[8.27]

8.12. Some Special Materials: *Coral.* One of the most widespread building materials in the Pacific area is one that was generally regarded as suitable only for specialized work until the years of the Second World War. Coral very quickly came into its own, and before the end of the war it became well known as the "Pacific lifesaver." There are many types of this organically formed rock, but that most useful as aggregate occurs in reefs and ledges and has characteristics similar to those of soft limestone. At least 90 per cent of coral is calcium carbonate; common densities range from 70 to 110 lb per cu ft in loose volume. It fractures into large lumps and so does not give much of the fine material also required for concrete aggregate. So-called "finger-coral" is much lighter, with densities from 60 to 80 lb per cu ft, loose volume; it is soft, fragile, and porous and does not make good concrete. The best type of coral for building purposes is generally found on the ocean side of islands rather than on the shores of lagoons, and correspondingly on the windward sides; the best of all is found on shores perpendicular to prevailing winds where there is a strong current. Clearly, the reasons for these variations are biological rather than geological, but knowledge of the variations has been used with good effect in the selection of coral as concrete aggregate, not only during the war years, but since then for the construction of massive concrete structures in connection with nuclear test work. Coral has also been widely used as rock fill and has been found to have good self-binding properties, so that when mixed with small quantities of cement it will yield a satisfactory mixed-in-place stabilized mix for economical wearing surfaces. It is worth noting that coral concrete has been made with sea water in the absence of fresh water, and the results have, apparently, been successful.[8.28]

Lightweight Aggregates—General. Coral has been mentioned first because of its unusual geological interest. There are, however, a number of materials that are much more widely used as lightweight aggregates for concrete. These may conveniently be grouped into four categories: those occurring naturally, those produced as by-products in manufacture, those manufactured from natural materials, and those which result in unusually lightweight concrete. Pumice, lava, and tufa—all volcanic rocks—are materials in the first group; they have long been used as aggregate, as evidenced by the reference to pumice aggregate on page 273. Fairly widely distributed, these materials require little processing beyond washing and screening before use. Cinders provide a well-known member of the second group, but they are not generally regarded as a geological material, even though they are, ultimately, derived from the earth. The slag that is produced in the manufacture of steel has at least the appearance of a naturally occurring rock. It is used as aggregate both in its normal condition and after being processed by one of the several methods now available for producing a lightweight product; "foamed slag" and "expanded slag" are two terms in common use to describe this specially prepared by-product. Manufactured aggregates are largely derived from certain types of clay that possess the property of expanding rapidly, or "bloating," when heated to the point of incipient fusion. Bloated clays have been used for the making of concrete for several decades; most of the material of this sort is produced by one or another of the specialized methods developed for the actual process of "bloating." In areas where suitable rock for aggregate is scarce, the possible use of clay that can thus be processed should always be kept in mind. Other aggregate manufacturing methods under development, and in use to a limited extent, depend upon the well-known process of "sintering" commonly followed in metallurgical work. Finally, when very lightweight concrete is required, this may be achieved by the use of an expanded vermiculite, a special variety of mica, or of expanded perlite, a type of volcanic glass. In each case, the material has the property of expanding, or "popping," when heated to the point of incipient fusion, and this is used as the basis of the preparation of the material for use as concrete (and even plaster) aggregate.[8.29]

Volcanic Ash. In areas where there has been volcanic action, the possible presence of volcanic ash must be kept in mind, since this can be a troublesome material if encountered on construction. Its name describes its character, the fine-grained loose deposit formed after violent volcanic eruptions, often carried by the wind for surprising distances from its point of origin. It will readily retain its "fresh" character for long periods, especially when protected by vegetal or other cover. During the construction of Alaskan military bases at the start of the Second World War, volcanic ash was encountered that had originated in the explosion of Mount Katmai in 1912. In one project under development for military purposes, an 18-in. layer of ash was found all over the area. Its abrasive quality greatly increased wear on construction equipment and even affected wearing apparel and leather. During the building of a wartime road on the island of New Britain, the Seabees excavated a sharply sloped hill that was found to consist of volcanic slag, or compacted volcanic ash. Trials showed that, when naturally fragmented to the size of pea gravel and rolled into place, the volcanic material formed what was practically a monolithic slab, an admirable wearing surface for heavy traffic. Its use spread and it was put to good service in paving landing fields and service areas. Demand for the material became so great that difficulty was experienced with normal methods of excavation, since drilling the necessary holes for explosive charges was slow. With the ingenuity so often demonstrated in times of war emergency, those responsible soon solved this problem by bringing up a Sherman tank and firing 75 mm shells directly into the face of the pit. Armor-piercing shells were found to be most suitable, giving 10-in.-diameter holes 10 ft deep, and doing in half an hour three times as much work as had been possible for a normal crew working a 12-hr shift.[8.30] The method is not recommended for normal use.

Fly Ash. Another type of ash that is achieving importance in civil engineering practice, perhaps because of the increasing amount of it that is becoming available, is the ash collected in the flues of powerhouses in which boilers are fired with pulverized solid fuel. Admittedly it is not a naturally occurring geological product, but it is of such interest and of such increasing importance, that it calls for at least brief mention. It is usually a fine gray powder, having silica, alumina, and iron oxide as its main constituents. It is relatively inert but has the valuable property of producing a pozzuolanic effect when used in the making of concrete with portland cement. For such use, fly ash should have a silica content of not less than 35 per cent, and a loss on ignition of not more than 12 per cent. Other more detailed requirements can be specified. The material has a bulk density of between 50 and 70 lb per cu ft. Because of its pozzuolanic property, it gives increased resistance against chemical attack to any concrete in which it is used, a reduction in the heat generated during setting, a reduction in the rate at which the concrete will gain strength, and a corresponding extension of the period during which this effect takes place. Fly ash is, therefore, a valuable "man-made geological product." One of its main disadvantages is that, since it is man-made, its properties are very variable, even from the same power station, so that unusual control has to be exercised over its properties in order to ensure its satisfactory use as an addition to ordinary concrete.[8.31]

8.13. Conclusion. These brief notes provide but an introduction to an application of geology of singular interest and economic importance. To those expert in the fields touched upon, the brevity of the treatment may appear to be almost foolhardy. But the intention has been not to attempt detailed consideration of the geological aspects of any of the building materials mentioned, but by this general coverage, to illustrate the geological origin of many of the commonest materials used on construction. With aggregate delivered by rail or truck from some source off the job, with brick and tile delivered from a modern manu-facturing plant inspected and tested against standard specifications, with cement, lime, and plaster delivered in convenient bags "direct from the plant," and with even cut stone now delivered in packages, sawed to finished dimensions at the quarry and delivered on the job as a "finished product," it is all too easy for the engineer on the construction job to forget that these and the other materials mentioned are derived from the earth, have a geological origin, consist of minerals that can be pre-determined, and so are subject to study and analysis in just the same way as are other materials that are truly the products of the earth. Especially is this true of natural stone, whether in crushed or finished form. And with just a little care taken in advance, notably by carrying out a few check petrographical analyses, possible trouble can be avoided in those cases, fortunately few in number, when deleterious minerals are present. It is, perhaps, not without significance that one of the very few petrographic papers in the literature of civil engineering known to the writer is one to be found in the Proceedings of the In-stitution of Civil Engineers describing a "post-mortem" examination of bad staining in granite, naturally found to have been caused by the weathering of an unstable mineral, in this case a type of dark mica.[8.32] The great activity in concrete research circles in connection with alkali-aggregate reaction will probably ultimately have much beneficial effect, despite the difficult problem with which it is concerned. Because of the research being carried on in this field, more civil engineers than ever will realize that "rock" is not just an inert material to be accepted for use merely on the basis of mechanical tests, but is rather a complex assemblage of minerals, whose study is a procedure that may be of the greatest possible benefit to their own work.

Suggestions for Further Reading

Since the main purpose of this chapter has been to direct attention to the geological aspect of natural building materials, the best suggestion for further reading that can be made is to urge that, when the necessity arises, contact be made with the appropriate geological survey for copies of the papers it has available relevant to the material being investigated. Even brief examination of the lists of publications of geological surveys will reveal what a wealth of information is already available in print on this aspect of applied geology.

A singularly useful, general but brief introduction to the study of building materials as a group is provided by:

Handyside, C. C., "Building Materials," 3d ed., 340 pp., The Architectural Press, London, 1958.

There are also available many good general treatments of such divisions of the whole subject as building stones, clay technology, etc., but these will only be of full avail when correlated with specific local information. Engineering societies have devoted much attention to the testing of natural building materials. Attention may therefore also be directed to the many publications of the American Society for Testing and Materials (1960 Race St., Philadelphia) and the Highway Research Board (2101 Constitution Ave., Washington, D.C.), lists of which should be available for ready reference by all engineers concerned with the procurement and use of natural building materials. In the field of concrete technology, publications of the American Concrete Institute (P.O. Box 4754, Redford Station, Detroit, Mich.) and of Concrete Publications, Ltd. (14 Dartmouth St., London S.W.1, England) will be useful.

PERIODICALS AND TRADE JOURNALS

So much valuable information is available in the periodicals and trade journals associated with the production and use of natural building materials that this partial list is presented for convenience, as the papers listed, with two notable exceptions, will not normally come within the purview of civil engineers.

Cement and Lime Manufacture, bimonthly, Concrete Publications, Ltd., London.
Cement, Lime and Gravel, monthly, Birmingham, England.
Concrete and Constructional Engineering, monthly, Concrete Publications, Ltd., London.
Crushed Stone Journal, quarterly, National Crushed Stone Association, Washington, D.C.
Journal of the A.C.I., monthly, American Concrete Institute, Detroit.
Publications of the National Sand and Gravel Association, Washington, D.C.
Publications of the National Lime Association, Washington, D.C.
Pit and Quarry, monthly, Chicago.
Quarry Manager's Journal, monthly, Quarry Manager's Journal, Ltd., London.
Rock Products, monthly, Chicago.

Chapter 9

TUNNELS AND UNDERGROUND EXCAVATIONS

Ezekias fortified his city, and brought in water into the midst thereof: he digged the hard rock with iron, and made wells for water.

> Ecclesiasticus 48:17 (probably the earliest reference to the famous water-supply works for the city of Jerusalem.)

TUNNELING MUST have been one of the earliest constructional activities of man. It may be that natural tunnels and other results of water action such as "swallow holes," frequently found in limestone and similar formations, first suggested to early man the idea of an artificial passage through rock. The rock or cliff dweller may have been an example to other human beings in distant ages; but however came the inspiration, excavated underground dwellings and temples, the first tunnels, are to be found in many of the ancient civilizations that have been investigated in recent years. Excavated passages beneath the earth were early utilized for purposes other than residence. One of the first of the more general utilitarian purposes for which tunnels were specially constructed was for drainage, often in connection with mining and quarrying work. Water supply and road construction also necessitated the digging of tunnels at an early date in the history of man.

Today tunnels are used for the same purposes. They facilitate transportation and are often used in the generation of water power as well as in the provision of water supply. Exceptional uses are to be found, but tunnels generally can still be classed as they were 2,000 years ago either as aqueducts or as viaducts. It is indeed strange to reflect that this ancient branch of construction has changed but little in achievement, despite great advances in method throughout the centuries. A tunnel is and can be only a tunnel, having a certain length and a certain cross section. The long Alpine tunnels are indeed magnificent achievements, but so also are many of the long tunnels of the pre-Christian era, especially when the construction methods then in use are considered.

9.2. Historical Notes. Brief mention of some ancient feats of tunneling may therefore rightly lay claim to a place in even the most cursory review of the art. Although geology as a separate branch of science was not recognized in these early years, brief reference here to a few of these tunnels is instructive. Examples of tunnels of some sort are to be found in almost all ancient civilizations, notably in Egypt where some of the rock-cut galleries of the early Egyptian kings are over 750 ft long. In Malta one may see underground temples and gathering places, at least 5,000 years old, hewn out of solid sandstone with flints which must have been brought to the island from the mainland. These early tunnels were generally built through the softer types of solid rock, but some were excavated through unconsolidated materials and so required immediate lining for stability. A notable example was the tunnel under the river Euphrates, probably the first submarine tunnel of which any record exists. It was 12 ft wide and 15 ft high and was built in the dry, since the river was temporarily diverted.

The Romans were preeminent in early tunnel construction because of their achievements and because of the improvements in method that they effected. They appear to have introduced the use of fire into tunnel construction, utilizing the principle (known to others earlier) that a heated rock if suddenly cooled will crack to some extent and so make excavation easier. They also most probably employed vinegar instead of water as a cooling agent when working in limestone and similar rocks, utilizing the acid nature of the vinegar to disintegrate the rock chemically as well as physically. The sufferings of the slaves who had to apply such methods can hardly be imagined. It is known also that the Romans utilized intermediate vertical shafts and even inclined adits in the construction of their longer tunnels, notably of the tunnel built for the drainage of Lake Fucino; this tunnel is driven through limestone for a distance of $3\frac{1}{2}$ miles and is 6 by 10 ft in theoretical section. It is said that 30,000 men were employed for 11 years on its construction. Volcanic tufa was another of the softer rocks pierced by these intrepid builders; one notable tunnel through this material, that which gave the road between Naples and Pozzuoli passage through the Ponlipio Hills, was 3,000 ft long and 25 ft wide.[9.1]

There are many other examples from the past, but only one will be mentioned. Lake Copais is now an area of about 100 sq miles of dry land, fertile and well cultivated, located near the east coast of Greece. It lies generally about 300 ft above the level of the sea from which it is separated by a steep range of hills. The area was drained in 1886 by a French company. After drainage had lowered the water level, the engineers found that the ancient inhabitants (of the prehistoric Minoan period, 2000 B.C.?) had drained it previously. The ancient works then discovered led to some ancient drainage canals and to some of the *katavothras*, natural tunnels in the form of large fissures through the limestone rock. Unfortunately, although these interesting natural tunnels were so effectively used in the past, the largest of them is now blocked up, and so a modern drainage tunnel had to be constructed. North of the drained area in the pass to the sea at Laryma, there are 16 shafts which appear to have been put down by the prehistoric workers mentioned with a view to tunnel construction, although the work had not proceeded far. The whole region is of great interest to the geologist and the civil engineer.[9.2]

The Middle Ages saw no advance in the technique of tunnel building, and even the introduction of gunpowder (first used in tunnel work during the period from 1679 to 1681 at Malpas, France) had little immediate effect. It was the extension of canals and the introduction of railways that finally initiated the great advance of the last 100 years during which most of the tunnels now in use were constructed. Although so rudely built and simple in conception, ancient tunnel works were inevitably dependent upon geological considerations—not only in design but also in construction; this is evidenced by the possibility of the use of vinegar and the specially hard nature of the flints and corundum utilized for cutting tools. Simultaneously with advance in tunneling technique has gone the development of geology, and so today the two are intimately associated.

9.3. A General Note. Of all the activities of the civil engineer, tunneling is without question that to which the study of geology can most fitly and usefully be applied; geological problems alone affect design and construction methods once the general location and basic dimensions of a tunnel are determined. Except in the case of special tunnels, such as those partially driven through an artificial deposit of clay (e.g., the Sixtieth Street and the Fourteenth Street Tunnels in New York) and those isolated examples built as tunnel linings prior to having fill placed over them (e.g., the Golden Circle Railroad in the Cripple Creek mining district of Colorado, where the line was carried in this way across a future refuse dumping ground), all tunnels are driven through a part of the earth's crust. Accurate location and construction methods depend therefore on the rock through which the tunnel is to be driven; the necessity of lining must usually be determined by the behavior of the rock when exposed to the air and possibly to water. A thorough geological investigation before construction begins is, therefore, of paramount importance in all tunnel work.

Basically, accurate geological sections along all possible routes available for the tunnel are the first requirement; knowledge of the characteristics of the rock to be encountered is the second and of little less importance. With this information at hand, the engineer can decide whether or not the construction of the proposed tunnel is a practical and economical possibility. He can determine with some semblance of accuracy what cover of rock must be allowed between the tunnel line and the ground

surface in the case of a water tunnel in which the water is to be conducted under a pressure head (hereinafter called a *pressure tunnel*).
The necessity of, and the design of, an artificial lining for the tunnel
can be generally determined, and the likelihood of having to grout the
rock adjacent to the tunnel can usually be foretold from such information. Finally, such geological advice will give to the engineer at least
some indication (often quite accurate) of the percentage of overbreak
that he is likely to encounter when construction is under way and for
which allowance must be made in his estimates. To the contractor for
tunnel work, geological information is equally vital; his entire construction program and construction methods depend on the material to be
encountered, whereas his main hazards, such as underground water,
are determined solely by geological conditions. On at least one major
tunneling project, preliminary geological studies suggested the possibility
of finding valuable mineral ores within the tunnel, the sale of which
might have paid part of the construction cost. Unfortunately, not a trace
of ore was found.

These several aspects of the application of the results of geological
investigation to tunnel work will be considered in some detail and
illustrated by examples from practice. There are some general observations which first demand attention. Clearly, the ideal condition in tunneling is to encounter one easily excavated material only, which contains
no water-bearing fissures and is unaffected when exposed to air. Rarely
is anything approaching such an ideal material found; the London clay
which most of the London tube railway tunnels penetrate in part is
perhaps as close to the ideal as is obtained anywhere. Normally, tunnel
locations can be changed only for economic considerations, and so no
search for suitable tunneling material is ordinarily feasible; rock conditions at a particular location have to be accepted by the engineer and
explored thoroughly in order to render design and construction as certain
as possible.

In general, Archean or Precambrian rocks, the oldest types geologically,
are difficult to excavate; construction in such formations is consequently
relatively expensive. Paleozoic rocks, on the other hand (younger,
geologically), are usually the most simple to excavate and, consequently,
they afford more economical construction. Formations of recent origin
increase construction difficulties. Tunneling becomes generally more
difficult as the formation becomes younger, and recent sand and gravel
deposits are particularly awkward to drive through. Novel methods have
been adopted in tunnel work for penetrating such materials; the practice of freezing the water in water-bearing strata is perhaps one of the
most ingenious. So far as is known, this method has been used
only once in tunneling (a tunnel for pedestrian traffic built at Stockholm, Sweden, during the years 1884 and 1886 by a Captain Lindmark,

through coarse gravel, sand, and clay, 80 ft of which was driven by freezing). It is said, however, that Siberian miners have long used the method in their mining operations. Grouting or cementation is a most valuable process for this kind of work, as will presently be described, and an even more recent development is the use of chemical solidification processes for water-bearing ground.

As in every other type of civil engineering work, economic considerations generally predominate in tunnel design and construction. Here, too, geology is of avail, since not only will the materials to be penetrated affect the actual cost of construction, but they will definitely affect the speed at which progress in excavation may be anticipated. From estimates, detailed comparisons of the costs of various alternative routes for the work proposed can be prepared. In the Kinlochleven hydroelectric scheme in Scotland (33,000 hp with a head of 1,000 ft), such a study led to the adoption of an open reinforced-concrete conduit, following the contour of the hillside, as the main aqueduct. In the neighboring Lochaber scheme (120,000 hp with a head of 800 ft), the main aqueduct is a tunnel; the selection of this route was based on a similar and extensive economic study, utilizing preliminary geological information.

9.4. Preliminary Work. Normally no deviation from general survey methods will be necessary in obtaining the requisite geological sections along possible tunnel routes. By their nature, however, tunnels will usually be located in such a way that accurate preliminary correlation of the strata to be expected in the tunnel with surface conditions will be difficult. Subaqueous tunnels, for example, can be readily checked only from indications on adjacent dry land; tunnels under cities will pierce strata covered by built-up city areas; and tunnels through high mountain ranges will be at great depths below the surface in some places—over 7,000 ft for the Simplon Tunnel in Switzerland. In many such cases, it will be impracticable, if not impossible, to put down the usual exploratory drill holes, which generally serve to confirm the deductions of geological survey work. It is for this reason that tunnel-construction records (to be mentioned later) are of vital importance.

Clearly, the first task of the geological adviser on a tunnel project is to indicate whether he considers the geological conditions anticipated favorable for tunnel construction. The civil engineer must then decide whether or not the tunnel can be constructed economically or if at all. It is of interest to note that in connection with the Simplon Tunnel, it has been stated that:[9.3]

Had the geologists been quite accurate in their preliminary investigation and reports, and had they truly and correctly anticipated the dangers and obstacles that were eventually met with in soft rock, the "Great Spring" or river of cold water, the high temperatures and hot springs, and the "creep" or lifting of the floor, no one would have dared to undertake the contract, and the tunnel would never have been constructed.

Perhaps it is as well for human welfare that in this instance preliminary geological advice was not perfect. It should be added that the geological structures met in the European Alps are some of the most difficult known in the science.

As has been noted, this tunnel is in places over 7,000 ft below the surface of the ground, piercing high ranges of the Alps, so that it is not surprising that preliminary predictions were not accurate; they did, however, give a reasonable conception of what rock would be encountered (gneiss, mica schist, and some limestone, or "sugar marble"). An even more serious result of incomplete preliminary information occurred during the construction of the Lötschberg Tunnel, from Kandersteg to Gopperstein, between October, 1906, and September, 1911. The tunnel is 9.04 miles long, and it was believed that it would penetrate solid rock (granite) throughout. Unfortunately, about 2 miles in from one portal, the drilling broke into an ancient glacial gorge, now filled with detritus and followed by the Kander River, and in an instant 8,000 cu yd of material rushed in and 25 men lost their lives. The heading had to be bulkheaded off and the course changed; only in this way was the tunnel eventually finished, finally being half a mile longer than had been anticipated.[9.4] Had geophysical methods of exploration then been available, trouble might have been avoided.

The accumulated experience gained in the several Alpine tunnels is being put to good use in the driving of the Mont Blanc vehicular tunnel. Linking Entreves in Italy (at 4,526 ft) and Hameau-des-Palerins near Chamonix in France (at 3,946 ft), the new tunnel will be 39,032 ft long —the longest road tunnel in the world. Designed to provide two lanes of traffic, it is so graded that near its midpoint it will reach an elevation of 5,232 ft so that drainage can be gravitational from both working faces. It will penetrate calcareous schist and granite and will, almost literally, go under Mont Blanc.[9.5]

The example of the Lötschberg Tunnel serves to demonstrate that in the case of deep tunnels, even expert geological investigation will not always reveal difficulties to be encountered. Another example of serious trouble in tunnel work occurred in the construction of the Las Raices Tunnel, Chile, for the Transandine Railway. It is 14,885 ft long and pierces a section of the Andes. Surface indications (and there were few rock exposures above the tunnel) suggested that it would be driven solely through porphyrite; thus, no trouble with water was anticipated. Driving disclosed that the porphyrite rock was generally firm, in some places cracked and fissured with bands of clay, and that there was some in-

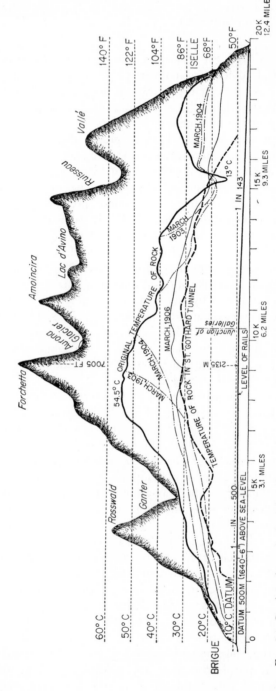

Fig. 9.1. Section through the Alps along center line of the Simplon Tunnel, showing temperatures encountered (and also in the St. Gothard Tunnel). (*Reproduced by permission of the Institution of Civil Engineers, from reference 9.3.*)

filtration of water. Practically without warning, a break-in occurred at about 1,750 ft from one face at a junction of a full section of the tunnel and a smaller leading section; a large amount of mud poured into the tunnel through quite a small hole and trapped 42 men. Fortunately, they were eventually rescued by means of a special rescue tunnel (the construction of which was a remarkable piece of work). The significance of the failure geologically, however, was that the break-in of 2,616 cu yd of material caused a hole to form in the ground above the tunnel. This earth movement greatly facilitated the investigations of the failure. It was found that, mainly from the presence of a boulder of granodiorite, the tunnel had tapped and drained an ancient glacial bed which had been filled in with river deposits. The official report stated, "The accident could not have been foreseen for a rivulet which joins the River Agrio, 150 meters upstream of the tunnel mouth, forms a waterfall, the lip of which is 30 meters higher than the roof of the tunnel, this seeming to show that the thickness of rock over the tunnel was ample." Again, it will be seen what trouble can result from underground conditions caused by glacial action of the past.[9.6]

Diamond drilling along the line of a proposed tunnel is made a supplement to preliminary geological investigation whenever possible. The results of this exploration are positive so far as they go; but their application to tunnel work must be considered in conjunction with the geological survey work also available. Cooperation of this kind has prefaced the construction of many important tunnels, among which are several of those that serve the great metropolitan area of New York. So important are these tunnels that a brief description of some of them will be useful.

9.5. Tunnels for New York. At the outset, perhaps, it should be said that some of the early experiences in tunneling in the New York area were not very fortunate. The first Hudson River tunnel was started in 1874, but apparently no exploratory work had been done in advance. The work met with repeated misfortunes; it was interrupted several times and was completed only in 1908. Another example of early work, in which test soundings were utilized but apparently not with geological correlation, is that of the East River Gas Tunnel, constructed between 1891 and 1894 for the purpose of taking three gas mains across the East River to the city of New York. About 10 pipe soundings were made in the two river channels under which the tunnel was to pass, and these indicated a solid rock bottom throughout, on which assumption a contract was let and work started. Trouble with water was soon encountered, however, and eventually the tunnel ran into a vein of soft decomposed rock. Construction methods had to be radically changed; compressed air and a shield had to be used before the work was finally completed, somewhat naturally not under the original contract.[9.1]

Just after the turn of the century, the Board of Water Supply of the

City of New York initiated one of the greatest water-supply under-takings that the world had yet seen, the Catskill water-supply project, which even in this day of great projects is still a monumental piece of engineering. It consisted essentially in the construction of two large impounding reservoirs in the Catskill Mountains, to the north of New York, and of an aqueduct 110 miles long to convey the water so obtained to the city area, together with other associated works, some of which are themselves of considerable magnitude. Two large pressure tunnels were also constructed beneath the city for the distribution of the Catskill water; City Tunnel No. 1 was completed in 1917 and City Tunnel No. 2 in 1936. The successive chief engineers to the Board of Water Supply have been aided by many distinguished consultants, only three of whom can be mentioned here—Professors W. O. Crosby, J. F. Kemp, and C. P. Berkey, all famous geologists, who were appointed in 1905 and 1906 to advise on geological matters affecting the works. From the very start of the work in 1905, the prosecution of this great enterprise was char-acterized by the closest possible cooperation between geologists and engi-neers. In the words of Dr. Berkey:

In this project virtually nothing was taken for granted. Every new step was the subject of special investigation with the avowed purpose of determining the conditions to be met; and, when these were determined, the plan of con-struction and design of the structure were brought into conformity with them. In this manner specifications could be drawn with sufficient accuracy to avoid most of the dangers, mistakes, and special claims commonly attending such work. Very few features or conditions were discovered in construction that were not indicated by the exploratory investigations, and such as were found proved to be of minor significance and were cared for at moderate expense.

When it is considered that the country traversed by the aqueduct (as is shown so clearly by the accompanying geological section along the whole route) "exhibits so great a variety of natural features and physical conditions that virtually every individual section of this aqueduct pre-sented special geological problems" and that the dam sites were generally marked by great deposits of glacial drift with ancient river valleys thus covered from view, this remarkable result will be more fully appreciated.

Fortunately for the engineering profession, the results of this co-operative work were made generally available by those in charge of the work through technical books, papers, and articles contributed to engi-neering journals.[9, 7] The paper by Dr. Berkey and J. F. Sanborn, presented to the American Society of Civil Engineers in 1923, is already an engi-neering classic; it is safe to say that the practice that it describes is respon-sible for some of the change in attitude of the civil engineering profession toward geology which has taken place since the turn of the century,

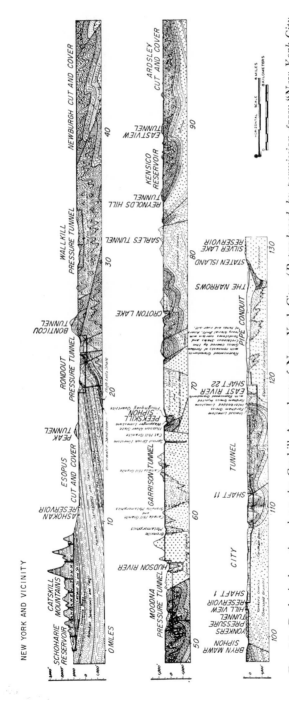

FIG. 9.2. Geological section along the Catskill Aqueduct of New York City. (Reproduced, by permission, from "New York City and Vicinity," Guidebook 9 of 16th International Geological Congress.)

293

certainly in North America. For those interested in a brief account of the geological features affecting engineering work in and around the city of New York, reference may be made to "Guidebook 9," prepared for the Sixteenth International Geological Congress held in 1933. Two of Dr. Berkey's statements from this interesting handbook have already been quoted; the following quotation is a description of one of the most unusual parts of the Catskill Aqueduct, the Hudson River crossing, the general location of which can be seen in the geological section (Fig. 9.2):

On the basis of preliminary field studies, therefore, the Storm King crossing was selected because it appeared, from field evidence, that at this place a tunnel could be driven in a single formation of essentially the quality of a granite without encountering a fault beneath the gorge. . . .

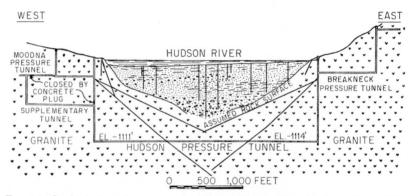

FIG. 9.3. Geological section across the Hudson River, New York, at Storm King, based on exploratory borings for the Catskill Aqueduct crossing (indicated in the section). (*Reproduced, by permission, from "New York City and Vicinity," ed. by Dr. C. P. Berkey, Guidebook 9 of 16th International Geological Congress.*)

It was commonly believed, however, that the Hudson River followed a great fault throughout much of its course and that this was the chief reason for its straight course and apparent independence of other structural control. In the preliminary studies therefore, three important questions had to be determined before suitable specifications could be drawn—first, the depth of the channel, so that the grade of the tunnel could be fixed; second, the kind of rock to be penetrated, so that cost could be estimated; third, whether any special weaknesses or dangers were likely to be encountered, so that suitable provision for them could be made.

When explorations were undertaken at this particular site great difficulty was encountered in determining the depth of channel, and very much greater depth was found than was anticipated from previous geologic knowledge. . . .

The difficulty was increased because the Hudson carries a heavy river traffic. The boring equipment had to be anchored in midstream in the main traffic channel, where there was always danger of interference. Furthermore, the gorge is filled with mixed material in which large boulders are numerous.

It was necessary to begin a boring with very large casing (18-inch) so that reductions could be made in passing through these obstructions.

After more than a year, borings to bedrock were successfully made on both sides of the river, finding granite on both sides. The gorge was found to be at least 500 feet (152 meters) deep for a width of 3,000 feet (914 meters). How much deeper it might be out in the center of the gorge no one could tell. A boring placed in mid-channel finally succeeded in getting to greater depth, reaching 765 feet (233 meters) without touching the rock floor. . . .

This fact, together with the slow rate of progress being made by the borings, finally led to the adoption of another plan for testing the ground beneath the river. The final working shaft on each side of the river was put down to a depth of about 200 feet (61 meters), and at that level a room was cut in the side wall, where a diamond drill was placed. This was set up to drill at an angle so as to penetrate the ground beneath the gorge out under the river. The first two borings, one on each side, were set to reach a depth in the center of 1,400 feet (427 meters) below sea level. These were successfully run in sound rock, and it was then decided to drill two others at a smaller angle, cutting the central ground at a maximum depth of 950 feet (290 meters) below sea level. In these borings sound rock, of granite type, was found continuously across the gorge. By this time the boring in the river had reached its maximum depth of 765 feet (233 meters) without touching bottom. With these data in hand, it was considered unnecessary to carry explorations further. . . .

When construction was finished the conditions uncovered in the Hudson River pressure tunnel were essentially as indicated by the exploratory and other investigations. The Storm King granite is continuous across the gorge. There are no great faults in the gorge at this point. The rock is sound and presented no special construction problem.

This extensive program of exploratory work is typical of the work done by the Board of Water Supply. On the 18-mile City Tunnel No. 1, for example, 46,000 lin ft of exploratory borings were put down, and more than 50,000 ft were drilled for City Tunnel No. 2; all were put down in conformity with geological advice. The same pattern was continued and the experience gained on the earlier tunnels was applied when New York undertook the much greater Delaware project, which involved the most extensive tunneling work ever carried out on any project. From the Rondout Reservoir, west of Poughkeepsie, the main aqueduct runs as a deep pressure tunnel for 85 miles to the Hill View Reservoir of the Catskill scheme; together with the connecting City Tunnel No. 2, the total length of this one tunnel is almost 105 miles. The East Delaware Tunnel (25 miles) connects the Pepacton and Rondout Reservoirs, and the West Delaware Tunnel (44 miles) connects the Cannonsville and Rondout Reservoirs; the latter was holed through in January, 1960, and marks the beginning of the last stage of this vast water-supply project, designed to satisfy the water demands of New York City until the end of the century.

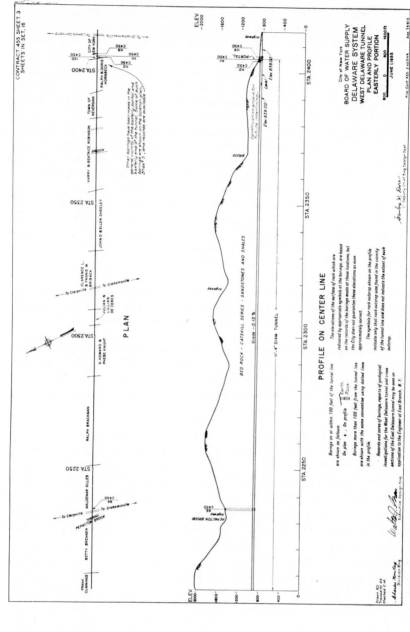

FIG. 9.4. A typical contract drawing for a New York water-supply tunnel. (*Reproduced by permission of the Board of Water Supply, New York.*)

296

A succession of papers by T. W. Fluhr has kept the profession informed of the geological conditions experienced through all this hardrock tunnel work and has presented to geologists details of geological structure that would otherwise have been unknown.[9.8] To summarize the geology of the Delaware Tunnels is clearly impossible; suffice it to say that the rock formations encountered were similar to, and an extension of, those already described in connection with the Catskill Tunnels. A number of major faults were encountered, but as a result of careful preliminary work in test drilling from the surface, and in some cases drilling ahead from working faces, soft ground conditions were always predicted and successfully planned for in the tunnel driving. One of the most critical sections was where the main tunnel passes under the Kensico Reservoir of the Catskill scheme; poor ground was detected in this area. The grade of the tunnel was therefore dropped to an elevation of −650, or more than 1,000 ft beneath the water level in the reservoir; special precautions were taken in driving, after unusually careful test drilling, and the tunnel was driven and then lined without trouble. This experience showed that faulting and rock decay, under the conditions here encountered, diminish rapidly with depth. The methods developed for driving through major faults on the Delaware Tunnels have provided a wealth of valuable information, now fortunately available on record for the information of all who encounter similar difficulties in tunnel work elsewhere.

The vehicular tunnels which so greatly aid traffic to and from Manhattan Island were also marked by unusual geological conditions. Possibly the most difficult of all was the Queens Midtown Tunnel, holed through successfully in 1939. Figure 9.5 shows the geological character of the ground penetrated by this tunnel. Even in this summary form, it can be seen to be unusually complex, involving tunneling with a shield in soft ground, artificial ground (formed by the clay blanket), and solid rock; in some sections the lower parts of the shields were in rock and the upper in loose soil. Compressed air naturally had to be used; a maximum pressure of $37\frac{1}{2}$ psi proved to be necessary. Illustrative of the conditions that had to be faced is the fact that at one time, one of the working faces was in 8 ft of lumps of coal (deposited long before in the river bed) of egg size and larger at the top; then 9 ft of sand, clay, gravel, and boulders; and finally 8 ft of sound rock in the invert. Under such conditions air was lost at surprising rates, even breaking up and eroding the clay blanket in the river bed, but the face was never lost and the tunnel driving was completed without a single fatality due to bends. It is difficult to imagine a more hazardous tunnel job; its successful completion is a tribute alike to the contractor's skill and to the very detailed foreknowledge of the subsurface conditions that was made available by geological studies.[9.9]

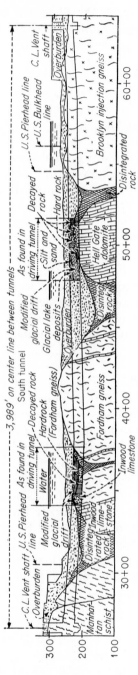

FIG. 9.5. Diagrammatic section across the East River, New York, showing geological conditions encountered during the driving of the East River Vehicular Tunnel. (*Reproduced by permission of the Editor, Engineering News-Record.*)

There may finally be mentioned the Wards Island Sewer Tunnel which was constructed during the period from 1935 to 1937. Preliminary borings although carefully taken, did not disclose the extremely soft, almost fluid, consistency of some decayed and disintegrated rock deep underground which finally necessitated a complete change of grade in the river section. The tunnel was constructed to deliver sewage from interceptor sewers on Manhattan Island to the new treatment plant on Wards Island in the East River, and the original plans were made for a depth of 297 ft. This proved too shallow, and the tunnel was finally put through at a depth of 510 ft below water level. The conditions encountered are clearly seen in Fig. 9.6, which also shows the location of the drill holes originally put down and the additional holes drilled after the work was temporarily closed in December, 1936, following the discovery that the seam of soft chloritic mass (of the consistency of fine mud) made further progress at that level practically impossible. One of the original borings had passed through this material; but as the hole had been drilled from the river, it had not been possible to secure such reliable samples as usual, and the wholly unsubstantial quality of the material was underestimated. The cross section illustrates how the secondary drill holes disclosed satisfactory conditions at a lower grade; work was resumed in March, 1937, and the headings were holed through 2 months later.[9.10]

9.6. Underwater Tunnels. Visitors to London, England, who have occasion to use Wapping Station on the East London line of the London Underground may notice a simple plaque bearing these words, "Thames Tunnel at Wapping designed by Sir Marc Isambard Brunel (1769–1845) and completed in 1843. Isambard K. Brunel (1806–1859) was Engineer-in-Charge 1825–1828." Thus was the centenary of the death of the younger Brunel marked at the site of the first underwater tunnel ever to be completed; the plaque was erected in 1959 by London Transport. The tunnel is still in regular use; its completion marked a victory of unusual ingenuity and heroic courage over what seemed at times to be insuperable obstacles. The ground conditions encountered were almost as varied as those met in the Queens Midtown Tunnel, New York, although there was no solid rock present. The contrast between the two jobs, one done with crude and simple equipment, the other with all the aids of modern construction techniques, is a vivid reminder of the progress made during the last century in construction methods.

It is said that Brunel got the idea of the shield with which he built the tunnel while examining a specimen of *Teredo navalis* in a piece of oak; he noted how the little mollusc bored its way into the wood, working under the protection of its own shell. He presented the idea to the Institution of Civil Engineers in 1824; a company was formed; Brunel was named engineer. Test borings were taken across the river near the

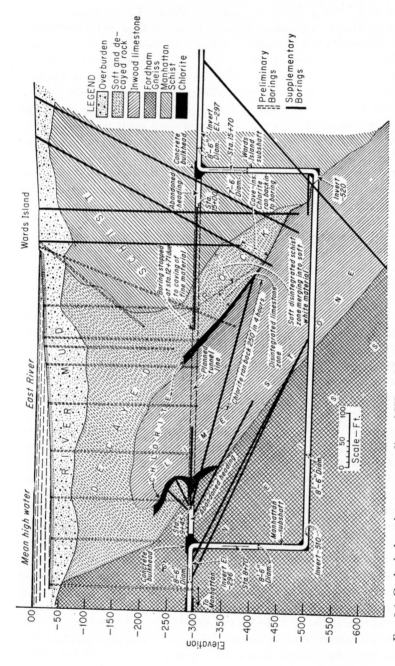

FIG. 9.6. Geological section on center line of Wards Island Sewer Tunnel, New York, as revealed by test drilling, showing necessary relocation of the tunnel because of chlorite seams. (*Reproduced by permission of the Editor, Engineering News-Record.*)

ferry that the tunnel was designed to supersede. The opinions of "eminent geologists" were obtained, to the effect that the tunnel should not go lower beneath the river bed than was absolutely necessary. This is one case in which geological advice was less than helpful. Trouble was encountered soon after construction commenced, owing to inadequate cover, and on May 18, 1827, a bad blow occurred and the tunnel was flooded. This was but the first of many worries. The works were shut down for 6 years because of lack of funds, but Brunel's personal enthusiasm eventually led to the resumption of operations in 1836, and the tunnel was successfully completed in 1843. His great granddaughter has told of Brunel's practice of personally examining samples of soil from the working face every 2 hr, day and night. Presumably on the insistence of his wife, Brunel had a basket arrangement rigged up outside his bedroom window so that the samples could be pulled up in the night for him to examine. Following his examination, he wrote his instructions, and these were sent down in the basket and back to the job. This went on for 4 years. It is not surprising to read that Brunel and his wife found themselves waking regularly every 2 hr throughout the night for many years after the tunnel was completed. In the face of such devotion to duty, it is sad to record that Brunel never did get paid all of his promised professional fee as engineer to this first of underwater tunnels.[9.11]

Better geological advice was obtained for the second Thames Tunnel, a small foot tunnel between London Bridge and Limehouse, still in existence but not in use. P. H. Barlow was the engineer; he also used a shield, although of a new design. Since he was advised by geologists of the thickness of the London clay in this area, he located his tunnel, which is 7 ft in diameter, well below the river bed and in London clay throughout; as a result, the job was completed between April 26 and October 8, 1869. In great contrast is the modern Dartford-Purfleet Tunnel, 4,700 ft long and 30½ ft in external diameter, which crosses under the Thames at a location that necessitated driving through solid chalk and a variety of soils including Thames gravel. The use of compressed air was essential; it is said to be the largest tunnel yet constructed under air. Even with air, however, some of the ground to be penetrated had to be pretreated by grouting with a specialized process; grout tubes were inserted from the surface of the river in advance of tunneling. A typical working face was 13 ft of clay, 7 ft of grouted sand and gravel, and 11 ft of solid chalk. Excavated chalk was pulverized, mixed with water, and pumped as a slurry to the surface.[9.12]

During the construction of the Almendares vehicular tunnel, connecting two of the most popular residential districts of Havana, in Cuba, unusual geological conditions were revealed by the intensive subsurface investigations carried out before completion of designs. Two approaches, totaling about 1,000 ft, join an underwater tunnel section 708 ft long. On

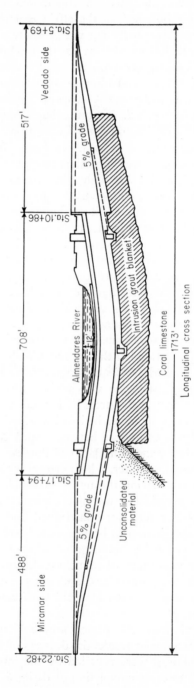

FIG. 9.7. Simplified geological section along the center line of the Almendares Tunnel, Havana, Cuba. *(Reproduced by permission of the American Society of Civil Engineers.)*

the Miranar side, ground conditions consisted of heavy layers of peat, overlying clay, and silt with sand and gravel lenses. Approximately halfway across the Almendares River, outcropping coral limestone was encountered which continued as an available foundation bed for most of the remainder of the structure. Extensive testing revealed that water could be controlled in the soil deposits by the use of well points, and the concrete approach structure was thus constructed in the dry. The coral rock was so porous that pumping it dry would have been impossible. A 25 ft depth of the coral was therefore grouted in advance of construction by means of the intrusion method. Thus, 67,000 cu yd of rock was "solidified," permitting the driving of steel sheet piling to form a cofferdam in which excavation proceeded in the dry to a depth of 38 ft below river level with only minor seepage. All expenditure on preliminary boring and testing was many times repaid by the ease with which construction was carried out after the precautionary grouting program had been completed.[9.13]

All underwater tunnels present some unique features of interest geologically; one more will be mentioned to show that tunnel geology is world-wide in its interest and variety. One of the greatest postwar Japanese engineering achievements was the completion of the Kanmon Vehicular Tunnel, which connects the southern island of Kyushu with the main central island of Honshu. Of the underwater tunnels so far completed, only the Mersey Tunnel, to be mentioned shortly, is larger. The Kanmon Tunnel replaces a busy ferry-boat service and roughly parallels a railroad tunnel completed in 1944. It is 2.16 miles long and provides two roadways on two levels with footpaths for cyclists and pedestrians. Penetrating diorite and porphyrite, it is a hard-rock tunnel throughout, but many faults had to be passed, since the rock had been badly affected by earthquake shocks that occur in this part of the world. Cement grouting on an extensive scale was necessitated in the underwater section of the tunnel because of the decomposed rock in the vicinity of the faults; the work was completed without trouble, although its construction (started in 1939) was delayed by the war.[9.14]

9.7. Tunnel Shapes and Linings. The lining of tunnels can naturally be considered under two general classifications, corresponding to the two general uses to which tunnels are adapted. In road and rail tunnels, a lining may be necessary to support the pressure exerted by the material in which the tunnel is excavated; it may likewise be necessary to cover up the exposed material on the tunnel perimeter to protect the material from atmospheric influences (and possibly the action of locomotive or automobile exhaust gases and vapors). Water tunnels, on the other hand, must often be lined to present a smooth surface to the flow of the water through the tunnel and thus to reduce friction losses to an economic minimum; it may also be necessary to provide an impervious lining to prevent leakage of water into the surrounding rock if this is at all fissured or pervious. Pressure exerted by surrounding material and, in the case of pressure tunnels, by the water inside the tunnel must be considered. Finally, the material penetrated must be protected, if necessary, from the action of continued exposure to water and, possibly, air. These distinctive functions of linings are emphasized here, since sometimes they appear to be confused. Brief consideration will show that water tunnels are generally lined irrespective of the material through which they are driven, while traffic tunnels may or may not need such additional attention before completion. The few tunnels constructed for the passage of canals through high ground are governed by the characteristics of both types of lining.

The determination of the final shape of a tunnel cross section will also be affected by the material penetrated. In water tunnels, a circular section is the most economical from the hydraulic point of view, but considerations of construction methods generally result in a horseshoe section with an inverted arch bottom. In soft ground and in poor rock, structural considerations of the design of lining will generally necessitate the use of a full circular section. Tunnel roofs are usually designed as semicircular arches even in quite sound and solid rock; the remainder of the section (in traffic tunnels) is proportioned on the basis of economic considerations. An interesting variation from this latter criterion is given by the Roman road tunnel, already mentioned, through the Ponlipio Hills; this tunnel has its cross section in the form of a pointed arch 25 ft wide, 22 ft high at the center of the tunnel, but 75 ft high at the ends; the increase was intended to improve the illumination of the tunnel. As the total cost of a tunnel varies almost directly with its cross-sectional area, the importance of the correct determination of this area will be clear. Economic considerations control this, but as has been indicated, in some cases the nature of the material to be penetrated will override basic financial factors.

An interesting side light on the early application of geology to civil engineering problems is given by the difficulty encountered by the younger Brunel (Isambard Kingdom) in directing the construction of the Box Tunnel on the Great Western Railway about 1835. Built on a gradient of 1 in 100, the Box Tunnel is today a leading feature on the main line of the Western Region of British Railways, and it is still, to a large extent, unlined. At the time of its construction, however, in addition to violent opposition from local landowners, Brunel had to put up with adverse comments from eminent geologists. The most severe critic was the famous Dr. William Buckland of Oxford, who maintained, even before the Institution of Civil Engineers, that the unlined portions of the tunnel (driven through sandstone) were dangerous; the "concussion of the atmosphere and vibration caused by the train," he said, would make the rock fall away. Brunel was unimpressed by this so-called "academic advice" and went ahead with the tunnel as he had planned it.[9.15] An equally famous railway tunnel in North America, the Hoosac Tunnel in northwestern Massachusetts, completed in 1873, then and still the longest railroad tunnel east of the Mississippi and the first tunnel in which nitroglycerine was used for blasting, was not lined and is still in excellent condition after continuous use since its opening.[9.16]

Methods of lining are not within the scope of this book. It may, however, be mentioned that in soft ground the use of segmental cast-iron or pressed-steel plates or precast reinforced-concrete block work is now almost universal as the lining for resisting ground pressure (having succeeded the brickwork once extensively used). If necessary, such linings can have a concrete surface coating applied to them for the purpose of presenting a smooth water surface. In solid-rock tunnels, timber framework used in construction may be left in place as a semipermanent lining in bad ground; it may be replaced by masonry or surrounded by a solid concrete lining. Mass or reinforced-concrete linings are now almost universal for covering up exposed surfaces liable to disintegrate. Concrete-placing methods follow standard practices, but there is at least one case in which geology may be said to have contributed significantly even to the placing of concrete lining. Twin 51-ft-diameter tunnels were built by the Hydro Electric Power Commission of Ontario in the early 1950s under the city of Niagara Falls, Ontario, to supply the Sir Adam Beck No. 2 water-power station. Centrally mixed concrete was used for the linings which gave a finished diameter of 45 ft. The invert concrete was placed by means of a self-propelled traveler working on rails, into which concrete was dumped from a "boot traveler" located beneath a number of specially drilled boreholes through which concrete was dropped from the surface. These holes were 12 in. in diameter, sunk by churn drills, and lined with steel plates that were grouted into place. The very regular geology along the tunnel route (to be referred to again shortly) permitted the adoption of this unusual means of concrete transport with certainty.[9.17]

As the cost of lining a tunnel may amount to one-quarter of its total cost, the importance of this feature of design will be obvious. Preliminary geological considerations will therefore be of great value in determining the design of the tunnel cross section. In igneous and metamorphic rock known to be solid, a lining will probably be unnecessary for a traffic tunnel. Should there be disintegrated or shattered rock, most treacherous conditions may have to be countered, not only requiring permanent linings but possibly giving trouble during the temporary support of the exposed material during construction. In the Simplon Tunnel, for example, much difficulty was experienced at a distance of about 2¾ miles from the Italian face because of pressures exerted by decomposed calcareous mica schist; even 16-in. rolled-steel beams used as temporary strutting buckled. Quick-setting cement provided the final solution to the problem then presented, although at a cost of £1,000 per yard of tunnel. In other places, rock in the tunnel floor was forced up; but in sections driven through solid rock, even at the maximum depth below the surface, no deformation occurred; the lightest type of masonry lining proved adequate.[9.3]

For a variety of reasons sedimentary rocks produce most tunnel-lining problems. As a result of their mode of origin, sedimentary rocks are likely to change in character within relatively short distances; their original depositional characteristics often make them susceptible to changes in pressure; and the combination of these two factors frequently renders them of an unstable composition, easily and quickly affected by exposure to air and water. Furthermore, the bedding planes of sedimentary formations naturally affect the stability of any tunnel section bored through them; the angle made by the line of the tunnel with the dip and strike of the beds is a most important feature. The underground water carried in fissures and along bedding planes will also affect the design of a lining. All these factors can be estimated, to some degree, from preliminary geological considerations.

9.8. Pressure Tunnels. The design of pressure tunnels presents to the civil engineer some of his most serious difficulties in tunnel work. Three separate problems always have to be faced. In some way, the engineer must make sure that the material surrounding the water will be impervious. A means must be secured for withstanding the pressures set up by the unbalanced head on the water passing through the tunnel. Finally, as a lining is almost invariably used both to satisfy these requirements and to reduce frictional resistance to the flow of water, the design must take into consideration the possibility that the tunnel will be empty and that ground water will tend to exert a considerable pressure on the outside of the lining. The engineer could naturally design a pressure conduit (of steel or reinforced concrete) that would meet all the requirements called for by the foregoing conditions and neglect entirely the existence of the surrounding rock. Such a course would be far from economical. True engineering is the attainment of the economic solution to the problems faced; and so in the design of pressure tunnels, the civil engineer seeks the cooperation of the geologist so that the best advantage can be taken of the rocks to be encountered in reducing the lining used to its economic minimum.

The three distinct problems must be emphasized; they each have a separate bearing on the final solution, although they are sometimes confused in discussion. All important pressure tunnels are lined today, and such linings are usually of concrete. Mass concrete has almost negligible tensile strength, and when under tension, even when reinforced, it will open up in minute cracks. If it is to be impervious to the water it is retaining, as it must be in the majority of cases (since the surrounding rock will not always be completely impervious to water), the lining must clearly be made from the finest quality concrete, placed carefully in position, and well compacted in the forms. This is essentially an engineering matter, but it is stressed here, since the rock excavated from the tunnel will probably be used, if possible, as aggregate, and a geological opinion of the rock's suitability for this purpose will have to be given before construction starts. The effect of the prolonged contact of portland cement concrete with the rock to be encountered must also be considered. A prediction of how the rock will break will aid in the preparation of estimates of lining-placing costs.

The structural design of the lining is governed by the anticipated maximum water pressure, from which can be calculated the total bursting pressure that will be exerted on the tunnel lining. This has to be resisted by the lining and the surrounding rock. At tunnel portals and where the cover of rock (the minimum distance from the tunnel perimeter to ground level) is small, the latter cannot be reckoned on at all, and the lining must be designed on standard lines as a reinforced-concrete conduit, neglecting entirely the effect of the surrounding rock. When the rock cover is appreciable, especially when it can be selected to suit design requirements, the geological nature of the surrounding rock is naturally of importance. Various methods have been suggested for arriving at the allowance to be made in design for the strength of the superimposed rock; the minimum assumption is that the actual weight of the column of rock vertically above the tunnel is all that can be assumed to resist movement due to the water pressure. Admittedly, any selection of the allowance to be made will be empirical, but a knowledge of the state and nature of the rock strata to be reckoned on in such calculations will tend to rationalize the decisions finally made.

Designing the lining for a pressure tunnel is an exercise in engineering judgment; although application of the laws of mechanics can suggest certain dimensions for the component parts, all calculations depend ultimately upon the accuracy of the assumptions made regarding the rock to be penetrated. Here again the absolute necessity of accurate knowledge of the rocks to be encountered during tunnel driving, as well as the necessity of samples so that the mechanical properties of the rock may be assessed for design purposes in advance of construction, cannot be too strongly emphasized. Study of rock mechanics is rendering assistance in such work, but again, accurate knowledge of the rocks to be encountered is the only basis upon which rock-mechanics results can safely be used. Of the many investigations made in the field prior to the design of a pressure-tunnel lining, one of the most extensive, as well as one of the most recent, was the study made in northwestern Canada for the Kemano power project of the Aluminum Company of Canada, Ltd. In an underground powerhouse, 1,400 ft from the access portal, 2.4 million hp will ultimately be generated, under a head of 2,590 ft. Two 11-ft-diameter pressure conduits, 4,450 ft long, lead from a steel wye at the end of the main tunnel for the initial half of the total installation, inclined at 48° to the horizontal, with two horizontal stretches, the second leading to a manifold from which water is supplied to the eight turbines. Hydraulic studies showed that the pressure conduits should be

Fig. 9.8. Special test sphere for the testing of rock penetrated by the pressure tunnel for the Kemano power project, British Columbia, Canada. (*Reproduced by permission of the Aluminum Co. of Canada, Ltd.*)

designed for a maximum dynamic pressure of 2,850 ft or 1,235 psi. The rock was determined to be a fresh, sound, medium-grained gray biotite-hornblende-quartz diorite with a slight gneissoid structure. Laboratory tests showed an ultimate compressive strength varying from 16,700 to 25,900 psi, and a modulus of elasticity averaging 6,997,500 psi.

It was decided to test the assumptions to be made in the design of the pressure-conduit lining by means of a test sphere. As soon as the exploratory tunnel to the approximate location of the powerhouse had been driven, a hollow sphere, fabricated from steel plate ½ in. thick and 10 ft in diameter, was concreted into a side adit and tested under pressures up to 3,600 psi. Extensive instrumentation was used in order to determine the modulus of elasticity of the rock and the action of the thin-walled steel vessel encased in concrete and rock. Although there were some difficulties, it was determined that the modulus of elasticity of the rock in place was about 2 million psi. Despite the reassuring results of the information obtained from the test sphere, it was decided to do further full-scale testing with the first of the conduits to be installed, concentrating especially upon the stresses induced in the steel liner plate. Tests were therefore conducted by filling the completed conduit with water and by creating increased pressures by pumping. Satisfactory results were obtained; the combined effect of concrete and rock encasement reduced stresses in the steel liner by roughly 70 per cent. Similar tests were conducted upon the second conduit when it was complete. Among the significant findings from this extensive investigation was the fact that strain decreases rapidly in the rock to the extent that at a distance of only 10 ft from the liner it appears to be negligible. The results obtained fully justified the adoption of the "cracked-zone" assumption for the design of the conduits. This was based on the idea of a ruptured zone in the rock immediately around the liner; it was assumed that the rock in the cracked zone would act as a series of individual columns. Permanent gauges have been installed in the conduits of the Kemano project so that information of still further value will ultimately result from the meticulous engineering studies that have characterized this great project.[9.18]

Carefully conducted studies were also a part of the design of another major Canadian hydroelectric project, the Sir Adam Beck No. 2 development at Niagara Falls, which was completed in 1956. Duplicating the existing Queenston development, with the new 1.2 million hp powerhouse adjacent to, but upstream from, the old one, the intake and main conduit arrangements for the new project differed from those previously used. Instead of using an open canal, skirting the city of Niagara Falls, Ontario, the Hydro Electric Power Commission of Ontario decided, after exhaustive engineering and geological studies, to convey the water from the intake for 5½ miles of its journey to the powerhouse through twin 45-ft-diameter lined concrete tunnels. Figure 9.9 illustrates the well-known succession of geological strata at Niagara Falls and the relation of the twin tunnels to it. Although some of the strata shown are not so competent as could be desired theoretically (some of the shales, for example, disintegrate upon exposure to the atmosphere), the rock in which the tunnels were driven was entirely adequate; the Irondequoit limestone which forms the crown of the tunnel is massive and competent, excellent in all respects for this purpose. Core samples were taken well in advance of design as part of the thorough exploration program; when tested, these gave a range of rock properties, so that a design could be prepared with confidence. From the start of construction, a careful program of measurement of possible rock movements has been carried out. The first significant results have been published and confirm design expectations. By extrapolation, a maximum inward movement of the walls of the first tunnel, on the major horizontal diameter, of 1.08 in.

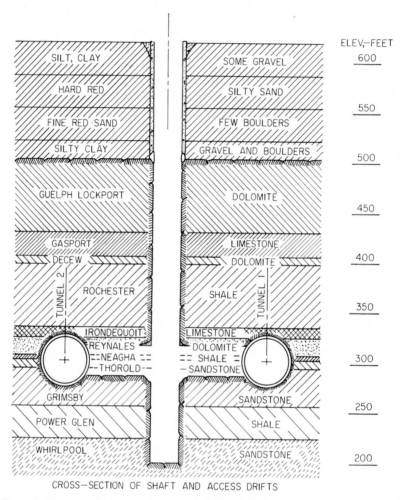

CROSS—SECTION OF SHAFT AND ACCESS DRIFTS

Fig. 9.9. Cross section of rock strata at Niagara Falls, Ontario, Canada, showing the location of the twin tunnels for the Sir Adam Beck power development near Construction Shaft No. 1. (*Reproduced by permission of the Hydro Electric Power Commission of Ontario.*)

30 years after placement of the lining is probable; this is based on the movement of almost 1 in. recorded by the time that the lining was placed, about 180 days following excavation. Of special interest is the fact that the corresponding inward movement for the second tunnel,

excavated after the first, was only about one-quarter to one-third of that in the first, as measured at several points; this is an indication of the stress relief in the rock due to the adjacent excavation. The instrumentation used and the records of rock movement so far obtained on this great project should be of special value to all concerned with pressure tunnels of comparable size and depth.[9.19]

Civil engineering literature contains some interesting references to pressure tunnels that have failed, one of which may usefully be summarized. During the years from 1923 to 1928, the city of Sydney, New South Wales, Australia, constructed a pressure tunnel under a major part of the city area in connection with its water supply. The tunnel is 10 miles long and was designed initially with an internal diameter of 10 ft; it is constructed throughout in Hawkesbury sandstone, of Triassic age, of varying character, fissured and jointed and marked by current bedding. Before the completed tunnel was put into service, sections of it were tested. During the test, the lining ruptured, to a varying extent, in all but one of the sections tested, although the pressures used were not unduly high. In general, the failures occurred (1) where bad rock and fissures had been encountered and (2) where the cover of solid rock above the tunnel was theoretically inadequate. The test water was found issuing at the surface of the ground, and from the accurate test readings taken it was seen that part of the lining and the surrounding rock had moved laterally $\frac{1}{2}$ to $\frac{3}{4}$ in. in the direction of the axis of the tunnel and at an inclination conforming to that of the bedding plane of the sandstone. As a remedial measure, the whole tunnel had to be lined with a solid and continuous steel pipe. The published description of the work is a fascinating engineering document and repays much study. Although the failure may have been due to faulty structural design, it was possibly associated with a lack of appreciation of the true nature of the sandstone rock when in place and also when used as aggregate for the concrete of which the lining was formed.[9.20]

9.9. Construction Methods. To attempt to deal briefly with tunnel construction methods in such a chapter as this is to be forced onto a course between the Scylla of a statement of somewhat obvious facts and the Charybdis of a detailed exposition of drilling, blasting, and excavation, features which belong more properly to a volume devoted solely to tunnel construction. Yet the attempt must be made, since, as in other features of tunnel work, construction methods depend primarily on the geological strata encountered. Broad classification of the material will determine generally the type of construction to be adopted. The exact nature of the material, together with local practice, will determine the detailed variations of the main method in use, as, for example, the use of top, bottom, or central headings in rock tunnels and the use of the English, Belgian, German, or other schedule of excavation in the case of soft-ground tunnels. These considerations all depend on the geo-logical nature of the materials, although methods will be determined by experienced construction men rather than by geologists. Special con-struction problems will almost invariably necessitate specialized investiga-tion, and attention will therefore be directed to a few of the more im-portant unusual conditions that may be encountered.

In very deep tunnels, underground temperatures may sometimes cause inconvenience and adversely affect the progress of tunnel excavation.

Table 9.1. Rock Temperatures in Leading European Tunnels

Tunnel	Mt. Cenis	St. Gotthard	Arlberg	Simplon	Lötschberg
Length, miles............	8.0	9.3	6.4	12.3	9.0
Elevation of portals, ft above sea level	{ 4,162 { 3,765	3,756 3,638	3,995 4,271	2,080 2,253	4,002 3,936
Elevation of "crown".......	4,248	3,788	4,297	2,312	4,067
Maximum elevation of moun-tain range in profile.......	9,673	9,384	6,658	9,315	9,568
Maximum cover...........	5,425	5,596	2,361	7,003	5,501
Maximum rock temperature, °F.................	85.1	87.4	65.3	132.8	93.2
Tunnel ventilation, cu ft air/sec, up to...............	247	35–71	106	1,236	388–883
Date constructed..........	1857–1872	1872–1882	1880–1883	1898–1906	1906–1911
Rocks encountered.........	Limestone, calcareous schist, gneiss, and schistose sandstone	Gneiss, mica schist, serpentine, and hornblende (fissured)	....	Slate, gneiss, and cal-careous mica	

SOURCE: Reproduced, with some additions, from I. Schoklitsch, Hydraulic Structures, vol. 1, p. 15, by permission of the publishers, the American Society of Mechanical Engineers, and the J. R. Freeman Trust Estate, New York, 1937.

The study of such temperature variation can proceed only on the basis of actual experience, and it is therefore not possible to predict accurately the conditions to be met. The temperature inside the Lochaber Tunnel in Scotland (during construction) rarely varied appreciably from 54°F. In the Simplon Tunnel, on the other hand, a considerable range of tem-peratures was experienced, as is shown in Table 9.1. Mine workings have given some useful data on this aspect of tunnel work. Exhaustive tests have been carried out on this matter at the Lake Shore Gold Mine in northern Ontario, Canada, which show that the rock temperature there rises 1°F with every 163.4 ft of depth below surface. In Great Britain, a corresponding figure has been found to be 1°F for every 60 ft of depth.

It has been during the construction of the long tunnels that pierce the European Alps that the most serious difficulties due to abnormal temperatures have been encountered. Table 9.1 summarizes some of the relevant information.

Other construction problems arise frequently on short tunnels and are often encountered in the usual course of civil engineering practice. They may arise from the proximity of other underground works, the

Fig. 9.10. Breakneck Tunnels, New York Central Railroad, New York. Old tunnel on left; portal of tunnel under construction on right. Note proximity of the siphon shaft house of the Catskill water-supply tunnel to right of new tunnel. (*Reproduced by permission of New York Central Railroad Co.*)

safety of which must be guarded. For example, an unusual problem had to be faced during the construction of the Breakneck Tunnel on the New York Central Railroad in the state of New York. An existing double-track tunnel, extensively used and only partly lined, had to be enlarged, and a new double-track tunnel had to be constructed parallel to the existing bore, with a 30-ft rock wall in between them. The material penetrated was a hard granite gneiss. The northern portals are close to one of the siphon shafts carrying the Catskill water supply from the deep-water tunnel under the Hudson River. Clearly, the excavation work had to be done in such a way that the siphon shaft would not be affected by the excavation methods used. Because of the compact nature of the gneiss, vibrations from explosions, if used, would be transmitted without much damping over considerable distances. The excavation of the rock was therefore all carried out by the drilling of 2⅜-in. holes, 6 ft deep, all around the final outline of the tunnel section, spaced at 3-in. centers. The ⅝-in. gaps between each hole were then broached, after which the isolated core of rock was broken up and removed by standard methods. The operation was successfully completed, and the

FIG. 9.11. New Breakneck Tunnel, New York Central Railroad, New York. View showing close drilling adopted for excavation because of the proximity of the Catskill Aqueduct siphon shaft. (*Reproduced by permission of the New York Central Railroad Co.*)

finished appearance of the rock surface is shown in the accompanying photograph.[9.21]

As indicated when linings were discussed, material may be encountered that is affected by exposure to air. Certain types of clay and shale are particularly susceptible to the influence of the atmosphere, and a common practice (as followed, for example, in Toronto tunnel work in Canada) is to spray the shale with a thin coat of cement as soon as it is exposed. Sometimes more elaborate methods have to be utilized, as in the case of the construction of the P.L.M. Railroad tunnels on the line between Nice, France, and San Dalmazzo, Italy. Rock consisting of almost pure anhydrite was encountered in the Col de Braus Tunnel for a length of about 1 km, and in the Caranca Tunnel for a few hundred meters. Water reaching the anhydrite in the former tunnel from adjacent Jurassic limestone caused the exposed rock to increase about 30 per cent in volume. The trouble became more serious during the time when work

Fig. 9.12. Equipment used for spraying the surface of exposed shale with cement grout, in water-supply tunnel for Toronto, Ontario, Canada; cement-coated shale may be seen on the right. (*Reproduced by permission of the Commissioner of Works, City of Toronto.*)

was halted from 1914 to 1919. When excavation and lining were finally completed, the water which had not been completely drained continued its action, and a portion of the masonry lining was badly ruptured. Aluminous cement was used for its reconstruction, and an elaborate drainage system was installed; it appears that a satisfactory result has been obtained. This experience was utilized in the later construction of the Caranca Tunnel. As soon as mucking was completed, the rock was covered with coal tar; the lining was built in with the least possible delay, using aluminous cement; and after its completion, coal tar was injected under pressure behind the lining. The tunnel was put into use in 1921, and has given satisfactory service since.[9.22]

Because of the nature of tunneling, little variation is possible in the methods used for excavating the rock or soil that has to be removed. Steady improvement has been made in methods of drilling and blasting for hard-rock tunnels, and mechanization has correspondingly increased the efficiency of mucking; Swedish practice has been notable in these fields. Shields are now used for hard-rock tunnels, as well as in soil where rock conditions are at all hazardous. The application of mechanical means of excavation in shale rock that can be cut has been noteworthy, starting with a simple application of adapted coal-cutting machines. In more recent years special tunneling machines have been developed and used with success by a number of contractors. An "electrified mole" with a 26-ft cutting face, for example, was designed for excavation of the tunnels on the Oahe Dam project in the Missouri Basin.[9.23] A smaller machine, but one capable of boring through soft limestone as well as shale, was designed and built for use on a new sewer tunnel in Toronto, Ontario.[9.24] Another type of machine, christened the "Teredo," was designed for use in tunnel work in Houston, Texas; on this machine, a rotating arm on a fixed face cuts away the "joint clay" to be excavated and breaks it up to such an extent that it can be pumped out.[9.25] With all such mechanical aids to excavation, accurate and certain knowledge of the rock to be encountered in every foot of tunnel to be excavated is absolutely essential. The presence of even small quantities of limestone, for example, caused considerable delay in the early use of the Teredo.

9.10. Overbreak. Unless the specification covering the construction of a tunnel under contract is most carefully drawn up, with due regard for all the geological conditions anticipated, the payment for *overbreak* is almost certain to be one of the matters that will cause the most trouble at the conclusion of the contractor's operations. The term "overbreak" is one now generally used in civil engineering practice to denote the quantity of rock that is actually excavated beyond the perimeter which is previously fixed by the engineer as the finished *excavated* tunnel outline. It will be realized that in the case of a lined tunnel, not only may the contractor receive no payment for rock excavated beyond this line, but also additional concrete filling will be necessary to fill up the resulting cavity. For engineer and contractor, therefore, the question of overbreak is an important one.

A close study of records and descriptions of early tunnels suggests that overbreak was not seriously considered in the early days of modern construction, possibly because many tunnels were then paid for on the basis of a unit length of completed tunnel. In modern work, payment is more usually made per unit volume of excavation and per unit volume of concrete or other lining. Under such circumstances, it will be readily seen that overbreak must be kept to a minimum; and as the quantity will depend primarily on the nature of the rock penetrated, given equally

Fig. 9.13. Special tunnel-boring machine being removed from tunnel after boring 11,500 ft through shale interbedded with well-cemented sandstone and hard crystalline limestone, Toronto, Ontario, Canada. (*Inset:* the pattern formed on the face of the 9-ft-diameter tunnel.) (*Reproduced by permission of the Foundation Co. of Canada, Ltd.*)

good driving methods, preliminary geological investigations are of great importance in estimating what overbreak will be.

In connection with soft-ground tunnels, the term is rarely met, since such works can generally be taken out exactly to the neat line of excavation, and construction equipment (shields, lining plates, etc.) can be designed to fit to this line. Close-grained igneous rock will usually break closer to the theoretical section than sedimentary or metamorphic rock, although certain types of chalk and compact sandstone will also give

FIG. 9.14. Main tunnel of the Lochaber water-power scheme, Scotland; view near heading 3E showing the effect of drilling at right angles to the strike of the mica schist. (*Reproduced by permission of Sir William Halcrow & Partners, Consulting Engineers.*)

good sections. As overbreak will depend on the detailed nature and structural arrangement of the rock strata encountered, it cannot often be determined with great accuracy in advance. When, however, the nature of the rocks has been determined by preliminary geological investigations, the tunnel engineers, because of their previous practical experience, and the geologist, because of his intimate knowledge of the characteristics of the rock types, will together usually be able to make a close estimate of the way in which the rocks will break. It will then be possible to prepare the relevant parts of the specification so that they will conform as closely as possible with the situations that develop as the work proceeds. The following represents a typical way of dealing with this matter; the items suggested refer to that part of a specification dealing with payment for excavation:

1. No points of solid rock must project beyond a line, called the *neat line* of excavation, fixed at a distance from the inside perimeter of

Fig. 9.15. Main tunnel of the Lochaber hydroelectric scheme, Scotland; view in heading 5W showing the effect on excavation of drilling along the strike of the mica schist. (*Reproduced by permission of Sir William Halcrow & Partners, Consulting Engineers.*)

the finished tunnel section equal to the minimum thickness of lining required.

2. No flat areas of rock of more than, say 3 sq ft must occur within a specified minimum distance from the finished perimeter, usually a few inches more than the minimum lining thickness.

3. All excavation and concrete lining will be paid for up to but not beyond another tunnel perimeter called the *pay line*, although all cavities beyond this line must be carefully filled, generally with concrete of an inferior mix.

The fixing of this pay line is usually the most difficult part of the cross-section tunnel design. The overbreak is the volume of excavation that actually has to be taken out beyond this line. Clearly, the engineer will want to fix the line so that a contractor will not be faced with the possibility of much overbreak, a feature that will be reflected in the unit prices tendered for excavation by those contractors who appreciate the significance of geology and in the disputes over claims made at the end of the job by those contractors who do not. The location of the pay line will depend upon the nature of the rocks to be met; the way in which they will tend to break; the necessity of temporary timbering and whether this will have to be incorporated in the finished lining or not; and last but not least, the anticipated dip and strike of the rocks to be met in relation to the axis of the tunnel.

Two photographs are reproduced showing finished cross sections of the Lochaber Water Power Tunnel in Scotland, as excavated. The first shows the shape of section obtained when the drilling was almost perpendicular to the strike of the mica schist; the marks of the drill steel are clearly visible; the overbreak here is very small. The second view shows the shape of section obtained when the drilling was approximately along the strike; the section is almost rectangular owing to the way in which loosened blocks of the schist have fallen away. These views illustrate more vividly than can any words the dependence of overbreak upon structural geological conditions as well as upon the nature of the rock that is penetrated.

9.11. Ground Water. The presence of ground water is often the main source of trouble in tunnel construction. It introduces at once the necessity of drainage facilities from all headings; and when the tunnel grades cannot be chosen to facilitate such drainage, the additional trouble and expense of pumping is necessitated. If water is present in any appreciable quantity, it will impede construction work of any kind; if the ground is soft and liable to be affected seriously by the drainage of water through or from it, the use of compressed air for all tunneling operations will become essential. Near Leadville, Colorado, a railroad tunnel was driven through dry compact glacial till without trouble or mishap. A drainage tunnel in the same area, through similar glacial till, encountered so many difficulties that part of the tunnel had to be abandoned; the difference was that, in the second case, the till was saturated and so had lost almost all its stability.[9.26]

It is of the greatest importance, therefore, before construction starts, to have as accurate information as possible about the ground-water conditions likely to be encountered. It may safely be said that no major civil engineering operations that are to be carried out below surface level should be started before something is known about the level and flow of ground water at the site. It is equally important to keep careful check on all water that is met with during construction. This will not only permit those in charge to determine the source of the water and therefore to seal the water off in some way, but it will also permit them to check so far as possible the course that the water follows and to make sure that no serious undermining or cavitation is being caused. In deep-tunnel work, plutonic water (water that has not come from the atmosphere or the surface of the earth) may be encountered; in this case, no such precautions can be taken. During the construction of the Simplon Tunnel, for example, alleged plutonic water was encountered at one point; a hot spring and a cold spring of water, differing by many degrees in temperature, issued into the tunnel within 1 m of each other. In contrast to this, in a test made during the construction of the Moffatt Tunnel in Colorado, calcium chloride was dumped in a lake 1,400 ft above the tunnel line, and traces of the chemical were found in the water entering the tunnel no more than 2 hr later.[9.27]

The more general factors affecting the presence of water in underground rock structures are considered in some detail in Chap. 5. These hold true for general tunnel work, although they are often complicated and sometimes present special features. The problem presented by ground water in tunnel work is the reverse of that usually to be solved, since the water is not wanted in the tunnel, and its flow must therefore be stopped if this is at all possible. Only rarely can an underground water flow be sealed off at its source, even if the source is known, although this was done in the Severn Tunnel, England. Grouting is therefore generally the first recourse of the engineer, provided that the quantity of water encountered is such as to render economic the expenditure of this additional money and also that it can be definitely stated, from knowledge of the geological formation concerned, that the grouting will be effective.

A separate note follows on grouting, in which an interesting application to tunnel work is described. There may usefully be mentioned, in addition, the experiences gained in connection with driving the two tunnels under the river Mersey at Liverpool, England, to which brief references have already been made. The Mersey is slightly less than 1 mile wide at its mouth, where it separates the cities of Liverpool and Birkenhead; its banks are largely taken up with the great system of tidal docks necessitated by its 30-ft range of tide. So great has been the traffic across the river at this point that a tunnel crossing was discussed as early as about the year 1800. In 1885, the Mersey Railway Tunnel, which still provides for an important electric railway service, was opened. And in 1934, the Queensway Vehicular Tunnel, still the largest subaqueous road tunnel in the world, was opened. The local geological formation is the Bunter sandstone, a red sandstone of the Triassic system; the tunnels lie almost wholly in the middle of three Bunter beds. The sandstone is hard, porous, massively bedded, and jointed; the strike is approximately north-south, and the dip is between 2 and 5°. Faulting is a characteristic of this geological structure, and a Liverpool geologist, G. H. Morton, suggested in 1861 that a fault would be found below the bed of the Mersey. Throughout the district the bedrock is covered with glacial drift, boulder clay, sands, and gravels, and these deposits extend across the river bed. In 1873, T. Mellard Reade, a distinguished Liverpool civil engineer and geologist, predicted that a buried river valley belonging to preglacial topography would be found under the present bed of the Mersey.

Construction of the Mersey Railway Tunnel started in 1879. Boreholes were taken, and Sir Francis Fox, the engineer for the work, talked to Mr. Reade. The latter stated in a paper that he maintained the correctness of his forecast of the buried valley:

. . . notwithstanding that I was given a section showing a series of borings taken by the first promoters of the tunnel, which was supposed to prove a rocky bed all through. Fortunately the engineers who carried out the work, forewarned, took further borings, with the result that the *level* of the tunnel was lowered. The trial headings found rock all the way through, but in the actual construction of the tunnel the bottom of the buried channel was cut through by the roof of the tunnel for about 300 feet, and I had the satisfaction of seeing the verification of my prediction without disaster to the undertaking. If the levels had not been lowered the result might have been disastrous failure.

The contractors met the buried channel suddenly and withdrew all their men from the workings, but the clay cover held, and work was eventually resumed and successfully completed. Mr. Reade's concise and modest statement illustrates vividly the value of this application of his studies of the glacial geology of the Liverpool district.

The fault predicted by Mr. Morton was also found, and both features were again encountered in the modern vehicular tunnel. When this tunnel was started in 1925, Professor P. G. H. Boswell undertook the extensive geological investigations that were necessitated by the increased size of the new tunnel (44-ft internal diameter), its location seaward from the Mersey Railway Tunnel, and the natural desire for economy in location and construction. Construction of the earlier tunnel assisted in these investigations, but a special study had to be made of the anticipated bottom level of the buried valley. This hinged on the elucidation of the fact that the old drainage system flowed in the *direction opposite* to that of the present river. Thus, the level of the new tunnel could be kept reasonably high; the actual minimum clearance between the tunnel excavation and the bottom of the valley was only 3 ft at one spot. The old valley, although filled with water-bearing sand, was

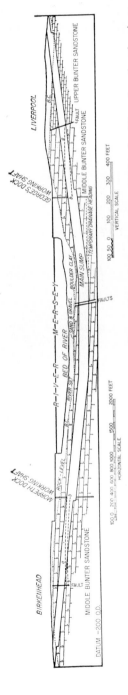

Fig. 9.16. Geological section along center line of the underriver section of the Queensway Vehicular Tunnel under the river Mersey, Liverpool, England. (*a-a.* probable water level after construction pumping stopped; *b-b.* water level under conditions of maximum pumping.) (*Reproduced by permission of the Liverpool Geological Society.*)

covered with impervious boulder clay, and so safety could be assured; because of the existence of this clay, which there came down to the rock surface, the railway tunnel could be completed even though it did pierce through the rock surface. It was not practicable to put down boreholes in the river (owing to the range of tide and shipping), and so all exploratory work was done by drilling *ahead* of the working face, up to 150 ft away. Many of these holes were used later as grout holes. The total cost of this extensive preliminary and exploratory work amounted

Fig. 9.17. Queensway Vehicular Tunnel under the river Mersey, Liverpool, England; view showing final phase of rock excavation and permanent lining in place. Scale may be judged by the size of the two men in the center background. (*Reproduced by permission of Mott, Hay and Anderson, Consulting Engineers.*)

to less than one-fifth of 1 per cent of the total cost; it was a remarkably good investment.[9.28]

A singular difference between the two tunnels is related to ground water. The lining of the railway tunnel was not made watertight, so that even today about 5,000 gpm (Imp) have to be pumped out of its drainage sumps; the water has the composition of the Mersey and comes through the fissures and joints in the sandstone. It is *not* related to the size of the tide, but it does vary sympathetically with the rainfall. Pumping had to be carried out during the construction of the vehicular tunnel, and this permitted many interesting observations with regard to ground water in the vicinity. The lining of the new tunnel is watertight, and the surrounding rock was grouted so that, after its completion, ground-water conditions reverted to their previous state.

In soft-ground tunnels, grouting may be equally effective but only for material, such as gravel, which the grout can penetrate sufficiently. Freezing has already been mentioned as another method (although of limited application) for sealing off troublesome underground water. Another method is to use the special well-point installations utilized in open excavation work, with the well points jetted ahead of the working face which is thus kept dry by the usual pumping process through the screens in the points. Finally, there is the more drastic procedure of actually lowering the underground water table to such an extent that the ground through which the tunnel has to be driven is above this level and so in the dry.

An early example of the application of this solution is almost classic. The construction of the Kilsby Tunnel near Rugby, England, proved an almost insuperable obstacle to the completion of the original railway line between London and Birmingham (now on the main western line from London to Scotland of British Railways); it was eventually completed in 1838 at a total cost of some £300,000 as against an estimated cost of £90,000 and only at the expense of some lives. Unfortunately, preliminary exploratory work missed striking a pocket of water-laden sand and gravel of the inferior oölites in the Lias shale; when the tunnel works encountered it, extraordinary difficulties were met because the deposit proved to be a veritable quicksand; at one time, construction work had to be stopped. But Robert Stephenson was the engineer, and that remarkable man solved the problem in a characteristically satisfactory manner. Shafts were sunk, and steam pumps were erected on the line of the tunnel. The following extract from his report is of interest:[9.29]

As the pumping progressed the most careful measurements were taken of the level at which the water stood in the various shafts and boreholes; and I was soon much surprised to find how slightly the depression of the water-level in the one shaft influenced that of the other, notwithstanding a free communication existed between them through the medium of the sand, which was very coarse and open. It then occurred to me that the resistance which the water encountered in its passage through the sand to the pumps would be accurately measured by the angle or inclination which the surface of the water assumed towards the pumps, and that it would be unnecessary to draw the whole of the water off from the quicksand, but to presevere in pumping only in the precise level of the tunnel, allowing the surface of the water flowing through the sand to assume that inclination which was due to its resistance. . . .

The simple result, therefore, of all the pumping was merely to establish and maintain a channel of comparatively dry sand in the immediate line of the intended tunnel, leaving the water heaped up on each side by the resistance which the sand offered to its descent to that line on which the pumps and shafts were situated.

This account was made in a report to the London and Westminster Water Company in 1841 and apparently forgotten until rescued by Prof. Boyd Dawkins and quoted in his James Forrest Lecture in 1898. It is a striking example of scientific observation, establishing the nature of the cone of depression set up by pumping ground water.

Consideration has been given to the handling of underground water in so far as it affects normal tunnel construction. Special problems in connection with such underground water arise, of which the following is an unusual example. The Boyati Tunnel, 8.33 miles long, 7.54 ft wide by 8.15 ft high, with a horseshoe section, is a part of the works for the supply of water to the city of Athens, Greece. Constructed between 1926 and 1931, it gave rise to many unforeseen construction difficulties, since no preliminary information was available and no borings were taken before work started. The trouble encountered soon demonstrated the need of borings, and therefore 12-in. holes, stepped in to 10, 8, and 6 in., were put down on the line of the tunnel at intervals of about ⅔ mile (the large size of the hole made it possible to use them for checking the tunnel survey and for leading electric power cables into the headings). The materials penetrated included compact marble, compact mica schist, a disintegrated chlorite schist (which smashed the concrete block lining 2 hr after setting and necessitated four sets of timbering before the squeeze was stopped), and crevassed and cavernous limestone. The latter was water bearing, and this water added to the troubles already encountered. Finally, at a distance in from the north portal of 13,700 ft, the water inflow was so great that the heading had to be bulkheaded off; the water pressure (estimated at 250 psi) was so great that it forced a large sandbag bulkhead over 3 ft back into the tunnel. Borings had disclosed that the dip of this crevassed limestone was inclined toward the line of the tunnel in the direction of tunnel driving, with a superincumbent bed of clay and conglomerate which was practically dry. It was therefore decided to tackle the tunnel by driving through the limestone, working into the bed rather than from "underneath" it, and for this purpose a special shaft was sunk on the line of the tunnel, wholly in the clay and conglomerate. This was first joined up with the south heading, and then driving was resumed into the limestone. Excessive water pressure was again encountered, and a detour had to be made from the original tunnel line, but the radical change in attack suggested by geological considerations was probably the keynote of the ultimate success of this notable work.[9.30]

No record of ground-water problems in tunneling would be complete without a final reference to what has been called the "hottest and wettest tunnel ever driven," the Tecolote Tunnel of the Cachuma project of the U.S. Bureau of Reclamation. The tunnel is 6.4 miles long and 7 ft in diameter; it conveys water from the Cachuma Reservoir on the Santa

Ynez River to the coastal area of California near Santa Barbara. It therefore penetrates the Cretaceous sedimentary rocks of the Santa Ynez Mountains, and it was known in advance that a major fault would have to be crossed by the tunnel. Trouble in driving was expected, based on experience gained with two roughly parallel tunnels driven many years before (the Mission and Doulton Tunnels). As one of the special precautions taken, therefore, the United States Geological Survey arranged to survey all springs and wells within 10 miles of the new tunnel, in

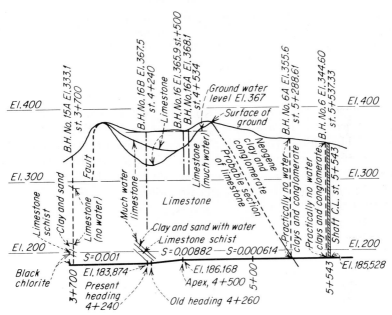

Fig. 9-18. Section along the center line of the Boyati Tunnel, Greece, in water-bearing area. (*Reproduced by permission of The Editor, Engineering News-Record.*)

case they dried up, since water flows, gas, and heavy ground had been encountered in the two earlier bores. Methane and hydrogen sulfide were found in small quantities and caused some trouble; deformation of temporary shoring also occurred. But it was a steady increase in the quantity and temperature of water entering the tunnel that was the real hazard, and led to a temporary shutdown of the work in 1953. Work was resumed the next year, and the tunnel was successfully holed through early in 1955, but only after further and almost incredible difficulty. The flow of water reached a maximum of 9,000 gpm, and the temperature reached 117°F; thus, working conditions at the face were almost unbearable.

Although hot water had been expected during the driving of the two earlier tunnels, since there is a well-known hot spring 2 miles away, none was encountered. A special combination of unusual geological conditions, at a rather local level, was responsible for the heat and water encountered in the Tecolote Tunnel; the heat was thought to be residual heat in the ground from geologically recent faulting. At first, attempts were made to grout around the tunnel in order to slow up the flow of water, but eventually the tunnel was completed without the aid of grouting; special pumping equipment was installed that, fortunately, was able to deal with the 9,000 gpm flow. Men going to work at the face had to travel through the "hot" section of the tunnel immersed in water up to their necks; they rode in dump cars specially provided for this job. It is small wonder that an Indian visitor described the job graphically as what he thought "the Christian hell" might be like. The experience is a salutary reminder that, even with the most expert geological advice, as was here available, minor local variations in geological structure in extremely distorted strata can give quite unexpected results; it points to the necessity of continual attention to every detail of the geology encountered in tunneling until the job is complete. This case also provides an illustration of how adversity can be turned to some good effect; the excessive flow from the tunnel was piped to the Santa Barbara area to relieve a serious water shortage; thus, the trouble in the tunnel proved to be the salvation of the local water authority.[9.31]

9.12. Grouting. Grouting, or cementation, has been mentioned already. It has been used extensively in tunnel work, mainly, but not exclusively, for reducing the flow of underground water into tunnels. Its application and the necessity of its application if anticipated before construction therefore depend on the geological nature of the strata to be encountered. The methods adopted for grouting in tunnel work are similar to those generally used; a cement mixture is usual, although sometimes special chemical additions are injected first to ensure cementation of fine cracks.

Fissures or joints must clearly exist in the rock if it is to be grouted satisfactorily. Fissures or general porosity of the rock is presupposed by the necessity of grouting. Excessive inflow of water, structurally weak rock unable to support itself across the tunnel arch, or material liable to disintegrate when further exposed to the atmosphere results from these characteristics. In all these cases, if the anticipated trouble is determined beforehand, as is generally possible by careful geological investigation, grouting can prove an effective remedy and prevent serious trouble. The construction of tunnels through water-bearing strata such as coarse gravel can be materially simplified in the same way.

Leakage of river water into the famous Severn Tunnel of the (old) Great Western Railway in England was practically stopped by the application of a specialized cementation process many years after the tunnel's construction. The construction of the new Mersey Vehicular Tunnel was greatly facilitated by the same process. Similar precementation in

water-bearing gravel facilitated the construction of some of the inclined
escalator shafts for the London tube railways. In a section of one of the
P.L.M. railroad tunnels in France (mentioned on page 315), a tar injection was successfully adopted to coat voids behind the tunnel lining
and to prevent further disintegration.

The work carried out in the Severn Tunnel may be mentioned in
more detail. The tunnel was started in 1873, but progress was slow; in
1881, the river water broke into the tunnel workings, passing through
open marl beds. These were successfully plugged up by depositing clay
from schooners sailing in the river above the breaks. Operating conditions
in the tunnel have always been troublesome, and the Great Western
Railway Company in the years 1924 and 1929 had to follow the earlier
practice and dump clay above obvious danger spots. After prolonged
investigation, aided materially by the geological record kept by the
original contractor (see page 17), it was decided to grout the natural
strata behind the brick lining throughout a critical section of the tunnel.
This work was carried out in two contracts; about 6.5 million lb of
cement was used in 2,100 holes, totaling 9,500 ft, in one contract; and
12 million lb was used in 2,400 holes, totaling 10,500 ft, in the second.
The existence of large voids between the brick lining and the surrounding strata, even beneath the invert of the tunnel, was proved by
the travel of the cement. The river bed above the tunnel was patrolled
at low tide during the grouting operations; but in only one instance did
cement actually travel to the surface; there it formed a protective
covering over the mouth of a fault in the marl.[9.32]

Chemical grouting has also played a part in assisting with the control of
ground water in tunnels; one recent application was in the tunnels of the
Pennsylvania Turnpike. More than 50 years after contractors quit work
on the ill-fated South Penn Railway, the seven tunnels then partially
driven were adopted for use on the great highway that now utilizes the
old right of way. The completed tunnels vary in length from 3,511 to
6,782 ft. About half the length of the turnpike tunnels represents enlarged
headings of the old railroad tunnels; the remainder are new bores. Detailed geological studies were made under the direction of A. B. Cleaves;
the local geology was unusually complex, involving 19 formations of
shales and sandstones. Careful studies of water seeping into the tunnels
revealed pH values from 3.4 (highly acidic) to 8.3 (highly alkaline); the
variation was in itself a reflection of the complex geology. Special pro-
visions were made for drawing off the highly acidic waters to prevent
damage to the concrete lining; vitrified clay tile drains were widely used
for this purpose. Gunited cover was provided for exposed rock in cavities
above the finished lining. After a decade, seepage of ground water
through the lining in some of the tunnels was proving to be a nuisance,
and a program for sealing them was initiated in 1953. A specialized

chemical grouting system was used in which an expanded shale light-weight aggregate served as backfill. Considerable success in sealing the tunnels was achieved.[9.33]

9.13. Construction Records. In all tunnel construction work, it is of the greatest importance that accurate, complete, and up-to-date geological records be maintained from the start of construction. This can be done most conveniently by means of a geological map of the tunnel route and a geological section along the line of the tunnel. The exact nature of the rock excavated must be observed after every round has been fired, and the direction of strike and dip of the rock must be recorded regularly. All this information should be carefully and continually compared with the geological section along the tunnel predicted from preliminary investigations before construction started and with similar records obtained at other headings in the tunnel. In addition, it must be compared with surface topography and geology above the tunnel and in its vicinity in order that as complete a picture as possible may constantly be available for study. In this way, a close check can be kept on the relation of observed to anticipated formation; any unusual departure from the latter can be checked as soon as it is discovered, and its implications can be investigated. Alternatively, if difficulties are encountered underground because of fissures or faulting, surface conditions may serve as a guide to future similar troublesome spots, once a correlation has been established.

The geological record so obtained is of great interest and importance in another direction entirely—to the geological surveyor; it gives him information obtainable in no other way, and if the tunnel is to be lined or used as an aqueduct, at no other time. Such records can therefore be of supreme value to the community as a whole, and all civil engineers in charge of tunnel work should therefore invite the attention of the director of the local geological survey to any section available for inspection and should furnish to the survey a copy of the final section obtained. The courtesy, involving no expense and but little trouble, should likewise be extended when possible to the head of any university geological department in the immediate neighborhood. The discretion of scientists is such that no engineer need ever hesitate to take the step here suggested.

There are today, most fortunately, many examples of tunnels that have yielded invaluable geological information, thanks to such cooperation as is here suggested. Even radioactivity in rocks has been recorded in some Swiss tunnels. Quite the most important instance known to the writer is recorded in the moving autobiography of the great German geologist, Hans Cloos.[9.34] Entitled "Conversation with the Earth" and available in English translation, it may be recommended without reservation to all engineers interested in geology; it is a most human and stimulating document, penned (as it was) shortly before the death of Dr. Cloos as a "valve and a means of salvation from the confinement, brute force, and untruth of the times." Dr. Cloos was greatly interested in the Rhine Graben, a geological feature of western Germany about which controversy had raged for many years. He tells of the interest to him, as possibly providing a clue to this geological riddle, of the proposal to build a new approach to the main railway station of the lovely city of Freiburg in the Black Forest near the Swiss border. Although the original contract for the work was signed in 1910, the years of the First World War and postwar conditions led to such a delay that it was not until August, 1928, that work was actively resumed. The tunnel had to be 1,696 ft long and was to pierce the Lorettoberg, below the line on the Gunterstal. Its western portal would be cut into sandstone and its eastern into gneiss, so that it might reveal the exact interrelation of the young sediments of the Rhine Valley (limestone, sandstone, marl, and clay) and the ancient gneiss of the Black Forest and the Vosges. Dr. Cloos visited the work regularly and in April, 1929, he was able to see the excavation completed, and the answer that he had so long been anticipating. "There it was," he writes, "right before my eyes . . . a furrow ran up the wall into the ceiling and down the other side, as neatly as if it had been done with a knife . . . dipping 55° away from the mountain and downward below the plain . . . I took pencil and paper and drew as much of the three-dimensional picture as I could reduce to lines and planes. For the wet spongy stone would not be there very long. It was to be sheathed in, and only a little window would be left open through which posterity may catch a glimpse of the extraordinary phenomenon that I have been privileged to see." Unfortunately, it has proved impossible to get a photograph of this unusual "window."

In addition to their vital importance to pure geology, construction records often have practical application and general utility. Should any trouble develop in the future operation of the tunnel, the cause may often be traced to some unsatisfactory condition of the surrounding ground if this information can be obtained from the records available. When tunnels, especially pressure tunnels, are being examined after continued periods of use, a geological section will always help to conserve time and increase the value of the survey by indicating the sections that need special attention. If a railway tunnel is to be increased in cross section, an accurate geological record of the original work will be of inestimable value. And if there should unfortunately be litigation with regard to the construction of a tunnel, as is sometimes caused by overbreak settlements, a geological record of the tunnel line will often be a deciding factor in a court of law.

As an example of a tunnel on which close attention to geology during construction was an important feature, the main tunnel of the Lochaber Water Power scheme (Scotland) may be cited. The tunnel extends from the main reservoir for the project, Loch Treig, to the side slope of Ben

Nevis (Great Britain's highest peak) overlooking Fort William, on Loch Linnhe; it is slightly more than 15 miles long and has an effective average diameter of about 15 ft. The tunnel passes through rock strata which, from the geological standpoint, constitute one of the most complicated parts of Great Britain. Many types of rock were encountered, from shattered mica schist to granite and baked schist of excessive hardness (some requiring three sets of drill steel in each hole drilled into them). Prior to construction, a survey of the route selected for topographical reasons was made by E. B. Bailey, later Director of the Geological Survey of Great Britain, who for many years past had made a close study of the rocks to be encountered. The preliminary information then obtained was confirmed to a remarkable degree by the geological section revealed by the excavation. During the construction of the tunnel, Dr. Bailey made a complete survey of it and collected many rock samples; in this way the detailed mapping of the surface above has been completed. Since several interesting facts, not shown by surface outcrops, were discovered, the public records were thereby enriched. Most of the staff of the resident engineer (the writer was a member for all too short a period) had a working knowledge of geology and so were able to observe and record the varying geological features encountered in the course of their regular engineering work. From among the many interesting features of the work, one may be mentioned. At the Loch Treig end of the tunnel, excavation proceeded in soft mica schist, much disturbed by faulting and lines of movement. There were seams of clay in this section, and the rock adjacent to them was soft; special timbering and cast-iron lining had to be used. After two of these disturbed areas had been passed, it was noticed that they corresponded to the lines of cliffs on the hill above the tunnel; accordingly, succeeding lines of cliff were surveyed, and the presence of bad rock in the tunnel was predicted thereafter to within a few feet of where it actually occurred. The value of such work to the contractors needs no elaboration.[9.35]

Two cases may be cited in conclusion in which the absence of construction records led to serious and unfortunate consequences. The first long railway tunnel ever to be constructed was the Woodhead Tunnel on the line connecting Manchester and Sheffield in the Pennine district of northern England. Twin single-line tunnels, one completed in 1845 and the other in 1852, are 15,906 ft long (the fourth longest tunnel in the United Kingdom). Disintegration of the brick lining made maintenance difficult, and daily traffic of over 80 trains on each line left little time available for the necessary repairs. In 1948, when the electrification of this important rail link was pending, it was decided that a duplicate double-track tunnel, parallel to the existing twin tunnels, would be constructed. Owing to a necessary slight realignment, the length of the new tunnel is 16,037 ft, (making it the third longest). In cross section, it was excavated as 30 ft 6 in. wide and 26 ft 4 in. high in the center; a mass concrete lining reduced the effective width to 27 ft. With the existing tunnels alongside, it might have been thought that construction of the new tunnel would be a fairly straightforward operation, but this did not prove to be the case. Since no technical account of the planning and execution of the old tunnels could be traced, no firsthand record of the behavior of the shale and sandstone rock that had to be penetrated was available. On the other hand, there was discovered a large and detailed longitudinal section along the original tunnel and through the five construction shafts, made in 1845 by the original resident engineer and deposited in the Geological Survey's Museum; it showed the strata encountered, the fossils found, and the limits of all geological features. In the report of the government's inspecting engineer (of 1852), reference was made to "bulging of the sidewalls" for a distance of about 50 ft, a condition that was corrected before the tunnel was approved for public use.

The new tunnel was completed toward the end of 1953; there had been a great deal of trouble with rockfalls and even with the method originally planned for excavation, owing mainly to the character of the black argillaceous shale that had to be penetrated for much of the total length. At about 900 ft from the Woodhead end of the tunnel, just as the transition from slabby sandstone into the shale had been made in the enlargement to final section of the pilot tunnel first excavated, a very large rockfall took place, involving a length of 100 ft of tunnel; the cavity thus formed extended to a height of 70 ft above the invert. The fall crushed the steel rib supports that had been erected, as shown in Fig. 9.19. The accident delayed work at this location by 6 months, but eventually the difficult section was passed, excavation completed, and the tunnel lined for final use. Construction records from the earlier tunnels would almost certainly have disclosed similar trouble, even though the bores were smaller in cross section. The case is a useful warning of the troubles that may be encountered with shale; the record that is now fortunately available of this tunnel job should be consulted by all who have major tunnel work to carry out in shale that is in any way of dubious character.[9.36]

The second case also comes from England; it involves the railway tunnel at Clifton Hall on a short branch line used for mineral traffic between Patricroft and Molyneux Junction, not very far from the Woodhead Tunnels. The tunnel was only about 3,900 ft long; it was straight in plan, lined with brick, of horseshoe shape, 24 ft 9 in. wide and 22 ft. 3 in. high. It was constructed in 1850 and used until the time of the Second World War. At that time it was closed, but was reopened for limited freight traffic in October, 1947. It was regularly and carefully inspected. On the morning of April 13, 1953, the "ganger" responsible for this stretch of line noticed a small amount of brick rubble on the track; he immediately reported this and swift measures for detailed inspection were taken by the railway engineering staff concerned. It was clear that the brick lining at the location noted was under stress; arrangements were made to have steel ribs made up so that the tunnel arch could be reinforced. Before these could be installed, early on the morning of April

Fɪɢ. 9.19. Roof collapse between 900 and 972 ft from the portal of the new Woodhead Tunnel of British Railways. (*Reproduced by permission of Sir William Halcrow & Partners, Consulting Engineers.*)

28, the tunnel crown failed, precipitating a mass of wet sand and rubble into the tunnel. In itself this would have been serious, but the debris and sand came from an old construction shaft that had been located at this point; the contents of the shaft were precipitated into the tunnel and a crater formed suddenly at the surface. Three houses had been built over the top of the unknown and completely hidden shaft; all collapsed into the shaft and the five residents of two of the houses were killed.

The official inquiry brought out the fact that the district engineer responsible had no knowledge at all of the existence of the old shaft, since tunnel records had been destroyed when the district engineer's office was badly damaged in an air raid in 1940, and the records that were left were lost in a fire in 1952. Records were found later that did disclose the fact that eight shafts had been used during construction and that the work had been difficult because of the presence of water-bearing sand. Considerable timbering had been necessary in the shafts. It appeared that some of the old timbers had been built into the brick lining and had decayed in the course of time; ultimate failure of the rotted timber had the tragic result described. No blame could be attached to any of those responsible for the tunnel, but Brigadier Langley, the inspecting officer for the Ministry of Transport and Civil Aviation, included this warning in his official report, a statement that well warrants quotation:

The loss of the tunnel records contributed materially to this accident, and the events leading up to it have shown only too clearly the danger that arises when vital knowledge is not readily available. The maintenance staff should know of the existence of old shafts and other features which may cause weaknesses but in many cases the only records are the original construction drawings which, with the growth in the number of documents to be preserved in engineers' offices, may possibly be overlooked. . . . I recommend, therefore, that all tunnel records be reviewed and that any special features be brought to the notice of the maintenance and examining staff.

This procedure was immediately adopted by the civil engineer of the London Midland Region of British Railways; it is one which could well be widely followed. The Clifton Hall Tunnel has since been filled in completely, and its traffic has been diverted to alternative routes.[9.37]

9.14. Underground Storage. Although natural underground cavities have long been used for storage purposes (see page 158), the demands of the Second World War led to developments in the use of specially excavated vaults for a variety of storage purposes, initially for defense but in postwar years for products for civilian use also. The engineering and geological features of such works are not different from those discussed in connection with tunnels; the shapes and sizes of the excavations alone are different. Because of the unusual character of some of these storage arrangements and because they depend for their success so completely upon geological factors, this summary note appears to be advisable.

In view of all that "Pearl Harbor" meant to the United States, it is not surprising to find that one of the first large underground storage installations was constructed during the late war years near Pearl Harbor in the Hawaiian Islands for the storage of naval diesel and fuel-oil supplies. Twenty cylindrical vaults, each 100 ft in diameter and 250 ft high, with domed inverts and crowns, were constructed as steel containers and set in a concrete lining within rock excavations of appropriate shape. Excavation was generally in a thick series of volcanic lava flows, with the Hawaiian names of *aa* and *pahoeboe*. Grounting was carried out when the tanks were completed in order to fill any interstices in the rock adjacent to the lining and also to prestress the concrete lining in compression before the tanks were filled.[9.38] When the war closed, it was found that vast underground storage facilities had been constructed in Germany, Japan, Italy, Czechoslovakia, and Sweden. In some cases, these large excavations were used not only for storage but also for manufacturing and allied activities. About 6½ million cu yd of rock was excavated from one part alone of one of the largest German installations, an indication of the extent of such defense facilities.

With the imperative of war removed, such unusual activities could not normally be considered for civilian use, but other ideas for underground storage were developed. One of the first of these was the result of studies by Harald Edholm of the Swedish State Power Board who wondered if the immiscibility of oil and water could not be utilized in underground storage facilities for oil. Using an abandoned feldspar mine on the east coast of Sweden, Mr. Edholm developed a system which worked exactly as he had predicted. The mine was cleaned out, and boreholes were installed to ensure a constant supply of water at the bottom of the vast storage cavern; the oil floated on top of this, and suitable arrangements were made for getting the oil into the "mine" and out again when wanted. Oil is now stored to a depth of 260 ft; the extent of the storage area is reflected in the fact that a special rowing boat has to be kept for inspecting the subterranean oil lake. It was estimated that a comparable "standard" oil-storage depot would have cost about five times what the use of the abandoned mine actually cost for full operation.[9.39]

The use of abandoned oil and gas wells for the storage of refined petroleum products is a regular practice in the oil industry; doubtless this practice was responsible for the development of the idea of using artificially made underground cavities for the same purpose. Notable among such modern installations is that of the Imperial Oil Company of Canada in the "backyard" of its large refinery at Sarnia, Ontario. A vast salt bed lies 2,200 ft below the plant and extends under much of this part of Canada and the adjacent United States. By means of rotary drilling methods, a borehole was sunk into the salt bed; two sets of pipes were installed in the hole, and solution of the salt began. In 3 months 384,000 gal of water was used, and 23 million lb of salt was dissolved; this created a natural storage cavern with a capacity of 30,000 bbl, which was later expanded to 50,000 bbl; an adjacent cavity was similarly formed with a 40,000-bbl capacity. Butane and propane were then pumped into the caverns and so stored; brine is pumped back as the lighter petroleum products are withdrawn from storage. The economy of this method of storage will be obvious; even the saving in the cost of the ground necessary for "normal" storage tanks is itself enough to pay much of the subterranean work.[9.40]

More than a million barrels of fuel were being stored in North America in this way by 1958, with probably more than 25 million barrels in abandoned oil and gas wells. These figures illustrate the remarkable scale of the vast underground storage project of the Standard Oil Company of New Jersey at Linden, New Jersey. Here there was no salt stratum easily to be mined, but only the red shale that characterizes so much of the geology of New Jersey. Through a 300-ft shaft only 42 in. in diameter, 140,000 cu yd of rock was removed after being mined out to form a vast honeycomb pattern of underground tunnels; these tunnels gave a total storage capacity of 675,000 bbl, all to be used for the storing of liquefied petroleum gas.[9.41] Perhaps the ultimate development in this direction is to be found in England near Stockton in Yorkshire. Here the Northern Gas Board has cooperated with Imperial Chemical Industries in arranging for the use of cavities which were formed in salt beds in the normal process of mining salt under the north bank of the river Tees. By sharing the costs, in order to have enough rock salt left in place to form gas-tight cavities, the Gas Board found that it could achieve for £100,000 what would cost £600,000 if a standard gasholder were used; this sum provides storage for about 10 million cu ft of gas under the 30 atmospheres of pressure that is possible in the deep underground salt beds.[9.42]

9.15. Underground Power Stations. Reference must finally be made to the remarkable development in the last two decades in the use of power stations located underground instead of in the more conventional building above ground. Well over 100 such plants are now in successful use throughout the world. Again, their design and construction follow generally the lines necessary for tunnel work, but the scale of the excavations involved and the critical character of the caverns thus formed give special interest to these examples of modern civil engineering.[9.43]

The first truly underground station appears to have been that built in the early years of the century at Snoqualmie Falls in the state of Washington. In Europe, the first such plant was that built in 1911 for the Porjus project in Sweden. The first Italian underground station was that at Coghinas in Sardinia; it was built in 1926. Today Italy is one of the leaders in this phase of hydroelectric design, having over 60 underground power stations already in use. Despite the fact that the local geology must give solid rock of excellent quality for such large excavations, there are even underground power stations now in the Highlands of Scotland, famed in geological circles for some of the most complex hard-rock geology to be found anywhere. And in the Ceannacroc station, the local schist is proudly exposed to view, as shown in Fig. 9.20. Canada has one of the pioneer stations to be built below ground; this is the Toronto Power Company's plant at Niagara Falls, opened in the first decade of the century. Unlike modern installations, this plant had the turbines at tunnel level connected with the generators at ground level by unusually long vertical shafts. At the other extreme is the station that is to date the largest installation of its kind to be built below the surface;

Fig. 9.20. Interior of the Ceannacroc power station in the Scottish Highlands, showing exposed mica schist. (*Reproduced by permission of Sir William Halcrow & Partners, Consulting Engineers.*)

this is the powerhouse for the Kemano project in British Columbia, in which 2.4 million hp will eventually be generated under a head of 2,590 ft. The excavation for the station measures 1,140 ft long by 82 ft wide by 139 ft high.[9.44]

It is, however, in Sweden that some of the most notable work in this field has been carried out, not only for power stations, but also for underground storage and manufacturing facilities. This is a reflection of the critical position of Sweden in time of war, a fact that is freely acknowledged to be the motivating factor behind the remarkable facilities that now exist below the surface of its land. There is, for example, a complete naval base in which one tunnel measures 96 ft high by 57 ft wide and is capable of sheltering a destroyer afloat. It is said that the entire Swedish navy can thus be taken underground. In Sweden, 160 ft is regarded as the minimum rock cover necessary for protection against atomic attack, if good solid granite be the local bedrock. The extent of Swedish underground work is further illustrated by the fact that over 7 million cu yd of rock had to be excavated for two power projects alone, those at Kilforsen and Stornorrfors. It has been reported that half the water power now generated in Sweden comes from underground plants; 80 per

Fig. 9.21. The main hall of the Kemano power station in British Columbia, Canada, during construction. (*Reproduced by permission of the Aluminum Company of Canada, Ltd.*)

cent of current construction in this field is underground. Thus, it is small wonder that Swedish engineers have developed hard-rock drilling and blasting to a degree unimagined a decade ago. The "Swedish method" is the name long since applied to the method adopted for rock excavation in recent years in Sweden; this method uses pneumatic pusher-mounted one-man rock drills and tungsten-carbide tipped drill steels. The geology of Sweden, marked by competent igneous rocks of wide extent, has assisted in this development. Records of Swedish developments are fortunately available for use by engineers elsewhere whenever they have similarly satisfactory geological conditions with which to contend.[9.45]

9.16. Conclusion. Many more examples could be quoted from the records of tunnel practice; the availability of this material is probably due to the fact that every tunnel job is unique at least in some one respect and often in several. Descriptions of tunnel construction consequently figure prominently in civil engineering literature, a fortunate feature in connection with any study of the application of geology to civil engineering work in view of the dependence of all tunnel work on geological conditions. This dependence will probably be clear from the examples that have already been quoted; the constructive contribution that the science has made to the art will be obvious. Notable among available records is the compilation by the California Department of Water Resources of complete records for 99 tunnels of various size, shape, character, and geology. Charts prepared from this study provide one of the most comprehensive estimating guides of this kind available in civil engineering literature.[9.46]

As a final note, reference may fitly be made to cases in which even the nature of the material encountered has permitted the use of special methods during construction. In connection with tunneling in soft ground, for example, the character of the clay encountered in Chicago, Illinois (and Winnipeg, Canada), permits its removal in large slabs "cut off" the working face by means of specially shaped power-operated knives. In great contrast to this work of peace may be mentioned the unusual procedure developed during the excavation of mine tunnels in the chalk of northern France during the First World War. In order to soften the chalk before excavation and to reduce the noise of the underground working, auger holes were bored into the working face and filled with vinegar, a strange reversion to the practice of the Romans![9.47]

Many great tunnels will still be built; the story of man's tunneling activities is an ever-widening one. Even as this volume goes to press, renewed consideration is being given to one of the most widely discussed of all tunnel projects not yet undertaken, that which will probably one day be built under the English Channel to link England and France. As early as 1800, a proposal to construct a tunnel was made; in 1867, the first definite plans appear to have been advanced; and thereafter public interest in the project has continued. A great deal of geological investigation was carried out; 7,000 soundings across the channel were taken in 1875, for example, and almost 4,000 samples were obtained from the sea bed. Exploratory shafts were sunk, and there exist today several trial headings which extend for some distance under the sea. The consensus of general geological opinion is that the proposed tunnel (39 miles long) should be constructed throughout in the Lower Chalk Measures, although the continuous existence of this formation across the channel can only be surmised. M. Fougerolles has worked out in detail a scheme for disposing of the excavated chalk by grinding it into a slurry and pumping it upward into the sea! A lengthy report on the project was made to the British government in 1930; it was favorable,

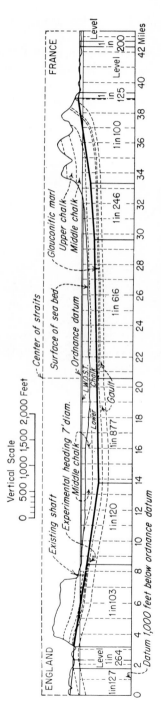

FIG. 9.22. Geological section along line of proposed channel tunnel between England and France, beneath the Straits of Dover. (Based upon the plan accompanying the report of the Channel Tunnel Committee, 1930, by permission of the Controller of H. M. Stationery Office, London.)

341

but the government subsequently decided against the project, not on any technical grounds but as a matter of policy.

For the benefit of those readers who may think that the foregoing reference to pumping out tunnel excavations is facetious, it may be mentioned that during the construction of sewer tunnels for the twin cities of Minneapolis and St. Paul, Minnesota, some tunneling work was carried out in the local white sandstone formation. Although this rock has a good appearance, it can be cut with a high-pressure water jet.

Fig. 9.23. Minneapolis–St. Paul intercepting sewer tunnels; view showing jetting of sandstone rock and pumping of sand slurry as an excavation process. (*Reproduced by permission of the Minneapolis–Saint Paul Sanitary District.*)

This means of cutting was adopted to break up the working faces; a $\frac{3}{16}$-in. jet at 300 psi pressure was used. The rock quickly disintegrated to the state of fine sand, and the resulting slurry was pumped, by means of centrifugal pumps, along the tunnel and up the working shafts to settling bins at street level.[9.48] And with this reference to solid rock being pumped through a 4-in. pipeline, perhaps this chapter should be brought to a close.

Suggestions for Further Reading

Most of the current textbooks on tunnel construction contain brief reference to the geological aspects of this branch of civil engineering, but the most helpful information will be found in individual records of major tunneling projects; the references cited in this chapter constitute a typical selection. In the case of some major tunnels, the organizations responsible have published complete records; an early but still notable example is "Geology of the Quabbin Aqueduct and Reservoir in Central Massachusetts," by F. E. Falquist and C. P. Berkey, published as Public Document 147 of the Commonwealth of Massachusetts, 1935.

From Vienna, there is available a volume devoted entirely to the geology of tunnels:

Stini, J., "Tunnelbaugeologie," Springer-Verlag, Vienna, Austria, 1950.

Chapter 10

OPEN EXCAVATION, FILL, AND DREDGING

Mr. Sopwith called the attention of the meeting to the valuable Geological Sections presented by the railway cuttings, and other engineering works now in progress; this was particularly the case on the North Midland Railway, where the crops of the various seams of coal, with the interposing strata, were displayed in the clearest manner, developing the geological structure of the country which the railway traverses.

At the Institution of Civil Engineers (London) February 2, 1841.[10.1]

THE DIGGING of a hole in the ground—for open excavation work is frequently so regarded—appears superficially to be a relatively simple matter. All experienced engineers know otherwise. The problems introduced are sometimes intensified by their very simplicity. The economics of engineering designs involving open excavation may be initially more indefinite and in consequence more involved than in many other branches of design work. Excavation methods and rates of progress are clearly dependent on the material encountered and its geological structure, the two factors that alike determine also the finished cross section of the excavation. All too often, these vital factors do not receive the study they deserve. The design and construction of embankments have generally to be empirical in a way similar to open excavation work. Unforeseen problems are not the same hazard as in excavation work, but the history of fill placement bears testimony to the fact that problems of serious moment are not unknown. These are often associated more with the effect of filling on existing strata than with the nature of the fill material itself.

Open excavation consists essentially in removing certain naturally formed material, within specified limits and to certain definite levels, in the most expeditious and economical manner possible. This necessitates knowing with some degree of accuracy the nature of the materials that have thus to be handled, their relative structural arrangement, their behavior when removed from their existing position, the possibility of meeting water during excavation, and the possible effect of the excavation operations on adjacent ground and structures. When these preliminary requirements are not fully answered before excavation begins, money is lost and trouble is encountered. This neglect of preliminary investigation work in open excavation is to some extent understandable: such work looks easy, and the unit prices generally charged are so low that it is often thought that a few cubic yards more or less will make little difference. The few can easily become dangerously many.

Preliminary investigations and constant check on excavation work as it proceeds are therefore clearly necessary. The preliminary work will follow the lines already suggested, with the addition of such special investigation as is found to be needed. The resulting geological maps should show rock contour lines where possible or the contour lines for any stratum so different from the surface material as to affect excavation methods and progress. The geological sections prepared will assist the engineer in visualizing the structure of the mass of material to be excavated. The usual care must be taken to investigate the possibility of encountering ground water. The sections prepared across and along the site to be excavated will show generally the relation of the hole to be made with adjacent strata and structures, and possible damage may in this way be foreseen. Complete and detailed records of all geological features encountered are just as necessary in excavation work as in other types of civil engineering work, since they will act as a constant check on the validity of information deduced from preliminary exploration and surveys and will often serve as a warning of possible unforeseen future troubles. Similarly, such records will be of interest to geologists and may reveal structural details of great value. A close watch should be kept for fossiliferous strata; and whenever possible, interested geologists should be granted permission to study fossil beds.

A typical example of modern excavation practice, illustrating the suggestions just advanced, is provided by the construction of the first subway in Canada, that of the Toronto Transit Commission. The railway is 4.6 miles long; it extends in a northerly direction from near the shore of Lake Ontario in downtown Toronto, and follows Yonge Street, the main traffic artery of the city. Prior to the completion of designs, every boring record that could be found for the central city area was studied. A test-boring program was then laid out on the basis of this study, and holes were put down at about 400-ft intervals right through the heart of the city. Soil samples were taken from the holes for soil testing, and ground-water levels were observed in some of them until construction commenced. It was found that the lower half mile of the subway box structure would be founded on shale, overlying which, and so constituting the bulk of all excavation for the cut-and-cover methods to be followed in construction, was a mixture of glacial till and glacial sands, gravels, silts, and clay. It was known that the geologically famous interglacial beds of the Toronto area would be encountered in the excavation. A local advisory geological committee was therefore formed in advance of the start of the work in order to provide liaison between interested geologists and the Transit Commission.

On the basis of the information obtained through these preliminary studies, designs and contract documents were prepared. Those tendering on the work were given access to all the information obtained on soil and ground-water conditions, with suitable qualifications as to its limitations; in the result, all bids received were remarkably close. Construction started in 1949 and was satisfactorily completed 3 years later. Excavation was generally by large diesel shovels; spoil was trucked up ramps to street level. Complete soil profiles were recorded in step with excavation; soil samples were taken at intervals of 50 ft and later lodged with the Royal Ontario Museum for safekeeping, where they are available for study by interested geologists. Much useful geological information was gained that has contributed to further understanding of the interglacial beds. The work was "unexciting" from the engineering point of view, because soil conditions proved to be almost exactly as predicted by the preliminary study. No unusual soil problems were encountered even in some of the difficult underpinning jobs that had to be done adjacent to the subway. Some claims were received by the commission after the work was completed (naturally), but all were settled satisfactorily and without recourse to law. As an indication of public interest, the Royal Ontario Museum arranged a special exhibit on the geology and construction of the subway; this is illustrated in Fig. 10.1; it attracted much attention.[10.2]

The preparation of limited areas of excavation for special foundations, as for buildings, bridges, and dams, will be considered in the chapters devoted especially to these subjects. In general excavation work, the dip of the strata to be encountered is a factor of major importance. If the strata are horizontal, or approximately so, excavation work will be relatively straightforward, and side slopes can be determined with some degree of certainty. If the bedding is appreciably inclined, excavation methods will be affected, and hazards possibly increased. The side slopes must be so selected as to be in accord with the natural slopes given by the bedding. Faults that cross the area over which excavation is to be carried out may cause serious trouble; in soft ground, it may be difficult, if not impossible, to detect them before digging starts, and hazards will thus be increased. Finally, all excavation work is influenced primarily by the nature of the material to be excavated. Broadly speaking, this can be classified as unconsolidated material (earth) and rock. It will be convenient if the general problems of excavation, already indicated, are

FIG. 10.1. Display model of soils encountered during the construction of the first section of the Toronto subway, of the Toronto Transit Commission, Ontario, Canada. (*Reproduced by permission of the Royal Ontario Museum where the model was displayed.*)

considered under these two headings. Note may again be made of the vital importance of adequate definitions in contract specifications of materials that have to be excavated, since the difficulties to which reference was made on page 16 most frequently occur in connection with open excavation. The suggestions already advanced for overcoming these difficulties are therefore of particular importance for this work.

Despite the apparent simplicity of excavation work, and the relative ease of defining what is meant by soil and rock, it is probably fair to say that more claims for extras have been received on civil engineering work as a whole on the basis of alleged incorrect classification of material to be excavated than for any other cause. For quite natural reasons, these claims are not often referred to publicly. So serious did they become, however, in connection with the building of the St. Lawrence Sedway and power project (on both sides of the border) that some reference to this particular instance is warranted, although final settlements are still under negotiation as this book is being written. The glacial history of the valley of the St. Lawrence is well known; there are some references to the tough overconsolidated glacial till and the critically sensitive marine clays of the valley in both geological and engineering literature.[10.3] Experience from the construction of the Messina Power Canal in 1897 revealed clearly the difficulty that these soils present in excavation; one contractor went bankrupt at that time. Despite the availability of all this information, which could have been studied in association with the official contract documents for the work, many large contractors submitted (at first) remarkably low bids for excavation, ranging from 34 cents per cubic yard up. On the first three major excavation contracts awarded on the American side, one contractor defaulted, one went bankrupt, and the third entered a claim for extra payment almost as large as his original bid. Experience on the Canadian side, although not quite so serious, was bad enough. Ultimately, it was announced in 1958 that five major American contractors had entered claims amounting to $27,625,603; they received settlements totaling $4,859,692.[10.4] Corresponding Canadian figures have yet to be released. It is clear that progress still has to be made in the proper application of geological information to civil engineering construction, even in such straightforward work as open excavation.

Naturally, there are construction projects on which the open-excavation work must be through material that actually varies from rock to soft unconsolidated deposits. Some unusual excavation work of this kind was encountered during the opening out of the Cofton Tunnel on the Birmingham to Gloucester section of the (then) London Midland and Scottish Railway (now British Railways) in England in 1925. The tunnel was constructed between 1838 and 1841 and forms a part of the route taken by this line of railway in crossing a fairly high ridge of

land immediately south of Birmingham. Because of modern traffic requirements, it had to be opened up and reconstructed as a cutting. The strata
shown up in the cuttings on either side of the tunnel were soft false-
bedded sandstones with thin beds of marl (north) and thick beds of
hard sandstone and beds of tough marl (south); for the civil engineer,
therefore, they can be classified generally as neither rock nor earth. No
records of the construction of the tunnel and the strata passed through
were available, but the geological survey map of the district showed a
major fault traversing the tunnel. Troubles due to earth movements

Fɪɢ. 10.2. Opening out of Cofton Tunnel, England; a hanging-wall slip in the
west slope on a fault plane. (*Reproduced by permission of the Chief Civil Engineer,
London Midland Region, British Railways.*)

were therefore anticipated, and some of a serious nature were encountered very early in the work. Before the final 80 yd of tunnel was
demolished, a careful geological survey of the surrounding country was
made in order to attempt a deduction of the hidden structure yet to
be encountered. The survey was considered in conjunction with the
records of dip and details of faults made from the start of the work. This
investigation was carried out in the midst of construction, and although
incomplete, it was of great service. The work was finally completed
satisfactorily but only after surmounting great difficulties. The evidence
tended to show that a tunnel, instead of an open cutting, had originally

been built because of a realization of the troubles to be encountered. Examination of the geological survey map showed that if the original line had been located either 200 yd west or 300 yd east of its actual position, little or no trouble due to the Longbridge fault would have been experienced. The paper describing the work is one of those rare civil engineering publications which deal with the surmounting of unusual difficulties in construction, and as such it is worthy of special study. At least one member of the staff of the Geological Survey of Great Britain was in constant attendance at the work.[10.5]

10.2. Economics of Open Excavation. The end of a tunnel is often the beginning of an open cut; the location of the change of section is always a matter demanding careful consideration by the designing engineer. The basic criterion, but not the only one, is the relation of the respective costs of construction of tunnel and open cut; geological structure is intimately associated with a study to determine such costs. Since tunnels have already been dealt with, little need be said about the estimated cost of their excavation. For an equivalent open cut, the volume to be removed per foot of length is naturally much greater, but the unit cost of excavation will be lower, since the work can be done in the open without underground hazards and with excavating machinery that cannot be used underground. If the side slopes can be trimmed off to a satisfactory angle, no equivalent to the lining of a tunnel will normally be necessary; but if the side slopes have to be restricted, retaining walls at the foot of the slopes may involve a greater cost than tunnel lining. Based on the figures thus obtained, comparative estimates of cost for tunnel and cut can be calculated; when these are applied to locations with increasing depth to grade, a section can be selected as that at which the change in type of construction can be made most economically.

Often this result will be the final one; but true economy has not been studied in investigations of this type, unless some consideration is given to geological structure. Geological sections along the center line of the proposed cut and at right angles to it (at several stations)—together with a detailed material study—are an essential. The relation of the cut proposed can then be seen in relation to underground drainage, the dip of the strata, and possible unusual underground structural relationships; important modifications of design may have to be made in consequence.

Consider such a section as that sketched in Fig. 10.3. In the tunnel, drainage of underground water need not be considered, as no water will reach the tunnel; but in the cut, drainage will certainly present serious problems. Water will be continually seeping out at contact A; and if the quantity of water is sufficient, it may tend to wash some of the sand out onto the face of the slope. In order to escape, the water must run down the face of the shale, thus tending to weaken it. There might even be some travel of water along bedding planes of the shale, lubricating them and giving rise to dangerously unstable conditions which might lead to serious slips. Alternatively, through this unrestricted drainage of the underground porous bed, unstable conditions might be induced in the clay stratum above, with the consequent possibility of serious earth movement.

In all such cases, and they are by no means rare, standard calculations of relative economy may not therefore present a true picture. In the particular case illustrated, it will be advisable, even at the expense of increased first cost, to extend the tunnel construction beyond the theoretical economical limit in order to avoid possibility of the difficulties indicated. Instances will occur in which no such simple geological structure as is sketched will be encountered. Faulted ground, for example, is a menace in both solid rock and soft material; and although it causes difficulties in

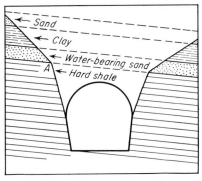

Fig. 10.3. Simplified geological section illustrating a possible relation between tunnel and open-cut excavation.

tunnel work, it may cause greater difficulties in open excavation, owing mainly to the greater freedom given to material on fault planes to move in large masses and thus to increase unnecessary excavation. The complications resulting from excavation in faulted ground which arose during

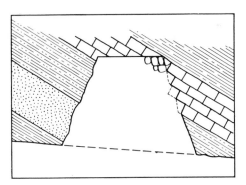

Fig. 10.4. Simplified geological section illustrating how the dip of rock strata may affect excavated cuttings.

the opening up of the Cofton Tunnel, described in the last section, serve as a good example; the factors there influencing ordinary economic criteria are clear.

In open excavation work not associated with tunnel construction, overall dimensions and depths to finished grade will normally be determined by considerations other than excavation costs, so that no question of relative economy will normally arise. Thorough preliminary investigations are necessary all the same, and these may reveal special conditions which do affect the economic aspect of the work undertaken. For example, subsurface explorations may show that a slightly different location can avoid troublesome material. Finally, geological conditions will have a bearing on the necessity of finishing off side slopes either with or without retaining walls, when there is no restriction on how an excavated area is to be bounded. The local geology will affect generally the economic cross sec-

Fɪɢ. 10.5. Sign displayed by the "Ontario Hydro" during the construction of the Sir Adam Beck development at Niagara Falls, Ontario, Canada. (*Reproduced by permission of the Hydro Electric Power Commission of Ontario.*)

tion of the cut desired in this case, since the structural relationships of the strata to be exposed will affect the nature of side slopes quite apart from the nature of the material. A point to be especially watched in this connection is the question of drainage, since the adoption of simple and relatively inexpensive drainage systems can readily lead to appreciable modifications in the side slopes adopted.

Each of the two great modern water-power projects at Niagara Falls provides an illustration of one aspect of excavation economics. For the Sir Adam Beck No. 2 Project of the Hydro Electric Power Commission of Ontario, the two large pressue tunnels (see page 309) lead to a final 2¼ miles of open canal, designed for a flow of 40,000 cfs, excavated through the upper strata shown on Fig. 9.9. Careful correlation of the cross section of the canal necessary for hydraulic reasons with the exact location of the rock strata, which are inclined slightly to the horizontal, showed that if the invert of the canal were kept in the Grimsby sandstone, drilling and mucking would be facilitated and a better canal section would be obtained from the structural point of view. The canal section

FIG. 10.6. Rock cut 140 ft deep at outlet (N) end of east conduit of the Niagara Power Project, Niagara Falls, New York. (*Reproduced by permission of the Power Authority of the State of New York; Uhl, Hall, and Rich, Consulting Engineers.*)

was therefore gradually widened, in pace with the gradual rise in the level of the surface of the Grimsby formation, in order to provide the requisite hydraulic cross section; this project thus provides one of the most vivid examples imaginable of the interrelation of geological conditions and civil engineering design.[10.6] The canal excavation was notable further in that it was depicted on a very large illustrated sign erected for the information of visitors to the great construction job while it was in progress; this sign is shown in Fig. 10.5.

Immediately across the Niagara River is the equally impressive Niagara power project of the Power Authority of the State of New York, constructed a few years after the Ontario hydro project, but similar to it in over-all conception. The great powerhouses face each other diagonally across the Niagara River, below the rapids that distinguish the Niagara Gorge. The American station is somewhat upstream from the Canadian; with the interconnecting high-tension lines clearly in view, they typify the joint development of that portion of the international waters that can be diverted from the world-famous falls without destroying their natural beauty. Since the Niagara project is the equivalent of the old and the new American stations, the capacity of its main water conduits is 83,000 cfs; water is abstracted from a point above the falls about 2 miles to the west of the Canadian intake. From the intake, the American water is conveyed to its powerhouse in twin concrete conduits, each equivalent in size to six double-track railroad tunnels. These are not pressure conduits, as on the Canadian side, but are reinforced-concrete arched structures within cuts excavated in the upper formations shown on Fig. 9.9. Because of the local topography and the route followed by the conduits, generally to the west of the city of Niagara Falls, New York, the depth of the necessary twin rock cuts was as much as 150 ft below the original ground surface, and maximum depth in solid rock was 145 ft. Figure 10.6 is a typical view of this impressive example of rock excavation; the total volume of excavation for the complete job of 39 million cu yd was in keeping with the majestic size of the twin conduit excavations.[10.7] The contrast between the designs of the main conduits for the two adjacent projects is striking to the interested observer; other factors, in addition to strict economics, were probably involved.

10.3. Open Excavation of Unconsolidated Material. Excavation in soft material may vary from work in good clean sharp gravel to digging in soft cohesive clay. Between the two extremes lie the many and varied substances classed generally as soils or earth or by some other such generic name, in nearly all of which cohesion is a property of some significance. It can be seen that in considering the mechanics of these materials, as distinct from solid rocks, conditions other than those considered in the ordinary strength-of-materials laboratory must be investigated. It is here that soil mechanics has made such a great contribution to this field of civil engineering; the determination of slope stability, based on laboratory investigations of the shearing strength of the soils to be encountered, is a notable part of soil mechanics theory. All that soil mechanics can do, however, is of little avail without accurate knowledge of the geology of the site to be excavated. The exact interrelation of the various soil strata, and particularly their relation to local ground-water conditions, must be known with certainty if excavation is to proceed as planned and without trouble. There is probably no branch of "soil work" in which soil mechanics and geology must be so closely associated as in the determination of slopes to excavation. That this is no new observation is shown by the comments made by Alexandre Collin more than a century ago and briefly quoted on page 106.[10.8]

In preliminary considerations of open excavation work, the bottom grade level will be determined either by factors depending on other parts of the works involved or by general economic considerations. In any event the effect of the side slopes on the total quantity of material to be excavated, and therefore on the total cost, will be considerable. In ordinary railway cuttings, for example, the volume of material to be excavated to form flat side slopes, nonproductive excavation as it might be called, can be far larger than the volume of material to be moved from that part vertically above the level base of the cut, the material that must productively be moved. It is clear, therefore, that side slopes must be as steep as possible, consistent with safety, in order to minimize the volume of material to be excavated.

In the preliminary as well as in the final determination of such side slopes, geological factors should be given the greatest consideration. In the past, this has not always been done; side slopes used in design have often been based on the past experiences of those concerned with the work. On the basis of practical experience, tables of angles of repose for materials of various kinds have been built up and are in general use today. Although these tables undoubtedly have their use, unquestioning reliance on them is inadvisable. Since it is almost impossible to correlate the broad material classification in these tables with the detailed results of test borings, the procedure is without a logical basis and so is the more surprising in view of normal engineering method. It is true that the side slopes of many cuttings stand up quite successfully; it is also true that trouble has been encountered with the sides of many such cuttings and that large quantities of material have probably been unnecessarily removed from the side slopes of many cuttings. The inevitable use of assumed angles of repose in very preliminary designs may be permitted; but it is suggested that before the completion of any final designs, a full study should be made of the geological structure of the complete prism of material to be removed, not only to discover the geological arrangement of the material but also to investigate the effect of removal of the prism on adjoining geological structure and to determine what soil mechanics investigations are advisable. Sands and gravels are usually unaffected by exposure to the atmosphere. Clays are different, and special attention must always be paid to the effect of exposure to the atmosphere on any clays that are to be uncovered during excavation. Moisture content of clay is a critical factor in such determinations; it can profitably be studied in the laboratory if undisturbed samples are obtained for testing. The old construction "dodge" of covering up exposed steep faces of clay was evolved in order to maintain unchanged the water content of clay; it is a device that will often result in considerable saving in excavation.

The foregoing comments on open excavation work in soil deal with points that are so obvious to all who have had any experience in this class of work that they are almost banal. Those, however, who have had experience will appreciate that, although the suggestions made are so obvious, they are often neglected or not even considered. Knowledge of all the strata to be penetrated in excavation work is absolutely essential before work begins, and this is true irrespective of the methods to be used for excavation. On large jobs, the use of automotive scrapers and tractors is now almost universal. So well have these construction tools been developed by their manufacturers that average unit prices for excavation on large North American jobs have actually decreased during the last 30 years, despite a threefold increase in the general price index. But as the experience on the St. Lawrence power project demonstrated in no uncertain manner, even the best of equipment will not operate efficiently in material for which it was not designed. Geological study, therefore, is a prerequisite for getting the best out of earth-moving equipment.

On more confined jobs, it is often necessary to limit the extent of excavation, or its effect on neighboring property, by the use of retaining walls of steel sheet piling, an aid to civil engineering construction whose use has grown steadily during the last three decades. Here, too, knowledge of the exact nature of the materials through which the piling is to be driven is an essential preliminary. The severe vibration set up by the driving of the piles, although relatively unimportant in sand and gravel, may produce strange results in clay, especially if the driving is under water. The author has encountered a small pier construction in which steel piles were driven into overconsolidated marine clay which naturally showed up in the preliminary wash borings as "very hard." When disturbed by the pile driving and consequent churning action, it changed character completely; it became almost fluid in the neighborhood of the piles, and gave a greatly reduced passive pressure as resistance to movement. While the pile-driving operations were in progress, a large dredge was engaged in excavating a channel in the clay. When some distance from the pier, the steel cutterhead of the dredge had to be used to break up the clay sufficiently for it to be pumped; but starting at about 400 ft from the site of the pile driving, a change in the nature of the clay became apparent. It became progressively softer as the neighborhood of the piles was approached until finally the steel cutter was stopped and the clay was removed by direct pumping.

The presence of boulders can be a serious impediment to the driving of steel piling; in the interpretation of the results of the preliminary test boring which is always necessary in this branch of work, an appreciation of the local geology can be of great assistance; knowledge of the glacial nature of strata encountered, for example, suggests the possible presence of boulders even if the test borings do not show any. Furthermore, if steel piling is to be driven through the full depth of unconsolidated

Fig. 10.7. General view of the south end of Steep Rock Lake, Ontario, Canada, after draining and the start of open-pit mining. The old shore line can be recognized near the crest of the surrounding hill; all the soil to be seen was potentially unstable. (*Photograph by R. F. Legget. Reproduced by permission of Steep Rock Iron Mines, Ltd.*).

material at a particular site in order to achieve toehold in the rock below, a study of the local geology will sometimes be the only means whereby a reasonable estimate can be made of the nature of the rock surface and whether or not it will be weathered to such an extent that the piles can penetrate it at least for a little way. In this branch of work, therefore, as in others, not only will an appreciation of the significance of geological features be of service to the civil engineer, but in many instances a direct application of geological information will assist in both the design and the construction of his works.

Instead of illustrating the foregoing remarks with what might be called a "conventional" example, attention will be invited to one phase of an excavation job which involved the moving of more soil than was moved in the building of the Panama Canal. Over 300 million cu yd of soil was moved from the bed of Steep Rock Lake in northwestern Ontario before all the valuable iron ore beneath the lake bed was accessible for open-pit mining. In 1943 and 1944 the lake, with an area of about 10 sq miles, was drained by a major river-diversion project. The natural bed of the lake consisted of varved clays with high sensitivity and a liquidity index always greater than 1; this soil index property was sometimes as high as 1.5. By a vast dredging operation the soil covering the ore bodies was removed easily, but the surrounding slopes had to be finished off in a stable condition. This involved careful cutting with high-pressure water jets to a finished outline that was based on most careful geological studies, closely associated with continuing laboratory studies of the properties of the soils involved. Basically, the method used was to trim the soil to a slope of 1 in 3 and to limit the vertical height of each slope to 20 ft. A horizontal berm, its width depending on the shear strength of the soil, was then excavated and graded gently away from the face of the slope to obviate drainage onto the erodible face of the excavated soil. In this way, all the slopes shown in Fig. 10.7 were successfully finished off; vegetation finally completed the stabilizing process. The most striking example of what could be achieved with this very unstable soil, which, due to its high-moisture content, ran like pea soup when disturbed, was the forming of a natural dam from the undisturbed material, 160 ft high, to retain an undrained part of the lake bed while excavation proceeded on the other side down to one of the ore bodies, 200 ft below the crest level of this unusual barrier.[10.9]

10.4. Open Excavation in Water-bearing Strata. Adequate surface-drainage arrangements are a first essential to success in all open excavation work. Consideration of the problems presented by the presence of ground water must inevitably be made in conjunction with geological studies, if possible waste of money and time are to be avoided. Pumping will be the engineer's first thought in determining how to handle these problems. But the provision of the usual sump when excavating into water-bearing gravel, for example, may be worse than useless. If preliminary investigations show that such water is moving, then a watertight cutoff must be provided before progress can be made. Interlocking steel sheet piling with watertight joints may provide a remedy if it can be tightly driven into an impervious layer beneath.

Alternatively, the job may be tackled with the aid of what is known as the "well-point system." Various systems incorporating well points (a self-descriptive term) are available for this type of work. Basically, the system consists of a special pump and a number of well points for lowering the underground water table below the lowest excavation level. In this way the material to be excavated is predrained and so converted from the wet state, in which its behavior may be treacherous, to the dry; thus excavation progress is facilitated and water troubles are obviated. The lowering of the ground-water level is achieved by means of special well points with riser pipes about 2 in. in diameter. The well points are fitted with special jetting nozzles, and immediately above these is wrapped a triple layer of bronze screen mesh; the standard area is 350 sq in.

The well points are jetted into the ground to a depth 5 ft or more below bottom grade level and are located close to the area to be excavated in such a way that they will not be disturbed when excavation is complete. They are spaced at certain distances apart so that the cones of

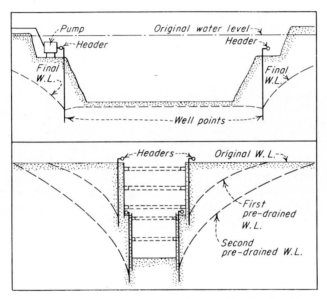

Fig. 10.8. Diagrammatic sketches illustrating the use of well points for open and for trench excavation in water-bearing ground.

depression around each well point intersect; thus, the water level midway between the points is lowered below any level at which it might cause trouble. All the points are connected with a header pipe leading to the pump which is set in operation when the complete system is ready for working. Successive cones of depression therefore completely surround the area of excavation. If the pumps are properly installed and of sufficient capacity, they will prevent the rise of ground water into the area, and excavation can proceed within the area in the dry. The system can be extended and modified in many ways, notably in the excavation of deep trenches; successive surfaces of depression are as indicated in Fig. 10.8. Bold and simple in conception, the system can naturally be fully effective only under skilled direction and with a sure and certain knowledge of the geological conditions obtaining at the site, since the success of its operation depends on the travel of the ground water in the strata encountered.

An example familiar to the writer may be cited; this was on the construction of the Victoria Park Pumping Station, a part of the duplicate water-supply system of the city of Toronto, Ontario, Canada. The buildings of this station cover an area 87 by 297 ft; during their construction, excavation had to be taken to a depth about 35 ft below the level of Lake Ontario, the shore of which was only about 100 ft away from one of the

Fig. 10.9. Excavation in swamp mud, predrained by a well-point installation (seen on right-hand side), for the placing of 84-in. precast-concrete pipe as an outfall sewer from Jamaica Sewage Treatment Works, New York. (*Reproduced by permission of the Moretrench Corporation, New York.*)

longer sides of the excavated area. Excavation proceeded through stiff clay for about 30 ft of the total depth of 46 ft; small water boils then made their appearance. Auger borings were taken all over the site to check those originally taken, and a few thin water-bearing sand seams were encountered. A well-point system was therefore put in, and well points were jetted down all around the area to be excavated to full depth. The excavation was then completed without encountering water. It is of special interest to note that methane gas as well as water was "pumped out" by the Moretrench pump; the gas, which was lit and burned, was believed to have been the result of decaying organic matter entrapped with the sand deposits.[10.10] A similar installation had been made some years before during the construction of the North Toronto Sewage Treatment Plant, an area of 170 by 250 ft and consisting of swamp mud, clay, sand, and gravel, which had its ground-water table lowered by 13 ft during the progress of excavation. In other cases the facility of working in the dry—made possible by the use of the well-point system—has permitted the simplification of foundation design. The large Holland Plaza Building in New York City was designed to be supported by a concrete-pile foundation placed in a clayey quicksand. A well-point system dried up the excavation, and a heavy reinforced-concrete mat foundation was used instead.[10.11]

At first sight, it would appear that the system would operate only in porous materials such as sands and gravels. However, it will give equally effective results even in some types of clay. The quantity of water pumped out of clay is naturally very much smaller than that pumped out of more porous material. Careful study has suggested that in such cases the suction caused by the pumping action causes a slight vacuum at the base of each point; this leads to an unbalanced pressure at the nearest exposed face, and atmospheric pressure outside prevents water from leaving the clay, and indeed, tends to hold the material at a slope far in excess of that at which it would naturally stand. At the other extreme, well points have been successfully used for dewatering softer types of rock. If the points can be driven into place, or placed in suitably drilled holes, they can frequently change a wet and difficult job into one that is as "dry as a bone," provided always that careful study of the strata to be drained has been made in advance.

Use of well points in sand fill is an obvious application; one of the most extensive of such installations was for the construction of an outfall sewer into Jamaica Bay, New York City, where excavation was carried out in an artificial peninsula of sand fill that was made of dredged sand deposited over some of the original muddy marginal bay bottom. So extensive had the installation to be, with three levels of well points in operation at once, that over 7,000 ft of 8-in. header pipe was in use at one time; the pumps handled as much as 800,000 gph.[10.12] During the construction of the Dennison Dam by the United States Corps of Engineers on the Red River between Texas and Oklahoma, an extensive well-point installation was used to dry up not only an area in which the closure section of the dam was to be constructed but also an area in which slumping had occurred and in which excavation had to be carried on under rigid control.[10.13] Water-bearing coarse gravel was successfully dried out by well points over an area of 250 by 200 ft during the construction of a power plant of the Pennsylvania Electric Company at Warren, Pennsylvania, immediately adjacent to the Allegheny River; on this job four *permanent* bronze well points were installed before construction was complete in order to provide a continuing pure water supply for boiler feed and general purposes.[10.14] Well points can frequently demonstrate their double utility in this way.

Deep excavations in the Key West district of Florida were not regarded with favor by contractors for a long time because of the ground-water difficulties encountered in the local oölite, a soft white rock composed of calcium carbonate, organically formed. In 1954, an attempt was made to drain this unusual material with the aid of well points; the initial installation at Key West was made for the excavation for a

Fig. 10.10. A well-point installation keeping dry an excavation in Miami oölite at Key West, Florida, U.S.A. (*Reproduced by permission of the Moretrench Corporation, and Powell Brothers Construction Company.*)

sewage lift-pump station, 40 ft square and 22 ft below the surface, with ground water standing 2 ft below the surface. Open pumping reduced the water level by 7 ft, and well points, placed in specially drilled holes, were successful in pulling the water down the remaining distance; special attention was paid to the spacing of the points in order to ensure proper approach velocities so that screen clogging would be avoided.[10.15]

Figure 10.11 illustrates graphically an unusual geological condition that was encountered during the building of the west anchorage for a cable-stiffened suspension bridge over the Lempa River in El Salvador. Well points here had three functions: to dry up the area in which excavation was to proceed; to reduce hydrostatic pressure in the underlying soil strata in order to eliminate any possibility of blowing in the bottom of the excavation; and to stabilize the soils adjacent to the large area excavated. Some trouble was encountered with boils caused by artesian water coming up unplugged test boreholes that had penetrated the underlying strata; this is a reminder of the necessity of plugging all such holes with clay, or preferably bentonite, when preliminary investigation is complete, lest the same holes cause unsuspected trouble when encountered again after construction begins.[10.16]

10.5. Graving Docks. An alternative means of controlling ground water during construction when large areas are involved, and one extensively developed in Europe, consists in the use of submersible pumps lowered

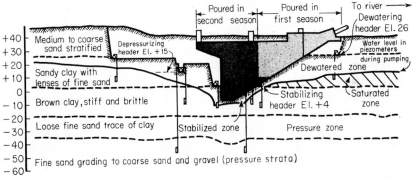

Fig. 10.11. Diagrammatic geological cross section at west anchorage of Lempa River suspension bridge in El Salvador, showing soil conditions which explain the necessity of the three-stage well-point system. (*Reproduced by permission of the American Society of Civil Engineers.*)

into specially prepared drainage wells. A water-lowering plant of this type was used during the construction of the Albert Canal in Belgium and also in the building of the King George V Graving Dock in Southampton, England. In this latter installation, ten 14-in. pipes gravel packed in 24-in. holes formed the drainage wells for dealing with the artesian water that was found by test borings under part of the area now occupied by this great dock.[10.17] Permanent ground-water relief pipes were installed in the completed structure. The construction of graving (or "dry") docks is naturally almost always an unusually difficult operation in civil engineering. The areas involved are always large; the very nature of the structures necessitates their being immediately adjacent to deep water. Unwatering problems have, therefore, accompanied the construction of most of these notable structures; they are not numerous even on a world-wide scale so that the record of each case is well worth careful study.

A wartime example of this type of structure may be described. The great West Coast Dock of the U.S. Navy at San Diego (the location was not mentioned in the published description of the work, dated 1944) with an entrance sill 45 ft below mean low water, was designed to accommodate the largest naval vessels. In view of the general character of the site, the original plans were to build the dock by underwater methods. Careful soil studies over the site, however, suggested that it might be possible to build the dock in the dry, and a full-scale field test by the U.S. Bureau of Yards and Docks confirmed this suggestion. The site was therefore dredged to grade, and then protected by a rock-fill sea wall behind which sand fill and an impervious silty-loam blanket were placed. Thirty-six 2,000-gpm deep-well pumps were then installed, as shown in Fig. 10.12, together with three rows of well points which circled the construction site and stabilized the soil slopes. In all, 1,600 well points were used in this way, yielding up to 2,000 gpm. Twenty-five days after all 36 main pumps were in operation, the entire site had been dewatered to an elevation of −62; the average pumping rate was 36,000 gpm. A continuous pumping rate of from 20,000 to 25,000 gpm was necessary to keep the water level down to the required level. Pumping was continued for 8 months, by which time the structure was complete. The deep-well pumps and motors were later used as the permanent pumping installation for the dock. Some settlement of adjacent ground was caused by the dewatering, but careful soil studies were able to contribute to the solution of the difficulties that might have resulted had it not been determined that the settlement was to be of limited extent.[10.18]

10.6. Excavation of Shafts. On a quite different scale, the excavation of shafts in water-bearing ground can prove equally difficult. All too many projects have foundered because of what appeared to be insuperable difficulties in "getting a shaft down." In the early years of this century, even so eminent and inventive a man as Thomas Edison was defeated by this particular civil engineering operation. By magnetic methods, Edison had located some ore in the Sudbury basin of northern Ontario, but when he attempted to construct a shaft through about 100 ft of water-bearing soil, in order to gain access to the ore, he found it impossible. (The main shaft of the world-famous Falconbridge mine was later discovered to be located close to Edison's.)

The first requirement is, as always, an accurate knowledge of the strata to be penetrated and the location (and possible variations) of the ground-water table. For shallow shafts, well points may be used, but the depth to which this method will be effective is very limited. Pumping at any great depth will usually be impracticable, not only because of the amount of water to be pumped, in view of the size of the cone of depression (see page 156), but also because of the possible effects of the pumping operation upon surrounding property, or at least upon local

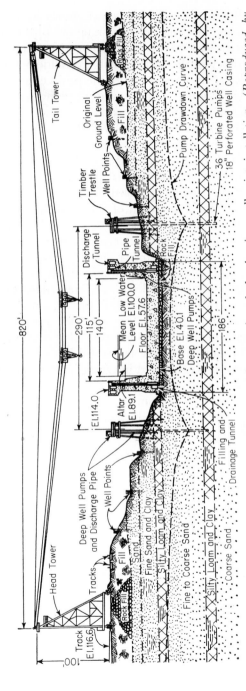

FIG. 10.12. Cross section through the site of the San Diego graving dock, showing well-point installation. (*Reproduced by permission of the American Society of Civil Engineers.*)

ground-water conditions. Accordingly, other means have been adopted for the sinking of shafts in water-bearing strata; one of the most common in recent years has been long used in mining operations, the freezing of the ground surrounding the shaft. Suitable conditions for such an application must be definitely known before the project can be considered; that is, there must be regular strata of water-bearing material in which water is present to such an extent that difficulty will be experienced in opening up the excavation in any other way. Once these conditions are determined, suitably sized pipes are sunk (generally by jetting) all around the area and connected to a refrigerating system which, when operating, gradually freezes solid the ring of material around the area of excavation; this ring acts as a natural temporary shell for the excavation work.

A major example of the application of this technique was for the excavation of large shafts used during the construction of a vehicular tunnel under the river Scheldt at Antwerp, Belgium, between 1931 and 1933. The shafts were 70 ft in diameter and 87 ft deep; and because of the construction method adopted, they were entirely free from bracing. They penetrated water-bearing sand with an interbedded turf layer. For the freezing process, 116 holes were bored, one set on a circle of 86-ft diameter, and one set on a circle of 78-ft diameter; the spacing between the holes was 4½ ft, and all were sunk to a clay stratum 90 ft below ground level. A 6-in. pipe was sunk and sealed in each hole, and a 2-in. pipe open at the bottom was inserted in each of the larger pipes to form the necessary circulating system for the brine solution which was used to lower the temperature of ground and water. In took 4 months to complete each of the requisite cylinders of ice and frozen ground; they were then maintained frozen until the shaft construction was complete.[10.19]

An early North American example was the sinking of a special exploratory shaft by the Tennessee Valley Authority for study of foundation conditions at the site of the Gilbertsville Dam. The ground consists of limestone bedrock overlain by about 50 ft of water-bearing soil. It was decided that a shaft would be the best means of determining soil properties, the character of the rock surface, and the way in which steel sheet piling behaved when driven through the local overburden; in addition a shaft would provide a means for inclined drilling into the bedrock. A ring of steel sheet piling was therefore driven to rock, and excavation was carried down in it in the open, with bracing installed as required. A bad blow occurred, however, 14 ft from bedrock, and it was then decided to freeze the soil around the shaft. This was done with equipment that the TVA had on hand, using a brine circulating system; thus, the shaft was unwatered and excavation was completed. Bedrock was found to be a dense, black siliceous limestone into which 25 of the 50 steel piles had penetrated, as deep as 5 in.; six of the interlocks between piles had, however, failed. Test drilling was then carried out from the bottom of the shaft, as shown in Fig. 10.13.[10.20]

A more recent application of the freezing concept was in connection with the access shaft for a new sewer tunnel under the East River in New York City. The New York City Public Works Department would not permit interference with the local ground-water condition at the necessary site of the access shaft in Manhattan because of possible settlement of adjoining buildings. The use of compressed air and freezing were the alternatives available. The contractor adopted freezing for the 14½-ft-diameter shaft that he had to sink to a depth of 123 ft in order

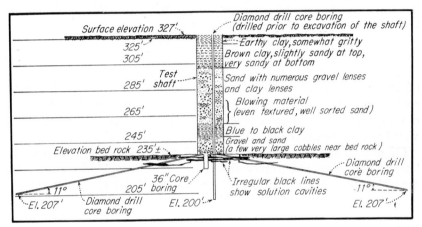

FIG. 10.13. Cross section through special test shaft at Gilbertsville Dam, TVA, showing the use of inclined test borings for subsurface investigation. (*Reproduced by permission of The Editor, Engineering News-Record.*)

to reach solid rock; the frozen shaft was then lined with concrete, and the freezing stopped as work continued down for another 200 ft in solid rock.[10.21]

The freezing process is not new, although with modern refrigerating equipment it has been refined to a degree not possible in earlier days. There are records of its use in mining operations well before the end of the nineteenth century. Shafts have been sunk to depths of 3,000 ft in unusual mining operations; one recent example on this scale was sunk to tap a valuable potash development some 30 miles east of Saskatoon, Saskatchewan.

Under very exceptional circumstances, other more specialized methods can be used in order to "solidify" soil that is giving trouble. Several chemical-injection methods are now available, some of a proprietary character. They have been successfully applied to shaft work but, like all other methods, they depend for their success upon an accurate foreknowledge of the strata to be penetrated. Since these methods require specialist knowledge for their successful application, their availability may be noted without any detail being given of their individual character.

10.7. Excavation of Rock. The problems that may be encountered in the excavation of solid rock are, in the main, similar to those met in rock tunnel work. They necessitate preliminary determination of the structural arrangement of rock strata, the nature of rocks to be encountered, the possible presence of water, and the resistance of exposed rock to weathering influences. The structural arrangement of rock strata will affect considerably the side slopes to be adopted in design, since if the general dip is toward one side of the cutting, there will be a tendency for shatter rock to fall off the ends of successive layers unless it is trimmed well back; a reverse effect will naturally be found on the opposite side of the cutting. Structural arrangement will also affect underground water problems; the arrangement of rock strata will determine the general lines of water movement, and in connection with the porosity or impermeability of beds, the levels at which water may be encountered. Angles of dip and other special structural features such as fault planes will obviously have a considerable influence on excavation methods.

Of great importance is the nature of the rock to be excavated. By "nature" is meant not merely the general classification of the rock but a vivid conception of the actual properties of the particular type of rock to be encountered all over the area to be excavated. The value of general classification is by no means unimportant—indeed, this is a first essential—but each class of rock can vary so considerably that, for civil engineering purposes, it must be further described by some indication of its physical properties. Thus, sandstone can vary from a hard and compact rock to material that is little better than well-compacted sand; granite can prove to one of the hardest of all rocks and yet it may be found in such a state of decomposition that exposure to the atmosphere will lead to its immediate disintegration. All preliminary geological information must therefore be checked thoroughly, and the general description of rock types, obtained from borings, must be considered in relation to the physical state of the rock samples so found. Similarly, it is essential to know with some degree of accuracy, before work begins, how the rock to be encountered will stand up after long exposure; this is necessary in order to obviate possible future accidents and to keep maintenance charges to a minimum.

If due allowance is made for exceptional variations in physical properties, the following notes will serve as a general guide. The stability and permanence of igneous and metamorphic rocks when exposed to the atmosphere can generally be relied upon unless the rocks are badly weathered. If they are badly fissured, jointed, or shattered by local faulting, the greatest caution must be observed in finishing off slopes. Caution is especially required for work done during severe winter weather, as in Canada, where frost action may temporarily consolidate local disintegration. Sedimentary rocks must be considered with great caution and judgment in such work. The presence of clay in any form, even as a shale which may be exceedingly hard when first exposed, must be regarded with suspicion, particularly if the bedding planes are inclined to the horizontal at any appreciable degree. The action of the atmosphere may soon reduce this material to an unstable state, with consequent extra trouble and expense. When clay is known to be present, ample allowance should be given in side slopes as designed, and the economics of protecting the exposed faces with light retaining walls should be investigated. Sandstone and limestone, if in a firm and solid state, will stand with vertical or almost vertical faces; but since both types of rock vary from a sound solid state to material that can be crumbled in the hand, every case must be considered on its own merits.

Adequate drainage facilities are naturally an important feature of all rock-excavation work. They will be provided by one of the standard methods available in civil engineering practice, but geological considerations may affect them to some degree. For example, in the construction of a new railway in Salvador and Guatemala (by International Railways of South America), many cuttings were made through a conglomerate called *talapete*. The side slopes in all these cuttings had to be left as steep as possible in order to carry off the torrential tropical rains before they led to erosion of the conglomerate.[10.22] Similarly, drainage in all types of shale, must be arranged to remove surface water as quickly and surely as possible in order to minimize its action on the rock. Limestone may also be affected by excessive contact with water.

The usual method of drilling and blasting may not always be suitable when the exact condition of the rock to be moved is known, as instanced by work carried out in preparing the foundation bed for the Prettyboy Dam in Maryland (described on page 505). A similar case occurred during the construction of the main spillway for the Fort Peck Dam in Montana, which is founded on local Bearpaw shale. This is a relatively soft rock, which can be excavated without the aid of blasting. To excavate the 200,000 cu yd taken out, three different types of cutting machine were used: an auger which drilled holes 5 ft in diameter, and two special adaptations of electrically operated coal-cutting machines, one used for cutting vertical slots between holes, and the other for horizontal undercutting. The Bearpaw shale disintegrates when exposed to the atmosphere, and for this reason a 4-ft cover layer was left in place over the excavated area at the start of excavation; the finally finished surface was sprayed with a bituminous paint against which the concrete was immediately placed.[10.23] Not only does this rock disintegrate when exposed, but it exhibits a slow rebound after excavation owing to the release of internal stresses previously resisted by the superincumbent rock now removed. This singularly unfortunate feature will be dealt with in connection with the founding of dams on shale such as the Bearpaw formation (see page 545).

Another example of interest is the excavation for the powerhouse substructure at the Wheeler Dam on the Tennessee River in the United States. Extensive preliminary exploration work disclosed that the rock

Fig. 10.14. Coal-cutting saw making horizontal cut in shale, excavating for training-wall foundation slab at the spillway for the Fort Peck Dam, Montana. (*Reproduced by permission of the Chief of Engineers, U.S. Army.*)

at the site consists of an "alternating series of nearly horizontal layers of pure limestone and a cherty siliceous rock, the latter occurring in much thicker strata than the former." More than 500,000 cu yd of rock had to be removed to depths varying to 57 ft below the existing stream bed, and owing to the nature of the rock to be encountered, it was deemed advisable to avoid any blasting close to the faces of the deep cuts in which the power units were to be placed. A system of close-line drilling was therefore developed and carried out with wagon drills all around the site; the rock so enclosed was drilled and blasted by the usual methods, except that no blasting was done within 30 ft of the line-drilled faces, from which the rock broke away cleanly. The undisturbed face of rock was of great importance in the structural design of the powerhouse, and the elimination of overbreak made the method quite economical.[10.24] Many other examples could be given, but the purpose of all would be but to confirm the importance of geological features in rock excavation.

In view of the basically elementary character of rock excavation as a construction operation, it is not surprising that no major advances in technique are to be found in the records of the last few decades. On the other hand, meticulous attention to detail and steady advances in the

Fig. 10.15. Line-drilled excavation for turbine pits in powerhouse area of the Wheeler Dam, Tennessee River, U.S.A. (*Reproduced by permission of the Chief Engineer, Tennessee Valley Authority.*)

equipment used for drilling and in the nature of explosives have greatly improved the efficiency of rock removal. In Sweden, rock-excavation practice (as well as tunneling) has been outstanding, especially in the adoption of small mobile one-man drilling rigs. Correspondingly, the wide adoption of removable bits and the improvement in the wearing properties of the bits have led to great advances in the handling of drill steel and therefore in the operation of drilling in general. Swedish rock experts have not hesitated to experiment with innovations in blasting techniques when conditions warranted it; one unusual example is the blasting of overburden and rock at the same time.

A new sea-level canal has been constructed to cut off a sharp bend in the Motala River between Braviken Fiord and the port of Norrkoping, some 90 miles southwest of Stockholm. The Lindo Canal will have an ultimate length of 4 miles; the first section is 2 miles long. Its depth is 31 ft and its bottom width 180 ft; thus it is wider than most of the major ship canals of the world; 5,000-ton vessels can pass each other while under weigh in the channel. The total project involves the removal of about 5 million cu yd of material, most of it by dredging; 26,000 cu yds is rock. At the entrance to the canal, glacial till with overlying clay occurred on top of the local bedrock to depths of 30 ft; the clay was saturated and thus awkward to remove, which would normally be the procedure before drilling the rock to be blasted. In order to obviate this difficult job, a technique was developed for drilling quickly through the overburden. With this technique, special drilling rigs with 52-ft feeds are adapted for driving a casing pipe simultaneously with sinking drill steel through the overburden, to be ready for drilling as soon as rock is encountered. Drill steel is withdrawn when the hole has been drilled to depth, and the casing pipe is left in place. Plastic pipe is then set in place, with the aid of a suitable collar, over the drilled hole, and the casing pipe is then removed. Loading of the holes is carried out by compressed air through the plastic tubing; as many as 40 to 50 cartridges can be loaded in one hole in this way and tamped into place. One major blast carried out in this way used 12,000 detonators and 123,000 lb of dynamite in 4,750 holes; the blast moved 36,000 cu yd of rock and 96,000 cu yd of overlying clay and till. The high ratio of dynamite to rock moved was due not only to the extra effort required to move the overburden but also to the necessity of fragmenting the rock to a finer degree than usual in order to facilitate its removal by dredging.[10.25]

Details of blasting technique have been mentioned in this example because of its unusual character; since these details are normally in the province of the expert, the geologist or civil engineer will not usually be directly concerned with them. But as in so many other branches of work herein described, even the best of blasting techniques will be of only partial avail if the geology of the work site has not previously been studied so that it is known with certainty. Especially is this so when blasting has to be carried out in proximity to existing structures. In the past, this difficult operation has generally been left to the expert. Many civil engineers must have had the joy of watching a really expert "powder man" carefully set his charges for some hazardous excavation work, such as the removal of rock to provide room for a new turbine installation inside a powerhouse containing operating machinery. But the innate art of such men should be capable of translation into measured terms; this is gradually being achieved.

Knowledge in this field was extended by some notable tests conducted in an area to be flooded by the St. Lawrence international power project (see page 348). In this series of comparative tests, observations were made of the effects of blasts set off at varying distances from abandoned houses founded on various materials.[10.26] As experience such as this is accumulated, vibrations due to blasting will gradually cease to be the hazard they can now sometimes prove to be when adequate precautions have not been taken before blasting to note all existing damage to buildings; cracking, especially, should be noted; if carefully recorded,

Fig. 10.16. "Double blasting" rock and overburden on the Motala River Canal, Sweden; this explosion was the result of detonating 56 tons of dynamite in 4,750 drill holes. (*Photograph by Gosta Nordin. Reproduced by permission of Skanska Cementgjuteriet.*)

it will often be found to coincide exactly with the damage reported after blasting has taken place. The author knows of a large rock-excavation job which had to be carried out in the vicinity of an important hotel. At the end of the job, the "usual" claim for damages caused by blasting was received; the claim, however, was not pressed when it was divulged that the contractor had rented a room in the hotel where he had maintained a vibration record throughout blasting operations; this record showed that the vibrations caused by the blasting were not so serious as those caused by heavy traffic.

10.8. Quarrying in Civil Engineering Practice. Building stone used in civil engineering will usually be obtained from an established quarry, and it is not often that large-scale quarrying operations will be necessary in the course of normal civil engineering practice. The two most common types of work requiring special supplies of quarried rock are the construction of rock-fill dams and the use of rock for the construction of rock embankments or special structures such as mound breakwaters. If the quantity of rock required for projects of this or any other kind is appreciable, the civil engineer will be well advised to obtain the services of a quarry expert. On some projects, however, civil engineers may be called upon to open up small quarries that do not warrant the employment of an expert; an appreciation of geology can then be of good service.

After the site of the quarry has been stripped, the exposed rock surfaces should be studied carefully; special attention should be paid to the dip and strike of the strata, to the presence of any unusual features such as folds, and particularly, to the jointing of the rock. On the strength of the information so obtained, the engineer will be able to open up a working face in the most advisable way, taking advantage of the direction of dip, strike, and jointing to facilitate both the blasting and the removal of rock; jointing is of particular importance. Methods of operation will depend on the amount of rock to be moved, the rate at which it is required, and the type of rock to be quarried. If a large output is not required, it may be desirable to utilize for drilling the regular job hand drills and jackhammers, in which case a series of low faces and narrow benches will probably prove most suitable. If the job is a large one, however, consideration should be given to the possibility of using larger drilling equipment, high faces, and deep snake holes which can be sprung before being finally shot, and thus lead to economy in operation.

The location and depth of drill holes and the necessary kind and amount of explosive to be used are matters that will have to be determined accurately for every new quarry face opened up. The problems involved are not dissimilar from those involved in the normal excavation of rock in grading work. As the U.S. Bureau of Public Roads has carried out field studies in connection with highway grading, some of the conclusions reached may usefully be cited even though they were obtained some years ago. A study of 71 different excavation projects showed that over half were poorly blasted, and only 15 were classed as good. The consequent average increase in operating time for steam shovels was 42 per cent; and as the volume of rock handled was less than the dipper capacity, the average over-all efficiency was only 50 per cent.[10.27] It is particularly to be noted that as rock drilling is an expensive operation (1 ft of hole is equivalent to about 1 lb of dynamite in North America), economic practice will tend to minimize drilling.

Only infrequently do civil engineering projects call for quarrying on a major scale, apart from the construction of rock-fill dams. One job that did need a lot of rock was the construction of the Hiwassee Dam of the TVA. All the aggregate, including even the sand, necessary for this great project had to be obtained from a specially opened quarry, as the rock from excavation was unsuitable. Good greywacke rock was found at a suitable location; in all, 1.7 million cu yd of rock was quarried. Interesting experiments were carried out in order to check the use of 9-in. drill holes as compared with 6-in. holes. The rate of drilling the two sizes was

Fig. 10.17. Blasting 2 million cu yd of quartzite in the quarry supplying fill for the rock-fill embankment of the Southern Pacific Railroad across Great Salt Lake, Utah, U.S.A. (*Reproduced by permission of the Atlas Power Company, and Morrison-Knudsen Company Inc., General Contractors.*)

found to be about the same, although the 9-in. holes when filled with explosive produced twice as much fragmented rock per foot of hole as did the 6-in. holes.[10.28] Far more extensive was the rock-quarrying operation called for in 1957 by the construction of the new rock-fill embankment across Great Salt Lake to replace the old trestle of the Southern Pacific Railroad. What was described at the time as "the biggest controlled explosion in history" involved the use of 1.79 million lb of explosive in one blast; this resulted in over 2 million cu yd of suitably fragmented rock. Location was Promontory Point on a peninsula extending into the lake from the north. Total quantity of rock required for the complete job was 13 million cu yd, all of which was a hard quartzite.[10.29]

Rarely will the use of an abandoned quarry turn into an engineering problem, but even this has been known. The Standard Oil Company of New Jersey, in a search for economic oil storage, found two adjacent abandoned slate quarries at Wind Gap, Pennsylvania. (Abandonment of the quarries is in itself a commentary upon changing building technology.) The company interconnected the two quarries and carried out the necessary rehabilitation work to make them serviceable for their intended purpose and to give a storage capacity of 42 million bbl. At the time (1954) this was the largest single oil-storage facility in the world. Because of the clean lines to which the slate had been excavated, it was not too difficult to fit the necessary pontoon floating roof; the tightness of the slate formation was naturally an essential part of the plan for the utilization of the quarries. As oil is pumped out of one quarry, water is pumped into it from the other in order to keep the top level approximately the same at all times. This project involves the principle of the immiscibility of oil and water that has been applied in even more remarkable manner for underground storage, as related in Chap. 9.[10.30]

10.9. Embankment Fill. The construction of embankments produces problems in many respects similar to those which arise in excavation, notably the determination of a safe angle of slope to use in design for the sides of the embankment. Although this will be clearly shown up practically as filling proceeds, it is often necessary to have an accurate idea of the slope that must be used before construction begins, especially if the ground area to be covered by the fill is restricted; thus, preliminary investigation and experimentation are often necessary. The correct placing and consolidation of fill material in ordinary embankments, exclusive of water-retaining earthen dams, are matters of standard construction practice. Associated with them are the problems of settlement and of bulking—the relation of the volume of fill material after deposition to the volume of the same material before excavation. Knowledge of this ratio is essential in accurate design work; it depends, naturally, on the type of material being handled. Bulking will depend principally on the undisturbed state of the material to be moved, on any change in the moisture content of the material between excavation and deposition, and on the methods used to consolidate the material after it has been placed in final position. The second two factors are of special moment in the case of sand and sandy materials; the first, in the case of clays and materials with a large clay content. When rock is used as fill material and has to be obtained by quarrying, the bulking may be exceptionally high.

Settlement of an embankment, the first of the two detailed problems mentioned, may be the result either of shrinkage of the fill material or of settlement of the foundation material upon which the embankment rests. If the fundamentals of soil compaction are properly utilized, based upon adequate preliminary soil mechanics tests on the soils to be handled, there is today no excuse for any appreciable settlement due to the first cause. The state of California, for example, regularly places finished pavements on top of its highway fills, up to 90 ft in height, shortly after completion without fear of trouble. Soil mechanics techniques are a regular part of its engineering control, as they now are in almost all highway organizations.

Unfortunately, the same cannot be said with regard to failures of embankment foundations, even though they are also susceptible to analysis, and so to control, on the basis of proper preliminary investigations including thorough test drilling over all the area to be affected by the load from the embankment. If the weight of material contained in even an average-sized embankment is calculated and reduced to the form of a load per unit area of original ground surface, the result will be found to be surprisingly high. Although it decreases toward the sides of the fill, this loading is directly comparable to that induced by concentrated structures, and the stress distribution in the foundation strata should be investigated accordingly. Progressive settlement will inevitably take place while the foundation beds take up their new loading, unless the fill stands on solid rock. If the strata are not uniformly strong, failure of one bed may occur, and the fill may collapse. The investigation of fill stability thus becomes a part of the study of soil mechanics; both the nature of the fill and foundation materials and the mechanics of the combined structure have considerable bearing upon the success of the fill construction. Stability investigations can be made only when accurate information on the local strata is available; thus, the need for preliminary exploratory work is again made clear. So many fill failures, great or small, will be known to most engineers that space will not be taken to mention one here; instances such as those in which a new fill completely disappears below the original ground tell their own story to the engineer whose appreciation of geology reminds him constantly of what may lie below a seemingly solid surface. It may be worth noting, however, that one of the many soil problems encountered in the Pittsburgh area is the stability of the dump piles of excavated soil from new highway construction and similar work. Excavation often has to be dumped in one of the many ravines that make this part of Pennsylvania scenically so attractive. This course has to be followed because of the limited availability of the level ground normally used for this purpose. The slides that sometimes occur in these "fills of excavation" are attributable to the steep slopes developed and to the apparent stability of the natural slopes of the ravines that can obscure, on occasion, the necessity of giving the same attention to slope stability here as on level ground.

10.10. Dredging. Filling of large areas, as distinct from relatively small embankments, is often economically carried out by pumping the fill material mixed with water. Settlement of the pumped material is one of the main problems, aside from those of construction method; this is also a part of soil mechanics. The colloidal material present in clays sometimes causes difficulty, but this can be foreseen if adequate preliminary tests are carried out. Dredging operations naturally necessitate a thorough knowledge of the material to be dredged so that suitable plant may be made available; adequate preliminary exploratory work is again the only way in which this knowledge can be gained.

Records of dredging practice contain descriptions of many projects with unusual geological interest. One of these, a combined flood-protection and navigation project for waterways in Florida, was initiated in 1930 to prevent a repetition of the disastrous floods of 1926 and 1928. Included in the project was the construction of 66 miles of levees around Lake Okeechobee. The material for the levees was to be obtained from the bed of the lake. Much of Florida is geologically new country; the bed of the lake was still in process of formation. Bed materials vary widely, and uniform deposits are exceptional; but under the recent deposits are strata of marl and limestone of varying thickness. The recent deposits often contain considerable quantities of sea shells, sand, and other material so finely ground as to be almost colloidal. From this brief description, it will be seen that the material was most unfavorable to dredging operations. Almost all the contractors who started on the work elected to use draglines for excavation, but later experiments with a powerful hydraulic dredge proved so successful that other dredgers were brought in. Special cutters had to be used at the end of the suction pipes; however, good progress was made at low cost, and the resulting levees were more satisfactory than those made with the draglines. The marl and limestone layers had to be broken initially by drilling and blasting, but the dredging equipment handled all material thereafter. The relatively new deposits proved their geological youth by the way in which they could be disintegrated.[10.31]

This example illustrates the fact that dredging is really only open excavation carried out under water; the submarine character of the work permits the use of floating equipment with its attendant economies. The basic principles upon which the work must be carried out remain unchanged. Adequate preliminary investigation is even more important for this kind of work than for excavation work in the dry since the material to be removed cannot be seen in advance. Removal of unconsolidated material usually revolves around the selection and the availability of suitable floating equipment for the dredging work. Suction dredgers fitted with cutter heads for disturbing the material to be excavated are perhaps the most common type in wide use; ladder dredgers are excellent for special purposes, and large dipper dredgers (in effect, excavating shovels mounted on barges) are suitable for shallow and heavy work. Of special importance is the possible presence of boulders. Suction dredgers should always be fitted with a rock catcher in the suction line; this is a simple trap device for catching all boulders and rock fragments, which may be sucked up the discharge line, before they get into the pumping unit and possibly cause damage to the impeller. The writer has had experience on two large dredging jobs, one in an inland lake and the other in the Gulf of St. Lawrence, where the only real problems encountered arose from the presence of boulders; in each case boulders were anticipated, but they still caused trouble with the dredging machinery.[10.32]

For underwater rock excavation two methods are in general use: under-water drilling and subsequent blasting with explosives, and alternatively, a floating rock breaker. In both methods, but especially when a rock breaker is to be used, accurate knowledge of the bedding of the rock and of the nature of the rock will prove to be of great value not only in planning construction methods but also in estimating construction schedules and in specifying the work suitably in relation to possible over-break. Many remarkable examples of underwater rock excavation testify to the difficulty of the work and its uncertainty.

One of the earliest as well as one of the most remarkable major ex-amples of underwater rock work was the removal of Flood Rock, a rocky ledge in Long Island Sound, New York; 80,000 cu yd was re-moved in this operation in 1885. The work had to be continued in later years, and a modern channel was completed only in 1920. Another in-teresting piece of work was carried out in New York in 1922 when a subaqueous reef in the East River was removed to improve navigation. The work had to be carried out under the water of a tidal river with a swift current and to a final depth which was only 15 ft above the roof of a busy subway tunnel. So accurately was the drilling and blasting of the crystalline Manhattan schist carried out, however, that the project was successfully completed without damage to the tunnel or interference with subway traffic. A feature of special interest was the extensive use of field seismographs to check on the extent of the vibrations caused by the blasting.[10.33]

The importance of the nature of the rock to be excavated in under-water work is well illustrated by experience obtained during rock-dredg-ing operations in the harbor of St. Helier, Jersey, one of the Channel islands. A rock breaker equipped with a 22,000-lb ram was used for breaking the rock of the local sea bed which varied from a syenitic granite to a true diorite. In the harbor area, the rock was badly fissured; but outside the harbor entrance channel, it was a purer and sounder diorite. The contractors estimated that the latter material cost five times as much to break as the former, even though the two were found in such close proximity.[10.34] The type of rock may also dictate the excavation method to be adopted, as is shown by a dredging contract carried out at Sunderland, England. Over 100,000 cu yd of rock was removed; work was carried to a maximum depth of 44 ft without the use of blasting or a rock breaker. This was possible because all the rock was a loosely bedded limestone, varying from a few inches to 2 ft in thickness, and it was broken up by the dipper of a large bucket dredger digging underneath the upper projecting stratum on the working face.[10.34] Some of the most extensive work in removing underwater rock was necessitated by the increase in the depth of channels in the St. Lawrence River associated

Fig. 10.18. Multiple-drill barge for rock excavation at work near Amherstburg, Ontario, Canada, in the Detroit River on deepening work in connection with the St. Lawrence Deep Waterway. (*Photograph by T. Ritchie.*)

with the international power and associated Seaway project of the 1950s. Much of the dredging fleet of the entire Great Lakes area was assembled for this operation; some new equipment was developed. Figure 10.18 shows the rather spectacular 20-frame drill rig used by Marine Operators for rock drilling in the Amherstburg Channel of the Detroit River in 1957.[10.35]

Under the exigencies of war, the same kind of equipment, but on a vastly different scale, was frequently developed from existing land equipment. The Seabees of the U.S. Navy, for example, were faced with the job of removing 22,000 cu yd of coral, ranging from soft to hard, in depths of water up to 18 ft, at a harbor in the Solomon Islands. Standard navy pontoons were lashed together to form a barge large enough to mount three standard 10-ton cranes with 35-ft swinging leads hung from 40-ft booms. Pile-driving equipment was used with the leads to drive steel pipes into the coral, in which dynamite charges were then set; the barge was moved 500 ft away for the firing, and then returned so that the blasted rock could be removed by a 1½-cu yd clamshell bucket, operated by a 25-ton crawler crane sitting on the bow of the work barge. Radio equipment, today not infrequent upon large construction jobs, was an innovation on this job; installed by the Signal Corps, it enabled the men on the barge to maintain contact with the shore and also with the crew at work surveying the channel for which the blasting was carried out.[10.36] In blasting through coral reefs in Samar, Philippine Islands, the Seabees adopted an alternative, and even simpler, technique—that of placing dynamite charges right on the surface of the coral to be removed with the help of divers, and firing it without the aid of any equipment. Using 60 per cent dynamite when available, they developed a pattern of blasting that could be varied according to the type of reef and the character of the coral. Although uneconomical in the use of explosive (requiring just over 4 lb of dynamite per cu yd, as compared with an average working figure of 1 lb per yd), the method was quick and was used when excavation had to be carried out without any suitable equipment near at hand.[10.37]

As an illustration of a combined dredging and filling operation with "soil mechanics overtones," there may finally be mentioned the preparation of an area for a new central market in San Juan Bay, Puerto Rico. The 100-acre site adjoins the mouth of the Puerto Nuevo River. When the river was dredged and rerouted in order to obviate troubles with flooding, some of the area developed for the market was used as a spoil area for dredged material. The site was an old mangrove swamp; soft organic silt extended from the surface to firm residual clay 25 to 40 ft below. The area was therefore first completely cleared, and a 4-ft sand blanket was pumped over it; this was used as a working area, and 33,500 sand drains, 18 in. in diameter, were installed to predrain the area. In order to speed up the required consolidation, the areas required for specific and immediate building projects were overloaded (i.e., covered with an excess amount of sand fill, which was later removed when the additional weight had caused the necessary consolidation of the silt). The amount of overloading was predetermined on the basis of the time of dredging, the duration of the sand-drain operation at each site, and the date at which it was required for building purposes. The extent of this site operation is indicated by the cost of almost $6 million for the first two phases, $912,000 for the river-diversion work, and $4.9 million for the fill and stabilization work.[10.38]

10.11. Conclusion. Some open-excavation work is called for on almost every civil engineering project; it is small wonder therefore that practice in this field is so diverse and so interesting despite the over-all simplicity of the basic operation. Improvement of well-accepted techniques may be expected to continue; new features will be added in matters of detail. Already, however, there are signs that some unusual methods may be available that can successfully be applied to excavation work. In rock excavation, for example, experiments in the fusion cutting of rock (and concrete) have been carried out. First tried in mining practice for the sinking of 6-in.-diameter blast holes in tough taconite ore, the method has been commercially applied to the cutting of holes through concrete, always a delicate operation in existing structures. Obviously costly at the present time, the method presents possibilities for special rock-excavation work that may one day prove worthy of exploitation.[10.39]

Borrowed from another field of engineering, oil-well drilling, is the technique of aiding excavation work by digging in a hole kept full of "drilling mud" or its equivalent. Tried out as early as 1939, with excavated clay used as a slurry, the idea of balancing the pressures exerted upon the walls of an excavation with the pressure of a heavy fluid has been applied in civil engineering work generally only in the late 1950s. The use of bentonite for this purpose is an old story in the oil fields; patented methods have now been developed for the use of the same material in civil engineering work. An Italian company has successfully applied the method for the forming of continuous walls of concrete piles through difficult ground for the purpose of forming the sides of a subway structure. This was in Milan; the name "Milan method" has already been given to the idea, which has now been applied to a variety of projects in a number of countries. The method was used on a test section of subway in Toronto, Ontario, in connection with the extension of the line mentioned at the outset of this chapter. The method clearly has great possibilities; economic considerations will determine its wider application. The fact that it uses bentonite and can only be applied when local ground conditions are suitable, ensuring certain tightness of the trench excavation (for example) so that the bentonite slurry will not be "lost," provides close links between this method and geology.[10.40]

Finally, there is already looming on the horizon of civil engineering practice the possible use of atomic explosions as an aid to major excavation. Experiments conducted by the United States Atomic Energy Commission, and carefully observed and recorded by engineering geologists of the United States Geological Survey, at the test site adjacent to Yucca Flats, Nevada, have provided vivid evidence of the potentialities of this peaceful use of atomic energy. The bedrock in which the Nevada tests were conducted is a volcanic tuff of three degrees of toughness. In the later blasts, exploded in underground chambers, "solid" rock 1,100 ft away from the blast was moved as much as 1 ft. After the largest explosion (up to 1959) a 5-ft fault movement of wide extent was observed at the surface. In many cases the flow of ground water was stopped by the blasts, which disrupted the strata and sealed joints in the tuff. Rock surrounding the blasts was brecciated all around, in one case for a distance of 80 ft from the center of the blast. And 1 year after the explosions had taken place, it was found that one-half the heat generated was

FIG. 10.19. The pool of Gibeon, near el-Jib, Jordan, part of the waterworks carried out by the Gibeonites in the eighth century B.C., for the collection of subartesian water; the shaft is 82 ft deep. This remarkable example of hand excavation in limestone, discovered in 1956 by Dr. James B. Pritchard, is a salutary reminder of the long tradition of open excavation work (see the Book of Joshua and reference 10.42). (*Photograph by Dr. J. B. Pritchard.*)

still in the ground around the blast center. These few facts, selected from the mass of information now available, at once point to the possibilities for the application of this extraordinary explosive power in civil work and serve also as a reminder that even the works of man can disrupt seriously what is so commonly called "the solid earth."[10.41]

Suggestions for Further Reading

Since most of the problems that develop in excavation work are caused by soils, the extensive literature now available on soil mechanics may well be remembered in this connection. References at the end of Chap. 4 (page 128) provide a guide. And as this ancient type of civil engineering operation advances, the most modern of scientific techniques may be applied to an increasing degree in this progress. Reference to the following bibliography, which contains a number of references to the use of nuclear explosives for excavation work, may be helpful:

Eckel, E. B., "Partial Bibliography of Unclassified Literature on Geology in the Nuclear Age (exclusive of Radioactive Raw Materials)," United States Geological Survey, Denver, Colo., 1959.

Chapter 11

EARTH MOVEMENT AND LANDSLIDES

> Diseased nature oftentimes breaks forth
> In strange eruptions; oft the teeming earth
> Is with a kind of colic pinch'd and vex'd
> By the imprisoning of unruly wind
> Within her womb; which, for enlargement striving,
> Shakes the old beldam earth and topples down
> Steeples and moss-grown towers.
>
> > Hotspur in King Henry IV
> > Part I: act III, scene i
> > William Shakespeare

EXCAVATION IS often associated in the minds of engineers with some form of earth movement—landslides or rockfalls—occurrences that so often interfere with the orderly progress of excavation work. The fact that landslides do occur is frequently accepted as a part of the natural order, certainly in some localities and with some classes of materials. In keeping with this attitude, it is all too often the case that such earth movements come to be seriously studied only after they have occurred, when damage has been done and when initial movement has interfered, perhaps seriously, with previously existing geological structure. References to landslides in literature, both classical and technical, are in keeping with this general position—even that passing reference in the works of Mark Twain to the farm in Nevada that slipped over to the top of another farm, and thus raised difficult problems of ownership. Few references, even indirect, are to be found in early writing, and so study of the subject does not lead to the interesting historical record that serves as a useful background to consideration of other branches of civil engineering work.

The general subject of earth movement, and of landslides in particular, is patently one of great importance, not alone because of the trouble and expense caused by unexpected earth movements during civil engineering construction but also because of possible loss of life through such movements of completed works or even untouched natural ground—catastrophes that civil engineering can sometimes avert. Any newspaper file will testify adequately to the validity of this statement, since hardly a month passes without a reference in the daily press to loss of life and property from this cause somewhere in the world. Fortunately, major catastrophes have not been frequent in recent years, but historical records show something of what has happened in the past by references to such occurrences as the fall of Mount Grenier in 1248, which buried five parishes, and the slide at Rossberg, Switzerland, which took the lives of 800 people.

In its major aspects, the subject of earth movement is of paramount importance to geologists and geophysicists; earthquakes, earth tremors, and land subsidence are being studied and analyzed as never before. The civil engineer is usually concerned with more detailed aspects of the subject, and in similar fashion, is pursuing with unusual vigor his research into the causes of landslides and the problems related to stability of earth slopes. His works, however, are affected to some degree by major earth movements in all parts of the world.

11.2. Stability of the Earth's Crust. The basic factor in all considerations of earth movement is that the crust of the earth is composed of ordinary solid materials which react to the stresses induced in them generally in a manner similar to structural materials which may be tested in a laboratory. This fundamental will be stressed elsewhere in this book; the risk of undue repetition is taken, since it appears to be a matter that is not always appreciated. If this essentially structural viewpoint is always remembered, earth movement will be better understood. Almost of equal importance is the fact that the constituents of the crust are under the influence of gravity. This simple statement is strangely important. It is a reminder that the principal cause of all minor earth movements, such as landslides and rockfalls, is the action of gravitational attraction functioning in the usual way. A mass of rock, for example, detached in some way from the bedrock of which it has been a part will not be held in position by some mysterious means if it is in unstable statical equilibrium. It may be expected to fall in just the same way as will any other solid body in similar circumstances. Similarly, if the underside of a loose mass of rock is inclined to the horizontal, and if that surface is well lubricated, then the mass will tend to move downward in just the same way as would any other similarly placed body.

Minor earth movements are, then, no matter of mystery but the inevitable result of instability of part of the earth's crust, and to a large extent they are subject to the ordinary laws of mechanics. This instability cannot always be foreseen prior to earth movement; but gradually, by an extension of experience and by continued study of records of landslides and similar phenomena, general knowledge is increasing. With instability admitted as the basic cause of movement, the question will be asked, what finally starts such movements? Construction operations are an obvious possibility; the great slides on the Panama Canal (see page 599) were the result of construction operations in connection with the excavation of the deep Gaillard Cut. Blocked drains may raise the level of ground-water tables and possibly affect the moisture contents of unconsolidated materials which thus become unstable. The burning or stripping of vegetation may loosen surface material which the vegetation has bound together. Earthquake movements can give rise to subsidiary earth disturbance. The cause of large earth movements such as major earthquakes is a sudden yielding of a part of the earth's crust to strains set up in it by an adjacent area which lacks balance or equilibrium. The civil engineer is not primarily interested in the detailed study of such causes; his main concern in designing works in regions subject to earthquakes is that they shall be safe. The matter is mentioned, however, since the stresses thus set up in the crust of the earth by natural forces can be duplicated on a small scale by the operations of the civil engineer. The construction of a great dam, for example, subjects the local part of the crust to unusual stresses; the design of dam foundations has to take this factor into account, necessitating unusual care in preliminary geological investigations, as is made clear in Chap. 13. New Zealand has provided a most unusual demonstration of what these stresses can do to a relatively weak rock formation; and as no better example could probably be chosen to illustrate the suggestions made at the start of this section (that the materials in the earth's crust will react to stresses set up in them), it will be briefly described.

The Arapuni water-power scheme is located on the North Island of New Zealand, about 120 miles south of the city of Auckland which it supplies with power. It was constructed between 1925 and 1932 under the direction of, and in the later portions by, the Public Works Department, since all public power supply in New Zealand is under government control. The scheme consists essentially of a main dam, of the curved gravity type, 192 ft high with a crest length of 305 ft on a 250-ft radius, which diverts the water of the river Waikato into an open headrace canal ¾ mile long, finishing with a spillway dam and penstock intake. Steel penstocks, built into rock tunnels, lead to the powerhouse, the ultimate capacity of which is 200,000 hp operating under a head of 175 ft. The geology of the Waikato Valley is complicated; the valley has been the scene of repeated volcanic activity, and as a result the course of the river and its gradient have varied widely and often. Old river courses have been filled with erupted matter, and consequent denudation has not always followed the old courses. The result has been that several old river channels now occur at varying heights above the existing river bed in the vicinity of the Arapuni works; one of these was utilized as the main part of the headrace canal. The rocks encountered were chiefly volcanic tuff and breccia. The vitric tuff is supposed to have been ejected as incandescent dust from vents in the ground and then to have fused together as it cooled. At the bottom of river valleys, however, where the probable presence of water caused quicker cooling, the rock, though of the same chemical and mineralogical composition as the solid tuff, is completely unconsolidated. The solid tuff may contain up to 30 per cent water

Fig. 11.1. General view from the air of the Arapuni hydroelectric scheme, New Zealand, showing location of the crack, the occurrence of which is described in the text. (*Reproduced through the courtesy of F. W. Furkert, sometime Engineer-in-Chief, Public Works Department, New Zealand.*)

which may be held in ultramicroscopic pore spaces, as the rock is durable and moderately hard. Below this tuff occur varying beds of tuff and breccia, including a pumaceous breccia on which the main dam is founded. Below this last stratum, softer tuffaceous material extends to great depths. These volcanic deposits were uneven; they also proved to be so elastic that "the absence or presence of 10 feet of water in the gorge as the diversion tunnel was opened or shut, caused decided and opposite tilts to be registered on the seismograph in the powerhouse." On June 7, 1930, while the dam was retaining water and the powerhouse was under load, a crack occurred in the local country roughly parallel to the flow of the river. It was widest (2 in. across) where the spillway joined the penstock intakes, and it extended for about 2,000 ft. Observations then made showed that "the whole mass of country, about 2,000 feet long, 150 feet thick, and 400 to 800 feet wide, was bent over towards the gorge." The power station was shut down, and the lake drained; "as the lake

Fig. 11.2. Arapuni hydroelectric scheme, New Zealand; view of the crack which developed in bedrock adjacent to the main intake structure. (*Reproduced through the courtesy of F. W. Furkert, sometime engineer-in-Chief, Public Works Department, New Zealand.*)

fell, the country recovered its position, the cracks closing except where jammed by drawn-in debris, and the powerhouse, suspension bridge, etc., regaining their original positions."

This most unusual occurrence was naturally investigated and studied closely by expert geologists and engineers. The consensus was that the movement was due to leakage of water from the headrace canal, which affected the adjacent volcanic rock to such an extent that movement took place. The remedial measures undertaken, therefore, centered on the provision of a waterproof lining to the headrace. After this was installed, apart from some minor troubles, the works functioned satisfactorily, and they do so today. While the remedial works were in progress, many unusual features developed. Thus, as the water level behind the dam was being lowered, gas consisting of 96 per cent nitrogen was found to escape from the rock in the headrace. The gas was unusual in that it contained no oxygen, and its volume may have reached the surprising figure of 50,000 cu ft (instead of the 25,000 cu ft mentioned in the published description). Much grouting was carried out; and while the necessary holes were being drilled, water was frequently lost; a fire hose was turned into one hole, finishing at a depth well below river-water level, without any trace of escaping water being found in the vicinity. In other holes, great difficulty was experienced because the drills encountered vegetation which had been growing on ground formed of early volcanic deposits when covered by later volcanic material. Timber was secured from holes and appeared to be quite sound; and although in the opinion of geologists it had been there for at least 10,000 years, the bark was still intact. The writer has in his possession a small cask assumed by many to be made of walnut, but which was actually made for him from a wood sample obtained from the deepest of the three lava-buried forests by F. W. Furkert, engineer-in-chief for all the work at Arapuni. In a notable paper, Mr. Furkert has described fully the troubles that developed and the remedial measures undertaken. It is a fascinating engineering document, as will be clear from even this brief summary, and it is an inspiring record of the successful surmounting of seemingly insuperable difficulties. The evidence thus presented by the rock movement at Arapuni shows clearly how the works of the civil engineer do affect the earth's crust. Although in most other cases the stresses set up in natural formations do not cause actual rupture of bedrock, the experience at Arapuni is a timely reminder of the strains that inevitably accompany such stresses, in rock as in other solid materials.[11.1]

11.3. New Zealand Experience. The geology of New Zealand is as interesting as this small country is beautiful and its people hospitable. Its remote location contributes to general lack of knowledge of the engineering achievements of New Zealand's engineers, aided as they so frequently are by geologists. Since there are few parts of the world where the instability of the earth's crust is so vividly demonstrated, a brief note on some further experiences with ground movement in New Zealand may be helpful. Geologically, much of the country is very "new." Movements along active faults are therefore something of practical significance. Even the capital city of Wellington is located on the site of severe earthquake movement that was observed by early settlers in 1855; a paper by an eminent local geologist bears the title: "For How Long Will Welling-

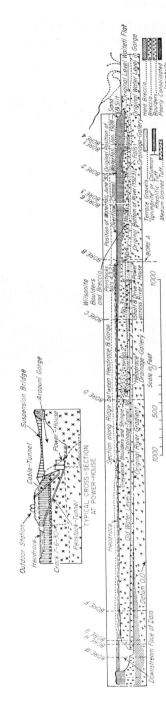

Fig. 11.3. Arapuni hydroelectric scheme, New Zealand, geological sections along headrace and overflow channel and through powerhouse. (*Reproduced by permission of the Institution of Civil Engineers.*)

ton Escape Destruction by Earthquakes?"[11.2] On the other hand, one of the country's most lovely lakes, with the musical name of Waikaremoana, was created by a majestic landslide that probably happened in historic times, for this is suggested by a fanciful but poetic explanation of the lake's formation, traditional with the Maoris.[11.3]

Within a distance of less than 20 miles, in the vicinity of the city of Dunedin on the southeast shore of the South Island, a remarkable series

Fig. 11.4. Abandoned Puketeraki Tunnel near Palmerston, on the main South Island line of New Zealand Government Railways, showing the relocated line in open cut on the left. (*Reproduced by permission of the Chief Civil Engineer, New Zealand Government Railways.*)

of engineering troubles occurred, all caused by ground movement. The writer had the privilege of being shown these classical cases by the late Dr. W. N. Benson who has described them in two notable papers.[11.4] Cornish Head is a good starting point: it is a notable headland that is itself scarred by major "landslides" of solid rock, caused by the yielding of the local Burnside mudstone over which occur beds of basalt and conglomerate. Not far away is the now disused Puketeraki Tunnel of the New Zealand Railways. Constructed in 1878, the tunnel is 516 ft long on a gradient of 1 in 66. It was excavated through the Caversham sandstone that is here located just over the Burnside mudstone. The tunnel, although this was not realized at the time, was actually driven through a slump scarp, movement of which has been aggravated in recent years by surface streams working through the overlying strata into the mudstone below the tunnel. Trouble with movements was experienced soon after the tunnel was opened. Starting in 1932 measurements of movements were regularly taken; it was soon found that the tunnel was actually being twisted by a movement of the entire rock mass that it penetrated. By 1934, a resultant total movement of up to 17.9 in. had been measured. With the geological cause of the trouble then realized, it was decided that the only course to pursue was to abandon the tunnel; the line was relocated in a cutting excavated between the tunnel line and the edge of sea cliff nearby.

A few miles down the coast is the site of a large mental hospital, 600 acres of beautifully situated rolling land which appear to be an almost ideal location for this therapeutic purpose. When the area was first proposed for hospital use, Sir James Hector (then director of the New Zealand Geological Survey) warned that "the clay would move—like any other plastic substance—with an almost molecular motion." His warning was disregarded. It is easy to realize why this was so as one stands on the upper part of the site, looking out over the sea, with good "firm" clay in evidence all around as a foundation material. Unfortunately, as later geological studies have shown, the entire site is underlain not only by the Burnside mudstone, but beneath it by the Abbotsford mudstone, an equally unreliable rock, with a major fault zone running across the building area. The weak character of the mudstones has led to severe slumping, so that much of what appears to be solid ground is merely surface evidence of successive slump scarps. Serious movements have therefore affected the hospital from its earliest days; the first main building had to be completely demolished a few years after its erection because of serious and irremedial cracking. Downhill movements of entire buildings have been measured in feet; differential settlements of many inches have accompanied such mass sliding. So serious has the instability of the entire site proved to be that it is to be abandoned as soon as other buildings can be provided.

It is therefore not surprising to find many and quite extensive landslides and mudflows (from the disintegrating mudstones) in the Dunedin area, although it should be added that these are evident only to the keen observer; the natural beauty of the area distracts normal attention from all such geological peculiarities. Even in the areas of bedrock much more competent than the mudstones, troubles have been experienced. About 25 miles west-southwest of Dunedin is a lovely little valley, the Waipori Gorge, in which is located a small municipal water-power plant, fed by water from an impounding reservoir at the head of the gorge, led to it through a tunnel that originally terminated at a point 680 ft above the river-bed level at the powerhouse site. Three 42-in. and one 60-in. diameter steel pressure pipes were installed on anchor blocks; the concrete was keyed into blocks of the local schist protruding from the steep surface of the side slope to the valley, which was known to be in solid schist. So solid did the rock foundation to the anchor blocks appear to be that no doubts at all were entertained when the plant was put into service. In 1929, however, following the thawing of an unusually heavy snowstorm, engineers in charge of the plant noticed what appeared to be slight movements of some of the anchor blocks, following some slumping of the slope surface. Careful measurements were instituted, and the movement was confirmed; the whole slope proved to be unstable; a maximum downward movement of 4.85 in. was detected. The movements of the different blocks were irregular, and this increased the complexity of the problem. It was then found that the anchor blocks were founded not on solid rock but on a mixture of rock debris, clay, and very large fault blocks of schist that had been mistaken for solid rock. The penstocks were therefore replaced by a continuation of the pressure tunnel, but even in this construction, difficulty was experienced when weathered schist was found to extend far below the surface of apparently solid rock.

11.4. Volcanic Action. If the engineers of New Zealand require any further reminders of the instability of the earth's crust, they have only to give thought to the hot springs that distinguish the central part of the North Island to have evidence of the relative proximity of the molten magma beneath the remarkably thin solid crust. The hot springs occur in an area 150 miles long by 30 miles wide; some emit steam and water at pressures up to 200 psi, which is evidence of minor volcanic action. The hot springs of Yellowstone Park are world famous; similar phenomena are found in many parts of the world, but particularly in northern Italy where the *fumaroli* have achieved fame not only as a scenic attraction but as the source of the first geothermal steam to be harnessed for man's use. Despite damage to some plants during the war, Italy had an installed capacity in its natural steam plants of 300 megawatts in 1956. New Zealand has built its first 80-megawatt plant, and has double that capacity in the planning stage. Plans for similar developments at the "steam wells" in California are under preparation.[11.5]

The utilization of geothermal steam is a vivid example of the engineering uses of unusual geological features, even though somewhat removed from the normal practice of civil engineering, as are also—most fortunately—full-scale volcanic phenomena. Both aspects of volcanic action are thus briefly mentioned, however, as further demonstration of the profoundly misleading influence of such commonplace expressions as "the solid earth" and "solid as a rock," expressions that may unconsciously mislead even the engineer into undue reliance upon inadequate information regarding the geology of his building sites. To see molten lava pouring forth from an active volcano, and—in the case of some of the Hawaiian volcanoes, for example—pouring back again into the earth through crevasses, is a sobering experience. To find complete mountains, such as Paracutin in Mexico, formed within a few years on what was previously level farm land, is a reminder that the earth is not the fixed and permanent sphere of the poets.

11.5. Earthquakes. Closely associated with volcanic action are those major natural earth movements termed "earthquakes": they have real

FIG. 11.5. Powerhouse in northern Italy operated by natural steam from the *fumaroles suffaroli.* (*Reproduced by permission of Messrs. Larderello, S.p.A., Pisa,* Italy.)

relevance to engineering. The earthquake that devastated Tokyo, Japan, on September 1, 1923, will be within the memory of some readers; it destroyed 140,000 lives and produced damage estimated at $3 billion. The earthquake that devastated Quetta, India, in 1935, took a toll of at least 35,000 lives in a few seconds. The earth movement that causes the quaking may be either volcanic or tectonic, the latter type being more common. In many instances, the permanent deformation of the earth's crust can be observed. Thus the San Francisco earthquake of April 18, 1906, caused movement along 270 miles of the San Andreas rift, a great fracture zone which runs almost parallel to the California coast line of western America. A maximum horizontal movement of 21 ft was after-

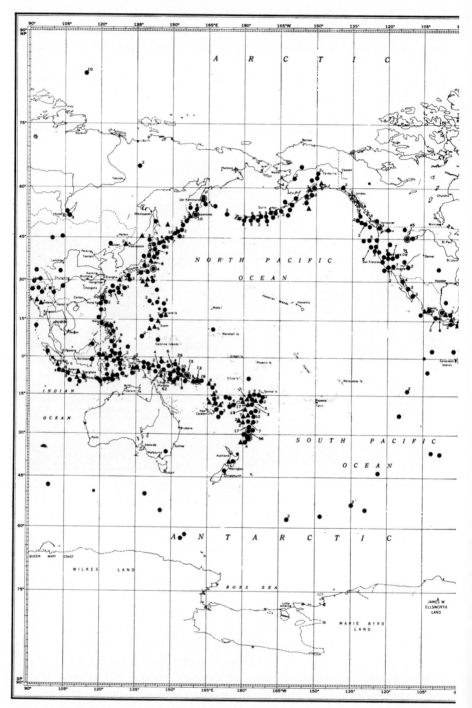

Fig. 11.6. Map showing the occurrence of major earthquakes throughout the world during

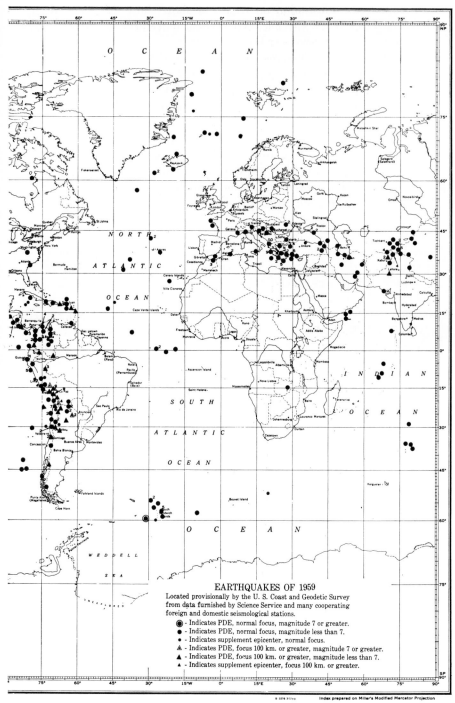

EARTHQUAKES OF 1959

Located provisionally by the U. S. Coast and Geodetic Survey
from data furnished by Science Service and many cooperating
foreign and domestic seismological stations.

⦿ - Indicates PDE, normal focus, magnitude 7 or greater.
● - Indicates PDE, normal focus, magnitude less than 7.
• - Indicates supplement epicenter, normal focus.
▲ - Indicates PDE, focus 100 km. or greater, magnitude 7 or greater.
▲ - Indicates PDE, focus 100 km. or greater, magnitude less than 7.
▴ - Indicates supplement epicenter, focus 100 km. or greater.

Index prepared on Miller's Modified Mercator Projection

1959. (*Reproduced by permission of the Director, U.S. Coast and Geodetic Survey.*)

ward found; the illustration on page 514 shows how this affected two dams that crossed the rift line. No vertical movement occurred; but in the Yakutat Bay (Alaska) earthquake of 1899 a vertical movement of 50 ft took place over a large area, completely altering the local topography and creating new waterfalls on local watercourses.[11.6]

Earth movements of this type and magnitude are generally restricted to certain parts of the world that have come to be known as "seismic areas." Seismic areas coincide generally with areas in which active volcanoes are found; both are usually close to the borders of continental land masses and so may be zones of weakness in the earth's crust. This factor may account for both phenomena. Earthquakes are not restricted to the main seismic areas; earth tremors probably occur in most parts of the world. Even in such an unsuspected area as eastern Canada and the bordering New England states, an earthquake occurred as recently as February 28, 1925; it was remarkable for its low intensity over a large area, but it caused much local consternation and did some damage to structures in the vicinity of Quebec and along the banks of the St. Lawrence River. Reinforced-concrete grain elevators at Quebec were badly cracked, as was also the adjacent ground; columns were wrenched off their foundation bolts. There was no direct loss of life, but there were several deaths from shock. The disaster served to focus attention on earthquake studies in North America. Its significance is due in part to another earthquake which is recorded as having occurred in the same region on February 5, 1663, probably in the vicinity of Three Rivers; landslides caused by this earthquake made the water of the St. Lawrence River muddy for a month.[11.7] Although much smaller in magnitude, and so causing less physical damage, the earthquake which centered on Cornwall, Ontario, on May 2, 1944 (close to the site of the new international powerhouse on the St. Lawrence River), was a further reminder of the wide extent of seismic disturbances.[11.8]

It must be emphasized that the actual earth movements are not the result of earthquakes; on the contrary, they are the cause of the quakes that follow them. The great masses of material involved in the movements naturally set up dynamic effects of magnitude. In the New Zealand earthquake of 1929, several observers witnessed the earth's surface undulating to such an extent that a ripple seemed to pass along the ground under observation. The main result, however, is the initiation of earthquake waves (or, more accurately, vibrations) within the crust of the earth. These travel great distances, and it is due to them that a localized movement of the earth can have disastrous effects over a wide area. Earthquake waves are recorded by means of seismographs, delicate instruments similar to those used in seismic prospecting but housed in special buildings and far more sensitive. Modern seismographs are, indeed, so sensitive that the instrument in the Bidston Hill Observatory near

Liverpool, England, regularly records the rise and fall of the tide in the adjacent Liverpool Bay and Estuary, which cause slight movement of the rock on which the observatory is founded. Seismologists have distinguished three types of waves set up by earth movements; two of these travel through the earth, and the third at the surface. All three can be

Table 11.1. Scale of Earthquake Intensities

I..... Not felt. Marginal and long-period effects of large earthquakes.

II..... Felt by persons at rest, on upper floors, or favourably placed.

III..... Felt indoors. Hanging objects swing. Vibration like passing of light trucks. Duration estimated. May not be recognized as an earthquake.

IV..... Hanging objects swing. Vibration like passing of heavy trucks; or sensation of a jolt like a heavy ball striking the walls. Standing motor cars rock. Windows, dishes, doors rattle. Glasses clink. Crockery clashes. In the upper range of IV wooden walls and frame creak.

V..... Felt outdoors; direction estimated. Sleepers wakened. Liquids disturbed, some spilled. Small unstable objects displaced or upset. Doors swing, close, open. Shutters, pictures move. Pendulum clocks stop, start, change rate.

VI..... Felt by all. Many frightened and run outdoors. Persons walk unsteadily. Windows, dishes, glassware broken. Knicknacks, books etc., off shelves. Pictures off walls. Furniture moved or overturned. Weak plaster and masonry D cracked. Small bells ring (church, school). Trees, bushes shaken (visibly, or heard to rustle CFR).

VII..... Difficult to stand. Noticed by drivers of motor cars. Hanging objects quiver. Furniture broken. Damage to masonry D, including cracks. Weak chimneys broken at roof line. Fall of plaster, loose bricks, stones, tiles, cornices (also unbraced parapets and architectural ornaments—CFR). Some cracks in masonry C. Waves on ponds; water turbid with mud. Small slides and caving in along sand or gravel banks. Large bells ring. Concrete irrigation ditches damaged.

VIII..... Steering of motor cars affected. Damage to masonry C; partial collapse. Some damage to masonry B; none to masonry A. Fall of stucco and some masonry walls. Twisting, fall of chimneys, factory stacks, monuments, towers, elevated tanks. Frame houses moved on foundations if not bolted down; loose panel walls thrown out. Decayed piling broken off. Branches broken from trees. Changes in flow or temperature of springs and wells. Cracks in wet ground and on steep slopes.

IX..... General panic. Masonry D destroyed; masonry C heavily damaged, sometimes with complete collapse; masonry B seriously damaged. (General damage to foundations—CFR.) Frame structures, if not bolted, shifted off foundations. Frames racked. Serious damage to reservoirs. Underground pipes broken. Conspicuous cracks in ground. In alluviated areas sand and mud ejected, earthquake fountains, sand craters.

X..... Most masonry and frame structures destroyed with their foundations. Some well-built wooden structures and bridges destroyed. Serious damage to dams, dikes, embankments. Large landslides. Water thrown on banks of canals, rivers, lakes, etc. Sand and mud shifted horizontally on beaches and flat land. Rails bent slightly.

XI..... Rails bent greatly. Underground pipelines completely out of service.

XII..... Damage nearly total. Large rock masses displaced. Lines of sight and level distorted. Objects thrown into the air.

SOURCE: Reproduced, by permission, from "Elementary Seismology" by C. F. Richter, W. H. Freeman & Co. Inc., San Francisco, 1958, pp. 137–138.

distinguished on the seismograms obtained from seismographs, and by means of suitable calculations, the origin of the waves, or epicenter, can be determined.

The area affected by earthquake waves is often extensive; in the case of the Assam, India, earthquake of 1897, it is estimated that an area of 1.75 million sq miles was thus influenced. Amplitudes and periods of vibration vary; the factor of most significance in engineering is the horizontal acceleration that the vibrations tend to produce. Various scales have been suggested and used to denote the differing intensities of earthquake shocks. One of the most recent is the modification of the Mercalli scale suggested by C. F. Richter.[11.9] This provides such a clear guide that it is reproduced in full (by permission).

Not only is geological action the cause of earthquakes, but local geological features can have a marked effect on the local results of earthquake shock. This is evidenced by the fact that earthquake shocks are not felt in deep mines located within seismic areas. Since the radiating vibrations travel at different speeds in different materials, it is to be expected that effects in rock and unconsolidated material will be different. This is found in practice; earthquakes cause much more trouble in areas of unconsolidated materials than in those with solid rock exposed at the surface. Greater amplitudes of vibration are possible in the former than in the latter; and consequently, greater accelerations are to be expected in the softer materials. In the San Francisco earthquake, the maximum acceleration recorded in marshy ground was about 10 ft per sec per sec; in corresponding rock outcrops, a figure as low as 0.89 ft per sec per sec was observed. Similar records have been obtained in other earthquakes. An expert Japanese committee has suggested that the relative intensity of earthquake damage on different types of terrain is approximately:[11.10]

Marshy land	1.5 (?)
Alluvial ground	1.0
Diluvial (older and more consolidated) ground	0.7
Tertiary rock	0.4

It follows that in civil engineering work in seismic areas, structures should be founded wherever possible on solid bedrock. Another reason for this is that under the action of the transmitted vibrations, unconsolidated material will fracture and be displaced much more easily than will solid rock. Actual experience with buildings and engineering structures in severe earthquakes is in line with this suggestion. When the local geology is such that a rock foundation bed cannot possibly be used, foundation design must take into consideration the unusual forces that may be exerted upon the structure following an earthquake; a raft type of foundation, so designed that it will withstand upward forces in addition to the usual downward loads, is one type that has proved satisfactory, as have also continuous foundations carried on piles driven so that they rest on an underlying rock stratum.

In built-up city areas, the shock from an earthquake is liable to fracture water mains; and as fire is always a consequent hazard, water-distribution systems have to be designed and constructed with special care in seismic areas. Underground conditions may be so affected that groundwater distribution will be changed; old springs may stop flowing and new ones may be formed. Unconsolidated deposits that are below the surface may react in strange ways. Fill material will very often be affected; the intense vibration may compact it to an extent not possible by any normal means. In the New Zealand earthquake of 1929, all made ground sank to some extent. One fill which had been in place for 6 years sank 3 ft, although it was only 22 ft high; the grass on the surface was not displaced.[11.11] A feature which is sometimes of serious consequence is the effect that an earthquake shock can have at exposed vertical or sloping faces such as the steep banks of rivers or those of artificial cuts. The action of the vibrations on reaching a sloping face has been likened to the movement of the last billiard ball of a row that is struck sharply at the other end. Although hardly an accurate picture, this may give the reader an appreciation of the severe landslides and rockfalls that so often occur on such faces after passage of an earthquake shock. Finally, and quite naturally, the damage caused by earthquakes to major engineering excavations, especially tunnels, that are adjacent to lines of major earth movement can be disastrous. The Arvin-Tehachapi earthquake in California on July 21, 1952, affected the area crossed by a steeply graded main line of the Southern Pacific Railroad on which there are 15 tunnels. Four of these were on a loop south of Calimente, adjacent to the White Wolff fault, upon which serious movement took place. Damage to the tunnels and the track within them was so serious that three of them had to be transformed into open cuts. The damage was economically irreparable; the total cost of this work was about $1 million.[11.12]

The importance of all these features to civil engineering design and construction will be clear. In seismic urban areas, local regulations usually govern the allowance to be made in structural design for the possibility of earthquake shock; a common rule is that a structure must be able to withstand a horizontal force caused by a horizontal acceleration of one-tenth that of gravity. In other areas, however, regulations will give the engineer no guide, and he will then have to study the past seismic history of the locality to see if any special features have been revealed. Local geology will be a necessary complementary study. The advisability of getting foundation beds of rock has been noted. Similarly, level ground should be selected in preference to undulating or hilly ground. Marshy ground should be particularly avoided, and the use of fill material should be kept to a minimum. Close vicinity of civil engineering works to natural cuttings such as river beds, canals, and coasts should also be avoided so far as this is possible.

Many of the features that have been mentioned to show the interrelation of earthquakes and engineering works were dramatically demonstrated by the effects of the Hegben Lake (Montana) earthquake of August 17, 1959. By a fortunate chance, two members of the Engineering Geology Branch of the United States Geological Survey were at work in the

Fɪɢ. 11.7. Trace of the Red Canyon fault, as exposed after the Hegben earthquake, looking west toward Culligan Ranch, showing typical damage to buildings. (*Reproduced by permission of the Director, U.S. Geological Survey.*)

vicinity, one above and one downstream from the Hegben Dam adjacent to which the major damage was done. There are available, therefore, detailed accounts of the geological aspects of the earthquake to associate with the seismological studies made possible through correlative seismogram analyses. Hegben Dam is an earth-fill structure on the Madison River in southwestern Montana; the structure has a concrete core wall, having been built in 1915 by a power company. It retains 300,000 acre-ft of water. The epicenter of the quake appeared to be close to the dam; major movement occurred along a well-recognized fault paralleling the lake formed by the dam and passing within 700 ft of the right abutment. A vertical displacement of possibly 15 ft took place on the fault. The dam was badly fractured, and settled as much as 4 ft, but it did not fail, even though overtopped at least four times as a result of the major waves set up in the reservoir by the ground movement. Far more serious was the massive slide which took place 7 miles downstream from the dam and which buried an unknown number of vacationers. At least 43 million cu yd of rock fell into the river gorge, completely blocking the river flow; the slide area was 1 mile long, and the debris rose 400 ft above the level of the stream bed. The United States Corps of Engineers quickly initiated emergency action and a relief spillway was soon excavated; this permitted the river to resume its flow, but the slide and the lake it created remain as grim reminders of the damage that an earthquake can cause.[11.13]

Although fortunately infrequent in occurrence, earthquakes can wreak such havoc when they do occur that it is somewhat surprising to find that their scientific investigation is of relatively recent date. The Lisbon earthquake of 1775 is really the first of which any scientific description exists. The first seismograph was not developed until the 1880s, following the pioneer seismic studies of Robert Mallet who published his first paper in 1862. His description of the great Neapolitan earthquake of 1857 (published in 1862) provided for the first time a sound basis upon which the science of *seismology* could be founded.[11.14] Mallet's papers include many excellent accounts of damage to buildings; the engineering effects of earthquakes have been a stimulus to the more fundamental study of seismic forces throughout the relatively short history of this branch of science.

11.6. Ground Subsidence. Sometimes a vertical displacement of ground accompanies earthquakes in addition to the main earth movement responsible for the quake. Thus in the New Zealand earthquake, to which reference has been made, the town of Karamea, located on a deltaic formation, sank 2 ft. Other similar natural depressions of large areas of land are constantly taking place. As outlined in Chap. 2, this gradual movement is also a part of the general geological cycle; it is usually so slow that it cannot be observed, but some instances can be and have been studied. For example, it is now known that the area in which are located the Great Lakes of North America is slowly tilting at the rate of about 5 in. per 100 miles per century. Although so small, this movement would in 1,600 years cause the upper Great Lakes to discharge by way of the Chicago River into the Mississippi Valley instead of into the sea by the St. Lawrence.[11.15] There are a few localities at which an even faster movement has been detected. Only in comparatively recent years has it been possible, through the medium of precise leveling operations, to observe such movement. Indeed, it has sometimes been in checking precise leveling results, especially of inland areas, that the movement has been discovered. A subsidence of 15 in. in the vicinity of Kosmo, Utah, was located in this way; it followed an earthquake which occurred on March 12, 1934.[11.16]

There is a further type of natural subsidence which may be briefly mentioned; this is the purely local phenomenon sometimes referred to as a "sinkhole." Such depressions occur when superficial unconsolidated material subsides into holes formed in underlying rock (generally limestone) which has been eroded in some way, often by solution in groundwater. Some of these holes are of unusual extent; Culpepper's Dish, a well-known feature in England, has a circumference of almost 600 ft; its sides slope to a depth of about 150 ft. A district in Jamaica is known as the Cockpit Country because of the sinkholes found there in the white limestone; they vary from shallow basins to pits 500 ft deep. An interesting case occurred in connection with the disposal of sewage from the city of Norwich, England; sewage was conveyed to a farm at Whitlingham, and the land on which it was discharged was soon covered with holes from 3 to 5 ft in diameter and of varying depth; the washing out of sand galls in the local chalk formation had resulted in a subsidence of the surface material.[11.17]

Ground subsidence so far discussed can be termed natural in character, but there are other types of subsidence for which man is responsible. Settlement of ground due to subsurface mining operations has long been recognized; it is briefly discussed in the next section. In more recent years, however, potentially more serious subsidences have been created by the removal of water and oil from the ground. In certain areas, subsidence due to these causes has become so serious that vast sums of money have already been expended for remedial engineering works. Ground movement of this kind can be likened to a large-scale demonstration of the process of consolidation, now so well recognized in soil mechanics.

Dr. O. E. Meinzer noted an early case of this type of ground subsidence in connection with his ground-water investigations in Dakota and in the Goose Creek oil field in the United States. He was apparently the first to treat this matter in a scientific manner, showing how the subsidence could be accounted for by the abstraction of water from underlying beds.[11.18] The abstraction of ground water is responsible for one of the best known cases of subsidence, that in the Santa Clara Valley, about 20 miles south of San Francisco, California. The area affected is 200 sq miles, and the maximum settlement has amounted to slightly more than 5 ft; this occurred in the business district of the city of San Jose, which has a population of 80,000. The subsidence was first noted during the progress of a survey in 1920. The results quickly became serious, as the area involved includes a part of the shore line of San Francisco Bay, which had to be protected by dikes. Settlement had virtually ceased by the end of 1937, when restrictions on well-pumping operations raised the ground-water level by 50 ft. The permanent subsidence, however, remains.[11,19]

More serious has been subsidence in the city of Long Beach, adjacent to Los Angeles in southern California. The largest oil field in California, and the second richest in the United States, was found under the coastal part of Long Beach—unfortunately, it might almost be added, in view of the damage it has caused. The first wells were drilled in December,

Fig. 11.8. View inside the U.S. Naval Dockyard, Long Beach, California, showing the retaining wall needed, as a result of land subsidence, to keep out the sea. (*U.S. Navy photograph. Reproduced by permission of the Commandant, U.S. Naval Dockyard, Long Beach, California.*)

1936, and the first settlement was noted shortly thereafter. Since the area in which settlement was first detected was located between two well-known faults, it was at first thought that the settlement might be related to the aftereffects of the 1933 earthquake in this area. As settlement continued to increase, however, it was soon found to be directly related to the withdrawal of oil, gas, and ground water from the underlying strata. By 1950, an elliptical area including much of the harbor, measuring 5 miles by 3, was seriously affected; the maximum settlement was 11 ft and this was increasing at the rate of about 1½ ft per year. Horizontal displacements were also recorded; a 6,000-ft base line had been shortened by 5 ft. First remedial work to engineering structures had to be undertaken at about this time; a major bascule bridge was jacked up 7½ ft, and protection walls and other works were constructed at the naval dockyard that was close to the area of maximum settlement. Maximum settlement had increased to 17 ft by 1952, with an anticipated ultimate maximum of 25 ft. Repressurizing of the strata from which the oil and gas were being taken was considered at that time to be impracticable for technical as well as for legal reasons, since so many owners were involved in the oil operation (including the city of Long Beach itself).[11.20]

By 1959, an area of 20 sq miles was affected, and maximum settlement had reached 26 ft; settlements of as much as 2 ft had occurred 9 miles from the center of the disturbed area. Since the United States Navy's $175 million dockyard was at the center of the area, it is not surprising that the American government had to take steps to remedy the situation; thus, an injunction was sought for the closure of the field. Over 800 million bbl of oil had been obtained from the field, and known reserves amounted to about half this amount. An emergency crash program was therefore initiated under the direction of a Subsidence Control and Repressurization Administration for the Long Beach Harbor Commission. Eight special pumping plants have been installed with an installed capacity of 37.5 mgd (to be increased to 44 mgd) which pump salt water out of special source wells; after treatment, the salt water is forced back into the oil-bearing strata, under pressures ranging from 850 to 1,250 psi. Cost of the plants, financed by the city, will be recovered through a surcharge paid by oil operators on each barrel of water pumped underground. By the end of 1959, almost 20 mgd were being pumped underground; it was then estimated that the subsidence under the naval installations would be halted in about 6 months. The remedial program is estimated to cost $30 million, but already over $90 million have been expended on rehabilitation work to engineering structures and services disturbed by the settlement.[11.21]

It is naturally in connection with coastal developments that land subsidence can be most serious. One interesting solution to the problems thus created was adopted in connection with the protection of a stretch of shore line in Venezuela. The area around Lake Maracaibo near Lagunillas in this South American state is extensively developed as an oil field. The ground is swampy, and so a drainage program was initiated in 1923, following which it was noticed that the ground was slowly subsiding. The rate of subsidence was about 12 in. annually, so that before long, properties of the operating oil companies were in danger of flooding. Various methods of protecting the lake front were tried, but finally a flexible type of reinforced-concrete retaining wall, with a sloping face secured by raking piles at the back, was evolved and constructed in 1932. The wall was subjected to a slight earthquake in 1933 but showed no signs of damage.[11.22]

Settlements at Mexico City are world renowned; they will be noted briefly in Chap. 12. Even the ancient and lovely city of Venice is said to be settling by as much as 1 in. every 10 years, but this may be evidence rather of a change in sea level as noted in Chap. 7 (page 221). Settlement in a city such as Houston, Texas, however, leaves no doubt of its reality or its cause. For a long time Houston was the largest city in the Western Hemisphere to draw all its public water supply from the ground; as much as 185 mgd were withdrawn from underlying water-bearing strata that were originally artesian. With a rapid increase in withdrawal of ground water, a corresponding increase in ground settlement has been noted; maximum subsidence in the Pasadena area (of Houston) was 3.5 ft by 1954, and this was expected to increase to 7 ft by 1970.[11.23] Corresponding settlements due to withdrawal of ground water have been noted in the vicinity of La Verne, affecting the Colorado River Aqueduct, and in the San Joaquin area of California's great Central Valley. Details need not be given; enough has been said to show how responsive the ground is to changes in subsurface conditions when it is of such a character that it can yield in response to removal of support.

11.7. Mining Subsidence. Subsidence has long been recognized in connection with mining operations in soft ground or with shallow workings. There is a long history of "mining subsidence" and of the measures taken to counteract its effects upon engineering and other structures. This is "predictable settlement" in one sense, since the execution of mining work is known in advance and its effect upon the surface above can often be predicted from previous experience. Despite this, troubles still occur. As recently as 1959, the Institution of Civil Engineers published the report of a special committee set up to explore the situation regarding mining subsidence in Great Britain, where mining has a history of many centuries. The report presents a complete survey of the various factors that must be considered in relation to the possibility of mining subsidence; it is accompanied by a bibliography that is a good introduction to European interest in a subject which is of such significance that special European conferences on ground movement have been held.[11.24]

In North America, the same problem exists, sometimes further complicated by legal features. In the Pittsburgh district, for example, some coal-mining companies through their ownership of coal and mineral rights state that these carry the right to mine coal without regard to the effect upon surface dwellings. Such companies cooperate with the public most helpfully with respect to local building problems, but if coal is left in place to provide the necessary pillars for roof support (and so for the elimination of surface settlement), in distinction to being mined outright, the surface owners have to make payment for this concession on the part of the coal companies.[11.25] Despite this type of cooperation, troubles with building settlements still occur around Pittsburgh and in similar areas. The cause is obvious; the solution equally so. And since in all mining operations the local geology must be well known, preliminary investigation at any building site that is even adjacent to an active mining area is absolutely essential; it can provide reasonable assurance of the safety of the site.

In most countries where mining is an important part of the national economy, mining regulations include stringent restrictions with regard to operations that may have any surface effects. The rules set out by the

Fɪɢ. 11.9. The result of subsidence above old mine workings at Hodbarrow Mine, Millon, Cumberland (the wall was once straight). (*Geological Survey of Great Britain photograph; Crown Copyright; reproduced by permission of the Controller of H. M. Stationery Office, London.*)

Dortmund Board of Mines are typical. With such control, trouble with subsidence caused by modern mining work is the exception rather than the rule. On the other hand, in areas where old mine workings exist, trouble is completely unpredictable. Somewhat naturally, it is in the Old World that mining subsidences of this type most frequently occur; there are on record many almost classical cases of unexpected subsidence when old mine workings were encountered. Ritchie records a case where old mine workings were found only when an excavator at work on a building site disappeared into shallow workings that had been penetrated, covered only by a thin roof of solid rock, boulder clay, and other deposits. The site had to be opened up and the old workings filled in before work could proceed. Old coal workings, previously unsuspected, were even encountered beneath the site for a new science building at the University of Glasgow, Scotland, and had to be fully investigated; necessary additional roof support had to be provided before the new building could be commenced.[11.26]

A somewhat extreme, but nonetheless interesting case may be briefly noted to show what mining subsidence can really do. The region around Barrow-in-Furness, immediately to the southwest of the lovely English

FIG. 11.10. The hole on the (old) Furness Railway at Lindale, near Barrow, Lancashire, England, into which a locomotive sank and disappeared in 1892. (*Reproduced by courtesy of E. H. Scholes.*)

Lake District, has been long famous for its iron mines. The local "ironstone" has been mined from underground workings for many decades, and earlier workings have never been fully surveyed. On September 22, 1892, locomotive No. 115 (a 0-6-0 tender engine) of the Furness Railway was shunting some iron-ore wagons into a siding at the railway yard at Lindale, near Barrow, when the driver felt the ground beneath his engine start to fail. He tried to reverse the engine, but the ground actually opened up before he could do this. He was able to jump off but was badly shaken; his fireman jumped also and was unhurt. As the cavity increased, first rails disappeared into it and then the locomotive and its tender. By the time the breakdown gang with their large crane reached the site, they were able to rescue only the tender. The locomotive quickly disappeared into an old mine working and has never been seen since; it is believed to be buried about 200 ft below the present surface.[11.27]

11.8. Landslides. Minor earth movements will be considered, for convenience, under the two headings "landslides" and "rock falls"; the latter term includes sudden falls of solid rock, and the former covers all other types of localized earth movement except subsidence. Landslides are so common and are often so serious in their effects that they have been the object of much study. Many official commissions have considered them, and two governments today—the Swiss and the Italian—maintain official organizations to deal with landslides and similar troubles. In many of these studies, attempts have been made to classify landslides in order to simplify their investigation; the classifications of Heim and Terzaghi are perhaps the best known. In this brief review, detailed classifications cannot be followed; reference may, however, be made to an exceedingly useful volume published by the United States Highway Research Board as its Special Report No. 29 (1958). "Landslides and Engineering Practice" is the accurately descriptive title of this report of a Committee on Landslide Investigations; it provides an admirable survey of all the major engineering aspects of landslides and landslide prevention. Together with a companion bibliography, this volume should be in the hands of all engineers concerned in any way with landslide-correction work.[11.28] Since it is an engineering study, it is perhaps natural that the report does not stress the fact that all landslides are geological phenomena. A study of local geology is, however, the only satisfactory way of starting an investigation of landslides, either actual or incipient. Geology is implicit throughout the report and in particular in the new system of classification that it presents, a summary statement of which is presented, by permission, as Table 11.2. Reference should be made to the report itself for a singularly graphic presentation of this logical classification.

All the types of slide shown are associated with movement of material constituting a part of the earth's crust, movement caused fundamentally by gravity and taking place because of some inherent instability in the arrangement of the materials concerned. All types are dependent completely on the nature of the materials involved and on their relative arrangement, in other words, on the local geology at the site of the slide. All types may occur naturally; all may develop during the course of civil engineering work. If they occur naturally, they must be regarded as an inevitable part of the general geological cycle, since they contribute to the erosion of parts of the earth's surface, and thus are important factors in the processes that are developing topographical features of the world today. If they occur during civil engineering construction, they betray some interference with the natural stability of the part of the earth's crust in which work is being carried out. In all cases, although the exact cause of the slide may be difficult to determine, they will be due to either one or a combination of several natural causes which can be determined if investigations are pursued in the proper directions.

It follows that although naturally occurring slides may be classed as "acts of God," if by that term is implied a part of the natural order of

Table 11.2. Classification of Earth Movements

Type of movement		Type of material		
		Bedrock		Soils
Falls		Rockfall		Soilfall
Slides — Few units		Rotational Slump	Planar Block glide	Planar Block glide · Rotational Slump
Slides — Many units			Rockslide	Debris slide · Failure by lateral spreading

		Rock fragments	All unconsolidated — Sand or silt	Mixed	Mostly plastic
Flows	Dry	Rock fragment flow	Sand run · Loess flow		
			Rapid earthflow	Debris avalanche	Slow earthflow
	Wet		Sand or silt flow	Debris flow	Mudflow
Complex		Combinations of materials or type of movement			

SOURCE: Reprinted by permission from "Landslides and Engineering Practice" published by the Highway Research Board, Publication 544, National Research Council, National Academy of Sciences, Washington D.C.

the universe, they cannot be so classified if the term is meant to suggest that the cause of a slide is a mystery. Slides do not develop their essential instability suddenly (if those due to earthquake shocks are excepted); the movement that develops is merely the indication that a critical point has been passed. Therefore, it should be possible to anticipate many landslides if the necessary preliminary investigations are made, that is to say, if the local geology is studied with unusual care. The fact that all too often such investigations are made after a landslide has occurred is probably the reason why the value of preliminary studies is not better appreciated.

Natural landslides may affect the work of the civil engineer in many ways. Those which have taken place in the past may be responsible for topographical features which the engineer has to deal with in his work. Many major slides have blocked up river valleys, and the resulting

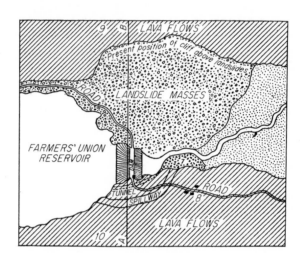

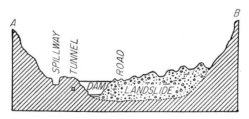

Fɪɢ. 11.11. General plan and section of the site of the Farmers' Union Dam (earth and rock fill; concrete core wall), Rio Grande River, Colorado, showing relation of dam to landslide mass. (*Reproduced by permission of the Director, U.S. Geological Survey.*)

constrictions give dam sites which at first appear to be admirable. In view of the nature of the material in slides, and its unconsolidated and often disturbed condition, sites of this kind may be very far from ideal. Dams have, however, been successfully founded at such sites. Some interesting examples have been given in a paper by W. G. Atwood,[11.29] one of which—the Farmers' Union Reservoir on the Rio Grande River in Colorado—blocks off only one-quarter of the width of the true valley in the local lava flows; the remaining three-quarters is dammed effectively, although with small leakage, by a great mass of landslide material. The incidence of another great landslide mass upon a major dam location is mentioned on page 559; the Bonneville Dam site was created by the deflection of the Columbia River by an ancient landslide. It will be clear, therefore, that recognition of ancient landslides is an important part of geological survey work. Local topographical detail will often be a helpful guide, but the composition of the unconsolidated mass will be a more certain one. Several distinguishing features may be mentioned: The rock fragments will be angular and not polished (unlike polished fragments in glacial deposits); all material will obviously be the same as those found in adjacent strata (again, unlike the mixed materials

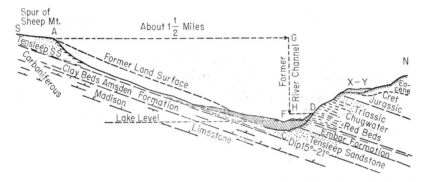

Fig. 11.12. Geological section across Gros Ventre Valley, Wyoming, showing the landslide of June, 1925. (*Based, by permission of the American Institute of Mining* and *Metallurgical Engineers, on a section in reference* 11.31*b*.)

in glacial deposits); and the disposition of the different materials in the mass will be irregular.

Dr. Terzaghi has described what must be one of the extreme examples of engineering use of landslide debris in the construction of the Cheakamus earth- and rock-fill dam in British Columbia. Founded on a thickness of 150 ft of landslide breccia, beneath which is a buried forest, the dam utilizes a site that was transformed by a major landslide about a century ago when a great lava face known as "The Barrier" collapsed and precipitated about 20 million cu yd of soft rock and mud into the Cheakamus Valley. The dam itself was constructed from rock fill and "Rubble Creek Wash," finer grained material derived from the landslide. The record of this unusual project shows clearly that design followed closely upon the most meticulous study of the geology of the dam site in the field.[11.30]

The motion of landslides, both natural slides and those caused by engineering work, may vary from an almost imperceptible rate to what may be appalling suddenness. The great Gros Ventre slide in Wyoming filled a river valley for 1½ miles of its course by a natural dam 1,000 ft wide at the top with an average depth of 180 ft. Eyewitnesses stated that the slide, whose total volume was estimated at 50 million cu yd, occurred in less than 5 min. It was later washed out by the natural flow of the river.[11.31] Figure 11.12 shows a typical section through the main slide from which it can be seen that the slide was essentially of the structural type; slipping occurred on a bedding plane.

One of the greatest landslips of which there is any record took place in Upper Garhwal, India, toward the end of the last century. Strictly speaking, it was a rockfall, but it is always referred to as the Gohna land-slide. Rising in the high Himalayas, the Birehiganga River is normally a small stream but is subject to high flood flows. It is 67 miles upstream of the city of Srinagar in Kashmir and is an important tributary of the Ganges. Reports coming out of the valley of this small river in the late fall of 1893 told of "a mountain having fallen." When the district sur-veyor visited the village of Gohna, he found that on September 22 a vast mass of rock had slipped down a distance of almost 5,000 ft, creating such a dust pall that villages around could not tell for some time what had happened; the dust settled to a depth of several inches for miles around. Another slip occurred on October 18, 1893; the final natural dam thus created across the river valley was 980 ft high above the bottom of the stream bed, 2 miles long at its base and 1 mile wide along its base. The slide consisted of pulverized and broken dolomite, varying from hand-size boulders to blocks of 2,000 cu ft or more. The British Superintending Engineer for the district decided that nothing could be done until the accumulating river flow overtopped the great dam. The timing of this was carefully estimated and all possible precautions were taken to avoid loss of life when the dam was overtopped. A telegraph line was run down the valley from the observation station at the dam so that ample notice of the flood could be given. In every town and village below the dam, stone pillars were erected to indicate the point below which it would be unsafe for people to remain when the flood occurred. Early on the morning of August 25, 1894, almost 1 year after the slide, the water began to trickle over the top of the dam. Within 24 hr, the level of the artificial lake had dropped 390 ft, and it was estimated that 10 billion cu ft of water had rushed down in a gigantic flood. Great material damage was done; towns and villages (including the whole of Srinagar) were swept away. Because of the precautions taken, how-ever, no lives were lost except for a fakir and his family who were de-stroyed not by the flood but by a slip in the face of the remaining barrier when they returned to their home after they had been unwillingly and forcibly removed.[11.32]

Talus slopes and similar deposits of eroded material which has fallen into place without the aid of water or glacial action are frequently affected by slides; instability arises from the way in which the material has reached its present position. Glacial deposits and materials deposited from water will not usually be affected unless there is some major change in their natural condition, such as that mentioned below; deposits containing clay are principally affected, since beds of pure sand and gravel rarely move unless they are seriously interfered with by construction operations. Instability in these cases arises from the variable character of clays, especially if moisture content is changed; the physical properties of sands and gravels, on the other hand, are relatively constant whether dry or wet. Solid-rock strata that have an appreciable dip and marked bedding planes, excessive jointing, or the essentially fissile structure of many of the metamorphic rocks will be found to be those most likely to give trouble through slides. Of common mineral contents, serpentine is that most liable to lead to trouble. It is an alteration mineral sometimes found in massive form; it feels greasy or slippery even when dry, and can be most troublesome when wet. It has been responsible for many serious slides. Another mineral that sometimes causes movements is anhydrite which will change to gypsum when exposed to the atmosphere by absorbing water; in so doing, it expands 33 per cent in volume, so that the resulting instability can readily be imagined.

The presence of treacherous materials alone is not sufficient to start a slide, but in combination with other causes, these materials can add to the troubles that movement will create. Earthquake shocks are always a potent cause of movement. The process of erosion is another common cause; it may act in one of several ways. Differential erosion of strata of varying stability may leave overhanging material of a harder stratum which will eventually break away and cause a slide. Erosion of the toe of a slope of unconsolidated material may remove the essential support from the material above which will start to move downward until stability is restored again. This will happen more easily on sloping bedding planes, which are always a source of possible weakness when bordering on any natural or excavated sloping face. Fault planes constitute another frequent cause of slides if they are so arranged that they isolate blocks of material which are thus left free to move; the work done in opening out the Cofton Tunnel (see page 349) is an example of slides due to this cause. The equilibrium of material in its natural position may sometimes be affected if unduly heavy loads are placed upon it. This is often the case with excavation work; the dumping of excavated material too near to the cut being made is responsible for many slides. The slides on the Panama Canal may be included among these, although the slides there were due to a combination of causes of which this was only one. Erection of buildings on unconsolidated material will sometimes have the same effect. The growing of carnations has been blamed for serious landslides near Menton, France, that took 11 lives. Local farmers uprooted so many olive trees in order to get ground on which to plant carnations (a more valuable crop) that the stabilizing effect of the tree roots was destroyed and the results were disastrous.

Probably the most important factor of all is a change in ground-water conditions. This may be caused by interference with natural drainage conditions, excessive evaporation from normally damp ground, or an increase in ground water due to excessive rainfall. This last is probably the most usual way in which ground-water conditions are affected; it is especially serious because excessive rainfall will also increase surface runoff, which may result in erosion of material at the toe of a slope and so intensify sliding tendencies. Rarely will surface erosion of itself lead to trouble; the landslides that often accompany this result of intense rainfall are generally due to a corresponding change in ground-water conditions. If, however, surface erosion strips off vegetation and leaves bare ground exposed to future rainfall, this may lead very quickly to an increase in ground water and so to slides. The presence of water underground has three main effects: it will increase the effective weight of the material that it saturates; it will tend to lubricate any sliding planes, especially if these are formed by materials, such as shales and clay, that are affected by moisture; and it will tend to weaken many materials, including the weaker kinds of rock and unconsolidated materials with any clay content. The combination of one or more of these effects with other consequences of heavy rainfall will show why many slides occur in wet weather and why drainage is so often an effective remedy for sliding.

The presence of excessive ground water is so generally realized as a potent cause of landslides that it may be difficult to imagine a slide caused by drought conditions. One such case, however, led to the wrecking of two trains, although the volume of material in the slide was only about 400 cu yd. The slide occurred on the Richmond, Fredericksburg, and Potomac Railway in Virginia in 1933. It took place in a cutting 1,000 ft long at a point on the west side where the cut was about 80 ft deep. Excavation was through sedimentary deposits of fine material derived from local metamorphic beds but containing no clay; deposition had been irregular, and induration had taken place to such an extent that the railway engineers classified the material as rock. They had found it difficult to excavate with a steam shovel and able to stand at a slope of about 60° in the lower part of the cut, flattening off to about 45° in the upper part. Three distinct strata were evident in the cut; the slide occurred from the third one and impinged on the tracks with the result noted. The strata were considerably jointed; expert opinion was that the slide was due to "the actual or incipient joint planes that parallel the west face of the cut [which] are the result of general shrinkage of the exposed beds because of excessive loss of moisture during a long dry period."[11.33]

Landslides occur frequently and come so often into the purview of the civil engineer engaged in general practice that it has been thought better to discuss them by means of the foregoing general notes than by the use of a few selected examples. The variety of slides is such that any examples so given can illustrate but a few of the many individual types; references are therefore given to publications that deal with slides much more fully than can be done in this short chapter and in which many

FIG. 11.13. Aerial view of the Elysian Park landslide, Los Angeles, California, U.S.A., November 26, 1937; the slide has special interest to engineers, since it wrecked part of the Riverside Drive concrete viaduct, seen in the photograph. (*Reproduced by permission of the City Engineer, Los Angeles.*)

instances are cited. The interest of the civil engineer in the geology of landslides is not in the geological features as such but only in so far as these may assist in remedial or preventive work. Further examples will therefore be given in connection with a discussion of this important branch of civil engineering work.

11.9. Preventive and Remedial Work. All engineering work directed toward preventing landslides or remedying the results of slides must be based on the fact that the movement betrays instability of the materials involved. If the slides are of undisturbed material, the fact that they are a part of the normal geological cycle must not be lost sight of; this may mean that they cannot be stopped but only anticipated and possibly controlled. If the slides develop during construction, their cause can usually be traced to a construction operation, and suitable remedial measures can be evolved, taking into account the construction work still to be done. But consideration of the over-all stability of the entire mass of material involved must always be of cardinal importance. If due regard is paid to stability, such remedial measures as removal of material at the toe of a moving slope and the construction of either pile or crib retaining walls at the toe of a slide will not be adopted except possibly as temporary emergency measures. In a few isolated slides of very small magnitude, these measures may be effective, but the general result of toe removal will be to remove some of the resistance to movement and so to increase the extent of the slide instead of stopping it. The use of piles, in particular, is usually clear evidence that those responsible for the remedial works do not appreciate the basic character of earth movement in landslips; the idea of retaining a deep-seated movement of a large mass of soil by means of slender piles is on a par with King Canute's efforts to stem the tide. The vibration caused by the operation of pile driving may even make matters worse if the soil in question is unduly sensitive. Piles are useful elements of civil engineering design when local soil conditions demand their use; remedial work on landslips is not such an occasion.

The use of retaining structures may also betray a neglect of the fundamentals of engineering design. Retaining structures should be designed for a predetermined load which they are to transmit to a foundation bed of known capacity. If constructed to stop a slide movement, unless the slide is of very small extent, they will have to withstand the load induced by movement of the whole slide—generally unpredictable with any accuracy—and will transmit the load, in many cases, to a lower part of the material affected by the slide. To illustrate the frequent failure of such measures to control slides would be to labor the point too strongly; examples will be found in several of the references given. There are two possible exceptions to this general unsuitability of retaining walls. First, they may be used in cuttings both banks of which are unstable and both of which can be held by retaining structures connected by solid struts across the bottom of the cutting. This measure sometimes proves economical; but usually it is more satisfactory to achieve stability of the slopes of the cutting, and thus to dispense with the need of such walls. Second, small walls may be satisfactorily used not so much as retaining structures but as protection for the lower parts of slopes combined with provision for drainage. A particularly ingenious example of this type of structure is provided by the use of *gabions*. These are "crates" formed of strong steel-wire mesh that are filled with hand-sized stone when in place; their appearance is clearly shown in Fig. 11.14, where they are seen in use by British Railways on a main line of the Western Region between Leamington and Birmingham. The crates, when built up to form walls of the desired height, provide a stable structure which has the virtue of being quite pervious to water. The gabions therefore act as continuous drains, and thus assist in the stabilizing of wet slopes by a combined action.[11.34] For locations where drainage at the toe of a slope is essential, they can often provide a simple but effective solution.

Three general preventive and remedial measures are available: consolidation of unstable material contributing to the movement, treatment

Fig. 11.14. Stages in the construction of gabions for bank stabilization at Ferndale Pendynis, Western Region, British Railways. Wire netting for forming the gabions is shown in foreground. (*Reproduced by permission of Chief Civil Engineer, Western Region, British Railways.*)

of the slopes that are unstable, and correction of ground-water conditions responsible for the movement. For some slides, special methods may have to be adopted, such as the protection of the toe of a natural bank from erosion by a river, protection of a weak stratum where differential erosion is taking place, or removal of unusual loads adjacent to slopes that have contributed to movement; but the three methods listed apply to all types of slides to some degree.

Consolidation of unstable material may be achieved by chemical means, by cement grout in certain special cases, and by freezing. The object of all processes is to render more stable material that is moving because of its own state, or to solidify it, if this term may be used in connection with the conception of a fluid or semifluid state of moving unconsolidated material. Such methods are necessarily expensive; they are therefore adaptable to emergency conditions where temporary stability is required, as on construction jobs. There have been some applications, particularly of the freezing process, that were not too successful; but one of the first applications of this idea, although now some years old, still provides an excellent example of the potential of the freezing process for stabilizing a difficult soil condition.

Freezing was successfully applied to the control of a slide, which might have been serious had it developed further, during the construction of the Grand Coulee Dam for the U.S. Bureau of Reclamation. The dam is located on the Columbia River, Washington, and is one of the major dam structures of the world. At the dam site, silt originally filled the valley of the river to a depth of about 500 ft, but the river subsequently wore this down to a depth of between 40 and 50 ft. During this erosive process, the river channel swung from side to side of the valley, with the result that slides of the silt were frequent. Excavation in the dried-out river bed encountered the toes of many of these old slides and in this and other ways so disturbed the stability of the remaining silt that many slides occurred during construction. The silt was a very fine rock flour, containing from 20 to 25 per cent colloidal material; when undisturbed, the material stood up well, but as soon as it was moved, it proved unstable on any slope steeper than 1:4 even when relatively dry. Drainage by wells and tunnels assisted in controlling slides, as did also slope correction; but near the center of the east excavation area, the bedrock was intercepted by a narrow gorge, 120 ft deeper than the average bedrock elevation, in which silt created an unusually serious slide. Since a 5-cu yd shovel could make no headway against the slide, the engineers finally decided to freeze an arch of the material in such a way as to form a solid blockade of the gorge behind which excavation could proceed. This was done with the aid of 377 special freezing points and a circulating ammonia-brine solution refrigerating system which had a capacity of 160,000 lb of ice per day. The frozen dam was about 40 ft high, and was located on top of a concrete and timber crib structure 35 ft high; it was 20 ft thick and 100 ft long, and cost $30,000. Although freezing started when the slide was moving into the excavation at a rate of 2 ft per hr, the dam was successfully completed and was estimated to have saved its own cost in the excavation which did not have to be done; in addition, several weeks of very valuable time had been saved in connection with work in the cofferdammed river bed.[11.35]

Slope readjustment, the second main remedial measure noted, really amounts to doing under control and in a limited way what a slide will do automatically if it is allowed to take place. Now that the stability of slopes can be theoretically determined with the aid of the techniques of soil mechanics, landslides caused by excessive slopes should steadily decrease in number. In earlier years, however, when civil engineering did not have the benefit of modern soil studies, the excavation of cuts with excessive slopes was a potent cause of earth movement; correspondingly, slope adjustment was frequently the major remedial measure. Since it cannot be assumed that this particular type of trouble has yet been completely eliminated from engineering practice, a glance at some examples is warranted.

Fig. 11.15. Flow of silt in the east excavation area at Grand Coulee Dam, Columbia River, Washington, U.S.A., stopped by an arch dam of frozen material. Refrigeration pipes may be seen near the center, at top of photograph. (*Reproduced by permission of the Commissioner, U.S. Bureau of Reclamation.*)

As an extreme case, there may be mentioned a statement made in 1894 by the chief engineer of the (old) London and North Western Railway of England that "there was neither a bank nor cutting between Euston (London) and Rugby that had not slipped at one time or other"; this statement deals with the first 100 miles of one of the main railway lines of England.[11.36] Railways have been very general sufferers from landslides, both in natural undisturbed material near to which railway lines have been located (as on hillsides, for example), and in the cuttings and fills constructed to carry the roadbed. It is perhaps safe to say that no railway line has suffered more than (although some of the South American lines may have suffered as much as) the Hill Section of the Assam Bengal Railway in India. It is 114¼ miles long and was opened to traffic in February, 1904; its construction was undertaken largely for military reasons, and it has been described by a Viceroy of India as a "millstone round the neck of the Indian Finance Department." From the very beginning of operation, slips and washouts gave trouble; in 10 years, about £100,000 had been expended in necessary maintenance, and the line had been closed on several occasions. In 1915, a further disaster, due to excessive rainfall, overtook the line and culminated in a fall of 26 in. in 48 hr. It was subsequently closed for 2 years while remedial work was carried out at a still further cost of over £225,000. Disregarding the financial aspects of the work, all engineers can appreciate the heroic efforts of the engineers concerned with the maintenance of this line in the face of the difficulties that the quoted figures suggest. The troubles were due in large part to the local geology; the rocks are of the Tertiary measures and consist mainly of alternating beds of carbonaceous shales and sandstones so affected by earth movements of the past that they possess little durability and break up into small fragments on exposure to the atmosphere. The shales vary from rock as hard as slate to material with the consistency of clay and the sandstones, from rock sand to first-class building stone. A detailed record of some of the major difficulties created by this material is fortunately available; the following account illustrates a notable case of slope readjustment—first by way of a slide, and subsequently by means of remedial measures coupled with other features of interest.[11.37]

Figure 11.16 represents a cross section at a point on the line near the south portal of the Chamartalla Tunnel; Fig. 11.16a shows how this was early in 1913. The slope of the cutting in the rock was at first taken out to a steeper slope, but after many falls of rock and earth had occurred, the slope was cut back to that shown. Revetment was also built to protect the newly exposed shale from exposure to the atmosphere. The retaining wall shown at river level was the cause of much trouble. When rebuilt in 1899, its foundation was on hard shale at river-bed level, and no erosion was anticipated; but in 1902, and again in 1908, the river in flood flow undercut this wall to a depth of 12 ft and eroded the hard shale completely; the wall had to be rebuilt again. In 1913, a great mass of material slipped from the hillside above onto the tracks; the load was so great that the retaining wall was forced into the river, and the whole railway formation was carried away for a length of 150 ft. Communication was restored temporarily within 15 days. Permanent reconstruction introduced many problems, but the final solution is shown in Fig. 11.16b; the design of the covered way was so prepared that it would offer a minimum obstruction to further slides that were intended to pass over it. A sloped cushion of earth fill and handpacked stone was to be

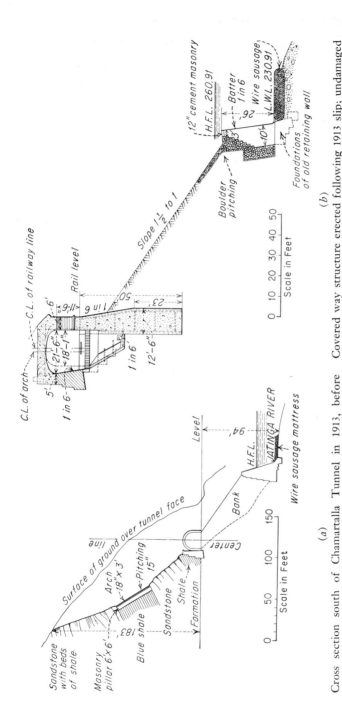

Cross section south of Chamartalla Tunnel in 1913, before major slip.

Covered way structure erected following 1913 slip; undamaged in 1915.

Fig. 11.16. Landslide remedial work on Hill Section of the Assam Bengal Railway, India. (*Reproduced by permission of the Institution of Civil Engineers.*)

permanently maintained on top at the slope indicated; the slope below the track was trimmed as shown. The foot of the retaining wall was protected with wire-sausage mattresses to secure it against future scouring. The piers for the covered way, as will be seen, had to be carried to a depth of 50 ft below track level in order to reach a solid foundation bed, since rock above this level was badly fissured. In 1915, when the major disaster to the line took place, a slip passed over the covered way without causing any damage. Fortunately, engineers are seldom faced with such difficulties as these, but the case is of great interest, because it shows how an exceedingly serious situation can be remedied by judicious work on the affected slope.

Drainage was the third main method to be listed. Surface drainage is generally envisaged as that necessary in most engineering work, including that dealing with slides. In a few cases, surface drainage may be effective; generally, however, it will be useless because the critical location in a slide is the plane on which sliding is taking place—usually well below the surface except at the extremities of the slide. At times, surface drainage may even be harmful. To be effective in preventing or remedying slides, drainage must intercept the ground water which is tending to promote the instability. Sometimes a very small amount of water can cause extensive slides. Examples from actual practice have shown that features such as thin beds of sand, only 1 to 2 in. thick and only slightly water bearing, and even a 1-in. seam of decomposed coal, can lead to extensive slides of the superincumbent material. Drainage can be applied effectively, therefore, only when those in charge fully know and understand the cause of the slides and the source of the ground water that is contributing to movement. This knowledge can be obtained by a judicious combination of geological survey work and test boring; needless to say, such work can be carried out far more easily and to much better effect before rather than after any movement has taken place.

In recent years, drainage has been widely recognized as essential to the maintenance of stable slopes and the avoidance of much trouble with earth movements. Many ingenious variations of standard drainage methods have been developed for use with unstable slopes. Highway departments, in particular, have special equipment and specially trained staff for such drainage work. In this branch of work, highway engineers have been able to profit from the experiences of railway engineers and to take advantage of all that modern soil studies can contribute. Highway construction in California now provides many notable examples of excellent drainage installations; the unusual troubles encountered with earth movements in that part of the United States are demonstrated by the fact that the cost of landslide-stabilizing works have, on occasion, amounted to more than one-third of the total state expenditure on highway maintenance annually.[11.38] Horizontal drains of conventional design can often be used; horizontal drains jacked into place, in order to avoid further disturbance of slopes, are a variant. The use of perforated pipes for this purpose is widespread, but almost every type of pipe and culvert has found application in some example of slope stabilization. There are now, fortu-

Fɪɢ. 11.17. Horizontal perforated 2-in.-diameter steel-pipe drains being installed on the Trans Canada Highway, west of Banff, Alberta, Canada; the second view shows the drains in operation in stabilizing the side slope. (*Reproduced by permission of the Department of Public Works (Canada), Highway Division.*)

nately, many hundreds of examples to show the efficacy of this preventive measure. To illustrate almost all phases of such work, an example will be cited that constitutes probably the worst individual landslide situation ever to be faced and solved by civil engineers.

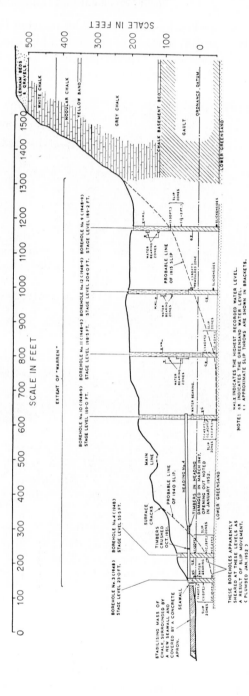

Fig. 11.18. Typical cross sections through the Folkestone Warren landslide area, showing something of the test borings and remedial works carried out. *(Reproduced by permission of the Municipal Engineering Publication Ltd., from the Eighth Annual Conference Brochure of the Institute of Highway Superintendents, London, 1958.)*

The main line of British Railways connecting the ports of Folkestone and Dover (previously a part of the Southern Railway) runs along the south coast of England where it is characterized by the widely known white cliffs of Dover. Between the Martello Tunnel near Folkestone and the Abbotsford Tunnel nearer Dover is a stretch of 2 miles of coast known as the Folkestone Warren. It has suffered extensive landslips from the earliest historical times, possibly since the breaching of the Straits of Dover in Neolithic times. The double-track railway line runs in a shallow cutting in the undercliff; the main cliffs rise about 500 ft above sea level. General conditions at the Warren in 1951 are shown in Fig. 11.18; Fig. 11.19 shows the appearance of part of it in 1915. In this

Fig. 11.19. Folkestone Warren Landslip, Kent, England, of 1915, showing the train involved at the west end of the slip movement. (*Reproduced by permission of the Chief Civil Engineer, Southern Region, British Railways.*)

year one of the most serious landslides of recent times occurred; another had taken place in 1877. Ever since the line was opened in 1844, however, those responsible for its maintenance have been plagued by earth movements; major remedial work was put in hand in 1948 following one of the most intensive programs of subsurface exploration of which the writer has knowledge. This work was started in 1939 but had to be stopped because of the war. Between 1940 and 1948, the position of the shear surface responsible for the major movement was clearly demonstrated in two of the timbered drainage headings that had been constructed before the war. The movement continued slowly throughout the war years, but fortunately, no major slide occurred. An extensive program of boreholes provided the basic information upon which an explanation of the movements and the main plan for the necessary remedial work could be based. This case, however, was one of the many in which engineering studies alone were not enough; the engineers in charge worked in the closest cooperation with officers of the Geological Survey of Great Britain, and their joint efforts eventually provided a reasonably complete solution to the century-old problem. In view of the discontinuities created by earlier slips which had caused gaps in the geological sequence, it was necessary to make a detailed study of the fossils found in the samples of the Gault formation obtained in boreholes in order to establish with certainty the stratigraphical succession in each particular boring. It would be hard to imagine a better example of the complete interdependence of such engineering and geological studies.[11.39]

Fig. 11.20. The weighted foreshore at Folkestone Warren, Kent, England; this is one of the landslide remedial works; the visitors are from the International Conference on Soil Mechanics and Foundation Engineering, London, 1957.

The Warren owes its existence to the facility with which northeasterly dipping Gault clay and chalk marl, forming the lower hundred feet of the Lower Chalk, are eroded by the sea. External factors affecting the earth movements have therefore been the effects of heavy rainfall and the erosive action of the sea. The Gault has marked swelling characteristics, so that any disturbance of it creates increasing trouble as the newly exposed material comes into contact with water. Figure 11.18 is a typical cross section resulting from the investigations carried out between 1948 and 1950; the figure shows one of the drainage headings and the foreshore loading (see above). The investigations showed clearly that the landslips penetrate to the base of the Gault and that failures had been generally confined to a plastic sheet of the Gault immediately overlying a thin layer of phosphatic nodules embedded in a concretionary grit, popularly known as the "sulphur band." When the cause was known, remedial works of a major nature were put in hand. These included a new drainage heading more than 700 ft long, constructed as a 6½ ft shield-driven tunnel, lined with precast concrete segments, whose purpose was to lower permanently the ground-water level in the disturbed area. In order to limit further erosion by the sea, over half a mile of the critical part of the coast was stabilized by weighting with chalk, held in place by concrete walls and slabs, and by carefully located groynes, constructed at right angles into the sea for added protection.

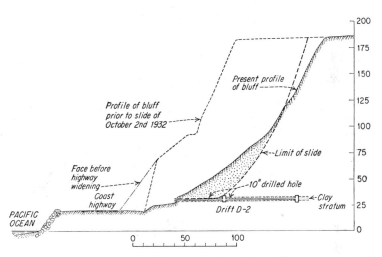

Fig. 11.21. General plan and typical cross section of landslide area at the Palisades, west of Los Angeles, California, U.S.A., showing the arrangements used for air drying. (*Reproduced by permission of Quinton, Code and Hill-Leeds and Barnard, Consulting Engineers.*)

The Folkestone Warren landslips are unique, but the records that the engineers associated with the recent investigations have published are invaluable guides even for remedial work on a much smaller scale. The case epitomizes successful drainage work in connection with landslides, except that it was carried out after a slide had occurred instead of before, as can often be done. The subsurface was adequately explored; the cause of the slide was found; and the main contributing cause was dealt with by a carefully planned drainage system. These steps characterize most preventive and remedial work in connection with landslides, although the exact method of dealing with the main cause of sliding may vary. When the slide is caused by normal ground water, special methods may sometimes be adopted in addition to regular drainage systems. Well points (see page 359) may be used to advantage in some places. One large hillside in California is being maintained in its present state only because of the successful operation of an extensive hot-air pumping system which circulated warm air through tunnels excavated in the clay bank in order to dry out ground water that was constantly seeping toward the hill face. This unusual scheme has worked so well that it has been possible to fill all the tunnels with gravel and discontinue drying, while leaving the general arrangement so fixed that drying can again be resumed in the future if this is ever necessary. The drying operation was carried on from 1933 to 1939, and it has not yet proved necessary to repeat the process.[11.40]

11.10. The Stability of Earth Slopes. The attainment of stability as a necessity in dealing with incipient or actual landslides has been stressed to such an extent that the question naturally arises, how can this stability be determined in the case of those sloping faces of unconsolidated materials which are so common a feature of civil engineering work. The sides of cuttings, the sides of deposits of fill material, and natural hillsides that have to be used in connection with civil engineering construction are the main types of earth slopes whose control can so often be a matter of great difficulty. Whenever such slopes are composed of material that does not occur in regularly bedded strata, the determination of stability becomes a matter of investigating the mechanical stability of a mass of unconsolidated material conforming to the outline of the slope under consideration. Once the physical properties of the material are known, it should be possible, by application of the laws of mechanics, to determine whether or not a specified slope will be stable. Today, this is a well-accepted part of studies in soil mechanics.

As early as 1846, this fundamental of the stability of slopes was recognized by a gifted French engineer, Alexandre Collin. He made field studies of extensive clay slips at 15 locations, primarily on the canals then being constructed with such vigor in France. He saw that they were all deep rotational slips, generally on a cycloidal surface, starting with a tension crack at the top of the slope. He carried out the first shear tests on clay, in order to determine the properties of the soils which he might then apply in the mathematical analyses that he also carried out.[11.41] In every sense, he was one of the great pioneers of soil mechanics, but his work was forgotten for almost a century. It was mentioned in connection with the studies made of the Panama Canal slides.[11.42] These were notable investigations, as were also those carried out in connection with slides on the Kiel Canal, and in particular, on the Swedish State Railways and in the harbor of Götenborg, Sweden. From these beginnings came the modern theoretical approaches to slope stability which are outlined in texts on soil mechanics. Not until 1956, however, did a translation of

Collin's book of 1846 become available in English. Reading the book is a sobering experience, for it is clear that Collin recognized the importance of quick shear tests in comparison with slow shear tests, the importance of what is now called "undisturbed sampling," and above all, the dependence of all theoretical studies of slope stability upon the local geological structure. This dependence is an essential counterpart of the most meticulous theoretical stability calculations.

To say this is not to belittle the value of the theoretical approach; it is essential. The assumptions made in calculations, however, must always be checked in the field, and any geological peculiarities of the site must

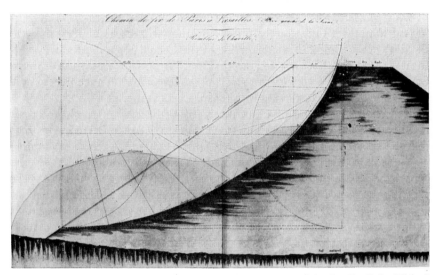

Fig. 11.22. A typical plate from Collin's book on "Landslides in Clay" (published in Paris in 1846), showing cycloidal form of failure surface.

be carefully investigated so that the relevance of mathematical computations may be realistically assessed. The presence of and the possible future changes in ground water must, in particular, be carefully considered. Geology, therefore, must play a part in all investigations of slope stability.

Such studies can often be aided by observing natural slopes that have been formed, and have proved to be stable, under the same general conditions as those being considered in connection with engineering work. The correlation of natural and artificial slopes has been outlined by Ward.[11.43] Skempton has published an intriguing account of the natural slopes found with the London clay.[11.44] Other regional studies are available so that it is not surprising to find that, well over a century ago, Collin had noted the same thing: "Must we not, in going from the observation of fills and of cuts made by man to the observation of mountains whose sides are or seem to be immense slopes of natural fills or cuts created by upheaval or erosion, find in one as in the other material traces of the permanent force which so acts on all bodies of our planet as to submit them to its immutable laws."

11.11. Mud Runs. In the classification of landslides in Table 11.2, a large grouping is designated *"flows."* Although much less frequent than the types of landslides so far described, earth movements consisting of soil or rock in the form of streams that either are flowing or have obviously flowed are encountered in many localities; they can cause serious problems for the engineer. Most interesting geologically are the flows associated with rock-talus slopes that sometimes take on the character of *rock glaciers*, a descriptive name to be found applied to them in geological literature. Only rarely do engineering works encounter this type of flow, but a section of the main line of the Canadian Pacific Railway was located across the debris fan at the foot of such a flow near Mount Stephen. Mud slides cover the track on the average of once every year and so constitute a continuing maintenance problem.

Mixtures of rock and mud are more serious because of the havoc they can create, even though they are normally restricted to barren areas that may be subjected to sudden high rainfalls. *Mud runs*, as they have come to be called, are generally confined to tropical countries; they are especially severe in India and in parts of South America where they are locally known as *huaicos*. Extreme climatic conditions will promote rapid disintegration of relatively weak rocks such as shales; the corresponding concentrated rainfall acts as an efficient transporting agent. If mud runs, for example, reach bridge openings that have been designed to take normal stream flow (of water), the consequent restriction of movement may block the opening and the results may be serious. Several sections of the Bolivia Railway had to be relocated for this reason (see page 628[11.45]).

Far more widespread and far more serious in their consequences are the mud runs, *flow slides*, or earth flows caused by the disturbance of unusually sensitive clays with high natural moisture content. Although stable in their normal position, these clays can quickly lose their apparent stability when disturbed; their excess moisture content may be released from its intermolecular structure to provide immediately a transporting medium for the soil particles; the resulting mixture will flow like pea soup. Marine clays such as those found in the lower Ottawa and St. Lawrence Valleys in eastern Canada, and correspondingly, in southern Norway and Sweden, are particularly susceptible to this type of movement. This fact is reflected in the existence, in the province of Quebec, on the north shore of the St. Lawrence, about 65 miles downstream from Quebec City, of a charming little village named Les Eboulements (one of the French names for landslides). Some of these slides, in Scandinavia as well as in Canada, have had tragic aspects, taking a toll of many lives. They can readily be explained, after they have happened, when the characteristics of the local soil have been determined. They are, however, difficult if not impossible to predict with accuracy. Knowledge of

Fig. 11.23. A mud run of excavated glacial clay, after being dumped from a dragline bucket, into the partially drained basin of Steep Rock Lake, Ontario, Canada. (*Photograph by R. F. Legget. Reproduced by permission of Steep Rock Iron Mines, Ltd.*)

the local geology, however, will provide a guide to the existence of potentially dangerous clays, as was explained in Chap. 4.

Flow slides of this type are not confined merely to marine clays; they may be suspected wherever clays have natural moisture content exceeding, or even close to, their liquid limits. Clays formed by deposition in glacial fresh-water lakes, accordingly, may be of this type, as has frequently been found on the Precambrian shield in Canada. Recent deposits, such as those found in the bed of Steep Rock Lake, Ontario, after it had been drained, were of the same nature. In every case, if the geological history of a clay can be determined, it will provide an invaluable guide to the sort of behavior that may be expected should the clay be disturbed, a guide to be checked and confirmed by detailed soil tests upon carefully obtained soil samples. Here, once again, geology and soil mechanics can be and always should be inseparable partners.

Fig. 11.24. Aerial view of the flow slide in Leda clay at Nicolet, Quebec, Canada, in which three lives were lost and the local cathedral (in center of view) just escaped destruction. (*Photograph by Spartan Air Services, Ltd.*)

11.12. Rockfalls. Rockfalls, in general, are more determinate and understandable than other types of minor earth movement. They occur when a mass of rock becomes detached from surrounding bedrock in some way and thus becomes free to move downward if its position will permit. The loosening of blocks of rock will almost always be associated with such features as bedding planes, joints, cleavage, or a local fault zone or plane. The immediate cause of loosening will be a change in the material adjacent to the planes of possible movement, which will usually be the result of weathering. Natural rockfalls are evident at any steep mountain face; talus slopes are a direct result. Many are of great extent, but great

Reference must finally be made to the rockfalls that have characterized the steep and rocky coasts of Norway. The topography of the western part of this country is widely known from the many photographs of its most beautiful scenery. Much of the fiord country consists of meta-morphic rocks of Cambrian and Silurian age; most rockfalls occur in the

FIG. 11.29. Installing rock bolts in the sandstone cliffs at the site of the Glen Canyon Dam on the Colorado River, U.S.A. (*Photograph by Bethlehem Steel Co. Reproduced by permission of the Commissioner, U.S. Bureau of Reclamation.*)

older metamorphic rocks of Caledonian origin. Records show that about 200 major rockfalls took place between 1640 and 1900 and that 50 have taken place since the start of this century. Most of them occur in the spring or the fall of the year, being clearly related either to freezing conditions or to excessive runoff. Over 350 people are known to have been killed in rockfalls; many of this number perished as a result of the six catastrophic rockfalls on record. These occurred generally in narrow fiords, where the fall of rock causes great waves in the narrow waterways and the consequent tragic flooding of little villages that are at once so picturesque and so vital a part of the Norwegian economy. Descriptions of these tragic happenings are available. Study of the records of such rockfalls and careful study of rock conditions in the vicinity of

Fig. 11.30. Automatic rock-movement gauge installed by the Norwegian Geotechnical Institute on the Flofjell, north of Loen, Norway, at the head of the Nordfjord (Lake Strynsvannet is seen in the background.) (*Reproduced by permission of the Norwegian Geotechnical Institute.*)

known falls have elucidated the causes of such accidents, so that preventive measures are now possible. The Norwegian Geotechnical Institute has been engaged in this important work and has designed and installed special extensometers for measuring slight differential rock movements (such as across an open seam) that may be anticipated prior to a major rockfall. Since these must be installed in isolated locations such as on the tops of steep cliffs above deep fiords, the Institute has coupled its extensometers to automatic radio transmitters, from which messages which will indicate any change in rock conditions are sent at regular intervals to observer stations at the bottom of the valleys. Figure 11.30 shows such an installation on the mountain Flofjell, some 20 to 30 km north of Loen, approximately 1,000 m above sea level. This is on the Nordfjord about 110 miles north of Bergen.[11.57]

It is perhaps not inappropriate to leave this vast and important subject standing, in imagination, amid some of the most beautiful scenery of the world, with a modern electronic instrument nearby to remind the engineer and the geologist of the inexorable progress of the geological cycle, of the possible instability of even the most solid-looking rocks, and also of the modern studies that are now possible for the investigation of such potential instability—work that should in the course of time greatly benefit the human race by steadily eliminating loss of life due to all that is implied by the simple term "earth movements."

Suggestions for Further Reading

Engineers who are concerned in any way with earthquakes and their effects will find the following volume a helpful introduction to the whole field of seismology and its extensive literature:

Richter, C. F., "Elementary Seismology," W. H. Freeman & Co., Inc., San Francisco, 1958.

Important as are landslides in the practice of civil engineering, only two references for further information need be listed, as the volume cited is so complete a guide to the subject and the bibliography so comprehensive a review of useful literature in this field:

Eckel, E. B. (ed.), "Landslides and Engineering Practice," Special Report 29 from the Committee on Landslide Investigations of the Highway Research Board, NAS-NRC Publication 544, Washington, D.C., 1958.
"Bibliography on Landslides," (prepared by the above noted committee), Bibliography no. 10, Highway Research Board, Washington, D.C., 1951.

The difficulties with slope stability in the Los Angeles area (see pages 429 and 479) have directed attention to the geological aspects of the local engineering problems to such good effect that geology is now recognized in relevant municipal regulations. Partly as a result of this, there was formed in 1958 the California Association of Engineering Geologists (P.O. Box 4164, Sacramento 21, California), the annual meetings and other activities of which are clear evidence of the keen interest in engineering geology now current in this area.

Chapter 12

BUILDING FOUNDATIONS

If a builder build a house for a man and do not make its construction fair, and the house which he has built collapses and causes the death of the owner of the house, that builder shall be put to death.

The Code of Hammurabi
(2130–2088 B.C.)

ALL ENGINEERING structures must be supported in some way by the materials that form the upper part of the earth's crust. There thus exists an inevitable connection between geological conditions and foundation design and construction. Dams, bridges, and structures associated with transportation routes are usually of considerable size and so achieve in the popular mind an importance not strictly in accord with fact, for the major part of engineering construction is made up of a large number of smaller projects. It is to this great group of miscellaneous structures that many civil engineers have to devote their attention. They know that small works may cause trials and difficulties no less than large projects; among these difficulties, foundation problems are far from being unimportant. To describe the supporting elements of this great miscellaneous group of structures as "building foundations" is to use a general term in a singularly wide way. But so varied are the types of work involved that generalization is inevitable. On the other hand, the main types of foundation design are so well recognized that a general discussion of them can safely be made without fear of oversimplification. In addition, the founding of building structures represents a relatively large part of this miscellaneous foundation work, and many of the associated problems are common to general foundation practice.

For many years, building-foundation work was largely a matter of rule of thumb, restricted only by such building regulations as were relevant. All too often, construction methods, which are of vital importance in many foundation operations, and sometimes even the final details of foundation design were left entirely to building contractors. In the hands of a competent construction company, this practice may not have been

444

too objectionable; but in other cases, it led almost certainly to unsatisfactory foundation work. Today, the foundation of structures is coming to be adequately recognized as an important part of building design. On many projects, large and sometimes small, architects are cooperating with engineers in this branch of building work which is essentially in the domain of the engineer. Preliminary investigations are more thoroughly made, and building plans are frequently prepared in association with a definite scheme of construction; the contractor is thus protected against the uncertainties that he might otherwise have to face. Simultaneously, the science of foundation design has been developing. Theoretical design methods are being correlated with the results of their application in practice; and by the improvement of field and laboratory soil-testing methods, better advantage is being taken of the possibilities that many building sites present.

The design of building foundations, and of all other foundations, consists in three essential operations: (1) calculating the loads to be transmitted by the foundation structure to the strata supporting it, (2) determining exactly the nature of the foundation beds that are to act as a support, and (3) designing a foundation structure to fit the conditions ascertained as the result of operations 1 and 2. Building loads may be affected in a general way by the local geology; but as a rule, for any particular region, they will be related only to structural design. Design of the foundation, however, is completely dependent on the nature of the ground underlying the building site. The determination of ground conditions is essentially a geological problem. When the foundation-bed conditions are known, selection of the type of foundation to be used is a matter of engineering judgment. In the actual preparation of design features, due account must be taken of all geological details liable to affect both the construction and the successful performance of the foundation. Soil mechanics studies make a major contribution to design work of this kind, but even the accurate design made possible in this way may be invalidated if a full study of the geology of the underlying strata has not also been made.

This broad outline provides the necessary background, so that consideration may now be given to leading aspects of the application of geology to building-foundation work. The fact must be emphasized that geological conditions alone are to be discussed—a warning necessary in view of the incomplete picture of foundation engineering that the following pages display. Adequate determination of geological conditions at a building site is but one of the three essential components of complete foundation design, and its isolation from the other two parts and particularly from the final detailed correlation of loading and ground conditions necessarily distorts its significance in foundation work. Foundation failures, however, are rarely due to faulty structural design; it is safe to say that, in general, they are related in some way to failure of the foundation beds to carry the loads put upon them. It is, therefore, an extremely important part of foundation work that is here discussed and one that, either directly or indirectly, is associated with the design and construction of every civil engineering structure.

12.2. The Influence of Geological Conditions on Foundation Design. Ground conditions at a building site may be one of three general types:

1. Solid rock may exist either at ground surface or so close to the surface that the building may be founded directly upon it.

2. Bedrock may exist below ground surface but at a distance that may economically be reached by a practical form of foundation so that the building load can be transmitted to it.

3. The nearest rock stratum may be so far below the surface that the structure will have to be founded upon the unconsolidated material overlying the rock.

The influence of geology is evidenced directly by this broad classification, since the three types of ground condition are the result of geological processes of the past. The city of New York typifies the first general type, in certain parts; some of the buildings of Manhattan are founded directly on the Manhattan schist which used to outcrop over part of that famous island. Much of the area covered by the city of Montreal, Canada, is of the second type; in this city Paleozoic bedrock is overlain by unconsolidated materials of the Pleistocene and Recent periods which vary in thickness, but which in some places reach more than 100 ft. The city of London may be taken as an example of the third type; the great London Basin with its deposits of London clay, sands, and gravel overlies the chalk, rendering impracticable the foundation of buildings on rock. It would be of interest to study the influence that ground conditions of these broad types have had on architecture, but engineers will readily appreciate the significance of the groups without the aid of this comparison.

Determination of a ground condition of the first type will be a relatively simple matter, even though it is a rare one in urban areas (possibly because cities are usually founded on riverbanks where unconsolidated deposits are the rule rather than the exception). The only additional services of geology will be in connection with the estimation of the soundness of the rock, with a determination of the significance of any structural features revealed, and possibly with a determination of the allowance to be made for seismic disturbances. Rarely will there be a question of whether the bearing power of rock is sufficient to withstand building loads; but if compression tests of the rock are made, great care should be taken to see that they are made with specimens loaded in a direction corresponding to that at the site. The difference in the bearing power of sedimentary rocks when tested parallel to the stratification and at right angles to it may be as much as 50 per cent. As sedimentary rocks include those rock types which have low bearing capacities, this point is sometimes of importance. Typical figures for slate are: 7,220 psi at right angles to bedding and 5,180 psi in the direction of bedding. These are average figures obtained in connection with the foundation of the Boston Parcel Post Building in the United States.[12.1] Values for the usual bearing stress utilized for various rock types will be found in engineering handbooks and treatises on foundation design; independent tests for all but the smallest projects are usually advisable. Provided that no serious structural defects exist in bedrock, this first general type of ground condition provides the most satisfactory of all foundation beds.

12.3. Foundations Carried to Bedrock. Where rock does not outcrop at the surface in the vicinity of a building site, underground exploratory work will be essential. If this discloses the existence of bedrock within a reasonable depth below the surface, thus suggesting the possibility of the second general type of ground condition, test boring and drilling should be carried out as extensively as possible all over the site in order to determine accurately the contours of this rock surface. Simultaneously, ground-water observations should be made. The word reasonable, although frequently so objectionable, is here used to cover the many variable local conditions that may affect the depth to which it proves economical to carry foundations to rock. The maximum depth so far utilized appears to be 250 ft; this was for the foundations of the Cleveland Union Terminal Tower, Cleveland, Ohio.[12.2]

A variety of engineering methods are available for transferring the building load down through the overburden to the bedrock. Choice of the method will depend upon a study of the economics and feasibility of the alternatives; such a study can be carried out with full satisfaction only against a background of complete information regarding subsurface conditions. If the depth is not too great and if the soil is free of boulders, the use of end bearing piles is a method frequently followed. If steel piles are to be used, the possibility of corrosion must be studied; methods are now available for checking this possibility in advance of construction. If concrete piles are to be used, the possibility of high sulfate content in the ground water must be investigated, so that any necessary precautionary measures may be taken. If cast-in-place concrete piles are to be used, the greatest care must be taken in studying the character of all soils to be penetrated to make sure that they are appropriate for the use of this type of foundation unit. Some cases of serious building settlement due to failure of this type of pile have occurred. If wooden piles are contemplated, similar care must be taken to study all possible variations in ground-water level; the reason for this will be evident when page 461 is reached.

For greater depths of overburden, for ground that contains boulders, and for carrying very heavy building loads, the use of some type of caisson or cylinder of concrete, either cased or uncased, will often provide an appropriate solution. For soft blue clay such as is found in the Chicago area, for example, a simple type of open caisson (the "Chicago well") has proved satisfactory for depths well over 100 ft. If ground water is present, air pressure may have to be used; some of the most difficult foundation jobs yet undertaken have had recourse to this type of foundation unit. In every case, however, accurate subsurface information is the first requirement.

Experience in the Detroit area shows how important it is also to know the full character of the underlying bedrock. Detroit is located in the glaciated area of North America; and the foundation-bed conditions there, although unusual, are not unique and may be found in other cities similarly located, e.g., Winnipeg, Canada. The bedrock is fissured limestone, overlain by clay strata of varying types with a layer of very hard glacial till ("boulder clay," or "hardpan") immediately above the rock. Depths to this impervious layer vary up to 120 ft. If it is not pierced, foundation design and construction is not unusual; shallow foundations may bear onto clay strata, and deep foundations onto the impervious layer through the medium of piles or concrete piers. If the glacial till is pierced at all, or if a crack is encountered in it, subartesian water may rise as high as 100 ft above the rock. During the construction of the Greater Penobscot Building, 565 ft high, having a total foundation load of 200 million lb, these conditions were encountered, and bell-mouth open concrete caissons which were to have been founded on the im. pervious layer had to have compressed air applied to them and be carried right to rock. The water has an unusually high sulfur content, which made it injurious to concrete. Efforts to counteract this additional trouble included grouting of the bedrock around the base area of concrete caissons before the impervious layer was pierced.[12.3]

Not only must the character of the bedrock be known with certainty, but the contours of its surface must also be known. In many areas, a relatively flat bedrock surface can be almost guaranteed, but even so, one or two test borings strategically located will always be a good insurance policy. If the uniform surface of the bedrock is in any doubt at all, then adequate test boring must be carried out to make sure that the nature of the rock surface is known over the whole of the building site. One glance at Fig. 12.1 should be enough to establish this point in the mind of the most skeptical of readers. This is a model illustrating, to scale, the foundation of a modern office building in the center of Oslo, Norway, on Fridtjof Nansen's Plass, close to the famous town hall of the lovely Norwegian capital city. One corner of the building is carried on concrete piers resting directly on rock; the other is supported on steel piles 50 m long, driven to rock through the soft sensitive clays that distinguish this part of Scandinavia (as they do the St. Lawrence Valley in Canada). In view of the almost phenomenal foundation conditions, the foundation shown has proved to be quite successful; maximum settlement (despite troubles during construction) has amounted to no more than $1\frac{1}{2}$ in.[12.4]

FIG. 12.1. Cutaway view of modern office building on Fridtjof Nansen's Plass, Oslo, Norway, showing variation in foundation-rock surface. (*Reproduced by permission of the Norwegian Geotechnical Institute.*)

In mining areas, special attention must be paid to the location of mine workings in relation to buildings that are to be located above them. The Pittsburgh area presents many examples of foundation difficulties due to the neglect of, or to the insufficient attention given to, this feature. On the other hand, it presents also some notable examples of successful solutions to problems of this sort. An outstanding example is provided by the foundations for the United States Veterans Administration General Medical Hospital, a 10-story building with two basements located over an abandoned coal mine 100 ft below the surface, no details of which were initially available apart only from the evidence given by some surface cavings. Subsurface exploration, not so much of the rock as of the voids from which ore had been abstracted, was conducted by means of 3-in. (NX) core borings, supplemented by three 30-in.-diameter calyx holes. Comparative estimates of the cost of the alternatives presented by the subsurface conditions led to the decision to grout up the old mine workings, since these were partially backfilled, after experimental grouting had demonstrated satisfactory results. All the old workings were therefore consolidated in this way at a cost of $524,151, and on this artificially "reconstructed" rock foundation this great building stands today, a landmark of greater Pittsburgh.[12.5] In Zanesville, Ohio, on the other hand, an 800,000-gal elevated steel water tank, that had to be constructed over old mine workings for which no adequate plans were available, was supported on one main central and 12 circumferential concrete columns, all carried about 50 ft below ground surface and so about 35 ft into rock, to a level below the mine workings. Of special note is the fact that the columns were reinforced only for their upper portions, where the supporting sandstone rock was relatively weak; the lower parts in hard shale were plain concrete.[12.6]

Economic studies will show in some cases that the best solution is to excavate all the overburden down to bedrock, utilizing the space thus excavated for building basements. In the construction of the electromagnetic plant of the Clinton Engineer Works in Clinton, Tennessee, toward the end of the Second World War, excavation to rock was carried out and two contrasting situations developed owing to a change in rock type on the two sides of the small valley in which the plant is located. On one side, the Conosauga shale was encountered; although seamy and weathered in its upper layers, it forms an admirable foundation bed below a depth of about 12 ft and was used for the plant foundations. On the other side of the valley, limestone of the Knox formation (to be mentioned several times in this volume as a particularly difficult rock with which to deal) was encountered. The surface was very broken; limestone pinnacles and large boulders made exact exploration of the surface difficult, and some of the flat-topped boulders at depths of up to 25 ft were particularly deceptive. Grouting was carried out, but eventually, owing to the emergency character of the work, a large concrete slab was placed over the entire rock area, and the buildings were founded on this.[12.7]

Finally, as an indication of what can be encountered in such an area as the island of Manhattan, Fig. 12.2 is reproduced; it shows a section through the foundation excavation for the Chase Manhattan Bank's head

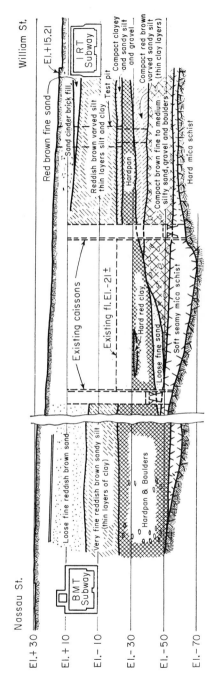

Fig. 12.2. Simplified cross section through the foundation of the Chase National Bank, lower Manhattan, New York City. (*Reproduced by permission of the American Society of Civil Engineers.*)

451

office building in downtown New York. Water-bearing silt and the presence of the boulders in the so-called "hardpan" made the final stages of excavation most difficult; the Joosten chemical solidification system was applied at the east end of the building site and at other trouble spots, and the excavation was completed satisfactorily without any loss of soil, which as can be seen from the section, could have had serious effects upon adjacent structures.[12.8]

It is of importance to note that if the surface of the bedrock slopes at an appreciable angle, special precautions may have to be taken in designing and constructing a foundation. This restriction is obviously important in the construction of buildings founded directly on rock. Such a restriction is also of some significance in buildings constructed on the third type of ground condition where solid rock is within a moderate distance of the ground surface although it is not actually used as the foundation bed. The action of gravity naturally affects all loose material lying above a solid-rock surface; and if the latter is lubricated (by ground water, for example), the whole mass may slip down the slope of the rock. This was the explanation generally recognized by engineers familiar with the serious movement of the Cahuenga Pass multiple-arch retaining wall constructed in Los Angeles in 1925. This wall is 450 ft long and its height varies up to 60 ft; the centers of buttresses are 30 ft apart. The wall was founded on bedrock at its ends but not in the central portion. Rock was here 40 ft below ground level; spread footings were therefore used and carried to a depth of 20 ft. Movement of this central section was observed before all the fill had been placed; it continued even after the loading on the wall had been reduced, and in July, 1927, amounted at one place to 17 in. outward and 15 in. downward. The load on the spread footings was limited to 8,000 psf, but the underlying rock sloped steeply away from the wall, so the conclusion was that soil strata and wall were moving down on the rock surface as a unit.[12.9] An allied problem is to have stratified bedrock available as a foundation stratum but dipping at such an angle to the horizontal that the stability of the upper layers is doubtful. In parts of New York City, the Manhattan schist is so inclined; it is a feature that is encountered elsewhere not infrequently. Local details will determine the best solution of the problems thus presented, but a usual method is to drill the surface rock and anchor it by dowels to layers that are so far below the surface as to be beyond the range of possible movement.

12.4. Foundations on Soil. The third general type of ground condition, where soil is used as the foundation bed, is probably the most common of all, particularly if due consideration is given to the vast number of small structures that could be founded on rock (by methods already described) but that need not be, because of their relatively small weight. Adequate subsurface investigation is again imperative if the foundation design is to be satisfactory. There was a time when it was generally thought that to carry test borings down as far as the length of bearing piles was enough; today, this limitation of test boring would often properly be regarded as tantamount to waste of the cost of what exploratory work was done. Even before the type of foundation to be used has been selected, accurate and extensive knowledge of subsurface conditions is essential. As a general rule, exploratory work should give definite results for a depth at least equal to twice the width of the structure and greater than this if possible, especially if the presence of relatively soft strata is suspected. The extra cost of a few feet more penetration of test borings, when once the boring equipment is set up, is negligible compared to the value of the results so obtained.

The vital necessity of obtaining subsurface information to such depths can be illustrated by a brief glance at one of the fundamental concepts of soil action. It may first be observed that foundation loads may be transmitted to unconsolidated strata in two general ways: (1) by constructing a continuous raft or spread footing which rests directly on the surface stratum, and (2) by forcing piles into the soil or by constructing piers therein, their tops structurally connected in a suitable way to the bearing columns of the structure. A variation of the first type is to have the load from a single structure distributed through a number of isolated footings. The second method may depend for its stability on the bearing of the ends of the piles or cylinders resting on a reasonably hard stratum, or the bearing may be the result of skin friction. Other minor variations might be listed, but these methods include generally all leading classes of foundation structure for unconsolidated strata.

How do these transmit the load from the building to the soil on which they rest? Some discussions would suggest that loads simply disappear into the ground in some mysterious manner. Figure 12.3 is a graphical illustration of the way in which they are actually dissipated by transfer of stress to steadily increasing volumes of soil as the distance from the foundation structure increases. The lines of equal pressure indicated in Fig. 12.3 are colloquially termed "bulbs of pressure," a convenient figure of speech, even though terminologically inexact. The proportional reductions of stress shown are typical values; exact figures for any set of assumptions made can be calculated for any given set of conditions; this is one of the great contributions of soil mechanics to foundation design. Simple though the diagram is, it is at the same time one of the most significant in the study of foundations; it shows at a glance the vital necessity of having accurate knowledge of subsurface conditions to a depth of at least twice the width of the structure to be supported.

When this precaution is not taken, and a building is erected without accurate subsurface information, trouble may develop if, for example, there is a buried stratum of weak soil beneath the site. There are on record all too many cases in which serious settlement has occurred from this cause. The following account is typical. A large building was carefully planned and designed; test borings were taken and the results carefully studied before construction began. Prior to its completion, this building was discovered to have moved out 4 in. and settled 4 in. at one place in its front wall. New borings were put down to a depth of 87 ft; the original borings had stopped at 42 and 31 ft, respectively. In the new tests, it was found that a stratum of "very soft black clay and fine

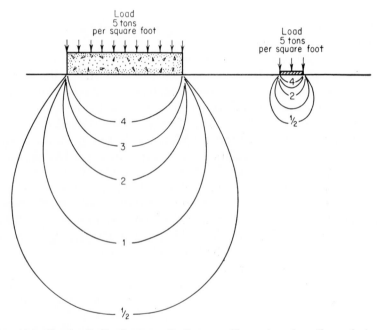

Fig. 12.3. Simple "bulb-of-pressure" diagrams illustrating the effect of the size of a foundation upon the stress distribution beneath it.

sand" existed at a depth of 55 ft below the surface; the upper strata were clay, with some sand of varying consistency. The front of the building was about 90 ft wide. The necessary underpinning and pile driving to correct the unsatisfactory condition thus discovered cost about $18,000—"probably four times what the cost would have been had the piles been driven before the wall was built."[12.10]

This aspect of foundation design on soil strata is so important that a further example will be cited, again not an exceptional case but one from ordinary practice having general significance. The Westinghouse Electric and Manufacturing Company Building in Philadelphia, Pennsylvania, was constructed on a building site, boring records for which were supplied by the previous owners. These showed 8 to 10 ft of loose fill and then uniform clay and sand to rock level, 45 ft below the surface. Bearing pile foundations were therefore decided upon for the 10-story building. The concrete pile contractors drove test rods to determine the length of piles, which was fixed at between 25 and 30 ft, a penetration shown by the test rods to be satisfactory. When 8 of the 10 stories had been constructed, the building was found to be settling noticeably. It had already sunk 4 in. on one side. New core borings and an open test caisson were therefore put down to rock, a mica schist which was found 57 ft down; the strata passed through were 27 ft of fill, 4 ft of peat, 1 ft of gravel, 15 ft of silted peat, 8 ft of silt, and 2 ft of coarse sand and gravel instead of

FIG. 12.4. The National Museum Building, Ottawa, Canada; the inset view shows the appearance of the entrance porch as originally constructed and before the tower had to be removed as a safety measure. (*Reproduced by permission of The Director, National Museum of Canada.*)

the fill, clay, and sand expected. The weakness that permitted the excessive settlement was at once obvious; an elaborate and ingenious underpinning operation had to be undertaken immediately, and the footings had to be supported on 15- and 16-in. pipe piles, concrete filled and carried to rock.[12.11]

Accurate knowledge of subsurface conditions at a building site naturally includes full information regarding the properties of the soils to be encountered. These are obtained by careful laboratory testing of good (undisturbed) soil samples. From basic soil properties and the application of theories of consolidation, it is now possible to calculate in advance of construction the probable total settlement of the building and also the rate of settlement. This is the settlement of the building to be expected because of the increase of stress in the soils supporting it; the fact that all buildings founded upon soil settle to some degree is now generally recognized. Correspondingly, safe bearing capacities for soil can be calculated, safe against excessive settlement and against over-stressing of the soil immediately under the foundations. These are matters in the province of the engineer; they are mentioned here in order to emphasize the absolute necessity of accurate subsurface information at building sites, a matter with which the geologist can frequently assist.

With the progress being made in the development and application of soil mechanics to foundation engineering, foundation failures should steadily decrease in number and magnitude. Study of failures of the past, carried out with constructive intent, can, however, be of real assistance to modern design. An extreme example of the difficulties caused by ignorance of soil behavior is provided by the National Museum Building in Ottawa, Canada, a massive red sandstone structure built in 1910 and now somewhat unusual in appearance since the elaborate upper part of the entrance-porch tower had to be removed shortly after the building was opened. Serious settlement was noted before the building was completed; before the tower was removed, the main porch had separated from the rest of the building by 14 in. at roof level. Modern study has shown that the supporting soil was just at the point of actual shear failure when the load was so fortunately reduced. The inside of the building even today exhibits, to those who know where to look, evidence of differential settlement that almost has to be seen to be believed; at least 12 in. of settlement is visible in one restricted area. Curious suggestions about the cause of the settlement were made at the time of the trouble; one eminent geologist stated that there must be a fault beneath the site. The real explanation is that the building was founded on over 100 ft of the sensitive marine clay already mentioned (see page 127), which was not strong enough to carry the heavy stress concentrations induced by this splendid example of Victorian "wedding-cake" architecture.[12.12]

The four main types of foundation structure for buildings on soil have been mentioned; the selection of the appropriate method is essentially a matter of economics and construction feasibility. Even here, however, geology can make a contribution. If, for example, it can be shown that the site is underlain by sensitive clay, such as that just mentioned, pile driving must be viewed with extreme caution, since in many of these clays, the vibrations set up by pile driving are enough to reduce their effective bearing capacity by partial "liquefaction." There is in the province of Quebec, Canada, a large church that had to be completely underpinned after having been founded on piles in complete disregard of the extremely sensitive clay on which it was founded; piles had proved satisfactory for supporting a church in a neighboring village which happened to have quite different subsurface conditions.

In many cases, particularly in very weak or sensitive soils, the floating or box type of foundation will provide the most satisfactory and economical solution to the foundation-design problem. Design of such foundations is an exacting task in civil engineering; its success depends upon adequate information on the supporting soils. There are many notable examples in North America. One of the largest is the head office building of the New England Mutual Life Insurance Company in Boston's Back Bay district; this building is 10 stories high and has a 290 ft tower. Ground conditions, from the surface down, were found to be 20 ft of man-made fill, 20 ft of alluvial silt, 10 ft of oxidized hard

Fig. 12.5. Floating "box" foundation being sunk into position, near Georgetown, British Guiana. (*Reproduced by permission of Soil Mechanics, Ltd., and Demarara Sugar Terminals, Ltd.*)

yellow clay (on which the building was founded), 70 ft of glacial clay, and finally 30 ft of compact sand and gravel above bedrock. Ground water is only 10 ft below the surface. The final design consisted essentially of a 40-ft-deep concrete box, the excavation for which just about balanced in weight the total building load of 130,000 tons, thus inducing no basic change of stress beneath the final foundation.[12.13]

A corresponding example from Great Britain is to be found at the Grangemouth Oil Refinery of Scottish Oils, Ltd., on the Firth of Forth. Here the subsurface conditions consist of a very soft (and weak) clay for a depth up to 30 ft underlain by a 9-ft layer of stony clay, below which gray silty (estuarine) clay extends more than 100 ft. Previous structures at the site had settled with a bearing pressure as low as ½ ton per sq ft, and a 110-ft chimney had settled 2 ft out of plumb. Even with cast-in-place bulb-ended concrete piles, the new structures also settled. For the latest structures, therefore, and after careful soil testing, a total load of 37,000 tons was carried on 15 separate cellular caissons, which were sunk to depths up to 24½ ft, forming, in effect, a set of floating foundations for the refinery. The largest of the caissons was 170 by 170 ft. They were made with thin reinforced-concrete walls, constructed in the first instance at ground level, resting on reinforced-concrete pads which were removed when sinking had to start. Soil within the cells was excavated by grab; a concrete plug sealed the bottom of each cell when the correct depth to give the required buoyancy was reached.[12-14] Looking at the new refinery today, with its complex equipment and highly instrumented operations, one finds it hard to credit that all the structures are supported on such weak soil, so successful has this foundation design proved to be, based as it was on a very thorough survey of subsurface conditions.

Japanese engineers have used a not dissimilar method, which depends to an unusual degree upon complete and accurate knowledge of subsurface conditions, for the construction of 18 buildings in the Tokyo district. When the subsurface conditions are known with certainty, and are suitable, a cutting edge is built on the surface of the ground and upon this the basement of the building is constructed as a "superstructure" above ground. When the resulting structure has the requisite weight, sinking is started by excavating beneath it; control is exercised by the progress of excavation under the cutting edge, and sinking is induced by the weight of the structure. Construction procedure for this daring method is naturally an engineering matter of unusual interest, but it will be appreciated that its success depends entirely upon exact knowledge of subsurface conditions. Boulder-free soils are obviously desirable; the most appropriate conditions are those given by alluvial or lake deposits of uniform soft or medium clay. The largest building yet to be constructed in this way is the Nikkatsu International Building in Tokyo, which has a four-story basement, nine stories above ground, and a three-story penthouse; it measures 325 by 220 ft along the streets at right angles on which it faces, and occupies a full triangular city block. Six borings and five wells were sunk to depths of 150 ft in determining subsurface conditions. Beneath the subsoil, a blue-gray clay extends for 50 ft, underlain by gravel and sand beds. Ground water was encountered at a depth of 40 ft, but not in any quantity until a gravel bed was reached. These are almost ideal conditions for the sinking method. Three basement floors were built above the ground before sinking started; the caisson then weighed 25,000 tons. The record of the successful and speedy completion of this $5 million project is an outstanding example of fine engineering based upon adequate preliminary geological information.[12.15]

For some buildings, deep basements are not required, and yet potential settlement of weak soil may have to be faced if a site must be used at which the only material available to an economical depth consists of

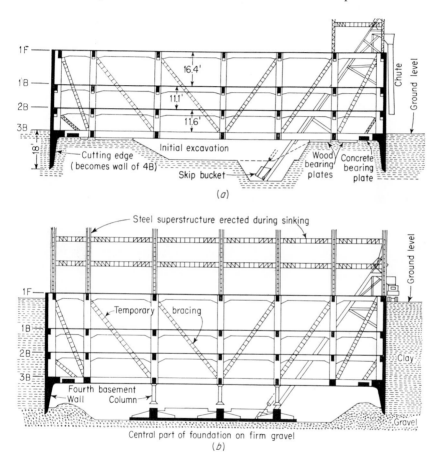

Fig. 12.6. Sections through the "foundation caisson" for the Nikkatsu International Building, Tokyo, Japan, showing the way in which this was transformed into the permanent foundation structure. (*Reproduced by permission of the American Society of Civil Engineers.*)

unconsolidated soils of low strength. Here again adequate preliminary information and full knowledge of the geological history of the soil can assist with the necessary engineering solution. If laboratory tests upon good soil samples show consistent values for the consolidation characteristics of the soil, it is possible to calculate how to induce a degree of consolidation of the soil in place by preloading it with a load that can be removed when necessary settlement has taken place. If the permanent structure can then be constructed, excessive settlements can be eliminated; the actual amount of settlement will be controllable to a reasonable degree of accuracy. The method is an old one, frequently practiced in the past (on the basis of "horse sense") for approach fills to bridges and similar earthworks. The application of the techniques of soil mechanics, coupled with accurate subsurface exploration in advance of construction, has converted this very practical approach into a refined and predictable procedure. Again, the details of its application lie in the

Fig. 12.7. Preconsolidating the site of the Cathedral of Mary, Our Queen, Baltimore, Maryland, U.S.A., by overloading with soil. (*Reproduced by permission of the Turner Construction Company.*)

field of engineering; again, the success of its application depends upon accurate subsurface information. Of the many examples now available from modern practice, there may be mentioned the construction of the Cathedral of Mary, Our Queen, in Baltimore, a monumental structure 375 ft long and up to 94 ft wide, with two stone towers 133 ft high. Here preloading in the form of a pile of earth 30 ft high, spread over an area of 120 by 70 ft, was carefully designed to obviate the differential settlement that would have resulted in the underlying soil formed of weathered micaceous rock from the extra load imposed by the two towers.[12.16]

12.5. Influence of Ground Water on Foundation Design. Ground water has already been mentioned several times in this discussion of foundations; its significance is even greater than these references might suggest. Although its importance is most evident when structures are founded on unconsolidated material, ground water is frequently a vital factor when foundations have to be taken through soil strata to rock. As indicated in the discussion of foundation methods for this latter type of ground condition, if ground water is present, the use of piers excavated in the

Fig. 12.8. Upper sections of timber piles under the Public Library Building, Boston, Massachusetts, U.S.A., showing deterioration attributed to varying ground-water levels. (*Reproduced by permission of the Boston Public Library.*)

dry to rock is automatically eliminated. In certain very stable kinds of soil, open dredging of small piers may be possible (as is sometimes the case in bridgework), but frequently the presence of ground water means that a more elaborate construction method must be adopted—usually a compressed-air plant, but including also such special methods as well points and freezing. The possibilities that ground water thus presents in the selection of a suitable kind of foundation design will make very evident the necessity of obtaining accurate preliminary information on ground water.

More than this, however, is involved in ground-water conditions. A large percentage of building foundations, more particularly those of the past, utilized timber bearing piles as an essential supporting element. It is well known that most kinds of timber have a long and useful life if kept either always wet or always dry (alternate wetting and drying is the exposure condition liable to cause rotting). Many timber bearing piles have been driven into ground in which the water table was near the tops of the piles. If, therefore, this water table varies in elevation, the timber piles will be alternately wet and dry and consequently may deteriorate. How frequently this condition occurs is only now being realized as older buildings are gradually being renovated and their foundations investigated.

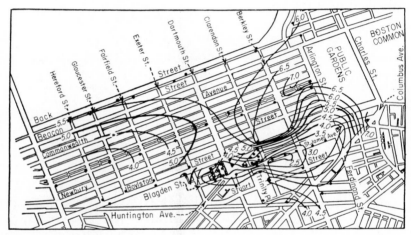

Fig. 12.9. Typical ground-water contour map for part of Boston, Massachusetts, U.S.A., showing relationship between area of low ground water and low-level sewer in St. James Avenue, as prepared from the ground-water survey described in the text. (*Reproduced by permission of The Editor, Engineering News-Record.*)

An interesting and historic example is that of the great tower of Strasbourg Cathedral, designed in 1439; its stone footings were originally supported on timber piles. The installation of a new drainage system in 1750 lowered the water table appreciably and in time caused the tops of the piles to decay. Serious settlement of the tower resulted. Some years ago, the tower was jacked up after its columns had been encased in concrete and new reinforced-concrete foundations installed.[12.17] Several other European buildings of historic interest have been similarly affected; but as a second example, there may be mentioned a famous building of the New World, the Boston (Massachusetts) Public Library. About the year 1929, cracks were noticed in the building; and after investigation by the city authorities and their consulting engineers, it was found that the tops of many of the timber piles supporting the structure had decayed, some having rotted completely. About 40 per cent of the building had to be underpinned; affected pile heads were cut off and replaced with concrete. The foundation strata in this part of Boston consist of boulder clay, blue clay, and silty sands overlying bedrock; pile foundations are therefore usual in this city area. The trustees of Trinity Church, which is adjacent to the library building, were alarmed at the possibility of similar trouble and had an investigation made in their behalf by X. Henry Goodenough, Inc., consulting engineers of their city. Their detection of the cause of low ground water in this vicinity is an interesting example of ground-water exploration carried out at relatively low cost; they finally revealed, in association with city authorities, that ground water was leaking away into a low-level sewer constructed about 1912 through the area being investigated. The sewer was partially blocked off by a suitable dam, and ground-water levels in the area rose to some extent. The test dam was therefore left as a permanent feature. Figure 12.9 shows ground-water contours before the leakage was checked; as a telling piece of evidence showing the possible danger of ground-water leakage in pervious soil strata, it would be hard to equal.[12.18] Although the construction of the dam in the sewer was to some extent effective, further remedial measures were taken in 1955. At the northeast corner of Copley Square, perforated metal pipes designed to serve as rechargers of the ground water in the affected area were connected to the sewer to take water from the flow through the sewer which is high even under dry-weather conditions. It is also thought that the Boyleston Street Tunnel of the Boston subway had an influence upon this ground-water situation, which is under continued careful observation.[12.19]

The problem of falling ground-water levels is not peculiar to Boston; it is, indeed, one of the most widespread effects of civil engineering works. In San Francisco, a 14-story building near Sansome and Bush Streets had to have its entire load transferred from 1,100 wooden piles to 210 concrete piers as early as 1930 for exactly the same reason.[12.20] In Milwaukee, Wisconsin, as in all too many cities, the same problem has, unfortunately, had to be faced. How can such foundation troubles be prevented and remedied? One method, followed in some building regulations, is to make sure that all piles are either cut off or embedded in concrete at a level well below the minimum elevation possible for the local ground water. An alternative method is to use "composite" piles in areas of fluctuating ground-water level, i.e., to use protected sections for the range of water-level variation and timber below this. Another practice was followed in connection with the foundation of the North-western Mutual Life Insurance Building in Milwaukee, Wisconsin. Foundation beds consist generally of glacial strata, with bedrock 250 ft below ground surface; the water table at the time of construction (1930) was 17 ft below the surface. Timber bearing piles were used, and lengths of 4-in. pipe were built into the foundation slabs, fitted with screw caps and strainer bottoms. Readings of the water levels in these observation pipes have been taken every three or four months since the building was completed. It has proved necessary to add water to about one-fifth of the pipes in order to maintain the ground-water level at the required elevation, but this has been done without difficulty and the foundations have performed satisfactorily. Naturally, a complete record of the levels of the ground water observed in the pipes is continuously maintained.[12.21]

Not only timber-pile foundations are affected by lowering of the local water table. The bearing power of soils, particularly of clays, may be appreciably changed by an alteration in their moisture content. Allied troubles include the shrinkage of clays as they dry out and the possibility that the finer particles will be washed out of waterlogged sand as ground water recedes or is drawn from it. All these conditions have been responsible for notable foundation troubles. To take another Old World cathedral as an example, the troubles experienced in connection with the foundations of St. Paul's, London, are related to local ground-water conditions, apparently having begun with the start of excavation for a deep sewer close to the cathedral site by the Corporation of the City of London in 1831. "Hundreds of tons" of quicksand or silt were removed by steam pumps set to work at a construction shaft; but after protests by many eminent engineers and architects (including Thomas Telford and John Rennie), the work was abandoned, and the shaft was filled up; damage, however, had already been done. Following careful investigations, all foundation work in the neighborhood of the cathedral is now subject to severe restrictions.[12.22]

Ground water may cause troubles with building foundations in a manner exactly the reverse of that already described, i.e., by being at such a level that a building foundation will tend to "float," to move upward instead of downward, as is usually the case. In the construction of the new General Care Building of New York's Harlem Hospital (mentioned on page 133 in connection with the unusually high temperature of the large volumes of water encountered in the excavation), the volume of water handled by the well-point system installed by the general contractor was so great that the system was kept in operation until 12 stories of structural steel and the first 3 concrete floors were in place; this was done in order to give sufficient dead weight to counteract the calculated hydrostatic pressure. Despite the intensive study given to this water, no agreement about its origin was reached among the experts consulted.[12.23]

When similiar circumstances are encountered with structures that do not have sufficient intrinsic weight to offset anticipated hydrostatic pressure, other measures have to be taken. When the sewage-treatment tanks of the Ley Creek plant at Syracuse, New York, have to be emptied for maintenance or repair (about once every 3 months), the super-intendent must first set in operation a permanent well-point installation that lowers the ground-water level around the tanks to a sufficient depth to avoid floating the empty tanks. Soil conditions in this area include a thick stratum of what is locally known as "black sand," a medium to medium-coarse sand high in calcium and iron salts, underlying a loam and clay blanket at the surface.[12.24] On a much larger scale, the Shawnee Steam Plant of the TVA, on the Ohio River downstream from Paducah, Kentucky, is surrounded by 84 relief wells, all connected by a large header pipe so arranged that a pumping installation can be set in motion in 7 wells should flood levels be reached by the river water. The great plant is founded on a permeable bed of sand and gravel overlain by an impervious stratum of loess. Experience with the use of relief wells on Mississippi levee works was applied in the design of the Shawnee installation.[12.25]

More unusual was the problem faced during the construction by the New York City Housing Authority of five 14-story apartment houses adjacent to the boardwalk at Coney Island. Figure 12.10 shows the local soil conditions, and the proximity of two of the adjacent buildings which could naturally not be disturbed during construction of the new blocks. Careful laboratory study of samples of the organic silt from both beds showed that this material had been overconsolidated in the past by an overriding sand dune, approximately ¼ ton in excess of existing over-burden conditions. This showed that the foundations of the large apartment blocks would have to be so located as to give some degree of buoyancy, in order to reduce the additional pressure they would exert on these silt beds, deep below the surface though they are, and this meant excavation below the level of existing ground water; this, in turn, meant unusually careful control of ground-water lowering opera-tions to ensure the safety of the existing adjacent buildings. Following detailed pumping tests, and only after the installation of a large number of observation wells through which the changes in ground-water level could be continuously observed, the job was completed successfully by a judicious combination of a well-point system pumping water *out* of the excavation for the apartment blocks and a diffusion system, operating simultaneously, pumping water back *into* the ground in the vicinity of the existing buildings. The full system was in operation between the months of June and September, during which period the foundations for all five apartment blocks were completed. When the system was closed down, careful checks showed no evidence of any settlement of the existing structures or of any damage because of the manipulation of the ground-water conditions in the area.[12.26]

It is believed that this was the first installation of such a diffusion or recharging system in association with a well-point installation; condi-

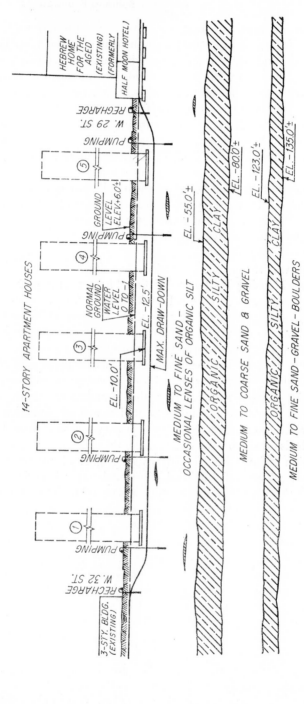

Fig. 12.10. Section showing the location of building foundations at Coney Island, New York, in relation to ground-water conditions. (*Reproduced by permission of the American Society of Civil Engineers.*)

tions were unusual, but the success of the project depended upon the most complete study of subsurface conditions made as a preliminary to planning and design. In great contrast are the problems met almost every day in areas where the local subsoil is a shrinkable clay, as is so frequently the case. Here, even small houses may be affected by the drying out of the clay. An unusually dry period or even the action of tree roots may cause a serious ground-water depletion. The waving profiles of some of the beautifully tree-lined streets of the city of Ottawa, Canada, are graphic examples of the influence of trees on ground settle-

Fig. 12.11. The sidewalk of Metcalfe Street, Ottawa, Canada, showing the effect of tree roots in causing differential soil movement. (*Photograph by M. Bozozuk, D.B.R., N.R.C., Ottawa.*)

ment; on these same streets there are examples of house-foundation settlements (due to desiccation of the underlying Leda clay by the roots of trees) that are classical to students of foundations, although serious indeed to the respective householders.[12.27] Trees are such beautiful features of any landscape that it is unfortunate that foundation engineers, and so geologists, have to take this jaundiced view of their presence near structures, but it has been clearly shown that in areas underlain by shrinkable clays, trees should preferably be kept as far away from the nearest structure as the height to which they are likely to grow.

Just as the shrinkage of clay can cause foundation troubles, so may its swelling when its moisture content is increased. An interesting case of this has been reported by Giesecke. The foundations of the University Baptist Church in Austin, Texas, were built as concrete walls carried to rock, thus surrounding a 6-ft layer of clay (decomposed shale) under the building proper. Owing to an increase of its moisture content, the clay expanded vertically by as much as 4 in., lifting the church building by breaking concrete footing slabs; the expansive force of the clay overcame the tensile strength of the concrete footing wall.[12.28] Unfortunately, this is not an isolated case. Much of the prairie part of Canada is underlain by expanding clays that give much trouble with foundations; it has been said that there is not a single concrete basement floor in the city of Winnipeg that has not been cracked by the expanding clay beneath. In South Africa, and indeed in many other parts of the world, the same problem is experienced to a varying degree.

Attention to the possible action of ground water, whether absent or present in foundation strata, is thus an absolutely vital part of subsurface exploration work for building foundations. The necessary studies can most usefully be made in association with test drilling. If the information then obtained is not sufficient, observation wells can be installed simply and at low cost. (Those used in the Boston studies already mentioned cost only $45 each.) Any such study will tend to confirm the necessity of strict control of ground-water resources, the depletion of which is of great importance in connection not only with public health but also, as will now be seen, with the stability of many building structures.

12.6. Settlement of Buildings. The foundation troubles to which reference has so far been made have been generally in the nature of excessive settlement. Structures that are supported on bedrock, directly or through piles or piers, will settle by extremely small amounts only, provided that the rock-foundation strata are sound. The displacement of such structures will generally be of negligible importance. If a foundation has to be supported by unconsolidated strata, appreciable settlement is always to be expected unless a buoyant design is adopted. Modern practice takes this settlement into account; foundation structures are now usually so designed that uniform settlement may be obtained throughout the building in order to obviate serious structural distortion.

The extent and kind of foundation subsidence will clearly be dependent on the nature of the soil strata. When these have been thoroughly explored and tested, it may be found that major settlement is unavoidable with the loads to be carried unless special measures can be taken. With buildings this may not be very serious, but with bridges and similar structures it may; jacking devices are therefore sometimes incorporated into foundation designs subject to this disadvantage. Geological study may suggest other occasions when the incorporation of provision for jacking in an original design may be a useful and economical safeguard. An interesting example is afforded in the special form of support and foundations for four circular reinforced-concrete water tanks, each 36 ft in diameter with its top about 32 ft above ground level, designed by H. C. Ritchie for the Urban District Council of Heanor, Derbyshire, England. The tanks were built in 1937 to replace a reservoir that had failed because of subsidence of supporting ground, which had colliery workings beneath. The same site had to be used; and although the foundations could be carried to a stratum of hard shale, future subsidence of the substrata had to be anticipated. Each tank is therefore carried on

Fig. 12.12. Reinforced-concrete water-storage tanks at Heanor, Derbyshire, England, showing unusual three-point foundation arrangement. (*Reproduced by permission of Ritchie and Partners, Consulting Engineers.*)

three points of support (instead of the usual four or more) in order to obviate indeterminate stresses at any stage of irregular settlement. The feet are not structurally continuous with the supporting foundations but rest freely on them, and the load is transmitted through special steel bearing plates and shoes which will permit the jacking up of the structure at each individual support so that the tanks may be raised and releveled as subsidence takes place.[12.29]

An alternative method has been adopted by the Nottingham County Council in England for the design of new school buildings that are known to be located over coal mines and so liable to damage from ground subsidence. Modern in design, the school buildings have light structural-steel frameworks. These were constructed on flexible concrete-slab foundations, reinforced to take up variations that might develop in ground level, and an adjustable joint connection was incorporated in the cross bracing adjacent to column bases; thus the design was given sufficient flexibility to take care of all "normal" settlements due to mining

Fig. 12.13. Structural-steel framework developed for school buildings in Nottinghamshire, England, with detail of special adjustable joint to allow for differential settlements. (*Reproduced by permission of the County Architect of Nottinghamshire.*)

subsidence. Details of the steel design are shown in Fig. 12.13. The design has been widely adopted in other areas where settlement due to mining subsidence is a problem.[12.30]

The records of engineering contain all too many accounts of major building settlements attributable to neglect of subsurface conditions prior to design and construction. Subsequent subsurface exploration has enabled civil engineers to force some undamaged tilted buildings back into place. Interesting though these examples are, they have really only a sort of pathological interest in this context, since the tilting should never have happened in the first place. Brief reference may, however, be made to two cases, the first probably the most famous of all such examples in the history of civil engineering.

FIG. 12.14. An unusual photograph of the failure of the Transcona grain elevator, Winnipeg, Manitoba, showing the upheaval of clay caused by the soil shear failure. (*Reproduced by permission of the Foundation Co. of Canada, Ltd.*)

Construction of a large grain elevator at Transcona, Manitoba, was started in 1911 adjacent to one of the world's largest railway yards, just outside Winnipeg, to facilitate the rapid handling of grain from the Canadian prairies. The drying house was 60 ft high and measured 18 by 30 ft; the adjoining workhouse was 180 ft high and 70 by 96 ft; and the bin structure was 102 ft high, and 77 by 195 ft. The 65 circular bins, arranged in five rows, were capable of storing 1 million bu of grain. A reinforced-concrete raft foundation 2 ft thick supported the bin structure, which weighed 20,000 tons when empty. Storage of grain started in September, 1913. On October 18, when 875,000 bu were in the bins, a vertical settlement of 1 ft occurred within an hour after movement was first detected. The structure began to tilt to the west and within 24 hr was resting at an angle of 26°53′ to the vertical; its west side was 24 ft below its original position, and the east side had risen 5 ft. Fortunately, because of the monolithic nature of the structure and its sound construction, no serious damage was done to the bins apart from their displacement. Accordingly, and through an outstanding underpinning operation, the bins were forced back into a vertical position, supported on concrete piers carried to rock, and the entire elevator rehabilitated. It has been in steady use ever since and can be seen today by travelers to Winnipeg on the Canadian Pacific Railway. The site is underlain by Ordovician limestone upon which rest deposits of glacial till, sand, and gravel. Then come 40 ft of glacial lake clays in two distinct layers of equal thickness, clays deposited in glacial Lake Aggasiz, to which reference was made in Chap. 4. Ten ft of recent alluvial deposits and outwash complete the subsurface profile. How much was known of the subsurface conditions when the elevator was constructed is not now clear, but recent investigations of the failure, using the techniques of soil mechanics, leave no doubt that the failure was caused by overloading the glacial clay. Ultimate bearing capacity determined on the basis of laboratory tests on samples was found to be 6,420 psf, as compared with a calculated bearing pressure at failure of 6,200 psf, a reasonably close agreement that confirms the value of studies in soil mechanics for foundation design when associated with accurate knowledge of subsurface geological conditions.[12.31]

Admittedly, the failure of the Transcona Elevator is (fortunately) an extreme case. Closer to the normal practice of civil engineering was the slight tilting of a reinforced-concrete water tower at Skegness in England. The 110-ft tower was founded on a reinforced-concrete mat; it tilted 2 ft out of plumb when first filled with water. Test boring revealed that the subsoil consisted of about 30 ft of water-bearing sand with some interbedded peat, naturally irregular, all underlain by glacial till which, if it had been investigated before construction commenced, could have been used as the foundation bed without difficulty. As it was, the tower base had to be surrounded with steel sheet piling, driven to varying depths, deep on the "low" side and shallow on the "high" side. Open large-diameter boreholes were then drilled on the high side with their bottom elevation well below the bottom level of the steel piling. This side of the tower base was then loaded still further with sandbags, until the excess pressure started to force some of the subsoil from beneath the footing up into the holes. Control of settlement was effected by removing varying quantities of the extruded soil from the open boreholes. In a period of 6 weeks, the tower had righted itself; when the tower was level, the steel piling was all driven down to the glacial till, thus enclosing the remaining subsoil beneath the tower which, under this constraint, gave all the bearing capacity required.[12.32]

All records of building subsidence are reminders of the fact that the earth's crust is not the solid immovable mass so popularly imagined. When solid rock outcrops at the surface, it provides a foundation stratum of material that is as susceptible to stress and strain as any other solid matter. If unconsolidated material constitutes the surface layer, it provides a foundation bed even more liable to evidence movement under load—possibly long-time settlement in the case of some clays if loaded beyond a certain limit. Modern foundation design aims not at eliminating settlements—the impossible—but at so controlling them that the structure supported will exhibit no undesirable effects. Should there be any reader of these words to whom the idea that all buildings settle is strange, let him reflect on the quite typical fact that a part of the Tower of London—that symbol of stability—is now known to rise and fall as the tide in the river Thames ebbs and flows.[12.33]

Fig. 12.15. The Leaning Tower of Pisa.

12.7. Some Famous Examples. The Tower of London is the third old building to be mentioned in this summary treatment of building foundations. It may be helpful to mention briefly a few other famous examples, not in any recriminatory sense—for all the buildings in question were erected long before foundation engineering had even been recognized as an important aspect of construction—but to illustrate still further the vital dependence of even the most beautiful of buildings upon the geological conditions beneath the ground on which they stand. The Leaning Tower of Pisa naturally comes first to mind in this connection. Located in northwestern Italy, the famous tower was started in 1174 but not completed until 1350. It has continued to tilt since then; the present displacement is over 16 ft in its total height of 179 ft. Its foundation consists of a circular slab 64 ft in diameter, with a central hole 15 ft in diameter. Whether or not there are piles under the slab is still uncertain. Foundation strata consist of a bed of clayey sand 13 ft thick, underlain by 21 ft of sand resting on a bed of brackish clay which is of unknown thickness. Prewar investigations and laboratory tests suggested that the tilting is attributable to the clay layer 28 ft below the foundation slab. A careful study was conducted, and remedial work was begun. The masonry of the foundation slab and ring wall was strengthened with cement grout under low pressure, and, as a final measure, the sand stratum surrounding the foundation was consolidated by the use of a chemical method employing a single gel medium injected at a low viscosity. There is some doubt whether this treatment was really effective, since movement of the tower continues, as recorded in a special modern observation room in the tower about 30 ft above ground level; the movement now is at the rate of 0.04 in. per year. It is estimated that it will take 200 years, at this rate of movement, before the tower is in real danger. Many suggestions have been advanced for rectification of the trouble, so it is to be hoped that this estimate will not be put to actual test. Since the bearing pressure under the base has been estimated to be 8 tons per sq ft (on the strata noted above), the wonder is that the tower has not settled more than it has.[12.34]

Not very far from Pisa is the city of Florence of whose buildings many tales could be told. Let it merely be noted that when Arnolfo di Lapo was ready to construct the Cathedral Church of Santa Maria del Fiore, he had a number of deep wells dug at intervals all around the site so that any vapors arising from the interior of the earth might thus escape before building started; the cathedral was protected in this way from earthquakes which were causing much damage in Florence at that time, a period—it should be added—when earthquakes were thought to be caused by gaseous vapors escaping from the earth's interior.[12.35] In the East, also, there are beautiful buildings which might be referred to in this account. The Taj Mahal in Agra, India, is widely regarded as one of the most beautiful buildings ever to be erected. Fortunately, it is in no such state as the quite beautiful Tower of Pisa, but to the observant eye even the Taj Mahal betrays the fact that, despite its ethereal appearance in moonlight, it is not supported in any mysterious way but rests, as do all buildings, upon the ground. The north wall is not often seen by visitors; it abuts on the river Yamuna, and its foundations are therefore subject to varying water levels, especially in time of the monsoon floods. Cracks in the cellar immediately beneath the plinth terrace on the north side and in the eastern superstructure of the mausoleum can be attributed to trouble with the foundations of the north wall many years ago, troubles which were so satisfactorily dealt with at the time that no evidence of any recent movement has been observed. Examination of the foundations of the north wall some years ago revealed the condition shown in Fig. 12.16, a prosaic representation indeed of this lovely monument to a beloved wife, but one which, at least to readers of this volume, may add still further to appreciation of this masterpiece of Indian building and architecture.[12.36]

One of the most notable artistic buildings of the New World has

(a)

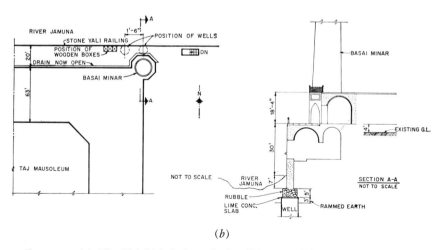

(b)

FIG. 12.16. (a) The Taj Mahal, Agra, India. (*Photograph by the Information Service of India; Courtesy of the Press Attaché Ottawa*). (b) Sketch of part of the foundation of this beautiful building.

achieved fame also because of its settlement; the Palace of Fine Arts in Mexico has already settled 10 ft, and its elevation is falling at the rate of 1.5 in. per year in relation to streets outside the influence of the building. The building was begun in 1904 and completed 30 years later. It consists essentially of a structural-steel frame with its exterior covered with Italian Carrara marble; interior partitions are brick. The building measures roughly 267 by 390 ft; its total weight of 57,500 tons is carried

FIG. 12.17. The Palace of Fine Arts, Mexico City. (Instead of the more usual detailed view of differential settlement, a general view of this monumental building is shown so that the settlements noted in the text may be better appreciated.) (*Reproduced by permission of The Director General, Mexican Institute of Fine Arts.*)

on a concrete-mat foundation, which weighs 46,000 tons. Subsoil conditions at the site of this building consist of about 165 ft of so-called "clay" with some interbedded layers of sand and sandy clay; the high moisture content of the main stratum is generally responsible for the remarkable settlement. The building was designed by an Italian-American architect on the basis of an architectural competition for the design that he won. Although the architect spurned engineering advice (a recorded saying of his was that "if the structure is pleasant to my eye it is structurally sound"), it has been stated that he did engage an engineering consultant to design the foundations, although no records appear to exist of the design assumptions. The architect was advised to tear down the beginnings of the building when serious settlements were discovered at the start of construction, but he refused to take this course, and the results are all too well known today.[12.37]

Even so famous a North American symbol as the Washington Monument in the heart of the capital city of the United States has had settlement troubles. This great masonry shaft, 555 ft 5 in. high above its foundation, weighing 81,120 tons, settled about 5¾ in. in the 50 years after its completion to full height in 1880. It is believed that further settlement is improbable provided that the ground around the monument is not disturbed; this has already interfered with plans for landscaping in the vicinity. Started in 1848 by public subscription, the monument had risen to a height of 150 ft by 1854 when funds ran out. In 1876, before Congress appropriated funds for completion of the shaft, a committee of engineers was appointed to study what had already been done. It was then found that the shaft was 1¾ in. out of plumb, and that the area and depth of the footing should be increased before the tower was completed. These recommendations were followed, and the incomplete shaft was brought back into plumb by an ingenious system of loading in connection with the underpinning, a job which was personally supervised by Gen. T. L. Casey. It is significant to note that, under General Casey's supervision, test borings were sunk, but only to a depth of 18 ft; thus they were still in the water-bearing sand and gravel stratum upon which the monument rests. The fact that these borings were not carried deeper is clear indication of the state of the art of foundation engineering at that time. When deeper borings were put down in 1931, a complex pattern of subsurface conditions was revealed; a layer of soft blue clay overlies bedrock which was reached about 90 ft below the present ground level at the foot of the monument. Since the thickness of the clay stratum varies considerably beneath the footing, the initial differential settlement is not surprising.[12.38] It is this same blue clay that underlies the Lincoln Memorial, not far away from the Washington Monument, and which caused such troubles with the construction of that most noble memorial. Much better soil conditions were fortunately found under Washington's most famous building, the White House, when it was reconstructed in 1951, but even here a layer of clay, 45 ft beneath the surface, gave cause for some concern in view of the loadings to which this soil would be subject from the reconstructed mansion. The techniques of soil mechanics were applied to the foundation design. In contrast with the sad record of other famous buildings noted, it is satisfying to record that actual settlements here agreed very closely with those calculated before reconstruction began, and were minimal.[12.39]

12.8. Precautions with Sloping Ground. There is still another geological problem with building foundations but one of a more specialized character than those already discussed. It is, therefore, much more local in incidence and can be mentioned here only briefly; but when it does arise it can be serious indeed. It is the possible instability of sloping ground when used for the foundations of buildings. Since large buildings necessarily need level areas for their siting, the sloping-ground problem usually affects residential construction. Sloping sites would not normally be chosen for building, but the mounting value of real estate in developed city areas has increased their use, especially where beautiful vistas further enhance the value of the land so used. Slope-instability problems, therefore, in relation to building foundations are found mainly in city areas,

FIG. 12.18. Slope failure on Madelaine Avenue, St. Johns, a suburb of St. Louis, Missouri, U.S.A. (*Photograph by A. B. Cleaves.*)

especially in those cities having hilly terrain. The west coast of North America immediately comes to mind, but other locations have had similar troubles.[12.40] In the area of greater St. Louis, Missouri, where the local loess is a soil most susceptible to water, many houses built too near the tops of slopes have shown evidence of damage after heavy rains or when drainage was interfered with. In the beautifully named suburban municipality of Bellefontaine Neighbors, for example, a slide in a steep slope into a borrow pit in 1957 damaged 10 houses on St. Cyr Drive; three of them were, unfortunately, a complete loss.[12.41]

It is in the Los Angeles area, however, that this type of trouble has been most widespread and serious. In 1952, when heavy rains occurred in Los Angeles following 7 very dry years, extensive damage was caused to many hillside properties; estimates of the value of the damaged property ran into millions of dollars. Many lawsuits resulted, since in areas of developed property, damage on one site may be effected by, or may itself affect, other adjacent properties. Before the following winter, the city of Los Angeles passed a grading ordinance, which amended the city building code and placed some 60 per cent of the city's area under special regulations. Rains in more recent years have caused further damage. Local studies have continued, and public interest has been aroused. In 1957, for example, a voluntary Geological Hazards Committee of the City of Los Angeles was formed by local geologists and engineers to assist civic authorities in dealing with this problem. Most dramatic and personally tragic are the losses of actual homes due to movements of soil and rock on slopes; such movements are usually due to the action of uncontrolled water. But masses of soil and rock are moved irrespective of houses, destroying useful land and causing all kinds of interference with normal municipal services.[12,42]

The causes of such trouble are exactly the same as those outlined in Chap. 11 and so need not be repeated; the problem of building foundations on sloping ground is only a special example of ground instability. Along the coast roads in the Los Angeles region, there is the added hazard of undercutting by the sea, but even here it is the effect of uncontrolled surface and ground water that causes most of the trouble. The application of geological principles to the problems encountered in constructing buildings on sloping sites is probably the most perfect example in engineering work of the old tag that "a stitch in time saves nine." For the expenditure of a very small sum, an examination of any site for a proposed small building can be made by a competent professional adviser. If good advice so received is followed, damage that might run into thousands of dollars can often be avoided. A few simple hand borings, examination of the local geology, study of ground-water conditions in the vicinity and of surface drainage arrangements, and above all, a close scrutiny of the records of local weather—such simple steps when followed by an expert can lead to sound advice on how a sloping site can be used or, alternatively, whether it should be avoided.

Once again it is necessary to stress the importance of local weather records and the convenience of studying them by means of hythergraphs; a typical hythergraph in this connection is reproduced as Fig. 12.19. In common with most people, engineers probably joke about the weather but they can give the lie to Mark Twain's witticism that "nobody does anything about it" by giving it consideration in all their environmental studies. Nowhere can it be of more significance than in considerations of the stability of steep slopes, especially in developed areas where building operations and street paving have interfered with natural runoff arrangements. In Portland, Oregon, intensive rain has caused small slides of soil and rock in some of the steeply graded streets of this northwestern American city. Figure 12.20 shows what some interested householders did about it; this use of plastic sheets for slope protection was quickly and naturally dubbed "using plastic raincoats." Reference to such an article of attire in a treatment of geology and engineering might appear to be incomprehensible out of context, but the very novelty of the reference may help readers to remember the vital importance of surface

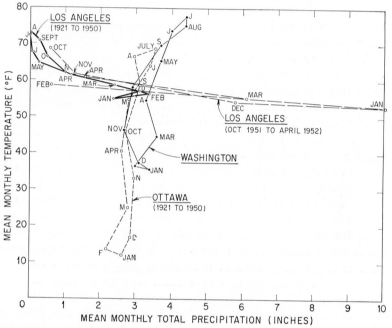

Fig. 12.19. A hythergraph, showing the average climates of Washington, D.C., Ottawa, Canada, and Los Angeles, California, U.S.A., with an additional record to illustrate the unusual rainfall at Los Angeles in the winter of 1952–1953.

protection against intensive rain when natural conditions have been disturbed and property has to be protected.

12.9. Preliminary and Exploratory Work. The investigation of subsurface conditions at all open building sites follows generally accepted methods; geological studies and test-boring operations are carried out as intensively as necessary. In urban areas, especially for buildings that are to be constructed on sites already occupied, the matter becomes a difficult one. Frequently it will be impossible to make test borings until existing buildings are demolished, before which time foundation designs have to be prepared at least in outline. In many cases, direct geological investigation will be impossible,

For preliminary work in cities, therefore, those minor exploratory aids mentioned in Chap. 6 assume a major importance. All old maps of the locality should be examined; they will often show the site of old watercourses, possibly now covered, and sometimes will suggest the existence of recently filled land at a building site. Foundation engineers of wide experience have testified to the value of the Viele map of New York in connection with foundation work in that city.[12.43] The map was prepared in 1860 when much of Manhattan Island was open land and shows old

Fig. 12.20. Sheets of plastic used by householders in Portland, Oregon, U.S.A. to protect the stability of the sloping ground on which their houses are founded; "plastic raincoats" put to engineering use in keeping unwanted water off critical slopes in order to prevent further slides such as the small one seen on the left. (*Photograph by World Wide Photos.*)

watercourses, swamps, and a pond. Naturally, the use of old maps and old descriptive documents is of greatest importance in Europe, owing to the greater age of Old World cities as compared with those of North America and other newly developed countries. Ground-water conditions can usefully be studied from available water-level and pumping records of local wells and boreholes. If records are not available, observation wells can easily be put down. The best of all information, however, apart from actual test holes at the site, is that afforded by the foundation records of adjacent buildings and the borehole records obtained for their construction. When reliable information of this kind can be procured, preliminary foundation designs can often be prepared, although it never obviates the necessity of confirmatory tests at the actual site when these can be made.

An interesting example of exploratory work at a building site is that carried out in connection with the foundations of the unusually large Battersea (steam) Power Station of the Central Electricity Board. This station is located on the south bank of the river Thames in London and now dominates the local skyline, having become a "London landmark." Preliminary study of available records of borings in the vicinity suggested that the London clay might be reached at a depth of 30 to 35 ft. Some local records indicated that the clay was at a much greater depth, and one showed that a well at the Nine Elms Brewery had failed to encounter the clay at all. From a study of these records and of a map prepared by the Geological Survey, it was anticipated that, with the London clay at about the depths indicated, considerable depressions in its surface might be encountered. This proved to be the case.

Figure 12.21 is a key plan of the site; the irregular spacing of the boreholes represents the efforts made to trace the depth and extent of the depressions in the clay. In all 73 test holes were bored, and 8 trial pits were sunk. These showed the alluvial gravels of the Thames flood plain overlying the London clay. Since water accumulated in the pits, it was decided to surround the entire building site with a retaining wall in order to exclude the water, and to found the station on the London clay. The Geological Survey was given full information from the test borings and was consulted about the results. The two main depressions detected from the borings were later confirmed as excavation proceeded and were found to be of the "pipe" type and not a continuous channel. They may have been caused by subsidence of the clay, following solution of the underlying chalk.[12.44] The cost of the necessary preliminary work is often a difficult matter to estimate in any undertaking, and building construction is no exception to this. It will be useful to point out, therefore, that this thorough investigation for the Battersea Power Station is that featured in the table on page 174 and which will there be seen to have cost only 0.2 per cent of the total cost of the station structure—a percentage that is not unusual but illustrates vividly the economy of adequate subsurface exploration.

As showing the difficulties that may result from inadequate subsurface information beneath a building site, there may be cited—not in any derogatory sense but with constructive intent, and in tribute to a fine engineering solution to an unusually complex problem—the foundations of one of the great buildings that now dominate the famous Raffles Quay in Singapore. The Asia Insurance Building is a steel-framed 18-story structure, founded on a site reclaimed from the beach during the last century. The beach formation beneath the site varies from 10 to 14 ft in thickness; it was thought to be underlain by fill and decomposed shale

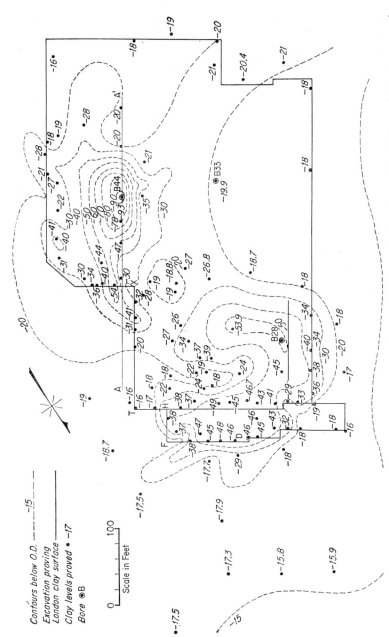

Fig. 12.21. Plan of the site of the Battersea Power Station, London, showing location of boreholes and the contours of the surface of the London clay. (*Reproduced from "Summary of Progress: Geological Survey of Great Britain," 1930, pt 2. Crown Copyright, reproduced by permission of the Controller of H. M. Stationery Office, London.*)

and sandstone. Four borings were sunk on the site in 1949 and came to refusal from 30 to 42 ft below the surface. A strong chisel was used to obtain chips from the sandstone encountered at the bottom of the holes, since there was no diamond-drilling equipment available in Singapore for penetrating deeply into the rock. A cylindrical type of foundation was then designed, with bearing intended for the hard layer encountered, and construction was started by a local contractor. It was soon found that the presumed bedrock was really boulders of weathered shale and sandstone of Triassic formation, common to Singapore. Granite boulders were also encountered, but these had originated in ballast deposited on the beach from ships using the port many years before. Lack of control over the cylinder sinking added to the difficulties by permitting soil boiling and consequent loss of ground in the area around. Work had to be stopped, therefore, and since proper drilling equipment was then available, further subsurface investigation was undertaken. Diamond-drilling operations did not readily distinguish between the hard clay that was encountered and the sandstone boulders, but clay was found to depths exceeding 100 ft, and samples were obtained. Cylinders already placed were therefore grouted up and then underpinned. This was a most critical construction operation but it was successfully completed; the bottoms of the new cylinders were belled out at appropriate depths to give the calculated bearing values determined safe for the clay on the basis of careful laboratory tests of the samples obtained during the diamond-drilling operations. The bearing pressure had to be reduced from the original value of 10 tons per sq ft to 3.5 tons per sq ft.[12.45]

Much of the interest of this job lies in the engineering methods followed in dealing with the revision of the foundation design, but as a "cautionary tale," the case is of great value. It vividly demonstrates the absolutely vital role that accurate subsurface information must play in the foundation design of buildings—large in this case, but size is not a determinant. Special note must be made of the fact that lack of proper test-drilling equipment in Singapore in the immediate postwar years was in part responsible for the trouble that developed. Similar neglect has been known, however, in other locations with no such limitations; only the fact that foundation-bed conditions have been so much better than those below Raffles Quay in Singapore has saved many another building from similar difficulties.

12.10. Urban Geology. In view of the fact that information on geological conditions in urban areas can be obtained only from a study of the test-boring and drilling records for numerous small building sites, it might naturally be supposed that there would be some generally recognized method of correlating these exploratory results. Unfortunately and surprisingly, this is not the case. There are all too few cities in the English-speaking world in which any cooperative venture in connection with subsurface information has been carried out. The situation in many cities is, indeed, almost the reverse of this. Private institutions of one sort and another regard information about foundation strata beneath buildings with which they are, or have been, associated as confidential and as their own particular property. This attitude is hard to understand. Were minerals of value involved, the situation would be different; but in the practice of foundation work, such secrecy appears to be singularly out of place. It persists, however, because, in general, legislation does not restrict it. Fortunately, there is another side to the picture. In a number of cities, engineers have cooperated with ready will and made available for public benefit accumulations of foundation information which are of unusual value in that they give composite pictures of foundation conditions for complete city areas. The following brief notes outline some typical examples.

New Orleans, Louisiana. Initiated in 1934 at the request of the Louisiana Engineering Society, a survey of foundation data was made as a project of the WPA of Louisiana. The results of the survey were published in a notable volume in 1937 ("Some Data in Regard to Foundations in New Orleans and Vicinity"). Through the cooperation of local engineers, architects, and officials, over 200 boring records and details of over 100 examples of foundation design in the New Orleans area were assembled. As the city is located near the mouth of the Mississippi River, the local geological formation is typically deltaic, consisting of sand and clay strata extending to depths greater than 350 ft. Several interesting features of these beds were noted: A layer of cypress tree stumps, whose trunks had been cut off, lies a few feet below the surface, and a second similar layer lies about 25 ft below mean Gulf level; a human skull was found in undisturbed clay at a depth of 37 ft below ground surface; and layers of oyster shells occur about 50 ft down.[12.46]

Winnipeg, Manitoba, Canada. At the instigation of the Winnipeg branch of the Engineering Institute of Canada, a Committee on Foundations in Winnipeg was set up in May, 1937. The function of the committee was to investigate and report on (1) why difficulties are experienced with foundations, (2) how best to repair faulty construction, (3) proper design for new foundations. In August, 1937, the committee submitted an interim report, discussing the formation of Winnipeg soils and subsoils, the foundation of new buildings, and the cause of settlement of existing buildings. Although described as an interim report, this document was unusually complete and is still used; it has remained the only such report, since the project did not advance further after its good start. More work is in prospect, however, and subsurface records obtained since this report was published may be made available. In general, limestone lies between 60 and 70 ft below ground level, and the intervening strata are a succession of clay and silt beds superimposed on a layer of glacial till, a common type of subsurface pattern for urban areas in the glaciated areas of central and eastern Canada and the north-eastern United States.[12.47]

Boston, Massachusetts. In the first published copy of the *Journal of the Boston Society of Civil Engineers* (1914) there appeared a paper by J. R. Worcester entitled "Boston Foundations" in which an assembly of boring records was featured. As a subsequent development of the interest aroused by this paper, the society set up a Committee on Boston Subsoils, the purposes of which were stated as follows: "The purpose of this Committee is to gather data regarding the character of the subsoils in Boston and adjacent areas, and to present it to the Society in such form as to add to the general knowledge and to make it available for reference by any who may wish to get a clear idea of the geological construction under this City."

This committee made an extensive report in 1931 and a second one in 1934. With the cooperation of those making borings in the city area, the committee has assembled over 9,000 records, locations of which are shown on 16 sectional maps. The borings are so well located that it has been possible to prepare six geological sections through the city at many points, to make maps of the rock and boulder-clay contours, and to locate old shore lines of Boston and Cambridge. The committee gave special consideration to the complex ground-water situation under the city area; it made tests of local soils and compiled a classification of these. The rock and boulder-clay maps were made by the geologist member of the committee who had started a study of the area as early as 1923.

This important work has continued through the years, still under the aegis of the Boston Society of Civil Engineers, latterly in association with the Emergency Planning and Research Bureau, Inc. Starting in 1949, the Society's Foundations Committee has published a series of papers giving in concise form and accompanied by key maps, full details of the boring logs they have available for various parts of the Boston area. The information is kept on file in the office of the society. This voluntary effort is an example that many other cities and local engineering societies might well emulate.[12.48]

New York City, New York. One of the most notable of all co-operative projects in the assembly of information on urban geology is that carried out by the city of New York and associated agencies; study of the geology of this great city was also one of the first such intensive geological surveys to be made. As early as 1902, the United States Geological Survey published the New York City Folio as No. 83 of its Atlas; this was followed in 1905 by the publication of Bulletin No. 270, "The Configuration of the Rock Floor of Greater New York," based on a study of over 1,400 borings. The Municipal Engineers of the City of New York have been active in this field since as early as 1915 and have published several notable papers in their journal. Planning the West Side Highway in 1933 provided a spur to further collection of boring records; these were assembled in the office of the borough president of Manhattan as the start of what has proved to be probably the most extensive collection of subsurface information available for any city. In the thirties a WPA project led to the preparation of "The Rock Map of Manhattan," enlarging still further the scope of earlier work. More than 17,000 borings were plotted on this map when it was first prepared; the number of records available has greatly increased in the years since then. A similar project was started at the same time for that part of New York outside the borough of Manhattan; for this "Mapping of Earth and Rock Borings" project, 27,000 boring records were used. Through the years, these fine record maps and compilations of subsurface information have been extended and improved. All records today are available for public consultation at the various borough offices. In view of the great concentration of building in New York, the variability of its bedrock surface, and the well-known difficulties that can arise even with the Manhattan schist as a foundation bed, it is particularly fortunate that New York has such a fine record of its urban geology.[12.49]

Ottawa, Canada. On a much smaller scale, and started only in recent years, the subsurface record for the capital city of Canada represents a similar degree of cooperation among many agencies; the records were collated, filed, and made available for public reference by a public agency. By agreement of the several groups concerned, the Geological Survey of Canada, with its headquarters in Ottawa, is the repository of the records; in association with the National Research Council of Canada, the Survey prepared the two maps upon which the information collected has been recorded. These maps, to a scale of 1 in. to 1,000 ft, show the drift-thickness contours, from which a clear picture of the bedrock surface beneath the city can be obtained.[12.50]

San Francisco, California. The United States Geological Survey has prepared, in a similar way, a bedrock map of the San Francisco area. Its scale is 1 in. to 2,000 ft. The ground surface is shown by contours at 25-ft intervals above an altitude of 25 ft, and at 5-ft intervals below that; bedrock contours are at 100- and 25-ft intervals, respectively. All who know San Francisco will appreciate how valuable such a map can be, not only because of the rugged character of the rock surface, which can be observed at the surface, but also because of the concentration of large buildings where the geology might be expected to be erratic. The published map confirms this inference; it shows, for example, that near the Ferry Building, at the foot of Market and Mission Streets, bedrock lies nearly 300 ft below the present surface, whereas it is exposed at the surface just a few blocks away to the northwest and southeast. The bedrock contours show clearly that this strange variation is due to an old buried river valley, a geological feature not uncommon but one that can play havoc with foundation designs if unsuspected and undetected. The local section of the American Society of Civil Engineers has also been active in assembling engineering information on subsoils, some of which has been summarized in a useful general paper.[12.51]

Prague, Czechoslovakia. The city of Prague is located in an area of complex geological conditions which have influenced the development of the city ever since the Middle Ages. The bedrock of the urban area consists of folded shales and quartzites of the Ordovician. The Paleozoic rocks are overlain by Cretaceous sandstones and marls, the nearly horizontal beds of which form the flat-topped hills at the outskirts of the city. The greatest part of the area is covered by Quaternary surface deposits—terrace gravels and loess sheets. Apart from this intricate geological structure, the activity of man has contributed to the complexity of local foundation conditions. Prague, having been inhabited continuously for at least 1,000 years, has had its surface conditions changed by excavations and man-made fills to such an extent that, in many cases, the original relief is difficult to ascertain.

The geological and foundation conditions of building sites have been investigated by various bodies; at present this work is mainly done by the Czechoslovakian Institute of Engineering Geology. The results of this research work are recorded in boring records and geological reports, maintained in the so-called Geofond kept by the Central Geological Institute in Prague. It is compulsory to deliver to the Geofond profiles of boreholes and duplicates of reports of all geological explorations carried out in the city area. The locations of borings are plotted on a 1:5,000 map and indicated by the numbers under which they are registered. These archives are available for the use of interested inquirers.

Since World War II a new map of foundation soils of the urban area to the scale 1:5,000 has been constructed under the sponsorship of the Board of Town Planning. It serves as the basis for new regulation plans and for the design of new districts. The map, which is gradually being extended, is also available to the interested public.

Former experience and records have been published in a series of papers dealing with the geological conditions of the Prague district. The inner city area was described in detail in a paper on the "Geological Features and Foundation Conditions of the City of Prague" (Czech with an English summary) by Q. Zaruba. A 1:12,500 map accompanies the paper. The work includes the results of researches and borings carried out for the design of the subway, hydrogeological conditions of the area, and a critical evaluation of earlier literature.

So the record can continue. In cities where no general cooperative effort has yet been started, there are often individual records, sometimes in the form of informative papers in the published records of engineering, that provide a first step toward the general picture of urban geology that is possible through cooperative effort. Correspondingly, there are occasional geological papers; these contributions provide good starting points for any concerted effort to assemble all available records. The Geological Survey of Canada, for example, published many years ago a paper on "The Pleistocene and Recent Deposits of the Island of Montreal" that has provided stimulus for a number of subsequent studies.[12.52] Bulletin No. 27 of the Minnesota Geological Survey deals with the "Geology of the Twin City Area" and was the foundation for subsequent studies of that area which includes the unusually interesting St. Peter sandstone that has been so intensively studied by the local office of the United States Corps of Engineers.[12.53] In New Zealand, the same pattern can be found; a paper presented to the Second Australasian Soil Mechanics Conference deals with foundation conditions in the city of Christchurch on the South Island; it was based upon a study of about 1,000 well logs and borings.[12.54]

It will be noticed that local engineering societies and local sections of national engineering societies have been prominently associated with these cooperative ventures. In the field of civil engineering, there seem to be few more useful tasks that such local groups of engineers can perform in association with local geologists—to their mutual benefit. The functions of the local engineering group are often in question. Here is an essentially local task requiring concerted action, which takes years to complete and which results in lasting benefit to the community. It is one that might usefully be adopted by many more engineering groups than appear yet to have entered this field; it would greatly benefit the profession by steadily removing uncertainty about subsurface conditions and would enrich scientific records. One of the happiest of all meeting grounds for civil engineers and geologists is in this joint study of what may be so truly called *urban geology*.

Suggestions for Further Reading

In view of the contributions that have been made from the study of soil mechanics to the proper design of building foundations, there is a growing volume of useful "case histories" in the literature of soil mechanics, to which the references cited in this chapter are but an introduction. Further reference may therefore be made to the guides to relevant literature at the end of Chaps. 1 and 4 (see pages 35 and 128). Local building regulations have not been mentioned in the chapter, but they will be found, in the case of some cities, to contain excellent sections on foundation design instead of the old "rules of thumb." In such cases, further investigation may bring to light local studies of foundation conditions that have not yet been recorded in the literature.

Chapter 13

THE FOUNDATIONS OF DAMS

Dams must stand. Not all of them do, and there are all degrees of uncertainty about them. Reservoirs must hold water. Not all of them do, and there are many ways by which water may be lost. The work must be done safely as a construction job. Not all of them are, and there are many sources of danger. The whole structure must be permanent and the work has a right to be done within the original estimates. Not all of them are, and there are many reasons for their failure or excess cost, most of them geologic or of geologic dependence.

Charles P. Berkey[13.1]

THE CONSTRUCTION of a dam to retain water causes more interference with natural conditions than does any other civil engineering operation. The validity of this assertion will be realized after even cursory consideration; the statement will later be amplified and explained, but of itself it constitutes a leading reason for the devotion of special attention to the foundations of dams. Equally striking is the critically important function that dams perform in storing water for domestic supply, for the generation of power, and for irrigation. The reliance that must be placed on structures carrying out these functions together with their existence in all parts of the world and in surprising numbers, ranging from the smallest timber-check dam to such structures as the Lloyd Barrage or the Hoover Dam, combine to provide further reasons for the devotion of particular attention to the design of dam foundations. Finally, although failures of civil engineering works are always of serious consequence, failures of dams are possibly more serious than others, since they generally occur during periods of abnormal weather, often without warning, and almost always with disastrous results. Defects in foundation beds are an unfortunate factor in many dam failures, and another telling argument is thus presented to support the necessity of neglecting no single feature of foundation beds that may possibly affect the dam that is to rest upon them.

Although the benefits to be derived from a critical study of engineering failures are duly stressed in other parts of this book, it may be noticed that constructive examples are offered, whenever possible, of works carried to successful completion with the aid of the methods and investigations described. A slight departure from this course will be made in the case of dams, and a brief review will be presented of some failures of the past. This is no descent to the almost hysterical attention devoted to dams whenever a failure does occur, at which times the pages of the popular press would almost lead one to believe that failures of dams are a regular occurrence. On these occasions, not a word is said of the thousands of successful dams performing their tasks, nor is the fact often mentioned that failures in many other branches of civil engineering, e.g., water purification, are far more liable to endanger the lives of people. Failures of dams are presumably "good news." It is not as news items that they will be considered here but rather as useful illustrations of some of the reasons for the failure of engineering structures and of the signif-icance of foundation-bed conditions among these reasons.

13.2. Historical Notes. Among dams of ancient times, that constructed by Joshua to help the Israelites cross the river Jordan is one of the earliest to be recorded, although the Marouk Dam across the river Tigris is even older, its construction having been carried out in almost prehistoric times. Built for river regulation, it lasted until the end of the thirteenth century. The first masonry dam of which there are good records is that built by Menes, first king of the first Egyptian dynasty, some time before 4000 B.C. Located 12 miles south of the ancient city of Memphis, to provide the site for which it was constructed to divert the waters of the Nile, it was 1,500 ft long and at least 50 ft wide. It was maintained for 4,500 years and then neglected. Another famous old dam was that near Yemen in Arabia, of which little is known beyond its construction date (1700 B.C.), its great size (2 miles long, 120 ft high, and 500 ft wide), and the fact that it failed about A.D. 300 in a flood recorded in Arabian litera-ture.[13.2]

These few examples are cited to illustrate the longevity of dam build-ing as a major branch of civil engineering. Further examples could be described; but as information about foundation-bed conditions is almost completely lacking in ancient records, they would have no particular reference to the purpose of this chapter. As an example of comparatively modern times, the Puentes Dam in Spain may usefully be mentioned. Constructed in the years between 1785 and 1791, it was 925 ft long, curved in plan, and 152 ft thick at the widest part of the base, with a maximum height of 167 ft, a perfectly safe design from the structural point of view. Constructed of rubble masonry and faced with cut stone, it was finished off with ornamentation befitting its standing as one of the wonders of Spain. Although the dam was apparently founded in part on bedrock, a gravel pocket about 67 ft wide was encountered near the center of the site and the founding of the dam across this gap was solved by an ingenious piled design carrying a grillage and protected by an upstream apron. This method of overcoming geological difficulties served satisfactorily just after the dam was built, but it was not reliable, and on April 30, 1802, that part of the dam above the earth pocket failed, following the washout of the underlying foundation beds. Still available is an eyewitness account of the disastrous collapse of this "plug" of masonry, which went out like a cork, leaving what appeared to be two massive bridge abutments with a gap between them 56 ft broad and 108 ft high.[13.3] This failure was somewhat exceptional, since other large dams constructed in the same period functioned successfully and thus inaugurated modern practice of dam design and construction.

13.3. Failures of Dams. The record of failures of dams in succeeding years provides a useful if a somewhat melancholy study. Analysis of the cause of failures indicates fairly definitely that the main reasons have been (1) the provision of inadequate spillway capacity, and (2) defective foundation-bed conditions; these two factors have accounted for the majority of all recorded failures. Spillway capacity is determined mainly from anticipated runoff from the catchment area above the dam, a subject on which geological conditions have a considerable indirect influence, as will be explained in Chap. 14. The second group of failures noted are all dependent essentially on geological features, although the specific reason for failure may vary from one case to another.

Several reviews of dam failures have been prepared, and the number of failures so listed is remarkable. Lapworth mentions that over 100 failures of dam structures due to undermining of water-bearing beds below the dam foundation occurred between 1864 and 1876.[13.4] Justin lists details of over 60 failures of earth dams alone between 1869 and 1919.[13.5] The study of failures in such numbers, although interesting and impressive, is not helpful with regard to avoidance of trouble in future work; a few special cases will therefore be referred to in detail. In his paper, Dr. Lapworth mentions several interesting cases, including the Hauser Lake failure which bears a striking similarity to the Puentes Dam failure, since a central portion 400 ft long, founded on water-bearing gravel, was destroyed in 1908 while the remaining sections were left intact.

An example from relatively recent practice is that of the Austin Dam which was constructed in 1893 to provide a water and power supply for the city of Austin, Texas. Difficulties were encountered during construction; the chief engineer responsible for the work resigned because of interference with his work. Eventually the dam was finished and placed in service; it was 1,091 ft long, of masonry, 68 ft high and 66 ft wide, resting on Cretaceous limestone, clays, and shales. The limestone strata were almost horizontal but alternated in texture, some much harder than others. It was said that the limestone was dissolved in places, giving rise to underground caverns, one of which was described by workmen but is not mentioned in engineering reports. The clays and shales were slippery and very broken, since the site was on a fault zone. Flood flows over the dam caused some erosion of weaker strata and at least one serious washout, which was repaired. This inevitably contributed to the sudden failure of the structure on April 7, 1900, when a central section collapsed completely; the dam was then overtopped by 11 ft of water because of severe flood flow. The concentration of flow through the

Fig. 13.1. The remains of the St. Francis Dam, California, U.S.A., after the structure had failed. (*Photograph by World Wide Photos.*)

resulting gap moved two adjacent blocks, each about 250 ft long, downstream for a distance of about 60 ft. The causes of failure are complex, but they appear to include removal by erosion of rock supporting the heel of the dam, the slippery nature of at least part of the foundation bed, and the presence of percolating water under the base of the dam.[13.6] The gap was closed and the dam placed in service again in 1915, but shortly thereafter another flood took out 20 crest gates and blocked the tailrace and turbine draft tubes with debris. Not until April, 1940, were the dam and the associated powerhouse finally put into continuing service; a thorough job of reconstruction included extensive grouting and foundation rehabilitation that can really be called underpinning, even though applied to a dam.[13.7]

The failure of the St. Francis Dam will be within the memory of some readers. This great gravity dam, 205 ft high and 700 ft long, was completed in 1926 by the Bureau of Water Works and Supply of the city of Los Angeles to assist in the storage of water for that well-known California community. It was located in the San Francisquito Canyon. Curved in plan and connecting with a long low wing wall, it created a reservoir with a capacity of 38,000 acre-ft. The dam was founded partially on schist and partially (for about one-third of its length at the southwest end) on a reddish conglomerate with sandy and shaly layers. The contact between the two rocks is a fault, generally recognized to have been long inactive. Although the schist is a relatively sound rock, the conglomerate[13.8]

. . . is by no means a strong rock. A test . . . gave a crushing strength of 500 pounds to the square inch. . . . When wet, the rock shows a considerable change, [a sample starts] to flake and crumble when placed in a beaker of water and in about 15 minutes slumps to the bottom of the vessel as a loose gritty sediment that can be stirred about with the finger. . . . So far as can be ascertained, no geological examination was made of the dam-site before construction began and no crushing or immersion tests were made of the conglomerate.

Seepage was noticed through the conglomerate when the reservoir first became full (in March, 1928); eventually, the dam failed on March 12, 1928, with a tragic toll of 426 lives and untold property damage. Boards of inquiry were appointed by the state of California and by the city of Los Angeles; both agreed that the main cause of failure was the nature of the rocks under the dam. Quoting Dr. F. L. Ransome[13.8] again: "The plain lesson of the disaster is that engineers, no matter how extensive their experience in the building of dams or how skilful in the design of such structures, cannot safely dispense with the knowledge of the character and structure of the adjacent rocks, such as only an expert and thorough geological examination can provide."

Just about 30 years later, an almost equally tragic failure occurred; 344 people were killed when the Malpasset Dam in southern France collapsed after several days of unusually severe rain. The dam was completed in 1954; it was a thin arched dam of reinforced concrete, its greatest thickness only 22 ft 8 in., and its height about 200 ft. Curved to a radius of 344 ft, it was built in a narrow gorge of Le Reyran River for the Department of Var to serve both irrigation and water supply. Its sudden collapse on December 2, 1959, resulted in a catastrophic flood that carried everything before it for 7 miles downstream; most of the people who lost their lives lived in the town of Frejus, which was in the path of the flood. The preliminary report of the commission of inquiry, established by the French Ministry of Agriculture, confirmed that the structural design, although daring, was sound. After reviewing all possible causes for the disaster, the commission was forced to the conclusion that the principal cause of the catastrophe was a rupture of the rock below the foundations, a rupture that induced substantial displacement, notably of the abutment, and so the destruction of the dam. The bedrock was a mica schist, reported to be sheared and jointed, with a wedge-shaped mass overlying a clay-filled seam. The official commission is undertaking a careful program of field testing; their final report will be a significant document, even though it is already known that, once again, geological

Fig. 13.2. The site of the Malpasset Dam on Le Reyran River in southern France just after this thin concrete arched dam had failed. (*Photograph by Keystone Photos.*)

defects led to the failure of such a notable engineering structure, again with appalling human suffering and loss in consequence.[13.9]

13.4. Review of Dam Construction. A return may now be made to the statement with which this chapter started, and consideration may be given to the effects of dam construction. A dam is an artificial structure erected to support a waterproof membrane designed to retain water above the level that it normally occupies at the site of the dam; suitable provision is made for passing a certain calculated flow of water past the dam, through it, over it, or around it, depending on local circumstances. The membrane may be and generally is an integral part of the dam structure. It may be supported in several ways by such varying designs as the following: an earth-fill or rock-fill dam, in which the membrane is either on the upstream face or in the center as a core wall; a gravity dam of masonry or mass concrete, in which the membrane is the upstream face of the dam itself; or a reinforced-concrete dam of the arched type, multiple arch, multiple dome, or some other special design, in all of which an unbroken reinforced-concrete skin serves as the waterproof membrane. It will be seen that dams can be generally grouped into two main divisions: earth- and rock-fill dams which depend for their stability on the natural repose of unconsolidated material, and concrete or masonry dams which depend for their stability on the structural performance of the material used for construction. The type of dam to be constructed at any location must be determined mainly from geological considerations; the actual kind of dam to be constructed, once its general type has been decided, will also be dependent to some extent on geological conditions affecting the supply of structural materials.

Since all dams retain water to a certain predetermined level, the flow of water in the watercourse being regulated is seriously affected below the dam site; the flow is generally regulated to a more uniform discharge than that given by the stream itself. In addition, the underground water conditions in the valley above the dam location are completely changed; the level of the ground-water table is raised at least to the water level of the reservoir near the water line, and changes of decreasing importance occur farther up the valley. Below the dam, the level of the water table may be lowered if normal stream flow is depleted. Between the two sides of the dam, there is thus set up a considerable difference in ground-water level. Although the waterproof membrane generally extends from side to side of the dam site, effectively isolating the two ground-water tables, this artificial condition will always exist while water is being retained. The structure will exert unusually high unit pressures on certain parts of the underlying foundation beds. The beds will be submerged well below water level in the reservoir area and so will be subjected to hydrostatic pressure, which may be appreciable in high dams. These are the main reasons underlying the assertion that a dam causes more interference with natural conditions than does any other type of civil engineering structure. In the special case of weirs, or dams founded on pervious strata, in which the waterproof membrane merely deflects the flow of ground water but does not stop it completely, the serious change in the underground conditions caused by the dam will be obvious.

In the case of all dams designed to seal completely the flow of water, surface and underground, down the valley that they cross, the action of the dam in resisting the pressure of the retained water gives rise to four main geological problems: (1) determination of the soundness of the underlying foundation beds, and their ability to carry the designed loading; (2) determination of the degree of water tightness of the foundation beds at the dam location and of the measures, if any, required to render the underlying geological strata quite watertight; (3) a study of the effect on the foundation bedrock of prolonged exposure to water; (4) an investigation of the possibility of earth movements at the site of the dam, and the measures to be taken as a safeguard. Some of the geological problems affecting the reservoirs formed by dams may be encountered also during construction; but for convenience, they will be considered

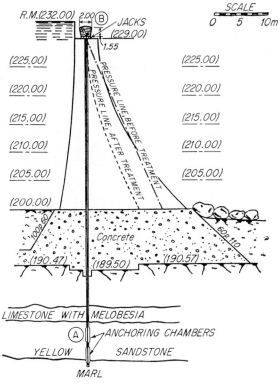

Fig. 13.3. Cross section of the Cheurfas Dam, Algeria, showing foundation strata and method of anchoring the dam to them. (*Reproduced by permission of the Institution of Structural Engineers.*)

separately in the following chapter which is devoted specifically to reservoir problems.

Dams founded on pervious foundations present their own special problems, mainly associated with the controlled flow of water beneath the structure. It may not be possible to make any dam foundation absolutely tight, but the slight leakage occurring with dams on so-called "impermeable" foundation beds, although associated with uplift pressure, is generally of no other consequence. For those dams on admittedly permeable foundation beds, the exact nature of the flow of water through

Fig. 13.4. General view of the Cheurfas Dam, Algeria, as reconstructed, and a close-up view of the head of one of the anchorages. (*Reproduced by permission of M. Andre Coyne.*)

the underlying strata is a vital part of the design; thus, accurate knowledge of the water-carrying properties of the unconsolidated materials encountered becomes a matter of importance. The accumulation of silt above dams, deposited as the water comes practically to rest in the reservoir formed by the dam, is another associated geological problem; it will be studied generally in Chap. 19. The scouring out of exposed strata immediately below dam structures, because of the excessive velocities of flood flows discharging over or around the dam, is also a matter of importance in the design of dams; it, too, is reviewed in Chap. 19.

Many special problems naturally arise in connection with the construction of dams, so varied are the sites in location and nature and so great are the possibilities for different designs. Since special problems, interesting though they may be, do not usually have a general application, they cannot receive attention here, apart possibly from one installation which was, for a time, unique. This is the Cheurfas Dam in Algeria, constructed in 1882, with a maximum height of 107 ft. Soon after construction, one abutment of the dam was washed away, but it was reconstructed and served well until recent years. An examination in 1927 disclosed serious weakness; and as the most economical means of strengthening the dam, 10-in.-diameter holes 13 ft apart were drilled from the crest of the dam to the foundation and then to a depth of 70 to 80 ft into the calcareous sandstone, limestone, yellowish sandstone, and argillaceous marl on which the dam is founded. Specially prepared steel cables were then anchored in these holes to the foundation strata, secured in special caps on the dam crest, placed under great tension, and then anchored; their effect was to "tie down" the dam to the foundation strata.[13.10] The same system of tying down a dam into its foundation beds was successfully applied to the Tansa hand-placed masonry dam after the structure was found to be in an unsafe condition.[13.11] The Tansa Dam is 173 ft high; it serves the water supply of Bombay, India. This method was also employed to raise the spillway level of the Steenbras Dam in South Africa by $6\frac{1}{2}$ ft in order to provide a quick and economical increase in the reservoir capacity for the water supply of Cape Town. The character of the Table Mountain sandstone, upon which the Steenbras Dam is founded, is such that percussion drills could not be used successfully; holes for the post-tensioning cables had to be sunk by diamond drilling. All cables were carefully grouted into place and tested beyond their design load; 6 cables only of the total of 326 failed to meet the stringent test conditions.[13.12]

A final observation of a general nature, which must be made before passing on to consider individual problems in detail, is that as the material status of Western civilization advances, the best sites for dams will be progressively used up, leaving for further development sites of increasing difficulty. Admittedly, this is a general tendency only, but there can be little doubt that it represents accurately the trend of dam construction. It will necessitate, or more correctly it is already necessitating, increasing attention to the geological conditions of new dam sites.

13.5. General Preliminary Work. Since the location of a proposed dam will generally be restricted by topographical, economic, and social consid-

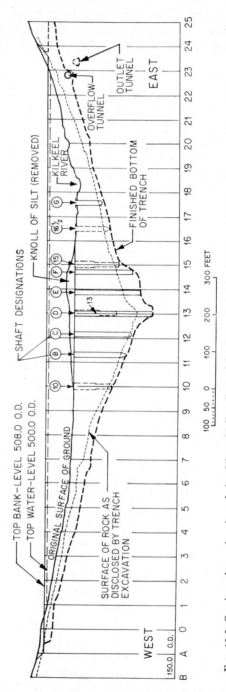

FIG. 13.5. Section along the site of the Silent Valley Dam, Northern Ireland, showing the bedrock levels as determined during construction. (*Reproduced by permission of the Institution of Civil Engineers.*)

erations, the areas to be examined as possible sites will be fairly well defined. In general, preliminary studies will follow the lines already suggested in Chap. 6. Accurate geological sections along possible lines for the dam will be a major requirement. The nature of valleys will sometimes mean that bedrock is some distance below ground level, and therefore the determination of the rock surface across the valley will often be a first step in the preparation of the section. Geophysical methods can be of great assistance in this work when utilized in connection with strategically placed boreholes. The existence of buried valleys must be checked carefully, not only from test-bore results but also from general studies of the local geology, for valleys 70 ft deep have been found between two boreholes as close together as 50 ft.

The possible presence of boulders is another danger to be guarded against, especially in glacial formations; the greatest care must be taken with test drilling. The almost insuperable difficulties met during the construction of the Silent Valley Dam for the Belfast City and District Water Commissioners in Northern Ireland were due very probably to the assumption that granite boulders encountered by the original test boreholes were solid rock. Although a rock foundation bed had been anticipated at a depth of 50 ft below ground level, the cutoff trench actually had to be carried to a depth of 180 ft through running sand of such a nature that the use of the maximum working pressure of compressed air served to reduce the water level by only a few feet. The final solution of the problems thus encountered provides a fascinating but sobering study.[13.13]

In the determination of the geological sections, local topographical detail and, more particularly, local geological features must always be given special consideration in valleys that have been subjected to glaciation. It was from surface observations at the site of the Vyrnwy Dam for the water supply of the city of Liverpool, England, that Dr. G. F. Deacon (joint engineer with Thomas Hawkesley) deduced that the valley was the site of an old glacial lake, held up at one time by a rock bar. The center line of the dam, which was the first large dam to be built in Great Britain, was located for the necessary parliamentary plans along the inferred position of the rock bar. Subsequent detailed investigation by trial holes and shafts proved the inference to be practically correct, and the dam was built as originally located. Dr. Deacon estimated that a deviation of the center line up or down the valley of only $\frac{1}{8}$ mile would have added £300,000 to £400,000 to the cost of the work.[13.14] As a contrast to this example may be mentioned a small dam known to the writer, which was constructed without any such preliminary studies of the rock surface; as a result several thousand dollars were wasted because the center line was only 50 ft upstream from what would have been a better location.

Whenever feasible, the rock surface should be traced right across the valley being investigated. This is not always possible, since faulting sometimes provides clefts filled to great depths with unconsolidated material. The author has carried out some investigations in the northern part of Ontario, Canada, in a rock gorge barely 50 ft wide through which passes the whole flow of a fairly large river. Solid diabase extends for a great distance on either side of the gorge, yet diamond-drill holes carried

Fɪɢ. 13.6. Excavation in progress for the Vyrnwy Dam in northern Wales for the water supply of Liverpool, England; southwest end of the site, as exposed in June, 1882, showing glaciated surface of rock (and incidentally, a very early example of a civil engineering "progress photograph"). (*Reproduced by permission of the City Water Engineer of Liverpool.*)

180 ft below water level in the river bed failed to reveal solid rock; the holes passed through boulders, gravel, and finally over 100 ft of compacted sand. This is typical of valley faults, quite a number of which are to be found in Canada; they always demand very careful study. When rock cannot be found at reasonable depths, the necessity of obtaining accurate information on all unconsolidated strata assumes increased importance.

The records thus made available will usually enable those in charge of the engineering work to decide on the general type of dam to be used and to begin their economic and design studies. If, for example, the

rock floor cannot be reached by ordinary drilling methods, an earth-
or rock-fill dam or a "floating" concrete structure may be necessary. If a
rock bed is found to be available at reasonable depths, economic considerations will guide the designer in his choice between an earth-
or rock-fill dam and one of the gravity or other structural type. The
choice of the kind of dam to be used, although so closely related to
geological conditions, must be left for study elsewhere, since it is
essentially an engineering problem. Enough has been said to indicate
the amount of geological survey work necessary before even a choice
can be made. Once the choice has been made, geological work must
continue, specially adapted to serve the particular requirements of the
kind of dam now contemplated; and it must be carried to such a stage
that, from the information so obtained, assurance can be had that construction of the dam as proposed can be completed within the estimated
cost.

13.6. Exploratory Work during Construction. It has already been indicated that investigations of the geological conditions underlying the
site of a dam do not cease when active construction work begins; on
the contrary, the start of excavation means, in many cases, that geological study can be extended, actual rock surfaces examined, and
previously formulated opinions checked. For all major dams, the services
of a geological expert will be advisable, and his work should most
certainly be continued until all excavation has been completed and construction begun. The final inspection of the foundation bed as prepared
for use will be the most critical part of the investigation work.

The start of active construction operations will generally mean that
equipment and power supply will be available for the use of aids to exploration other than those possible in ordinary preliminary work. The
digging of more extensive test pits is a first possibility but one that is
merely an extension of work included in most preliminary investigations.
A further extension is the excavation of shafts into rock and of exploratory tunnels. The purpose of such shafts and tunnels is to permit
visual inspection of the actual rock structure in checking on the geological
sections across the site, previously prepared, and on the soundness and
strength of the rock in relation to the designed loading. In many deep
gorges especially suitable for dam sites but where borings cannot easily
be taken in the river bed, underwater tunnels drifted from shafts sunk in
the gorge sides can prove invaluable. Exploratory excavation work of
this type can often perform a double purpose by providing access to
rock well below the foundation-bed surfaces into which cement grout
may be injected, if this is necessary to render the foundation strata
watertight. In this way, grouting can be made thoroughly effective and
more extensive in its influence than is possible from surface operations.

As an example of a dam at the site of which exploratory tunnels were widely used, there may be mentioned the main dam of Le Sautet water-power development in the south of France on Le Drac, one of the head-waters of the Rhone. Located in a magnificent gorge 600 ft deep and ½ mile long, the dam is 414 ft high and yet has a crest length of only 263 ft. The dam proper is an arched structure, bearing onto the walls of the

Fig. 13.7. Le Sautet Dam, powerhouse, and gorge, Drac River, France; the dam is 414 ft high. The extensive exploration of the limestone on which it is built is described in the text. (*Reproduced by permission of le Société Forces Motrices Bonne et Drac, Grenoble, France.*)

gorge, but it is backed with lean concrete designed to buttress the two sides of the gorge; the resulting cross section is almost that of a gravity dam. The rock in which the gorge is located is a limestone formation, which called for most careful exploratory work. The preliminary investigations and surveys extended over a period of 10 years, and 1,650 ft of exploratory tunnels were driven. As a result of this study, it was determined that the rock was as sound as could be desired, without faults or other imperfections. Watertightness of the gorge sides was assured by an extensive grouting program; about 20,000 ft of grout holes were drilled and grouted, absorbing about 6 million lb of cement under pressures as high as 500 psi. Much of the grouting was done from the tunnels, some of which have been left open so that further grouting can be done in the future if inspection shows this to be necessary.[13.15]

Another major aid to construction is the use of special drilling machines capable of taking out drill cores up to 72 in. in diameter, as described

Fig. 13.8. General view of excavation at the site of the Prettyboy Dam for the water supply of the city of Baltimore, Maryland, U.S.A. (*Reproduced by permission of the Chief Engineer, Dept. of Public Works, Balitmore.*)

on page 206. The use of large-diameter drill holes at the Prettyboy Dam in Maryland was then mentioned. The highly foliated nature of the schist revealed in the foundation bed of this dam resulted in such overbreak and general rock movement after blasting operations that other methods had to be tried for the excavation of the necessary cutoff trench. After repeated trials, a novel expedient was adopted. Wire-rope saws were rigged up between pairs of the calyx drill holes, and with these the necessary trenching work was successfully carried out; this was probably the first occasion on which wire saws were used on a highly quartose rock. Figure 13.9 illustrates two of the wire-saw rigs used at the site of the Prettyboy Dam.[13.16]

The continued study devoted to all the geological aspects of the construction of the Hoover Dam provides an unusually good example of the invariable requirements of dam construction work—close inspection of all rock surfaces as they are stripped and a final and thorough in-

FIG. 13.9. Wire-rope saws in use for rock excavation at site of the Prettyboy Dam for the water supply of the city of Baltimore, Maryland, U.S.A. (Drill holes were also used for subsurface examination of rock by geologists.) (*Reproduced by permission of the Chief Engineer, Dept. of Public Works, Baltimore.*)

spection before concreting is started. In 1928, a board of engineers and geologists recommended after much study that the dam be located at the Black Canyon site on the Colorado River. The canyon walls were formidable, defying intimate inspection; the gorge floor was buried deep below the swift-flowing water of the river, heavy boulders, and river sediment. Predictions were made, however, explorations were renewed, and active construction soon started; by 1933, the canyon floor had been cleaned up (the river flow was diverted through tunnels), and the geological formation was thus available for direct inspection. Dr. Charles P. Berkey was a member of the original board, and he made a final inspection at this time. It revealed that every major contention and assumption made by the board 5 years before had been confirmed by intimate examination of the gorge in the dry. The report need not be referred to in detail since many of its features are discussed in the

Fig. 13.10. A general view of the site of the Hoover Dam as finally excavated, showing the canyon walls and the "inner gorge." (Photograph taken as the second bucket of concrete was being placed, June 6, 1933.) (*Reproduced by permission of The Commissioner, U.S. Bureau of Reclamation.*)

publications describing this famous dam. All the rock formations of the gorge were found to be thoroughly capable of bearing the load and resisting the thrusts of the dam. Stability and general watertightness of the walls and floor as well as of the four great tunnels in the canyon walls exceeded all expectations, although grouting had to be carried out to obstruct leakage and otherwise guard against the great pressure of the water to be retained in this unusually deep reservoir. The rock of the foundation beds was found not to soften under prolonged submergence. The gorge did not follow a fault zone, but a most interesting feature revealed by excavation was the existence of an "inner gorge," forming a narrow and tortuous channel roughly along the center of the main gorge at a depth of 75 to 80 ft below the rock benches on either side. The side rock benches were generally smooth and uniform (although showing some potholes); but the inner gorge was pitted and fluted, being generally very uneven in form and depth. This form suggested that the whole of the previously superincumbent mass of sediment had moved in great flood "tides," being subject to scour, whereas in the center there had been a considerable whirling action which set up "pothole erosion" at greater

Fig. 13.11. A close-up view of the final excavation and clean-up work in the deepest section of the "inner gorge" at the site of the Hoover Dam, showing some of the river gravel deposit. (*Reproduced by permission of The Commissioner, U.S. Bureau of Reclamation.*)

depth. Although this would seem hard to believe, it was proved beyond doubt by the essential continuity of river fill from top to bottom and also by the finding of a sawed plank of wood embedded in the gravel at the edge of the inner gorge, a position that it is believed could have been reached only by burial during a recent flood. On this site now stands Hoover Dam, a tribute alike to those by whom it was planned, designed, and constructed.[13.17]

13.7. Soundness of Bedrock. It is now necessary to turn from general considerations to special geological problems that may be encountered in dam construction. The essential soundness of the strata on which a dam is to be founded is a prime requirement that must be investigated.

Two questions that the civil engineer desires to have answered well before his construction operations are to start concern the probable nature of the rock surface as it will be exposed on excavation and the possible presence of disintegrated rock, since his estimates of cost will depend on the answers. Test pits, if carried to rock surface, may give some indication of the answers to these questions; test drilling likewise may give an indication, although with certain types of disintegration the rotten rock when still in its original position may give surprisingly good cores, showing up in its true nature only when exposed to the atmosphere. Thus it is that a careful geological study is a most necessary aid in determining whether or not disintegration is to be expected. A geologist may be able to deduce this from knowledge of the essential nature of the rock type to be encountered and of possible disintegrating influences and from a detailed study of cores obtained from test drilling.

In Washington, D.C., a bed of granite was found which had decayed to a depth of 80 ft to such an extent that it could be removed with pick and shovel. In the state of Georgia, limestone has been found decomposed to a depth of 200 ft; in Brazil, shales have been found disintegrated to a depth of 394 ft below surface level.[13.18] These figures indicate how serious this problem can be. Actual examples from construction practice will elucidate the problem even further. Before the start of construction of the Assouan Dam on the river Nile in Egypt, in 1898, it was assumed that in the deeper channels of the river bed, where drilling could not be carried out because of the swift currents, all decomposed granite would be eroded. When the site was unwatered, it was found repeatedly that there were depths of decomposed granite at the bottom of most of the channels; the removal of this material added greatly to the cost of the work. In one season, five times the estimated quantity of rock had to be removed; for the complete structure, excavation was 100 per cent in excess of that calculated. It is of some interest to note that Sir Benjamin Baker, engineer for the work, consulted Sir Archibald Geikie, then director of the Geological Survey of Great Britain, about possible fissures in the granite, but apparently in London and not at the site.[13.19] At the Sennar Dam on the Blue Nile in the Sudan, the reverse experience was encountered; the excavation necessary was less than originally calculated, and there was a consequent saving in cost. In a North American example, a cutoff wall resting on andesite had to be carried 40 ft lower than the level originally suggested by core borings in order to reach what was finally considered to be sound rock.

An added difficulty is that of determining exactly what is meant (or desired) by "sound rock"; the term may have quite different meanings for engineer and for geologist. The engineer associates structural soundness with the strength of the rock and its impermeability, whereas the geologist may tend to consider the matter from the mineralogical standpoint. The subject is complex, therefore, and its consideration requires experience and a close cooperation between engineer and geologist. A final note of warning must be stressed with regard to rock structure near fault zones. As exemplified by the rock encountered at the Prettyboy Dam, rock adjacent to fault planes may quite probably be brecciated and useless as a sound foundation rock. Normally fractured rock can easily be detected from its appearance if not from its location, but under special circumstances this may not be easy. When work is proceeding in very cold weather, for example, the effect of frost may convert such breccia into an apparently solid mass. In the north of Ontario, Canada, the author has noted this effect; diabase which had been fractured into fragments of about 1 cc in size appeared to be quite solid when exposed at a temperature of $-30°F$, but revealed its true nature (detected from the location) only when subjected for some time to the action of steam jets.

The structural strength of rock in proposed foundation beds is a main requirement of soundness. Compressive strength is the property generally in question; dam structures (gravity, arched, or buttressed) are designed with a maximum unit pressure at the heel as one criterion for stability, and this is equated to the maximum permissible compressive stress in the rock. Although it seems probable that no dam failure has been directly due to a failure of a rock foundation stratum in compression, this in no way minimizes the importance of this aspect of the subject. The compressive tests usually carried out deal with rock specimens in the dry, whereas part, at least, of the rock surface supporting a dam structure will be exposed continuously to water. A further consideration of rock soundness therefore must always be the effect of prolonged exposure to water. The bedrock is to be exposed not only to water, but to water under appreciable pressure. Any failure of the rock under the influence of water may therefore lead to serious structural weakness; and if the weathered rock is for any reason displaced as it weakens, as it may be by seeping water, serious damage may be done. The failure of the St. Francis Dam provides at once a notable and most tragic example.

Preliminary testing can remove almost completely any doubts entertained on this matter, as has been instanced in many investigations. For example, tests made in connection with the Madden Dam site at Alahjuela, Panama Canal Zone, may be mentioned. Among the rock formations investigated was a bluish-gray fine-grained sandstone, known as the Gatun (?) formation, samples of which were tested by the National Bureau of Standards and found to have a compressive strength of 3,500 psi when dry but only 850 psi when wet. Similar figures for a light-gray medium-grained sandstone also tested, the Caimito (?) formation, were 2,300 and 550 psi, respectively. The figures quoted are extremes. Petrographic examination disclosed the presence in the sandstones of a clay mineral occurring as films coating feldspar and other grains; abundant glaucanite contributed to the weakness.[13.20] This example serves to show the importance of tests on thoroughly wet rocks; incidentally, it illustrates the troubles that may be encountered because of the unwanted presence of clay.

Another possibility of gravity dam failure is to some extent dependent on geological conditions—the possibility that the dam will slide. Various values have been suggested for the coefficient of friction between either concrete or masonry and mortar and rock surfaces. Tests reveal that, provided a rock floor is properly cleaned and prepared, the bond obtained between concrete and rock can be so efficient that failure will take place only by a shearing fracture of solid rock mass or of the concrete. Special preparation of rock surfaces may be necessary in the case of glaciated rock that may be worn so smooth that it must be roughened artificially in order to give a good bond. Perfect bond may be obtained between concrete and the rock surface, but the rock mass itself may slide forward under the influence of the pressure transmitted from the dam foundations. Movement of this kind will take place only along planes of weakness in the rock, such as bedding planes, and only when normal resistance to movement has been in some way removed. Naturally, geological structural arrangement will be the determining factor, since movement is possible only on bedding planes that are horizontal or that dip away from the dam. This arrangement can be determined only by adequate preliminary geological study. The Austin Dam already mentioned provides an illustrative example.

There is at least one dam under which the foundation beds were "tied together" by means of grouted steel anchor rods in order to achieve increased resistance to the downstream thrust upon the dam foundation exerted by the water pressure. The Harland County Dam on the Republican River in southern Nebraska rests upon Cretaceous chalk with interbedded bentonite seams up to 3 in. in thickness. There is a general upstream dip of about 2 per cent, and several faults cross the site diagonally. Faults were grouted along the upstream side of the spillway section of the dam and deep drain holes were provided in the chalk under the spillway in order to reduce uplift pressures and seepage. Anchor rods were grouted inside 6-in.-diameter drill holes, inclined upstream on a 2:1 slope, so arranged and designed as to ensure stability against sliding.[13.21]

When the foundation beds at dam sites are finally seen, after the necessary dewatering operations and subsequent river-bed excavation, it is not uncommon for unexpected geological features to be revealed. For this reason constant attention to all geological details is imperative. Few dams have probably undergone such difficulties with foundation bedrock after the site was cleared as the Bort Dam, key structure of the Dordogne power system in southwestern France. A gravity structure, curved in plan, its exact location and shape were determined by the necessity of utilizing two types of foundation rock, a sound gneiss capable of sustaining 15,000 to 20,000 psf and a weaker mica schist with a strength of only 5,000 psf; a crushed fault zone between the two formations crossed the gorge immediately under the site of the dam. Great difficulties were experienced during construction, notably with incipient slips in the mica schist when exposed in the side of the gorge. A series of reinforced-concrete "rockslide protection works" had to be constructed in order to hold up great masses of the mica schist that exhibited instability before the main mass of the dam had reached them.[13.22]

Difficulties of a different kind, but equally serious, were met during the construction of the Bhakra Dam on the Sutlej River in northern India. This great Indian engineering structure is a concrete gravity dam, 1,700 ft long, 575 ft wide at its base, and 740 ft high from the bottom of excavation. The dam is founded on sandstone interspersed with numerous seams of a claystone-siltstone formation. General practice was to excavate these seams, when encountered, to a depth of twice the width of the seam and then to backfill with concrete. One major seam was encountered, however, which was 110 ft wide at river-bed level and inclined at 70° to the horizontal as it crossed beneath the location of the dam. The consultants recommended that the seam be excavated to a depth of about 100 ft below the level of the river bed. Excavation proved to be most difficult, however, and it had to stop about halfway down to the desired elevation. The open cut so formed was then backfilled with concrete; 12-ft square shafts were left at 20-ft intervals, through which the excavation was eventually resumed. Mining methods were used, even to the extent of using light blasting charges, but the excavation was taken out only by blocks; each one was backfilled with concrete before the adjoining blocks were excavated. The work was successfully extended to the desired depth and the dam was completed.[13.23]

13.8. Possibility of Earth Movement. Earth movement in its relation to dam foundations is of vital importance. The nature of dam structures is such that, unless due allowance has been made in design, any movement of the foundation beds may lead to serious structural damage. In areas subject to earthquake shocks, allowance for seismic forces must always be made even for dams founded on the most solid of rock formations. A usual allowance is to consider an earthquake shock with a horizontal acceleration of one-tenth that of gravity; vertical acceleration is neglected. In connection with the application of this design requirement to the Morris Dam built in the San Gabriel Canyon near Azusa, California, to augment the municipal water supply of Pasadena, California, it was found that the natural period of vibration of the dam as a whole (328 ft high) was 0.16 sec or less. It was estimated that the volume of material in this dam had to be increased by 15 per cent to allow for the thickening necessary to resist seismic forces.[13.24] Special dam designs have been evolved to be proof against earthquake shocks even if quite severe. There is, for example, a special type of laminated concrete paving used for facing a considerable number of rock-fill dams in Chile; the rock fills are designed so that they will not flatten under shock; the slopes adopted (1.6 and 1.8:1) were arrived at after a long and careful study of rockslides, many of which had been caused by earthquake shocks, in the district adjacent to the dam sites.[13.25]

Fig. 13.12. The Morris Dam for the water supply of Pasadena, California, U.S.A., located in the San Gabriel Canyon over a fault (now a part of the Metropolitan Water District of Southern California). (*Reproduced by permission of the Chief Engineer and General Manager, Water Dept., City of Pasadena.*)

Many dams, especially those of old design, have failed as the result of earthquake shock, a fact that is not surprising in view of the relatively recent progress of seismic-research work. What is perhaps more surprising is that dams built at right angles across faults along which movement has taken place owing to earth movement have not failed. Two good examples are provided by earth-fill puddle-core dams built across the San Andreas fault in California in 1870 and 1877, respectively. The San Andreas Dam is 95 ft high above stream bed and 130 ft above the bottom of its cutoff trench; and the Upper Crystal Springs Dam is 85 ft high above stream bed and 190 ft above the bottom of its cutoff trench. Both were constructed on clay foundation beds; the fault passes almost at

right angles across their crest lines. The disastrous San Francisco earthquake of 1906 reached a maximum intensity of 10 on the Rossi-Forrel
scale; movement was concentrated along the fault line. At the two dams,
permanent displacement up to a maximum of 12 ft took place; and
although outlet tunnels around the dams were badly fractured, the dam
structures themselves remained stable. Despite the appreciable movement

Fig. 13.13. The Upper Crystal Springs earth-fill dam (of the San Francisco Water
Department) showing displacement of dam on either side of the San Andreas fault,
following the severe earthquake of 1906. (*Reproduced by permission of the General
Manager and Chief Engineer, San Francisco Water Dept.*)

of one-half of the dams, they remained watertight and so stand today
as seen in an accompanying photograph. A large mass concrete gravity
dam (the Crystal Springs Dam, constructed in 1877 and enlarged in
1888 and 1890) located only ¼ mile from the fault was undamaged.[13.26]
Earth dams in Japan have similarly withstood severe earthquake shocks
without serious damage. The design for a dam for the water supply of
Rangoon, Burma (in an area also subject to earthquakes), was based on
this experience. In the absence of any clay suitable for use as a puddled
core, the dam was designed with a flexible concrete core wall. The dam

is 126 ft high. The concrete core wall was built as a series of panels connected by means of ingenious grooved joints filled with asphalt.[13.27]

The example cited of what can happen at a fault plane is a fitting reminder of the importance to be attached to the presence at a dam site of geological faults—certain signs of past earth movement. It will be increasingly difficult to find sites for dam structures without some such defect, and engineering ingenuity has already been displayed to advantage in devising means of overcoming the difficulties in design thus introduced. At the site of the Morris Dam, California, for example (see page 512), a minor fault intersects the dam foundations near the base of the right abutment in a direction almost normal to the axis of the dam. Study of the stratification of old stream-bed gravels revealed the fact that no appreciable movement along this and other fault planes had taken place for a period of approximately 10,000 years. The fault received special treatment in design; an open joint with vertical sliding planes was provided in the dam structure over the trace of the fault from top to bottom of the dam between two of the blocks into which it was divided for construction purposes. The four sliding planes are at an angle of 45° with the horizontal and so lie in the direction of past movement. Planes of contact are separated by a bituminous filler

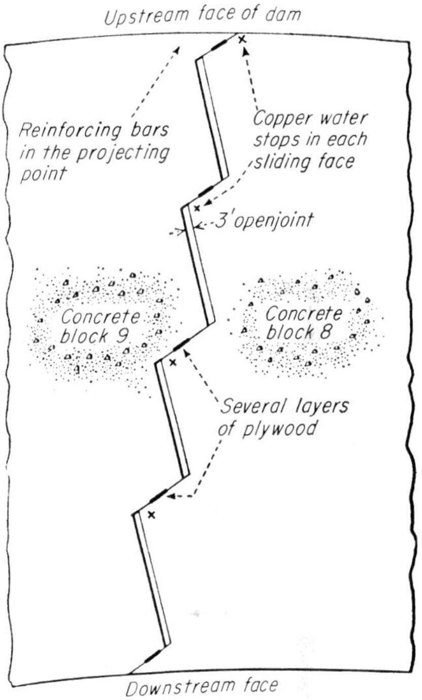

Fig. 13.14. Sliding type of joint which divides the Morris Dam (for Pasadena water supply, California, U.S.A.) into two units over an old inactive fault. (*Reproduced by permission of The Editor, Engineering News-Record.*)

which can yield slightly if motion is not as anticipated.[13.28] A somewhat similar type of sliding joint, but horizontal, was incorporated in the design of the 210-ft Lake Loveland concrete arch dam near San Diego, California, above a shelf in the left abutment in an attempt to eliminate cracking of the concrete at this location when the dam is under load.[13.29]

Another interesting and illuminating example is provided by the foundation-bed conditions at the site of the Owyhee Dam built about 1930 by the U.S. Bureau of Reclamation to serve a large irrigation project. The dam is 355 ft high above bed level but 530 ft high above lowest concrete level; it provides 715,000 acre-ft of storage on the Owyhee River in eastern Oregon.[13.30]

The dam site was formed by the present Owyhee River cutting a narrow gorge 400 to 600 ft. deep through a flow of rhyolite which blocked the valley subsequent to the deposition of the original tuff underlying the district. The outer surface of this flow of rhyolite moving on the original tuff—probably in contact with water—chilled comparatively quickly, producing a layer of pitchstone agglomerate, roughly about 25 feet thick, extending as a contact between the two materials. Subsequent erosion has removed the upper levels of this rhyolitic flow, and the river had cut its gorge down into the remainder. This rock, which forms the abutment and foundation material for the structure, is an extremely hard crystalline mass due to the slow interior cooling of the flow. Beneath it lies the stratum of more elastic pitchstone agglomerate as a transition material blending into the softer tuff.

A fault in the center of the streambed parallel to the canyon subsequently has occurred with horizontal displacement. Exploration of this fault zone with diamond drill borings showed that faulted material was evident in the hard rhyolite in the form of small shattered pieces, but indicated that the disturbance lessened in the more yielding agglomerate and practically disappeared upon entering the tuff. The original plan provided for the removal of this faulted material on the line of the upstream cutoff by means of a shaft to the undisturbed tuff. . . . Excavation work in this cutoff shaft and general foundation excavation along the upper portion of the fault revealed fractured and loose material, which made it advisable to remove the material in the fault zone throughout the entire width of the structure and refill the crevice with concrete to insure proper foundation conditions. This possibility had been foreseen as a result of the drilling and was provided for in the specifications. . . . Excavation proceeded through about 83 feet of faulted and broken rhyolite, 22 feet of the agglomerate and 10 feet into the practically undisturbed tuff to El. 2,145, at a depth of about 213 feet below low water level of the river. It is of interest to note that the level of actual excavation required to reach undisturbed material below the zone of fracture was within 2 feet of the estimated depth established by the exploratory borings in the zone.

This unusual foundation work is described in detail because of its special interest and the close relation between construction procedure and geological structure that it reveals. Practically all recorded cases of major dam construction over faults include some features of interest. Reference can be made, however, to two more examples only, which are of special interest; one is the arched foundation necessitated at the Rodriguez Dam on the Tijuana River near Tijuana, Mexico, constructed during the years from 1928 to 1930. The dam is of the Ambursen-buttress type, 240 ft high above lowest foundation concrete, having a crest length of 2,200 ft and providing a storage of 110,000 acre-ft.

Rock, which was exposed over much of the site, consists of rhyolite and granite with a fused contact, indicating watertightness on this plane. In the lower part of the gorge the rock surfaces were hard and fresh, although broken. . . . Cleavage planes are evident on either side, dipping toward streambed. As preliminary investigation nine borings were made in streambed and about fifty test pits were excavated at higher elevations. Cores could not be obtained in the other holes but two indicated sharp clean rock chips and the remaining two showed rather definite evidence of disintegration. . . . Foundation excavation work uncovered bedrock at depths of about 35 feet, as had been expected, but it proved considerably broken and unsuited for buttress foundations. A more serious difficulty was the finding of a pronounced

Fɪɢ. 13.15. The Owyhee Dam, Oregon, U.S.A.; a general view of the unwatered site, showing the canyon walls and the fault described in the text. (Scale may be gauged by the size of the crawler crane in the center foreground.) (*Reproduced by permission of The Commissioner, U.S. Bureau of Reclamation.*)

fault about 20 feet wide parallel to the stream along the sound rock of the east bank. . . . In addition, deeper excavation along the line of the cutoff showed that a weak, inferior bedrock could be expected to continue below the existing elevation of foundation excavation.

Further and more extensive geological inspection of the site was made in the light of foundation excavation. . . . Excavation in streambed over the foundation area revealed sound rock walls about 90 feet apart at the upstream toe and 50 feet apart at the downstream edge of the structure. . . . Excavation in the cutoff indicated that conditions could not be bettered by going deeper. The alternative was to provide a foundation structure across streambed to equalize that portion of the load which could be carried by the weaker rock and transfer the remainder to the sound rock of the walls.

Fig. 13.16. Rodriguez Dam, Mexico; close-up view of the special arch incorporated into the foundation because of the presence of a fault. (*Reproduced by permission of the Ambursen Dam Co.*)

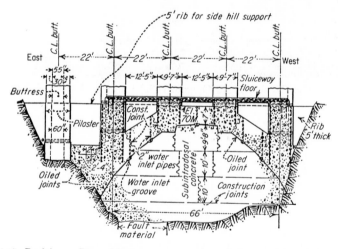

Fig. 13.17. Rodriguez Dam, Mexico; cross section of the special arch incorporated into the foundation near the downstream end. (*Reproduced by permission of The Editor, Engineering News-Record.*)

Eventually, after much study and approval by a consulting board, a concrete arch with a span across the stream bed varying from 86 to 76 ft, with the barrel 225 ft long, was designed; the space between the intrados of the arch and the stream bed was built up with lean concrete to provide a support for constructing the arch and to transfer a portion of the load vertically, although no allowance for this was made in the arch design. The arch was successfully constructed, and the dam completed.[13.31]

Fig. 13.18. The Pozzillo Dam of Eras, Palermo, from the left bank of the Salso River, Sicily, Italy, showing the special concrete-block construction: the dam is 56.50 m high and 195.84 m long on the crest. (*Reproduced by permission of Dr. Inq. Claudio Marcello, Consulting Engineer.*)

Finally, reference may be made to a dam incorporating in its design a considerable degree of flexibility not in anticipation of earthquake shocks or movement over faults, but because of the possibility of differential settlement between one part of the dam and another. The Salso River Dam is located in Sicily, Italy, near Pozzillo above the Catania Plain. Part is founded on sandstone but the downstream section had to be founded on clay. It is a gravity structure, 183 ft high and 770 ft long. The structure was built of individual blocks of concrete, suitably proportioned to give the necessary shape, approximately cubes of about 13 ft side. The upstream face was formed by a continuous metal plate, keyed into the sandstone, in order to provide a watertight membrane. The blocks were connected with specially designed joints, incorporating provision for some sliding in case of differential settlement when full load is against the dam.[13.32]

13.9. Permeability of Bedrock. The second essential requirement of a rock foundation bed for a dam is that the entire geological structure underlying the site of the dam, in addition to being strong enough to carry the designed loads, shall be sound enough to provide a watertight barrier to the water impounded by the dam. Although the requirement is so obvious, dams have failed because of its neglect, and an imposing and tragic list could be produced in confirmation of this statement. One example only will be mentioned, since it has been termed "the greatest object lesson that the history of engineering foundations had to offer." The Hales Bar Dam on the Tennessee River in the United States was founded on a pure but soluble limestone well known for its cavernous formation. Cavities were encountered to such an extent during the excavation of the dam site that completion was delayed several years, and the cost was increased far beyond the original estimate. Several hundred thousand barrels of cement were injected into the fissures and openings in the underlying rock. The dam site is located on a syncline, the lower side of which is especially susceptible to solution water. Further trouble due to this cause was foretold, notably by L. C. Glenn, not long after the dam was put into use.

About 10 years after the dam had been completed (in 1926), leakage through this limestone had become quite serious, and many unusual methods were used in attempts to provide an effective seal, including the use of various kinds of mattresses and the dumping of rocks, gravel, clay, and bales of hay. Success was achieved only by drilling a large number of holes to an average depth of about 90 ft and injecting into these hot liquid asphalt, the flow of which was assisted by ingenious devices; over 11,000 bbl of asphalt was used. The process was later repeated, and leakage was eventually stopped. By 1941, however, leakage had again increased, amounting then to 1,700 cfs, so that further remedial action had to be taken. The dam was now owned by the Tennessee Valley Authority. The geological and engineering staffs of the TVA made careful studies, and many rehabilitation schemes were evolved. It was finally decided to form a continuous curtain of concrete along the face line of the dam by means of continuously connected calyx drill holes, 18 in. in diameter. More than 200 holes were drilled to depths up to 60 ft; the total length of drilling exceeded 12,000 ft. The holes were lined with cement-asbestos pipe and then filled with concrete. Study of the Bangor limestone obtained from cores at this time showed a rate of solution much greater than would be expected for most limestones, a fact dramatically demonstrated by the troubles caused by leakage at the

Hales Bar Dam. The dam stands and serves well today but it is said to have cost over $10 million, and it took almost 20 years to stop the leakage beneath it.[13.33]

The first reason for having rock strata underlying dams as watertight as possible is obviously to make sure that no water escapes. Not only is this necessary from the point of view of water conservation, but it is also essential because any steady flow through a solid rock formation is certain to have some erosive action, which in all probability will gradually

Fig. 13.19. The Hales Bar Dam, now of the Tennessee Valley Authority, showing drilling in progress for the prosecution of leakage remedial works. (*Reproduced by permission of the Chief Engineer, Tennessee Valley Authority.*)

but steadily intensify the defective conditions causing the original leakage. The geological investigations already mentioned will indicate the underground structure to be encountered along the line of the dam, and from a study of this cross section a general idea, at least, of the effectiveness of the strata in retaining water can be obtained. Naturally, limestone and all soft rock formations are suspect until proved to be sound; limestone formations, especially, are unusually soluble and so characterized by underground caverns or open fissures.

Although limestone causes most of the geological troubles in foundations, it was a shale and sandstone combination that presented one of the most unusual examples known to the writer of a permeable foundation bed for a dam. The Santa Felicia Dam of the United Water Conservation District of California is a 200-ft rolled-earth dam located due north of Los Angeles on Piru Creek. It lies over sandstones and shales of Miocene age, much folded and tilted and known to be oil bearing. One oil well was actually located in the reservoir and further drilling was contemplated. The District had therefore to pay for the abandonment of this part of the oil field and for the capping of producing wells in the reservoir area; this cost $200,000. Oil at the dam site was therefore suspected, but as test drilling proceeded, oil was encountered in every one of the test borings and in the 70 grout holes drilled into the old stream bed. Gas under pressure was struck by some holes. All holes had to be sealed off, and oil seeps (of which there were many) had to be capped just before earth fill was placed over them. Anticipated water pressure would more than counteract the oil and gas pressure when the reservoir was filled, but this unusual "permeability" of the foundation strata made the construction of the Santa Felicia Dam a somewhat uncommon operation.[13.34]

In addition to study of all relevant geological information, including the detailed results of all boring, tests should be carried out whenever possible by means of the boreholes used for obtaining core samples. The use of carefully controlled and observed water-pressure tests in these holes provides a fairly reliable confirmation of underground structural soundness. If the holes hold water under the maximum test pressures, it is clear that the strata penetrated by the test holes are watertight in the neighborhood of the holes. This qualification is a necessary reminder that water-pressure tests in drill holes are not an infallible guide; when considered in conjunction with ascertained geological structural data, however, such tests can be a reasonably reliable indication of watertightness. Pressure tests of this nature were utilized in connection with the geological investigation of the Madden Dam site in the Panama Canal Zone, although in this case water was forced under pressure into flowing wells to see whether they would provide underground connection to other wells or any other possible means of escape for the test water. For tests of this kind, the use of color dyes, which will be dealt with in the following chapter in connection with leakage from reservoirs, is often of value. Tests were also carried out, during the Madden investigation, on the permeability of test specimens of the rock types encountered; the tests were made on core samples taken from drill holes. The apparatus employed was not unlike the standard type used for testing permeability of unconsolidated material; the specimens were packed into sections of steel pipe with lead wool and steam packing and subjected to a head of 80 psi.[13.35]

In addition to the possibility of major leaks, an almost equally serious problem is presented by the danger of minor leaks, especially on the site of the dam structure itself. Springs are included in this category; if noted either before or during construction, or if preliminary investigations suggest that they may tend to form at constant planes after construction is complete, the most careful precautions must be taken to box them out when the lower courses of the dam are being built so that they may be suitably connected with the drainage system.

This last possibility is probably the most difficult to investigate before construction and the most potentially dangerous, since the slight leakage of water that may occur between rock surface and dam structure after completion will probably give rise to what is generally known as "uplift pressure." Uplift pressure was not, as is sometimes suggested, neglected in all early dam designs; this is made clear by the following quotation. Dr. Deacon, describing the design of the Vyrnwy Dam to which reference has already been made, stated (in 1896) that:[13.36]

> Although no visible springs of water issued from the beds of rock thus exposed, it was by no means certain that, when the reservoir was formed and the head on one side became 144 feet, springs subject to that pressure would not occur. Moreover, a mere moisture, rapidly evaporated when exposed to air might when sealed down acquire a pressure from the adjoining hills of far more than that due to the intended level of the lake . . . and the Author agreed with him [the late Mr. T. Hawkesley] in thinking it desirable to provide relief drains, which so far as he is aware, had not been done in connection with any former masonry dam.

The predictions of Messrs. Hawkesley and Deacon have been generally confirmed at many dams on which tests of uplift pressure have been made. Many of these are founded on perfectly sound rock strata so that the uplift pressures may be said to be independent, in these cases at least, of geological structure. At other dams the reverse is true and therefore uplift pressures may rightly be classed generally as a problem associated with the geology of dam sites.

Drainage has long been a matter for keen debate, but the general consensus appears to be that, provided the drains are carefully located and are of such a size and character that they cannot possibly become blocked, their installation is a wise precaution. Drainage trenches filled with crushed rock and provided with suitable outlets constitute a usual expedient. Inspection galleries inside a dam structure are often connected with the drainage system so that regular checks on the drainage can be made; and in a case known to the author, one of the inspection galleries is located on the rock floor itself in order that the rock surface can be periodically examined.

There remain to be considered possible means of increasing the impermeability of a dam foundation consisting of rock. Sometimes this work can change an unsuitable site into one that can be utilized with confidence. An obvious solution, often adopted to seal temporary cofferdams, is to use a blanket of impervious unconsolidated material, such as clay, upstream of the dam structure so that any leakage passing under or around the dam will tend to draw the material into the cavities and in this way seal them tight. When large cavities are known to exist, bulky materials, e.g., bales of hay, may first be used to block the main openings. Although these measures failed to stop leakage in the Hales Bar Dam, they have been successfully utilized elsewhere. Of more general application is the grouting or cementation of the underlying rock strata; this will be considered separately in the following section.

Fig. 13.20. Typical view in limestone cavern at the site of the Madden Dam, Panama Canal, prior to sealing by clay grouting. The reprecipitated calcite lining the walls may be seen. (*Reproduced by permission of The Governor, Canal Zone.*)

13.10. Grouting of Foundation Beds. Grouting may be generally described as the injection of suitable material into certain sections of the earth's crust, under pressure and through the medium of specially drilled holes, in order to seal any open fissures, cracks, cavities, or other openings in the strata encountered. Cementation is a word applied to grouting in some cases when a slurry of portland cement (either alone or mixed with a proportion of sand) is used as the sealing material; it is also used in a proprietary connection. In addition to cement, clay, asphalt, and various combinations of chemical solutions are used to form the necessary seal.

Clay was apparently first used on a major scale in the sealing of the limestone foundation beds underlying the Madden Reservoir in the Panama Canal Zone. The limestone formations encountered are badly weathered in central localities and contain underground caverns and fissures, which render them far from the watertight barrier required to form the bed of this reservoir. Cement grouting was considered impracticable because of the presence of a loamy sand lining the caverns and crevices, with which the cement would not bond. Considerations of expense ruled out the possibility of using asphalt, and so the board of consultants for the project suggested the use of clay. A valuable series of experiments was carried out, the results of which demonstrated that the best effects were obtained with mixtures of clay and water containing about 55 per cent water. Grout of this consistency traveled up to 50 ft underground and penetrated seams as narrow as $\frac{1}{2}$ in. It was found that the mixture had to be prepared with the aid of blungers, such as those that are used in the ceramic industry; screens were also necessary. On this job, 3- and 7-in.-diameter drill holes were used, and the pressure varied with the consistency of the grout. Excavation of small pits at surface blowouts showed up several well-grouted seams, and other specific test results demonstrated the special utility of this method of grouting for the cavernous limestone encountered.[13.37] Although clay does not give such a perfect seal as cement, for example, it can be employed where cement cannot be used and therefore is a useful tool of the foundation engineer.

Another example of a somewhat similar kind was the use of a fine, red, sandy loam, having a high clay content, mixed with a small proportion of cement (varying up to a mixture of 1 part cement to 6 parts soil) as grouting material for sealing an old earth-fill dam near Huguenot, New York, which supplies the Port Jervis community with water. No information on subsurface strata was available when the dam was raised, and serious leakage subsequently developed. To stop this, an extensive test-boring and grouting program had to be carried out to seal boulder and gravel strata previously unsuspected. The case is a good example of the expense that can be caused by lack of adequate construction records.[13.38]

French engineers have further developed the use of clay for grouting in recent years by adopting a finely powdered clay in suspension, so selected that it will have some thixotropic action. Such clays must have high liquid limits; sodium bentonitic clays have been found to be most satisfactory. Chemical grouting has also been adopted for special cases of trouble with dam foundations, but its application to this field cannot be expected to become widespread in view of its cost and specialist character. Aqueous emulsions of bitumen have also been used, especially when the main function of the grout was to reduce permeability rather than to fill open voids. Asphalt was used for the latter purpose in connection with the Hales Bar Dam, as has been noted. It was also used for forming the necessary cutoff wall at the Claytor Dam on the New River near Radford, Virginia. Founded on a stratified gray dolomite with shale and chert present in seams, the dam was located over some large solution channels that naturally had to be filled. After a study of various possibilities was made, the asphalt-sand mixture was decided upon. Mixed in a standard construction premix plant, the asphalt was, in general, dumped into place, but its consistency was such that it penetrated into fine seams and acted as a satisfactory grout.[13.39] Details of these and other methods are to be found in the references cited; they are noted here in order to show how engineers can overcome poor rock conditions when the geology of a dam site has to be accepted and used to best advantage.

Grouting with cement is the most usual method adopted, and civil engineering literature contains references to its successful application to many different types of work. The method depends essentially on the fact that if portland cement is mixed in a slurry with water, it will, in course of time, "set up" hard and bond satisfactorily with other materials such as rock with which it may be in contact. Originally, the grout was simply poured into open cavities and allowed to set freely. Eventually, the idea of forcing the grout into normally inaccessible cavities by the use of pressure was developed. The origin of cement grouting is a matter of conjecture; it seems probable that the Romans were at least familiar with the idea, even though they had no means of using pressure for injection. Pressure grouting was certainly used to some extent in the nineteenth century, but not until James Greathead invented his grouting machine at the end of the century for assisting in the construction of tube railway tunnels in London did it become a regular construction operation.

The first dam foundation effectively sealed by grouting of which the author has been able to trace written details was that of the Kinder Embankment of the Stockport Corporation, England. During the construction of this work (from 1903 to 1905), the bedrock was found to be so fissured and faulted that it could not support the originally intended masonry dam; a satisfactory shale bed was eventually found at a depth of 180 ft below ground level. In the construction of the trench to this depth, much trouble was encountered with water. The drainpipes installed to tap the water, as concreting advanced, were carried up until water ceased to flow from them and then grouted up under pressure, a practice now frequently followed.[13.40] One of the first dam projects on which pressure grouting was used in the United States was the Estacada Dam constructed in Oregon in 1912.[13.41]

Concurrently, the use of grouting in mining operations was progressing, especially for the sealing of water-bearing strata in such operations as shaft sinking. A pioneer in this work was Albert François. In the early years of the century, François worked out and developed the use of a special direct-acting pump capable of developing 3,000 psi pressure; flexible and reliable mechanical controls; the use of cementation pipes sealed into the ground; and the employment of special chemical solutions, lubricating in their action, to ensure the cementation of all fine cracks encountered. Development work has naturally taken place along general lines other than those associated with this particular process, so that it can now be said that cementation is an accepted part of foundation engineering practice, capable of accurate planning and control if considered with proper relation to the geological structure concerned.

British practice contains many interesting examples of cementation as applied to dam construction, including several cases in which its use has materially reduced the necessary depth of cutoff walls. Precementation has been another feature of British practice; the term is used to indicate the cementation of underlying strata before dam excavation is begun. The object of precementation is twofold: to consolidate effectively (by means of the cement grout) the material that has to be excavated and to obtain the benefit of the superincumbent weight of undisturbed strata over the fissures being sealed. This weight is necessary to prevent vertical lifting of rock strata above fissures which the pressure on the grout tends to cause, movement that has been readily observed in a number of cases. Precementation can be carried out even through surface strata of unconsolidated material if the drill holes used are suitably cased, but this introduces the risk of leakage occurring at the junction with solid-rock strata; it is always advisable, therefore, to strip unconsolidated materials before cementation is undertaken.

Considerable savings can be effected by the careful application of this method, as was clearly brought out in its use at the Scout Dyke Dam site in England. This is an interesting example, especially since vertical shafts were used from which horizontal drill holes, in addition to the usual vertical drill holes, were made. Work on the dam, which is an earth-fill structure forming part of the Barnsley Corporation Waterworks, Yorkshire, England, was started in 1924. Underlying the site are alternating beds of sandstone and shale; a bed of permeable sandstone outcrops in the stream throughout the length of the reservoir, and below this is a tight bed of shale. The sandstone bed was found, by means of trial borings, to be almost horizontal and uniform in thickness along the line of the dam. In order to avoid taking the trench down to the depths that the position of this bed necessitated (over 80 ft at the ends of the dam), cementation was resorted to, and afterward the trench was taken down only to the first sound shale or sandstone encountered. A series of vertical boreholes 25 ft apart was put down into the impervious shale underlying the sandstone encountered at stream level, and cement was injected into them. Later, when the trench was excavated, shafts were sunk 200 ft apart to

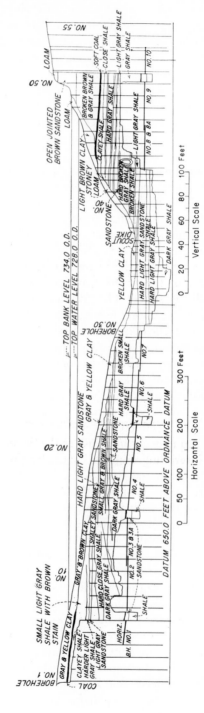

Fig. 13.21. Geological section along trench of the Scout Dyke Dam, Barnsley, England, showing boreholes used for precementation. (*Reproduced by permission of The Institution of Water Engineers.*)

528

the same level as the bottom of the boreholes, horizontal holes were drilled between them, and cement was again injected. In this way, any vertical joints possibly missed by the boreholes were sealed. All holes were drilled with a view to obtaining cores, and the evidence thus obtained was a valuable addition to preliminary information. It was found during the progress of the work that grouting pressures of not more than 400 psi had undoubtedly lifted strata so that the limiting pressure was reduced to 100 psi. Careful estimates of cost were kept which proved

Fig. 13.22. Abitibi Canyon power project, northern Ontario, Canada; general view of excavation for dam, looking upstream, showing main cofferdam, diversion-tunnel intakes, and deep shaft for excavation of unsound rock. (*Reproduced by permission of the Hydro Electric Power Commission of Ontario.*)

beyond doubt the great monetary saving achieved by this precementation program.[13.42]

Cementation under high pressure was carried out for a very different purpose in the construction of the Abitibi Canyon water-power dam in northern Ontario, Canada. This large structure, located on a river flowing into Hudson Bay, is founded on gabbro which preliminary test borings showed to be free from seams and fissures. When the site of the dam in the canyon was unwatered, it was found that along the stream bed there was a zone of rock which, for a width of about 40 ft, had been altered in composition and texture by possible faulting and by the passage of intrusive gases through the rock when molten. Since it was not known whether or not this zone would be impervious to water, a shaft was sunk to a depth of over 100 ft below river level at the upstream face of the dam. No water was encountered, and the rock appeared to be sound; but it was decided to carry on exploratory work by drilling from the bottom of the shaft, and when seams or porosity was found, to use cement grout at pressures not less than the full static head from the reservoir with water at top level. This course was followed, and the excavation was concreted up so that construction of the main body of the dam could continue; a smaller shaft was boxed out, measuring 10 by 12 ft, with an enlargement at the bottom. From this shaft, holes were drilled, and grouting was carried out at 10-ft stages in each hole, using pressures up to 250 psi. In addition, grouting was carried out in old exploratory drill holes in the canyon walls and from inspection galleries left in the dam; a total of 1,527 bags of cement were used with satisfactory results.[13.43]

The foregoing examples have been cited because of their major geological interest. It has been, however, in connection with the construction of large dams in the United States during the second quarter of this century that perhaps the greatest progress has taken place in developing the techniques of cement grouting. Notable have been the practices developed by the Tennessee Valley Authority, to mention but one of the several large American engineering organizations that have contributed to this advance. This has been of necessity, in view of the poor foundation conditions, usually in limestone, available for several of the large TVA dams. Early experience with the foundations for the Norris Dam may be cited in view of its extent and pioneer interest. The dam is a gravity structure located on the Clinch River about 80 miles above its confluence with the Tennessee River; it is 285 ft high and floods an area of 34,200 acres at normal pool level. The entire valley above and below the dam site is underlain by Knox dolomite; in many locations there are underground caves and porous beds. The dolomite was described in official reports as "a comparatively hard and substantial rock . . . quite massive, compact and sound. Some jointing has occurred . . . [with] occasional seams, of importance in regard to possible leakage." Complete exploration of the dam site confirmed previously expressed opinions of consultative boards to the effect that the foundation rock itself is characterized by massive thick strata of excellent rock interrupted at definite intervals by horizontal seams which are partly open, partly clay filled, and for a portion of the area in close contact. A comprehensive grouting program was laid out covering the entire base area of the dam, spillway apron, and powerhouse. The grouting treatment was divided into two parts: shallow, low-pressure grouting covering the entire area of the foundation; and deep, high-pressure grouting to form an impermeable curtain under the heel of the structure. On the reservoir rim, the work involved the determination of the location of those portions in need of treatment to prevent excessive leakage and the grouting of the parts found to be faulty.

Spacing of the drill holes through which grouting was done is shown in Fig. 13.23. A system of interlocking patterns was chosen for the shallow grouting. All seams were washed out by reversing air and water flow between adjacent holes prior to grouting. One complete pattern was first drilled and grouted to a depth of 20 ft. Following this primary

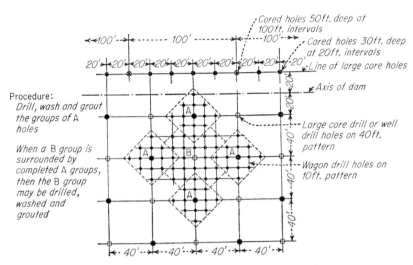

Fig. 13.23. Diagrammatic plan of holes used for grouting formation beds for the Norris Dam, Tennessee River, Tennessee, U.S.A. (*Reproduced by permission of The Editor, Engineering News-Record.*)

grouting, a system of 40-ft holes, evenly spaced betwteen those first drilled, was superimposed upon the original pattern, and the same sequence of operations was repeated. After the dam had been built to a height of 100 ft, deep foundation grouting holes were drilled from the lower gallery to establish a deep grouting curtain. This curtain is located approximately 6 ft downstream from the axis of the dam. The work of drilling and grouting the holes 10 ft apart in the galleries was divided into three parts. First, groups of three holes on 100-ft centers between groups were drilled, washed, and grouted, after which groups of three holes halfway between the first groups were similarly treated. This left space for two holes between the first and second groups, and these were drilled last. In general, a refusal pressure of 150 psi was used in the curtain grouting.[13.44]

At almost every one of the major TVA structures, new experience was gained with the art of grouting in limestone. At the Chickamauga Dam, for example, founded on a fissured and cavernous limestone overlain by 40 to 50 ft of overburden, ranging from good sandy-clay loam to mixed gravel, and finally limestone slabs and clay, subsurface conditions were found to be so variable that most of the original grout holes, on 100-ft centers, missed the worst areas. One large cavern was found as much as 90 ft below normal river level. Because of the size of caverns to be filled, grouting was developed in which a mixture of sand, bentonite, and cement was used.[13.45] Published records make the invaluable experience thus gained available to the public. Records exist not only for dams of the TVA but also for structures built by the U.S. Bureau of Reclamation. Brief reference to one of these, the Hoover Dam, must be made. All grouting work was specified in detail with regard to materials, pressures, and procedure. The contractors, Six Companies, Inc., developed special equipment for this as well as for other parts of the work. Wherever concrete was to be placed against rock, advance provision was made for forcing grout into rock fissures and seams, if any existed. While concreting was in progress, special pipe connections were installed through which grout could later be forced when the dam was carrying full water load, in order to seal effectively the contact between concrete and rock. By means of carefully planned drill holes, the attempt was made to provide a grout cutoff "curtain" in the bedrock across the dam site; and to assist in attaining this objective, grout holes were drilled from the outlet tunnels up to 150 ft deep. After the construction of the dam had advanced appreciably, grouting was also carried out from the inspection galleries left in the body of the dam. Checks on the efficacy of the grouting were made by taking out cores of grouted rock; these showed satisfactory results. Pressures used varied up to 1,000 psi; the average quantity of cement used (neat cement was used throughout) was 0.8 sack per ft of hole for all the longer holes.[13.46]

In other lands, too, grouting has become an almost essential part of the practice of dam construction. Many modern European dams, especially the daring arched dams that now distinguish many of the spectacular gorges in high mountains, are assisted in their functioning by hidden "grout curtains" carefully placed in the surrounding rock. The Saint Pierrett Cognet Dam, an important unit in the Drac development in France, may be considered typical. Although the dam is 75 m high, the gorge in which it is located is so narrow that the entire structure contains only 38,000 cu m of concrete. The gorge is in a highly fissured Bajocian Lias, reasonably watertight but subject to surface weathering. The rock surrounding the dam absorbed 300 *tonnes* of cement at the rate of 30 kg per sq m of finished curtain.[13.47] Figure 13.24 illustrates clearly the extent of the grouting necessary to seal marl and limestone strata at the site of the Foum El Gherza Dam in Algeria.

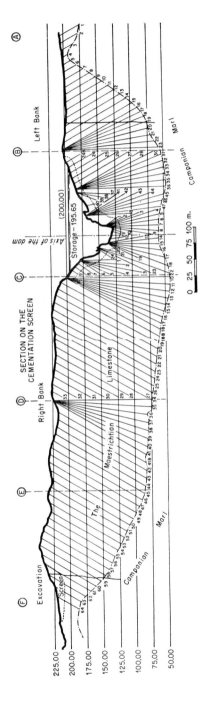

FIG. 13.24. Section showing the extensive grout curtain formed at the site of the Foum El Gherza Dam in the Sahara Zone of Algeria to seal the marl and limestone strata shown; sulfate-resisting cement was used. (*Reproduced by permission of le Société Nationale Electricité et Gaz d'Algérie, and the Editor of Travaux from Travaux, 282, August, 1958.*)

The most extensive use of cement grout known to the writer is not, however, in North America or in Europe, but in northeastern Iraq. The great Dokan project is a combined irrigation, water-supply, flood-control, and water-power development; the main retaining structure is an arched concrete dam, 116 m high, across the Lesser Zab River. The rock succession at the dam site starts at the surface with a marl, under which is thinly bedded limestone, and then dolomite; an important "contact zone" occurs between the weathered surface of the dolomite and the limestone. The dam is located almost at the top of an anticlinal fold, and the "contact zone" is exposed in both abutments. Careful preliminary work showed the necessity of extensive grouting; this had to be carried out, eventually, over a total length (including the dam) of 2,451 m. Special tunnels were excavated in both abutments to facilitate the grouting work which was carried out to depths up to 60 m, where a pressure of 40 kg per sq cm was used. Table 13.1 summarizes the main statistics of this

Table 13.1

Project	Area of curtain, sq ft	Total drilling, ft	Total injection, met. tonnes
Dokan......................	4,528,000	601,000	77,766
Hoover Dam...............	1,116,000*	190,981	13,250
Camarasa (Spain)............	3,102,000*	169,402	186,000
Chickamauga (T.V.A.).........	228,000*	477,427	59,500
Bin-el-Ouidane (Morocco)......	1,453,000	121,000	27,122

* Approximate only.

SOURCE: Reproduced, by permission, from G. M. Binnie, J. G. Campbell, P. F. F. Lancaster-Jones, and G. A. Gillott: The Dokan Project: The Flood Disposal Works and The Grouted Cut-off Curtain, *Proc. Inst. Civil Eng.*, **14**: 157-204, (1959).

grouting operation and shows comparable figures for four other dams, two of which have already been mentioned. It is not, therefore, surprising to find that the grouting work for the Dokan Dam, including the two tunnels, cost £2.85 million.[13.48]

From relatively insignificant beginnings, pressure grouting, or cementation, has developed into an important feature of all major construction operations. The actual performance of grouting operations is essentially an engineering matter, but successful application depends on an accurate knowledge of underlying geological structure, just as does the need for the application of grouting. Grouting must therefore always be a co-operative endeavor of engineer and geologist, and the success of the operations described in the foregoing typical examples has been dependent to a large extent on such joint action.

13.11. Dams on Permeable Foundation Beds. Discussion of dam foundations up to this point has been confined to structures constituting watertight barriers across a valley; watertightness was achieved either by founding the dam directly on impermeable rock or by having some type of cutoff wall constructed below the dam structure proper, connecting it to a solid-rock floor below. There are many sites at which dams have been required but at which solid rock exists only at very great depths below existing ground level. The unconsolidated deposits on which a dam structure must be founded at these sites present many unusual problems of design and construction. In permeable strata such as sands and gravels, the stability of "floating dams," as they are sometimes called, depends on a predetermined safe rate of flow beneath the dam; in impermeable strata, for example, clay formations, reliance must be placed on the efficiency of the clay as a seal against uncontrolled flow beneath the dam. In both cases, accurate knowledge of the nature of the unconsolidated deposits to be encountered is as essential for design as for construction.

Thus the importance of preliminary geological studies at dam sites again comes up for emphasis. Methods of investigation need not be detailed again, nor even an example given, since general procedure and the analysis of results are similar whatever the geological conditions at the dam site may be. Novelty enters in as a result of the fact that the unconsolidated deposits now have to be regarded as constituent parts of the structure, necessitating detailed testing prior to use in design, instead of as something to be got rid of by excavation or penetrated by cutoff trench or sheeting. Soil sampling must therefore be a feature of preliminary work. The soil characteristics to be investigated in connection with dams on foundation beds of unconsolidated materials are common to other branches of civil engineering work, but there is probably no other branch of civil engineering work in which close correlation of geology and soil studies is so absolutely essential.

13.12. Materials of Construction. The availability of suitable local materials for the construction of a dam will naturally be a determining factor in the economic studies of every dam project, and it may often affect the choice of the type of dam. Although the actual volume of material to be placed in a dam will be very much greater if it is built of rock or soil instead of concrete, the lower unit costs involved will always warrant consideration of the alternatives before a final decision is reached. In mountainous areas, rock-fill dams are frequently "obvious" solutions, but the difficulty of adequately sealing them impeded their widespread adoption for many years. With the development of sloping impervious blankets, however, a device applied in the design of the Nantahala Dam on the headwaters of the Little Tennessee River in 1942, rock-fill dams have gained new recognition and their number is steadily increasing. Requirements for sound foundations for rock-fill dams are the same as those for concrete and masonry dams. There is now the further geological requirement that the rock available must be suitable for the purpose intended; it must be known that the rock can be quarried in the sizes necessary and will be reasonably durable when in place in the dam and so submerged in water. Limestone is again a rock to be questioned for such use.

The use of rock-fill dams always calls for careful study of the material to be used. There may therefore be mentioned an example of rock-fill

Fig. 13.25. The Kenney sloping core rock fill on the headwaters of the Fraser River, British Columbia, Canada, just as impounding water was starting, showing access roads and borrow-pit areas. (*Reproduced by permission of the Aluminum Co. of Canada, Ltd.*)

dam construction which emphasizes several matters already generally discussed. The Los Angeles County Flood Control District was set up in 1915 to carry out flood-protection work and water conservation for Los Angeles County. In 1924, $25 million of the funds raised by bond issue were allocated for the construction of a concrete gravity dam of unprecedented size in the San Gabriel Canyon. Work was begun under contract in 1929, and completion of the dam was expected within 6 years.[13.49]

While excavation was still under way a serious earth slip at the west abutment resulted in holding up the work for a further study of foundations. Before the end of 1929 the contract for constructing the dam was cancelled.

Surveys for a new dam site developed what was thought to be a safe and satisfactory location just above high water level of the reservoir of the Morris Dam, constructed by the city of Pasadena lower down the San Gabriel Canyon. At this site it was proposed to build a rockfill dam . . . to have a height of 300 feet above streambed, a crest length of 1,670 feet, and a base thickness of 900 feet at streambed level. . . . A contract was awarded in the latter part of 1932. . . . After that contract was made, work in the quarry progressed satisfactorily, although the unexpectedly large percentage of material that had to be rejected resulted in low yardages delivered at the dam.

Fig. 13.26. San Gabriel Flood Control Dam No. 1, under construction in August, 1934; concrete toe wall in the foreground and Quarry No. 10 in the background. (*Reproduced by permission of the Chief Engineer, Los Angeles County Flood Control District.*)

. . . Up to October 1st, 1934, approximately 3,650,000 cubic yards of material, including stripping and waste, or the equivalent of about two thirds of the total volume of the dam, had been removed from the quarry. But little more than one tenth of this material actually went into the dam. [Quotation amended and corrected.]

After further conferences and reports, work on the new contract was temporarily held up, and the dam design was revised again to take into consideration the rock available from the quarry. On this basis, the work was satisfactorily completed in July, 1937. Over 10 million cu yd of material was finally placed in the dam; about 1 million cu yd was a sand-clay mixture used as an impervious blanket near the upstream face, and all other material was quarried rock. All loose rock fill was placed with the aid of sluicing; shrinkage approximated 6 per cent. The dam is functioning satisfactorily, having already been tested by severe floods. A smaller rock-fill dam, known as San Gabriel Dam No. 2, was constructed about the same period. No trouble was experienced with rock supply in this case; the main difficulty involved the settlement of the rock fill when near completion, which was attributed to lack of sluicing for compaction of the fill. These brief details of a notable water-conservation project (a full bibliography for which is noted) serve to illustrate the vital importance of material supply and, in particular, of rock fill. Geological advice was repeatedly taken in connection with this work, though some of the geological difficulties were unpredictable.

Although not generally so recognized, one of the greatest contributions to the practice of civil engineering from the still developing study of soil mechanics has been the requisite knowledge for the use of soil as a material in the construction of major dams. Even the most cursory examination of the record of dam building in North America and elsewhere will show that earth dams have steadily progressed in over-all size and in height since the formal recognition of soil mechanics in the mid-thirties. Approval has now been given for the construction of what will be the highest North American dam of soil, not concrete; this is the proposed Oroville dam of the Feather River project of the Water Resources Department of California. It will be 730 ft high, topping the 726-ft Hoover Dam. It will contain 79 million cu yd of soil, but even this quantity was exceeded by the Oahe Dam built on the Missouri River by the United States Corps of Engineers; the Oahe Dam contains 91 million cu yd. The Oroville Dam will be a composite structure; a gorge in the bottom of the valley of the Feather River will be filled by a 1-million-yd "plug" of concrete, over which the earth dam will be built. Material for the earth dam will be brought from old gold-dredge tailing deposits, 10 miles downstream; this material has been found to be almost perfectly graded for the formation of the pervious part of the dam; suitable material for the impervious core is also conveniently available.[13.50]

It is but rarely that such an ideal supply of soil is so readily available, although the highest earth-fill dam yet completed was almost as favorably situated. The Swift Dam on the Lewis River in southwestern Washington is 512 ft high; it was completed in November, 1958. It contains 16 million cu yd of material, most of which was available in the form of reworked mudflow material in large terrace deposits a short distance above the dam site on Swift Creek. Substantial deposits of relatively clean sand and gravel were found 1½ miles upstream; thus, the supply and handling of material for the dam was relatively economical and easy.[13.51] In some cases, soil has to be treated before use. For one or two earth dams, available soil had excessive natural moisture content and so had to be dried before use. Material for the Green Mountain Dam, a part of the Colorado–Big Thompson project of the U.S. Bureau of Reclamation, was obtained from a glacial moraine. This dam is 310 ft high and contains more than 4 million cu yd. The contractor for the work installed a specially designed sorting plant through which material larger than 3 in. in diameter could be separated out. This coarser material included large glacial boulders and was useful for the pervious part of the dam; provision of such coarse material, especially for riprap, is sometimes a problem in areas in which no solid rock is exposed.[13.52] Precast concrete

FIG. 13.27. The Swift River earth-fill dam, Washington, U.S.A., with its reservoir full; Mount Adams is seen in the background. (*Reproduced by permission of the Vice President and Chief Engineer, Pacific Power and Light Company.*)

blocks have sometimes been tried for this purpose but in at least one case they did not prove successful; instead, boulders had to be placed over a properly graded coarse filter.

If only as a reminder that earth dams are not peculiar to North America, brief reference may finally be made to the Serre-Ponçon Dam of Electricité de France. Another part of the Durance development, this notable structure is located in the French Alps at what appears to be an ideal dam site on La Durance River near the towns of Embrun and Gap. The river here flowed through a narrow gorge formed in limestone formations of the Lower Lias, close to a broad valley in Embrunais black marl. So obvious was this a site for a dam that explorations started in 1913. It was soon found, however, by means of many test borings and the driving of test shafts and tunnels that, although there was no buried glacial river course, the natural valley reached a depth below present surface level of 110 m and was filled with alluvial material. Even these deposits were unusual since rock scree, falling from the sides of the gorge, had become embedded with the alluvial material and in some cases was surrounded by a clay matrix. Subsurface conditions were further

FIG. 13.28. The Serre-Ponçon Dam on La Durance River, France, under construction; the view shows the apparently ideal site. (*Photograph by M. Barranger; reproduced by permission of Electricité de France.*)

complicated by the presence of thermal waters at a temperature of 60°C, highly charged with calcium sulfate, leached from the gypsum Lias below and seeping upward through faults and seams in the limestone. Plans for the "obvious" mass concrete or arched dam had therefore to be abandoned and the site was left unused until the progress of soil mechanics made an earth dam of requisite size an economic and engineering possibility. An earth dam has therefore been constructed on this interesting site; it is 600 m wide at its crest and 650 m long along the valley floor.[13.53]

In the cases cited, and indeed in every earth dam, geology is an essential aid to the engineers responsible not only in connection with the foundation condition but also in relation to the supply of the necessary construction materials. Pleistocene geology shows itself, once again, as the inevitable companion study to soil mechanics; in the selection of material for use in earth dams and embankments, the two disciplines should be inseparable.

13.13. Construction Problems. It is fitting to include at the end of this list of special problems a note on those which arise during construction operations. To emphasize the fact that study of geological conditions at a dam site must be continuous from the start of preliminary operations up to and beyond the final passing of the cleaned and prepared rock surface as the approved foundation bed, this section is inserted. A problem that may be regarded as essentially part of the construction operations consists in the removal of all rotten and disintegrated rock; keeping accurate records of all rock that is so removed is equally important. When finally the approved foundation bed is ready for undertaking the building of the dam, a complete and detailed survey of the bed must be made; this is one of the most critical duties of a resident engineer. Although record surveys of this kind may seem to be unimportant at the time, they can often prove to be of inestimable benefit; their value is incalculable because if they are not accurately made when the foundation bed is ready, they can never be obtained again. The author writes on this point from personal experience of a rock-surface survey so obtained in the depth of a Canadian winter which proved to be of great and unexpected assistance when an adjoining section of a dam was constructed in the following spring.

There are some detailed matters in connection with the preparation of a rock foundation bed which call for mention. One essential of construction is to get as good a bond as possible between concrete and rock. To obtain this, the rock surface must be clean, free from all loose particles of material (even though they be rock fragments), and free from standing pools of water, however small, when concreting operations start. Opinions differ concerning the methods to be used when a glaciated rock surface is encountered, but it is generally agreed that any polished surfaces should at least be roughened by "pop shots," even if excavation is not undertaken to break up the surface completely. Failure of the Gleno Dam in Italy has been attributed to sliding of the structure on a glaciated rock surface. Preliminary geological advice will generally be able to foretell the presence of such a feature, so that an appropriate construction schedule can be prepared. The exact location and regular discharge of all springs encountered must be most carefully recorded lest they prove to be possible sources of trouble. Any unusual springs should be immediately brought to the attention of the geological adviser so that he may examine them and advise accordingly. The detailed inspection of all unusual features, in addition to general supervision of excavation operations, is just as essential a part of the duties of the geological adviser as are the preliminary geological investigations.

Only during construction will the full extent of unusual foundation-bed features, revealed in part by preliminary investigations, be seen. During the construction of the dam for the Merwin Hydro Electric Project on the Lewis River in Washington (downstream from, and associated with, the Swift Dam, mentioned earlier), a buried gorge immediately below the location of the powerhouse in the 1,250-ft dam was

FIG. 13.29. Unusual pothole detected in preliminary investigations and uncovered during excavation for the foundation of the Noxon Rapids Dam, Montana, U.S.A.; the workers shown indicate the scale. (*Reproduced by permission of the Chief Civil Engineer, Washington Water Power Company.*)

detected in preliminary studies, but naturally, it was not fully seen until excavation was complete. It was then found to be 70 ft wide and 120 ft deep, a buried river valley from preglacial times. In a bold solution, a massive concrete arch was built to span this inner gorge and on this the powerhouse of the Pacific Power and Light Company has successfully performed since the dam was completed in 1931.[13.54] Not too far away, at the site of the Noxon Rapids Dam of the Washington Water Power Company in Montana, glacial action has had similarly significant effects upon the bed of the river, as was fully revealed only after dewatering. Figure 13.29 shows one of the potholes then discovered; it extended 80 ft below river-bed level and required 22,000 cu yd of concrete before it was completely filled. The site is on indurated argillite but lies in a wide valley that was once the bottom of glacial Lake Missoula. Failure of an ice dam in glacial times, about 25 miles above the dam site, led to strange erosional effects in the sediments already deposited and this led to complicated soil conditions which had to be dealt with in the construction of this dam. The final solution was a mass concrete spillway and powerhouse section, flanked by two large earth-fill wing dams.[13.55]

Geological features revealed during construction can sometimes affect progress schedules. During the construction of the Beechwood Dam and powerhouse for the New Brunswick Power Commission, on the St. John River 100 miles north of Fredericton, a relatively small fault in the argillite that made up the entire river bed was discovered during the second construction season despite a most careful preliminary program of test drilling. Some alteration of plans was called for in order to deal adequately with the fault zone; this was readily arranged but the change affected the schedule for the placing of earth fill in the adjacent wing dam. The delay meant that placing of soil had to proceed during Canadian winter conditions or be postponed until the following year. In an ingenious solution, an asphalt-mixing plant, hastily procured, was used to heat the soil before placement, and thus the work was finished almost as originally scheduled.[13.56]

A different kind of construction expedient was followed during the building of the Seminoe Dam of the Kendrick Project of the U.S. Bureau of Reclamation. Two faults, normal to each other, were found to intersect beneath the center of the dam; they were uncovered only when excavation was possible on the site of the dam after dewatering. The dam is a concrete structure, 260 ft high, arched in plan as it is located in a narrow gorge. After the dam had been started, engineers decided to clean out the two fault seams and backfill with concrete so that progress of the main structure would not be impeded. This involved what can only be called another mining operation; shafts were left in the concrete base of the dam through which access to the fault zones was obtained and through which all muck was removed and concrete transported for the backfilling operation. Despite the hazard of the work, 3,500 cu yd of seam material was removed and replaced with concrete without accident. Concrete placing in the main dam was completed 6 weeks before the last placement of concrete in the foundation.[13.57]

Cutoff walls, when necessary, as they so frequently are in the abutments to dams and under earth-fill structures, always provide the contractor with a construction challenge. Geology has contributed to this phase of dam construction also. The Mount Morris Dam, on the Genesee River in northern New York, was built on a site characterized by limestone and shale formations similar to those encountered in the area of Niagara Falls, to which reference has already been made. The dam, designed for flood control only, is a mass-concrete structure 250 ft high, but it was necessary to carry cutoff walls well into the two abutments. The shale rock made excavation for these walls difficult, but the contractor solved his difficulty by tunneling into the walls of the gorge and then stoping (upward) into the shale, mucking out through the access tunnels. Excavation was carried vertically in this way for a distance of

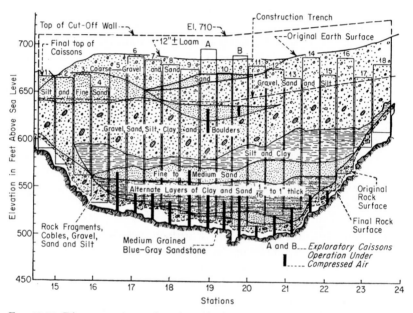

Fig. 13.30. Diagrammatic section through the soil strata encountered by the concrete caissons forming the cutoff wall of the Merriman Dam, part of the Delaware Aqueduct works for the city of New York. (*Reproduced by permission of The Editor, Engineering News-Record.*)

35 ft, and the process was then repeated after the open excavation had been filled with carefully placed concrete.[13.58]

A problem of an entirely different kind had to be faced in the construction of the Merriman Dam, part of the Delaware Aqueduct project for the water supply of the city of New York. Here, a complex assembly of glacial, waterborne, and lake-deposited sands, gravels, boulders, silty clays, and glacial till had to be penetrated to depths up to 180 ft in order to provide certain cutoff for the 200-ft-high earth-fill dam, designed to form one of the main reservoirs of the Delaware system. It was decided that the best way to achieve this would be by the use of caissons so designed and constructed that compressed air could be applied if and when necessary. Twenty reinforced-concrete caissons were used for this purpose; they measured about 12 by 45 ft, the height varying with the level of bedrock upon which they were finally founded. Free air was used for much of the excavation, but pressures up to 38 psi did become necessary in the final stages. Figure 13.30 illustrates, in diagrammatic form only, the heterogeneous character of the glacial soils that were penetrated by this unique cutoff wall; it illustrates, as well as can be done, the variation in soil conditions that must be expected in this type of glaciated country.[13.59]

Finally, it has been during construction operations that troubles due to overconsolidated shales have made themselves evident. When this type of shale is known to exist, a contractor can be forewarned and can adopt a method such as that followed on the Oahe Dam on the Missouri River. Here, the shale was excavated in relatively small areas; as soon as it was exposed at final grade, it was immediately covered with a bituminous coating; concrete had to be placed within 48 hr—in practice, it was usually in place within 24 hr. Only when this initial concrete slab had set were holes drilled through it and the necessary anchor bolts set in place for the purpose of holding the shale down and restricting its swelling tendency.[13.60]

13.14. Inspection and Maintenance. A note must be added with regard to the maintenance and inspection of dams. In some places, notably in Great Britain, this is a matter rigidly defined by law; annual inspections are obligatory for all structures above a certain size. The restriction of this legislative requirement to dams is a matter of some surprise to many engineers in view of the numerous other types of civil engineering work at least equally hazardous to human life. With or without state regulations, however, regular inspection of all dam structures is an essential. Naturally, examination is restricted to those parts of the dam which can be seen—together with the inspection galleries, tunnels, and shafts that have been left open after the completion of construction. The practice in certain large dams of leaving exploratory tunnels open has already been mentioned; this means of access is invaluable. One certain guide in inspection is the leakage of water through or around the dam. Records of this will naturally have been kept regularly, and any increase, either sudden or gradual, will be a call to remedial action. Study of the leakage, the sediment it carries, and its chemical content may reveal the reason for the increase and suggest remedial measures. Such study of leakage in extreme cases when the damage is irreparable will at least permit due warning of impending trouble. Failures should become more of a rarity as the years go on, especially so if, in the course of increasing the safety and reliability of dam foundations, due attention to the associated geological conditions is always regarded as a factor of the very greatest importance.

13.15. Conclusion. There are few civil engineering works which so attract public attention as do dams, large or small. There are few other works that so often seem to be a cooperative effort between man and nature. To see a thin arched concrete dam in a narrow river gorge or a massive concrete dam in a great river valley spanning between exposed

FIG. 13.31. A beautiful dam in an ideal setting, typifying the significance of the geology of dam foundations; the Escales Dam on the Ribagorzana River in northern Spain. (*Reproduced by permission of the Director Gerente, Empresa Nacional Hidro-Electrica del Ribagorzana.*)

rock walls is to experience a sense of aesthetic satisfaction that is but rarely aroused by the works of the engineer. Figure 13.31 illustrates but one striking example of the "aesthetics of dams," if the term may be allowed. It shows the impounding dam for the Escales hydroelectric project in northeastern Spain. It is a gravity structure, 125 m high and 200 m long on its crest. Water impounded above the dam is led through tunnels to a large underground power station in which three

16,800 hp units operate under a head of 117.5 m. The dam is located on the Ribagorzana River which has its headwaters in the Pyrenees. Flanked by supporting alternating strata of Cretaceous marls and limestone, which dip almost vertically, this dam—as do so many others in similar locations —shows a sense of fitness with its surroundings that makes it a fine symbol of the interrelation of geology with the design and construction of major civil engineering works.

Suggestions for Further Reading

As in many other branches of civil engineering, the most helpful sources of further information in this branch will be the records that are so fortunately prepared and published of the design and construction of most of the major dams of the world, especially if unusual features have been encountered. Typical examples will be found among the references cited in this chapter. In order to be of optimum use, these have been taken, whenever possible, from journals that are generally available to engineers, even though in some cases much more complete accounts are also available in volumes not readily consulted. Typical are the references to dams constructed by the U.S. Bureau of Reclamation and by the Tennessee Valley Authority, both of which have published several notable volumes recording in great detail the design and construction of some of their major dams and other engineering projects. Merely as an introduction to these volumes, full particulars of which can be obtained from the two agencies themselves, the following two records may be noted:

"Geology and Foundation Treatment: Tennessee Valley Authority Projects," TVA Technical Report 22, U.S. Government Printing Office, 1949.

"Geological Investigations," Bulletin 1 of Part III, Preliminary Examinations, Boulder Canyon Project, Final Reports, U.S. Bureau of Reclamation, Denver, Colo., 1950.

Another well-known and useful publication has recently been revised and brought up to date by the U.S. Bureau of Reclamation; copies may be obtained from the Superintendent of Documents, Government Printing Office, Washington 25, D.C. It is: "Design of Small Dams."

One of the pioneer volumes in the field of geology as applied in civil engineering dealt exclusively with dam foundations; it is still of interest and value:

Lugeon, M., "Barrages et géologie," F. Rouge et Cie, Librarie re l'Université de Lausanne, Switzerland, 1933.

The Proceedings of the International Congresses on Large Dams (Secretary's Office: 91 Rue Saint Lazare, Paris 9, France) will be found to contain papers with useful geological information in them incidental to the major questions that are considered at successive conferences of this international body.

Chapter 14

RESERVOIRS AND CATCHMENT AREAS

> The question as to the possibility of retaining water in rocks for summer use is decided by the annual and periodical operations of nature. For the means of altering or improving some of these natural operations, so as to render the irregular supply of water which falls upon the earth more convenient to the general purposes of man, we must have resort to geology.
>
> William Smith, 1827[14.1]

THE FUNCTION of dams, in general, is to retain water above the elevation at which it normally stands. This impounding may vary from the control of water levels within a few feet of normal elevation by a regulating weir to the creation of the immense lake now behind Gouin Dam in northern Quebec, on the St. Maurice River. Besides specially restricted cases such as low-head regulating weirs, a reservoir will be formed by a dam to serve as an artificial storage basin for the water that is retained. Usually the dam structure forms but a small part of the periphery of the reservoir; its bottom and the greater part of its sides (if this distinction may be used) will consist of the natural crust of the earth. A superficial assumption is that, provided the dam site is given due attention with regard to watertightness, all will be well. If this were always the case, this chapter would not be necessary.

As explained at the outset of the last chapter, the construction of a dam and the subsequent impounding of water behind it cause more interference with natural conditions than do almost all other works of the civil engineer. The problems created at the dam site are common to the whole reservoir above this site, although to varying degrees. In brief, a difference will be set up in the level of the water table corresponding to the height of the dam between the two sides of the dam; all material in the bed of the reservoir and especially close to the dam will be subjected to considerable hydraulic pressure; all flooded areas will in the future be subject to the action of water upon them; and finally the groundwater level up the valley in which the reservoir is located will be directly

548

affected by the rise in water level, generally for a considerable distance away from the actual shore line of the impounded water. In consequence, there will be a tendency for the impounded water to find some means of escape through any weaknesses that may exist in the structure of the ground. Materials in the sphere of influence of the impounded water and liable to be affected by exposure to water may fail to retain their former stability; landslides are one possible direct result of failure. Features such as wells that come within the area of influence of the reservoir and are dependent on previous ground-water levels will be correspondingly affected. Cursory consideration will show that all these matters depend fundamentally on the geological structure of the reservoir basin. A study of this geology is therefore an essential complement of geological investigation at a dam site, since only by this means can possible dangers be foreseen and suitable precautionary measures be taken in advance.

Another important reason for the careful study of the geology of reservoir sites is that an accurate estimate of the capacity of a reservoir can thus be made; this requirement often has associated with it the determination of the necessary height of dam. This figure must often be determined purely from the point of view of elevation when maximum working head is the criterion, as in the case of water-power plants. In other cases, especially with water-supply reservoirs, effective storage capacity is the determining factor. For a reservoir formed by a dam and a basin of impervious strata, the calculation of this capacity is a simple matter, and reservoir capacities are often calculated on this assumption. If attention is given to the geological formations underlying the basin, it may be found that large masses of pervious rocks are in contact with the impounded water and are so arranged that they can drain out (at least to some extent) as the reservoir water level is lowered. With the aid of reasonably careful preliminary geological investigations, an estimate of the additional storage thus available can be obtained, with consequent benefit to the economic aspect of the scheme.

14.2. Leakage from Reservoirs. Leakage from reservoirs is obviously a potential source of trouble. Surprising though it may seem, attention has not always been given to the possibility of leakage developing. Of the many examples that can be cited to support this suggestion, there need be mentioned only the abandonment of the Jerome Reservoir in Idaho and of the Hondo Reservoir in New Mexico as a result of excessive and uncontrollable leakage which occurred after the impounding dams had been built. That structures of magnitude should have to be abandoned not because of defects of design or construction but because of the undetermined nature of local geological structure is surely most telling evidence of the need of adequate study of every feature connected with the geology of a reservoir site.

It is, perhaps, not without significance that the two most remarkable examples of the interrelation of geology and engineering encountered by the writer in his own experience have involved reservoirs. One of these cases is that dealt with in the concluding section of this chapter, in which it will be seen that geological study was applied with constructive effect. The other example is, on the contrary, one of the most singular cases imaginable of what can result from the neglect of geology. Unfortunately, it must be described anonymously, but the lesson it tells does not suffer from this lack of identification. There is standing today in the northeastern part of North America a fine buttress-type reinforced-concrete dam about 40 ft high and ⅓ mile long, constructed in 1910 and still in good condition, even though it has never retained water. It was built by an owner who spurned professional advice. A cursory reading of a geological report then extant would have shown that one side of the valley crossed by the dam, one buttress therefore of the structure and one complete side of the intended reservoir, consisted of a glacial moraine made up of small boulders. As could have been foretold, the reservoir leaked like a sieve as soon as impounding of the water commenced. Not willing to be beaten by geology, the owner had a vast area paved with an asphalt-coated reinforced-concrete slab; later he had a cutoff wall, in places taken to a depth of 80 ft below ground level, carried up the valley from the dam. All to no avail; the reservoir still leaked to such an extent that the intended generation of the power from the water that was to have been impounded had to be given up. Penstock and powerhouse were dismantled. The dam stands today in mute testimony to what the neglect of geology can do. But as has happened before, the beavers who inhabited the stream that was to be dammed by the concrete structure did what engineers could not achieve. They built their own series of dams and did retain water; one of the beaver dams was carefully constructed around a sinkhole, the leakage through which was thus stopped by nature's own engineers.

Failure by excessive leakage may take place because of defects in the structural arrangement of the underlying strata, e.g., a fault or excessive fissuring; through failure of one or more of the rock types to stand up to exposure to water; as a result of the dip of pervious rock strata, which drains water away from a reservoir site; or through the absence of adequate impervious barriers at critical points in the topographic perimeter of the reservoir area. These different possibilities can best be explained by a discussion of typical cases.

As an instance of leakage from a reservoir most probably due to the first of the causes listed, the experience met with at Ewden Valley works for the water supply of the city of Sheffield, Yorkshire, England, may be mentioned. Construction of the two impounding earth dams in the Ewden Valley began in the year 1913; the respective reservoirs are known as the Broomhead and the More Hall; the former is for water supply, and the latter for compensation water purposes only. The Broomhead dam is about 990 ft long at the top of the embankment, and overflow level is 91 ft above lowest drawoff level. The configuration of the valley disclosed the presence of ancient slips near the dam site, and studies and test borings indicated a very disturbed condition of the underground strata, which consists of shale, sandstones, and grits with overlying yellow clay. Excavation for the cutoff trench confirmed this deduction; the trench had to be carried to a depth of 120 ft below stream level before the strata were found in undisturbed horizontal positions. Underground water flow in a band of grit was encountered and was tapped and drained as the trench was concreted up. Geological and specialist engineering advice was constantly taken as the works proceeded; but after the start of impounding water in May, 1928, increased flow below the dam was observed, which indicated leakage from the reservoir. Further geological investigations were made (also in connection with a serious landslip), including many more borings; as a result of these investigations, a program of cementation was initiated. In about 6 months (that is, up to July, 1930), 14 million lb of cement was injected, which reduced the leakage from 2,478,000 to 1,577,000 gal (Imp) per day. This latter figure has been still further reduced by additional grouting work carried out when the reservoir was drained and also by sluicing silt behind sandbag dams formed where rock outcrops were found in the bed of the reservoir. Leakage still persists through unknown underground passages; the works are a most striking example of the possibility of leakage occurring through rocks normally sound but locally distorted and fissured, despite most careful engineering work and geological investigation.[14.2]

As the dam site in a reservoir will usually be at the deepest part of the valley utilized to form the basin, the impounded head will be greatest at this location. Therefore, stuctural geological defects and the existence of rocks that may be affected by prolonged exposure to water are of special consequence and of greatest potential danger in the vicinity of the dam. Especially is this true of doubtful rocks such as those which are to any degree soluble in water. Rock salt is naturally the most dangerous of all; but as it is not of frequent occurrence, it is not of great significance. Gypsum, although less soluble than rock salt, is seriously affected by exposure to water and so is potentially dangerous. Of unusual significance in all reservoir investigations is the presence of limestone. Although it is the least permeable of the rocks mentioned, its relatively wide distribution renders it comparatively well known. This general familiarity, although not perhaps breeding proverbial contempt, does lead to the tendency to form incorrect judgments regarding its soundness, especially when considered in conjunction with the relatively solid appearance of many outcrops.

All limestones are at least partially soluble in ordinary water. If through the movement of water the resulting solutions can be removed from contact with the rock and replaced by fresh water, solution will continue. In all limestone formations subject to movement of underground water, therefore, special precautions must be taken to make sure that no potentially serious zones of weakness exist. The well-known caverns found in many limestone districts are the result of water action. Sometimes these are the result of the action of flowing streams which for a part of their courses flow underground; parts of Derbyshire, England, are typical of similar well-known scenic areas to be found in many parts of the world. Some limestone caverns are the result of periodic movements of underground water tables. In consequence, a close study of existing underground water levels, although always of value in connection with the investigation of reservoir sites, is of special value in the case of those formed by limestone strata. Many examples from practice testify to the importance of close study of any limestone formation encountered in reservoir work. The troubles at the Hales Bar Dam (see page 520) were due to cavernous limestone. The pioneer work on grouting with clay at the site of the Madden Reservoir in the Panama Canal Zone (see page 525) was occasioned by the careful studies of the underlying limestone strata, which had been made in the preliminary geological investigations; all points of weakness were effectively sealed up before the reservoir was filled. The Malad Reservoir, near Malad, Idaho, represents another example. A dam 440 ft long and 70 ft high was projected to impound water, and construction was started in 1917. Work had to be stopped when the crest had reached a height of only 50 ft; although the level of the water being impounded had risen only 10 ft above normal stream level, leakage was occurring at a relatively high rate. Investigation suggested that the leakage was occurring through a bed of soluble limestone 500 ft long and 25 ft wide in outcrop on the side of the valley near the dam but effectively screened from view by a talus slope. These examples include cases previously noted in order to illustrate the close relationship between the geological conditions affecting dam sites and those germane to reservoirs and catchment areas.[14.3]

The possibility of leakage through a pervious stratum dipping away from the reservoir valley is best explained by means of a simple diagram (Fig. 14.1). This is not an unusual geological section; and although the figure is diagrammatic only, many actual sections of a similar type can be found. The inclined structure of pervious and impervious strata will naturally result in any water in contact with the pervious beds in valley A (as, for example, water impounded in the valley by a dam with crest level about X) flowing underground until it is discharged into valley B. Discharge might take the form of springs. The structural arrangement shown is as simple as possible; it is capable of much variation without the fundamental source of leakage being changed. For example, the lower pervious stratum might not outcrop in valley *B* but remain underground with no natural outlet for the entrapped water if the surface stratum were impervious. Artesian pressure would thus be set up, and a potential supply of underground water would be provided.

Finally, there always exists the possibility that leakage may take place through some permeable stratum at a low point in the ground encircling

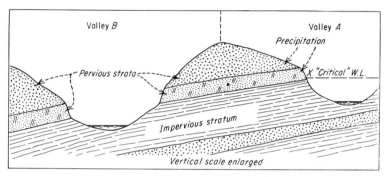

Fig. 14.1. Simplified geological section, illustrating possible leakage from a reservoir and catchment area.

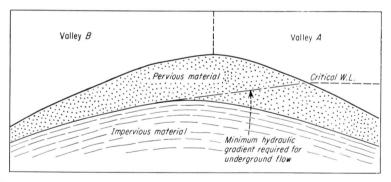

Fig. 14.2. Simplified geological section, illustrating another possible means of leakage from a reservoir.

the reservoir. Rarely will the topography be such that there is no indication of any low spot in the perimeter of the reservoir site. Any depressions will inevitably call for special geological study, since the fact that they are a departure from the regular topographical feature is an indication that some unusual process has been at work at some time in the past. Glacial action is frequently responsible for depressions—"saddles," they may be called, if they take that particular form between two valleys. A section through a simple saddle in which the rock level has been worn down well below surface level, pervious deposits making up the observed level of the ridge at this location, is shown in Fig. 14.2. If water is impounded above "critical WL," and the broken line extending through "pervious material" is the necessary underground hydraulic gradient for flow through that material, it is clear that leakage will occur from valley *A* into valley *B*. In addition to causing loss of water from the reservoir, this underground flow of water may cause trouble in valley *B* if there is any instability there of unconsolidated deposits which might be intensified by the presence of excessive underground water.

There are available all too many descriptions of losses from reservoirs due to this cause. One of the most remarkable examples is that given by the Cedar Reservoir in the state of Washington, briefly noted in a number of references which prompted J. Hoover Mackin to undertake a careful study of the case many years after it had first given trouble.[14.4] In 1914 the city of Seattle constructed a concrete dam in a gorge of the Cedar River, a tributary of the Snoqualmie River, with a crest length of 795 ft and a total height above bedrock of 217 ft. Before the dam was built, the city was advised by its consultants of the danger of severe leakage around the northeast abutment, but this advice was neglected. Filling of the reservoir started in 1915, but before it had proceeded far, leakage was reaching a volume of 30 million gpd. Despite this, filling was slowly continued; leakage increased and finally washed away the small town of Moncton, whose 200 inhabitants were relocated. A new board of consultants was appointed, and test holes were put down. The findings of this board were just the same as those of the earlier consultants, namely, that the northeast abutment of the dam was part of a large glacial morainal deposit of open-textured gravel, occupying a deep and capacious preglacial valley of the Cedar River.

Much effort was exerted and large amounts of money were spent in attempts to seal the reservoir. Presumably to test the efficiency of the sealing operations, water was allowed to rise again in the reservoir toward the end of 1918. Leakage again appeared and increased rapidly. Around midnight on December 23, a great earth movement occurred on the eastern part of the northeast face of the morainal embankment (i.e., the part on the face of the moraine removed from the dam), approximately 6,000 ft from the dam. Well over 1 million cu yd of material was washed out by the rush of water; the initial discharge when the failure occurred was estimated at between 3,000 and 20,000 cfs. The resulting flood rushed down a small creek valley to the Snoqualmie River, taking out the small town of Edgewick, sawmills, and other property, and destroying some track of the Milwaukee Railroad; good fortune alone obviated a major loss of life, for no train was passing at the time. Subsequent legal actions dragged on for the next decade but eventually the city of Seattle had judgment rendered against it of over $300,000. The dam still stands, but somewhat naturally, no attempt has again been made to use it for its intended purpose of impounding water. Mackin's paper on the failure gives a detailed treatment of the geology of the morainal ridge and provides a rational explanation of the exact happenings at the time of failure.

14.3. Detection of Leakage. Leakage from a reservoir will generally be so obvious as to call for no special aids in detection. Sudden increases in stream flow below a dam site without a corresponding increase of rainfall will be a direct indication of some escape of water; and the appearance

Fig. 14.3. Undershot water wheel in Cephalonia, Greece, operated by the flow of the sea *into* the island. (*Reproduced by permission of John Blake, Ltd., Accrington, England.*)

of springs, boils, or other surface indications of underground water in locations previously dry and stable will also indicate unsatisfactory conditions. Minor leakage may be more difficult to trace, especially in connection with the investigation of solution channels in limestone. The use of dyes in cases of this kind can be invaluable; small quantities of dye can be added to the moving water at a convenient station, and samples taken from the suspected source of leakage. Various chemicals have been used for this purpose; permanganate of potash is perhaps the most common; in some cases, ordinary bluing can be used. The use of bacteria has been suggested; but for practically all special work, a chemical indicator is used. Many chemicals are thus employed, among them fluorescein and its sodium salt, uranin. These give water a characteristic color which can be detected even when diluted to the extent of 1 part in more than 10 million parts of water.

Even with the use of such sensitive dyes, however, leakage sometimes cannot be traced. An interesting, although possibly unique, example which may be mentioned is a small water-power installation in Cephalonia, one of the islands of the Ionian Archipelago (Greece). The undershot wheel of the installation is operated by the flow of sea water from the Mediterranean into the island. The strange stream so formed eventually disappears from view in the caverns and fissures of the limestone of which the island is there constituted. During British occupation of the island, large quantities of petroleum were poured into the sea water as it passed the mill, and the island was surrounded by boats whose crews were on the lookout for any signs of emerging petroleum. None appeared, and repeated tests have failed to reveal where the water goes.[14.5] Although petroleum is a somewhat unusual indicator of leakage, it is sometimes so used where it can be with safety and convenience. The case is cited in view of its unusual interest and also because it presents yet another example of the vagaries of a limestone formation.

Another of the peacetime applications of atomic energy is placing into the hands of the geologist and engineer a new tool of great potential for the tracing of subsurface water flow. The use of radioactive isotopes for such a purpose is an obvious use of these newly developed chemicals. There are many difficulties in the way of their widespread adoption: the possibility of interaction with the aquifers, their relatively high cost, biological and radiation dangers, and the varying half-lives of different isotopes. The converse of these difficulties provides, of course, the desirable features of isotopes for ground-water movement tracing. A number of isotopes have been successfully used in this way. One of the early applications was in an isolated location in the Libyan desert of Egypt where Sir C. S. Fox checked on the watertightness of a proposed reservoir site by using isotopes to show that ground water was not moving, rather than the reverse.[14.6] Rubidium chloride was specially prepared for this application at Harwell, the British Atomic Energy Research Establishment, flown out from London to Cairo, driven immediately to the site, and put to use within little more than a day after its preparation. Similar applications have been made in several countries; interesting applications using a cobalt isotope are reported from Israel, for example, where a radioactive hexacyanocobaltate was found to be the most suitable isotope for use with Yarkon River water in the limestone aquifer in the Lydia well field. Naturally, background for freshly pumped water has to be determined before the radioactive material is introduced.[14.7] The single-well pulse technique has been found to be reasonably effective and economical, even though results so obtained have to be interpreted with care if the aquifer being studied is extensive. Expert assistance must still be utilized for all such use of radioactive materials but they do hold promise of extending very greatly subsurface water investigations.

14.4. Prevention and Elimination of Leakage. If the preliminary geological investigations already described are applied to the study of reservoir and catchment areas when a dam construction project is planned, most of the possible sources of leakage from the reservoir should normally be discovered. The various possibilities of leakage have been noted, and the nature of the means of leakage will be some indication of whether or not it can be prevented by anticipatory remedial works. In the case of strata dipping across a valley into adjacent areas, little, if anything, can be done to interfere with the natural direction of underground water flow. When saddles occur with low spots in the bedrock elevation, as indicated in Fig. 14.2, cutoff dams can be constructed to seal effectively the open waterways thus available for underground flow. The simplest type of structure will suffice for this purpose, provided that a cutoff wall of some type is carried to the rock floor between the points at which it ceases to be above reservoir water level.

In other cases of possible leakage, especially where localized fissuring of rock is encountered, grouting may effect a satisfactory seal if carefully carried out in close association with complementary geological study. Grouting operations may similarly be employed for remedial work if leakage is discovered after a dam has been completed and the storage of water within a reservoir has begun. As it is seldom that a reservoir can be emptied completely, or even partially, for more than a short time after it has been placed into active service, remedial work to eliminate leakage from a full or partially filled reservoir is often an extremely difficult matter. Another method of reducing and possibly eliminating leakage is to employ natural sealing material, such as clay or the silt content of the watercourse feeding the reservoir, to block up the openings in the reservoir through which leakage is occurring when these are definite and not too widespread. If the exact location of the area of weakness is known, sluicing or dumping suitable material into the reservoir immediately above this area may often be effective. Even mattresses or fascines, similar to those used in river-training work, may be used if the area of weakness can be accurately located. The process may be a natural one. W. L. Strange has described how the Much Kundi Tank in Bijapur, India, formed by a masonry dam on schistose rocks, was sealed and made tight after 12 years of natural silting.[14.8] In the discussion of Strange's paper, a Yorkshire (England) reservoir was mentioned, formed by an 80-ft dam, which leaked as much as 440,000 gpd (Imp) but which silted up and sealed itself tight in 2 years. The permanence of any self-sealing operation will obviously depend on the nature of the leakage. If the sealing is completely in basalt and similar rocks, then it may be permanently effective; but if it is only partially successful in a limestone formation, then the constant flow of the small amount of leakage still persisting may be sufficient to enlarge existing leakage channels by further solution and cause a recurrence of serious trouble.

A variety of other methods have been used in achieving economical sealing of reservoirs that leak. There is a record of a reservoir in the Italian Apennines, on the river Ripa, formed by a gravity-arched concrete dam 47 m high, leaking through a crevasse in the rock floor and through pervious rock, that was eventually sealed by successive applications of a cement-sand mixture applied with cement guns. The extent of the operation is indicated by the fact that the sealing operations cost over six times as much as the original dam.[14.9] The use of asphalt as a sealing medium by the TVA has already been noted in connection with the Hales Bar Dam (page 520). The TVA successfully used the same system in sealing the reservoir formed by the Great Falls Dam on the Caney Fork River in central Tennessee.[14.10] Clay has naturally been used for the same purpose; it assisted, for example in the partial solution of the many problems encountered by the Water Commission of the City of Kingston, Jamaica. This is a 700-million-gal water reservoir formed by low embankments around a suitably graded site. Clay was only partially successful in stemming the serious leaks that developed even before the reservoir was put to use; an asphalt, sand, and gravel grout was used in the final remedial work.[14.11] Finally, reference may again be made to the sealing of the reservoir on Treasure Island in San Francisco Bay by the introduction of sea water in order to promote base exchange in the clay lining, to which attention was directed in Chap. 4 (page 124). In all these cases, the solution was selected in the light of local geological circumstances after the leakage had been detected and its cause determined.

14.5. Secondary Effects of Reservoir Flooding. The function of an impounding dam is to store a predetermined quantity of water and, in the case of a water-power scheme, to raise the top level of the impounded water to a certain specified maximum. Areas of dry land must be flooded as the water rises, and the flooding will often entail extensive civil engineering construction of what may be termed a secondary nature. Buildings may have to be relocated, and sometimes whole settlements may have to be moved. Transportation routes, which often follow valleys, may traverse land that will be flooded when the reservoir fills. Relocation work can sometimes attain major proportions. In the planning of all such work, the effect of the ultimate maximum water level must be considered. This type of work will often be located on hillsides, and the possibility of landslides is one that must always be given special attention.

Unusual difficulties of this nature had to be faced in connection with the Bonneville Dam on the Columbia River, Oregon, construction of which started in 1934. The site of this dam is interesting, complicated as it is by the existence of the Cascade Slide, a great landslide which occurred about 1,000 years ago after the river had cut a deep gorge close to one bank estimated to have been at least 200 ft deeper than the modern channel. The slide deflected the river from its course and

Fig. 14.4. Bonneville Dam on the Columbia River, Oregon, U.S.A.; a view taken shortly after starting the impounding of water. The large area of land to the left of the dam is the ancient Cascade Slide; the old river channel was located on the other side of this. (*Photograph by Brubaker Aerial Surveys. Reproduced by permission of the Chief of Engineers, U.S. Army.*)

altered the topography all around the site selected for the dam; preliminary investigations, therefore, had to be carried out with unusual care. A railroad and a highway on each side of the river required relocation to bring them above reservoir level. The unusual part of this work was to obtain a stable location for the railroad on the Oregon shore some distance above the dam site, where an old landslide existed which had given the railroad company much trouble even before the dam construction started. The slide area is about 1½ miles long and 3,000 ft wide; its slow movement is attributed to the lubrication by ground water of an underlying stratum of shale. Solution of the problem included extensive drainage tunnels and the construction of a retaining wall, measures which were mentioned in Chap. 10.

Underground water levels will be materially affected in reservoirs, the top levels of which are appreciably above normal river elevation, and this change in a natural ground condition may have widespread effects. Building foundations, especially those on clay, must be carefully studied. Underground water-supply systems will clearly be affected. If there is

FIG. 14.5. View of the Columbia River, Oregon, U.S.A., immediately upstream of the Bonneville Dam, looking upstream, showing necessary road and rail relocation. The river here flows to the west; the work on the south bank was complicated by the Ruckel Slide area, which had long given trouble in the maintenance of the Union Pacific Railroad tracks at this location. (*Reproduced by permission of the Chief of Engineers, U.S. Army.*)

any possibility that minor seepage, apart from appreciable leakage, will reach catchment areas other than that in which the reservoir is situated, attention must be given to this contingency in case it should ever develop serious proportions. Peculiar problems may often arise due to special local circumstances. In a paper on dam construction in New South Wales, Australia, mention was made of the selection of a dam site for impounding water for the supply of the city of Sydney. Six sites were chosen. The first selected for construction was on the Cataract River and had a catchment area above it of 53 sq miles. The geological formation of the Cataract catchment consists of Hawkesbury sandstone overlying coal measures, and the area is bounded on its upper end by a range of high hills rising abruptly a short distance back from the ocean. Coal seams outcrop on the side of the hills facing the ocean and dip with a fairly rapid inclination underneath the Cataract catchment. The seams have been worked from the face of the hills for some time, and coal mining is carried out in the area.

It will be seen that there arises the interesting double problem that coal mining might interfere with dams and reservoirs, and that seepage from reservoirs might interfere with mining operations. The second appears to be the more probable although no trouble of either kind has yet been reported throughout this whole area. The New South Wales Mines Department has laid down marginal zones around areas of stored water in which bord-and-pillar extraction of coal is permitted. The Mines Department permits bord-and-pillar extraction under stored water, but total extraction of coal beneath stored water and the marginal zones is forbidden except with the permission of the Secretary for Mines. The widths of the zones and the sizes of bords and pillars are fixed by the Mines Department. The situation is complicated by the unusually complex local geology, which includes two series of fresh-water sedimentary rocks of the Triassic system. Some information on geology of an adjoining area is given in a comprehensive report upon the preliminary investigations carried out in connection with the Warragamba Dam. This dam will be just over 400 ft above river-bed level and will be the largest dam in the Southern Hemisphere.[14.12] Containing 1½ million cu yd of concrete, it will be the major structure of the Sydney Water Board and will give an additional storage capacity of 460,000 million gal for the water supply to the great metropolitan area of Sydney.

14.6. Catchment Areas. Brief consideration will show that the water impounded by dams will be obtained in all normal cases from the rain that falls on the area of the valley, or catchment area, above the dam. In the ideal case, all the rain would flow down the watercourse to be stored in the reservoir; actually only a percentage of the total is obtained for use in this way, and the relation of this "runoff" (to use the convenient engineering expression) to the equivalent rainfall is influenced by the geological structure of the catchment area. Indeed, it can be said that the relation of runoff to rainfall can be fully studied only if due consideration is given to the local geology.

A catchment area that was formed of a continuous exposure of impermeable rock would yield at any gauging station in the watercourse a runoff equivalent to the rainfall on the total area above the station less the amount lost by evaporation. In the usual catchment area, however, other losses must also be considered; the most important of these are the water that is absorbed by vegetation, the water that is temporarily absorbed into the underground water reservoir formed by any pervious rocks underlying the area, and the water that is deflected into adjacent catchment areas because of peculiarities of geological structure.

In the last case, a study of Fig. 14.1 will show that in a way similar to leakage of water from the reservoir, rain falling onto the side slopes of the valleys depicted may not, and in some cases will not, join the runoffs from the catchment area on which it falls. This diagrammatic section makes the source of loss so clear that elaboration is not necessary; suffice it to say that the preparation of corresponding geological sections through typical parts of catchment areas should always be a component part of hydrological studies, so that, in evaluating anticipated runoffs, the true effective catchment area may be used in calculation. Somewhat naturally, the smaller the catchment area the greater the possibility of appreciable loss from this cause.

14.7. Relation of Geology to Runoff. The calculation of rainfall losses is a vitally important part of hydrological study in connection with all engineering works dependent on assured water supply. Studies of the matter are to be found in many standard works, and many empirical formulas have been evolved to suggest a general relation between rainfall and runoff for catchment areas of different sizes and different climatic conditions. Of the factors affecting rainfall losses, two of those mentioned are fundamentally dependent on geological structure. It will therefore be seen that although general formulas are undoubtedly useful in limited application, they must be interpreted in the light of information on the local geology if they are to be effective and of use.

Loss of rainfall by percolation to underground pervious strata is the first of these two factors. Consideration of this possibility leads inevitably to a general study of ground water. In all but the most exceptional watersheds (such as those used at Gibraltar), some portion of the rain will fall on pervious material and so sink below ground surface. There it will eventually join that large body of water which is permanently held in the interstices existing in the underground strata, taking its part in the slow but steady movements of the contents of this underground reservoir. It is water derived in one way or another from this source that constitutes the flow in the corresponding watercourse during periods of dry weather when the flow obviously cannot be the direct consequence of rainfall. This "dry-weather flow," as it is termed in engineering practice, is the criterion on which fundamental calculations regarding water supply must be based. The determination of the minimum possible dry-weather flow at any gauging station is a critical hydrological investigation, since it will often be impossible to measure this by actual gauging before a water-impounding project is started. Records at the sites of works that have been constructed can usually be obtained, and these constitute a valuable guide to similar cases. It is in determining the similarity of catchment areas in this connection that geological structure must be considered.

D. Halton Thomson compiled a study of more than 30 records of various dry-weather flows for British streams, and these show discharges varying from 0.055 cfs per 1,000 acres on the river Alwen in North

Wales (drainage area, 6,313 acres) to 2.00 cfs gauged on the river Avon, Scotland (drainage area, 5,000 acres). The ratio of the two records from these catchment areas, almost identical topographically and in respect to climate, is 1:36. This is a surprising variation, and the explanation is wholly geological. Superficially, both areas might be regarded as impervious; the geology of this part of the Alwen Valley consists of Silurian shales and grits covered with boulder clay; that of the Avon is wholly granite. Based on this general comparison, it would seem that the dry-weather flows from the two areas should be almost equal. Further study discloses the fact that although the Alwen catchment area is watertight, as might be expected, and thus provides little or no underground storage, the granite over which the Avon flows is so fissured and decomposed that vast quantities of water are held in its interstices. The ample underground storage thus provided is drawn upon by the stream during persistent dry periods.[14.13]

Another interesting example is afforded by flow records at two different points on the river Exe in Devonshire, the lower one just above the range of tidal influence and the other near the headwaters of the river above the junction of two important tributaries with the main stream. Table 14.1 shows that the unit dry-weather flow for the whole area is

Table 14.1

	Upper Exe basin	Whole of Exe basin
Drainage area......................	240 sq miles	461 sq miles
Average annual rainfall..............	47 in.	42 in.
Dry-weather flow (aver. of September, 1911)...........................	22 cfs per 1,000 acres	87 cfs per 1,000 acres

almost four times that of the upper part of the area alone; the reason for the variation is, again, solely geological. About one-eighth only of the upper part of the area is formed of pervious rocks, the New Red sandstone, and the remainder is Devonian measures and igneous rocks; thus, practically no underground storage exists. The basins of the two tributaries that join the main river below the upper gauging station are largely formed of the pervious New Red sandstone, and in consequence, they are both well served with underground storage to the extent that their unit dry-weather flows are so high that they raise the figure for the whole catchment area to that indicated in the table.[14.13]

The examples quoted are by no means unusual, and they therefore illustrate vividly the effect that geological conditions have on dry-weather flows. This effect is felt to varying degrees for all stages of stream flow. Even during torrential rainfall, a pervious surface stratum will rarely be so completely saturated with water that rain falling on it will all run off, giving a flow equivalent to 100 per cent of the rainfall.

This is confirmed by the unique conditions that combined to cause the catastrophic floods early in 1936 in the eastern part of North America. Unexpectedly early rains fell on catchment areas that were still frozen hard, and thus constituted catchment areas almost "ideal" if considered

Fig. 14.6. Powerhouse and surge tank of the Aguasabon hydroelectric project in northern Ontario, Canada. Lake Superior is in the foreground; Blue Jay Reservoir (290 ft above) is seen in the background. (*Reproduced by permission of the Hydro Electric Power Commission of Ontario.*)

from the standpoint of impermeability. The resulting runoffs caused floods that broke all known records and in some cases exceeded the calculated "1,000-year maximum." That such floods do not normally occur is due to the regulating effect of geological formations, which determine to some degree the course of water from the time it falls as rain until the time it reaches the watercourse to join with the stream flow. The importance of this effect can hardly be overemphasized. The figures quoted illustrate how geological conditions alone can explain some variation in runoff records. By means of similar studies, not only can records be compared, but the accuracy of recorded flows can be checked as possible limiting cases.

14.8. The Aguasabon Reservoir, Ontario. Between 1946 and 1948, the Hydro Electric Power Commission of Ontario completed its Aguasabon power plant on the north shore of Lake Superior, about 130 miles east of Port Arthur. It has an installed capacity of 53,000 hp generated under a head of 290 ft. Water is brought to the small powerhouse, located on Terrace Bay, through a 15-ft-diameter tunnel, which leads to twin steel penstocks. The Aguasabon River enters Lake Superior about 2 miles to the east, its water having been impounded by a concrete dam about 1½ miles from the mouth. Because of unusual local topography, the reservoir so formed not only extends up the river in the usual way, but floods through a narrow gorge just above the dam into a large basin-shaped area to the west of the river, extending to within ½ mile of the shore of the lake and yet 290 ft above it (at reservoir water line). Superficial examination suggested that the rock ridge might continue under the overburden between the reservoir site and the lake even though the ridge was covered with a mantle of soil. The usual careful preliminary test drilling of the Ontario Hydro, however, penetrated to depths well below lake level along this ridge and found nothing but sand and gravel; the presence of many boulders eliminated any possibility of constructing a cutoff wall (even to such a depth) between the adjacent rock outcrops.

Study of the natural basin directed attention to a small pond of water (Blue Jay Lake) in its center, a pool which could be retained only by underlying impervious material. The glacial history of this part of northern Ontario suggested that this might be a layer of glacial silt similar to other glacial lake deposits in this part of the Canadian shield. Trenching around the edge of the reservoir area and very careful test drilling (with a minimum number of holes actually penetrating the blanket) revealed a continuous bed of compact and almost impervious glacial silt over the entire bed of the basin, extending—most fortunately—to just about the intended top water level for the reservoir. Somewhat naturally, tests were made to determine by penetration the depth of the silt layer but where this was studied it was found that although in the middle of the reservoir area a thickness of some 60 ft existed, this thinned out to a relatively few feet toward the upper edge. With the existence of this natural reservoir lining known, planning of the project could be completed. The plant was built, and the reservoir was filled. There was a slight increase in the level of the ground water in the sand and gravel almost 300 ft *beneath* the reservoir, but this gradually leveled off and the plant has been in continuous operation ever since its opening, dependent for its water supply upon this natural "perched" reservoir.[14.14]

Chapter 15

WATER SUPPLY

But if anyone will note the abundance of water skilfully brought into the city, for public uses, for baths, for public basins, for houses, runnels, suburban gardens, and villas; if he will note the high aqueducts required for maintaining the proper elevation; the mountains which had to be pierced for the same reason and the valleys it was necessary to fill up; he will conclude that the whole terrestrial orb offers nothing more marvellous.

Pliny the Elder[15.1]
(23 to 79 A.D.)

THE APPEARANCE of a short chapter dealing with water supply may seem strange at first sight but the subject is presented in this way in order that its importance may be duly emphasized and that the relation of geological considerations to water supply may be clearly defined. All too often the "geology of water supply" is featured in a manner not in keeping with the importance of the engineering side of water-supply work, to which geology can be no more than a serviceable aid. That geological conditions have a profound effect on sources of water and on the means by which water is supplied for public use cannot be denied. Geological conditions are, however, a part of the natural order and cannot well be altered, whereas the task of the civil engineer in designing a water-supply system is the utilization for the public good of the particular natural conditions with which he has to deal, often a task of great difficulty.

Much can be written even in summary form about the importance of water supply; it can hardly be overemphasized. It is a prime requirement of public health, an essential to cleanliness, and a fundamental requirement of almost all modern manufacturing processes. Indeed, a satisfactory public supply of pure water is one of the engineer's greatest gifts to his fellow men and at the same time one of his greatest responsibilities. So vital is the maintenance of a public water supply that no possible risks can be taken in connection with the necessary engineering design. Few cities are in the fortunate position of having a duplicate water-supply system

566

to safeguard them against serious trouble if anything should interfere accidentally with the functioning of the main supply. Unusual precautions have to be taken, therefore, in providing temporary storage facilities; for this reason, conservatism in water engineering design and practice is often justified. Correspondingly, in no branch of civil engineering are geological considerations more important than in connection with water supply: the most careful preliminary geological investigations are always absolutely essential.

15.2. Historical Note. This importance is reflected in the attention that was paid to water-supply systems by some of the earliest engineers. The inscription on the Moabite stone, dating from the tenth century B.C., contains references to water conduits and cisterns. There is evidence to suggest that reservoirs for water supply existed in Babylon as early as 4000 B.C. The Bible contains not a few references to water-supply systems; some of these systems were of considerable magnitude, and parts of them have remained in use up to the present day. Notable among these were the waterworks for the city of Jerusalem, which were installed in Solomon's newly conquered city about 900 B.C. and showed highly developed technical skill. They were extended by King Hiskia in 700 B.C.; an inscription records that his engineers successfully bored a tunnel almost a mile long by working from the two ends. The Romans also augmented the supply, and parts of the original installation are still used today to supply the Mosque of Omar.[15.2] Works in Asia Minor at Priene (dating about 350 B.C.), a town of only 5,000 inhabitants, are hardly excelled by those of any modern town, since every house was connected by earthenware pipes to mains supplied from a large and steady spring on the hillside above the town.[15.3]

The waterworks of ancient Rome are widely known and appreciated, but the fact that the supply to the city is estimated to have exceeded 80 million gpd is not perhaps so generally realized. The principal sources of the Roman water supply were springs in the great beds of limestone in the valley of the river Amio. Many of the springs fed into one of the 11 aqueducts that were constructed to carry the supply to the Imperial City, those monumental undertakings even the ruins of which testify to the engineering skill of their Roman builders. Fortunately, a contemporary description of these works exists, written by Sextus Julius Frontinus, water commissioner of Rome in A.D. 97. This earliest of engineering authors was an enthusiast, commenting in one place thus: "Will anybody compare the idle Pyramids, or those other useless though much renowned works of the Greeks, with these aqueducts, with these many indispensable structures?" This has a modern touch, as indeed has much else of what Frontinus wrote; his descriptions are worthy of study by all engineers interested in the history of their art. It will be found that he does not neglect geological features.[15.4]

The Middle Ages were not devoid of their water-supply engineers. The modern emancipation of women is possibly reflected in the fact that the first post-Roman artificial water-supply system in England appears to have been that installed by St. Eanswide, of whom it is reported that "she haled and drew water over the hills and rocks against nature from Swecton a mile off to her Oratoria at the sea-side." The good lady in question was the daughter of Eadbald, King of Kent (A.D. 616–640), and was the first prioress of St. Peter's Priory near Folkestone.[15.5] So the fascinating story can be unfolded; it will be found related in detail in more appropriate places, but enough has been presented to show that the water engineer of today is following in a great tradition and that, in some respects at least, modern problems were reflected in these ancient works.

15.3. Sources of Water Supply. This plural subheading is almost a misnomer, since the source of practically all water supply is the fall of rain; the use of the plural implies that the natural cycle may be broken into in this way for classification purposes. The estimation of the quantity of rain that will fall upon an area is always of importance in water-supply studies, whether the supplies are to be drawn from catchment areas, lakes, rivers, wells, or springs; these are the features that are usually referred to as sources of water supply. The quantity appears to depend on many local factors, including the physical configuration of the district, its elevation above sea level, and its relation to mountain masses, prevailing winds, and the proximity of the sea. It is a matter only indirectly related to geology. There appears to be some reason for believing that the presence of forests has an influence on rainfall. If this is true, geology, in so far as it has been favorable or not to vegetable growth, will indirectly influence rainfall.

In the study of what happens to rainfall when it reaches the ground, geological conditions assume importance. Part of the rain is evaporated; part will run off the surface; part will be absorbed by the vegetation on which it falls; and part will eventually find its way into the subsoil. Cursory consideration will show that all four processes depend to some extent on the geological nature of the ground on which the rain falls. Only a portion of the rainfall on any area is therefore available for use. That which runs off the surface to form the flow of streams and rivers is clearly of special interest to water engineers. The available runoff naturally includes also that part of the water which eventually finds its way into watercourses by seepage through the local ground formation. Geology has therefore an appreciable effect on the relation of runoff to rainfall, as was pointed out in the preceding chapter.

The most satisfactory method of evaluating probable runoffs is by means of stream gauging in conjunction with the study of rainfall records. If a measure of actual stream flow is thus obtained, the various reductions in quantity of water from the amount falling as rain are automatically taken into account. This does not mean that study of the geology of the catchment area can be neglected; it cannot, unless long-term stream-flow records are available, since after varying intensities and durations of rainfall, geological peculiarities may affect the relation of runoff to rainfall to a varying degree and consequently interfere with the regularity of stream discharge. The loss of water through evaporation into the atmosphere and absorption by plant life is of interest to the water engineer only in so far as it represents a quantity of rainfall that cannot be used. That which percolates into the ground, in addition to representing an amount that has to be determined as a loss in the rainfall-runoff relationship, goes to replenish the great volumes of underground water which are of such vital importance to life on the earth's surface. Clearly, the amount that thus enters the ground is directly dependent on the geological nature of the exposed surface and on the type of vegetation growing thereon.

15.4. Water Supply from River Flow. Probably the simplest and most straightforward method of obtaining a supply of potable water is to abstract it directly from the flow of a river or from a fresh-water lake; it is also probably the first method ever used, if imagination may be allowed to range back to the activities of early man. Today, some of the greatest cities in the world secure their water supplies in this way— London, from the river Thames; Montreal, Canada, from the St. Lawrence; Chicago and other American and Canadian lake cities from the Great Lakes. What relation does geology have to this branch of waterworks engineering? There is, first, the indirect influence that geological conditions have on the rate of river flow. The local geological structure at the site of the water intake will affect to a considerable degree the type of structure adopted to provide the necessary intake. At Toronto, Canada, for example, the intake for the city's duplicate water-supply system was designed as a tunnel in the local shale for a distance of 3,300 ft out from the lake shore, finishing in a vertical shaft leading up to a series of precast concrete and steel pipes laid on the lake bed in a trench, at the ends of which are located the actual intakes, suitably screened. The location of the necessary control buildings for intake conduits from rivers or lakes, adjacent to a watercourse or shore line, will often introduce unusual geological conditions in the foundation beds that have to be used.

The abstraction of water from a river may be undertaken in a manner similar to that followed in Toronto; in general, Montreal and London obtain their supplies in this way. In some instances, however, when a river is bordered by porous beds of sand or gravel, advantage is taken of this geological feature, and the water is abstracted through the porous stratum and not directly. This method has many advantages, the most important of which probably is that the water is naturally filtered by its passage through the porous stratum; the use of artificial slow sand-filter beds in other water-supply schemes is a special adaptation of this process. Many such installations are to be found on the continent of Europe on some of the highly industrialized rivers. The cities of Berlin and Frankfurt in Germany and Göteborg in Sweden obtain at least a part of their water supplies in this unusual way, as do many cities in the great Ruhr industrial area of Germany. Hamburg, Germany, in addition to obtaining water that has filtered through from a river bed, uses two irrigating channels into which river water is pumped as additional "distributors," located to

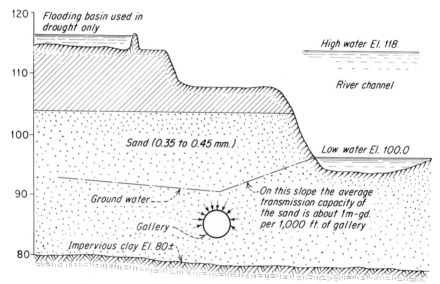

Fig. 15.1. Diagrammatic section showing intake arrangement used for the water supply of Des Moines, Iowa, U.S.A. (*Reproduced by permission of the Secretary and General Manager, Des Moines Water Works.*)

the north and south of the boreholes from which the city supply is finally obtained.[15.6] The city of Breslau, Germany, has used a similar practice. The devices used to abstract the water from the porous strata vary, but in some cases they are similar to the well points used on construction projects to dry up water-bearing ground (see page 358). Thus, Düsseldorf, Germany, uses borings 70 ft apart with gravel-packed suction pipes 12 in. in diameter, the yield of each being about 24,000 gph (Imp).[15.7]

This interesting method is not confined to Europe. The city of Des Moines, Iowa, has long obtained its water supply in this way from the Raccoon River which flows through a valley about a mile wide consisting of impervious material with a superficial deposit of water-bearing sand. Collecting galleries consisting of reinforced-concrete pipes 4 ft in diameter are located parallel to the riverbank and about 200 ft away from it.

They are located in this way in order to obtain fairly uniform percolation; a minimum good-quality supply of 300,000 gpd is obtained.[15.8]

A somewhat more unusual installation of this kind is that which supplies the city of Kano in northern Nigeria, Africa, an important center with a population of over 100,000. Prior to the construction of the new

Fig. 15.2. Sinking intake well No. 3 for the water supply of Kano, Nigeria, West Africa. (*Reproduced by permission of Binnie, Deacon and Gourlay, Consulting Engineers.*)

waterworks, the necessary supply had been drawn from wells dug in the local laterite. As this was unsatisfactory, a new installation was completed at a cost of about $1 million. Five large intake "wells" in the form of reinforced-concrete cylinders with internal diameters of 9 ft (three) and 15 ft (two), respectively, were sunk by grabbing from the interior to depths of between 35 and 52 ft. The wells rest on rock and penetrate the sand which constitutes the local river bed; they are located in the river bed over a stretch of about 2 miles. Intake pipes of 4-in. diameter are installed in two of the wells and porous concrete blocks in three; these are located near the rock surface through which water is drawn from the surrounding sand; the sand acts as a filter and also as a storage reservoir during dry seasons. A daily flow of over 500,000 gal (Imp) has been obtained.[15.9]

To include here reference to a water supply from ground water flowing beneath a dried-out river bed may appear to be stretching the title of this section rather far, but the inclusion is literally correct. A somewhat similar example from North American practice is to be found in Virginia. The city of Harrisonburg was led to the consideration of augmenting its water-supply system on account of a water shortage during the great drought of 1930. Surveys and investigations finally led to the conclusion that this could be obtained from ground-water flow in the valley of the Dry River from the normal stream flow of which the city already drew its main supply. It was found possible to extend an existing concrete diversion dam across the river bed for a distance of about 900 ft through a relatively level part of the bed of the valley as far as a steep rock cliff. This necessitated a thin reinforced-concrete wall, varying from 12 to 24 in. in thickness and keyed into the underlying fine-grained closely cemented Pocono sandstone rock for a distance of 16 in. The entire wall was backfilled on the upstream side with selected stone, obtained to some extent from excavation. At the location of the lowest level of the rock, a suitable concrete collecting gallery was constructed upstream of the dam, from which a 14-in. supply main leads to the city. The valley bed consists of products of disintegration and erosion varying in size from fine sand to large boulders; and in this deposit, 12 underground streams were encountered in definite courses, carrying such an amount of water that it caused difficulties during excavation. This flow is now permanently collected in a perforated concrete pipe laid under the stone backfilling and connecting with the collecting gallery. An average flow of about 700 gpm is obtained from this unique installation, which has performed satisfactorily since its completion.[15.10]

15.5. Water Supply from Impounding Reservoirs. When water for public use cannot be obtained directly by abstraction from river or lake, an obvious alternative is to utilize a distant source of supply such as the streams found in mountain areas, impounding these artificially and conveying the water thus obtained by means of aqueducts to the cities for which it is required. Although these schemes are always bold engineering conceptions, they are not a development of modern engineering, as a glance at the records of the Roman aqueducts will make clear. These ancient water-supply systems have now been eclipsed in size and conception by those of modern times, but they will always retain their interest. Water is conveyed today for city use in aqueducts hundreds of miles

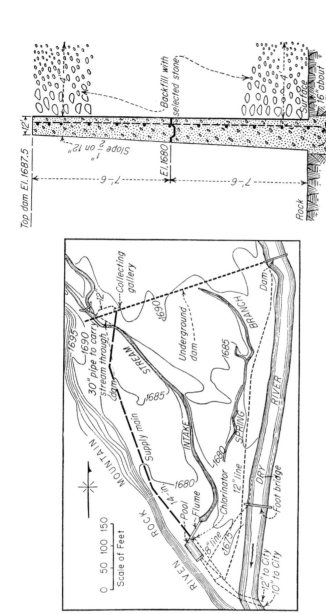

FIG. 15.3. Underground dam for the water supply of Harrisonburg, Virginia, U.S.A. (*Reprinted by permission of The Editor, Engineering News-Record.*)

long; that for the water supply of Los Angeles, California, brings water 250 miles to the city from the Owens Valley, 43 miles of this being made up of 142 tunnels of varying length. This installation is but one of a distinguished group of major engineering enterprises of this type which in the United States include the Hetch-Hetchy scheme supplying San Francisco and the Catskill and Delaware systems for New York, and in Great Britain include the Vrynwy scheme supplying Liverpool, the Rhyader supplying Birmingham, the Haweswater for Manchester, and those that supply other inland cities of England.

A typical water-supply scheme of this type consists of a catchment area, part of the rainfall on which is impounded behind a storage dam. From the reservoir formed by the dam, water is led away through an intake structure into the main aqueduct in which it is conveyed to a point on the city distributing system, generally a storage reservoir. It will be seen that the engineering problems introduced by the works mentioned are not peculiar to water-supply engineering; all of them are important parts of many water-power schemes, for example. In so far as the relation of geology to the works indicated is concerned, no unusual features are introduced by their use for water-supply purposes. The problems that they introduce can therefore be treated generally, as has already been done.

Although the engineering works for water supply derived from distant sources introduce no unique problems in relation to geology, individual examples of this type of project have provided the engineer with most valuable information on the general geological questions then introduced. Especially notable was the work of this nature during the construction of the Vyrnwy Dam for the water supply of Liverpool, England. The Ewden Valley works, also in England, have similarly been mentioned as providing most valuable information to engineers because of the geological conditions encountered. These and other English and European water-supply systems have involved works of great magnitude, but some of the North American water-supply schemes are even larger and may well be briefly mentioned.

The Catskill system for the city of New York, to which extended reference has already been made, is one such example. It includes two great tunnels, one going under the Hudson River 1,200 ft below water level, and two great dams; the close study of geology made in connection with this and other associated works was to a large extent pioneer work in this field. The Board of Water Supply for the city of New York continued to correlate geological study with its contract work and applied this particularly to the new Delaware River system which has now been put into service to supplement still further the water supply of the great metropolitan area of New York. The Delaware River aqueduct consists of 85 miles of tunnel, in six sections, the longest of which is 45 miles long;

the predominating rock types are shales, slates, sandstones, gneisses, and schists.

San Francisco receives its water supply from an impounding reservoir system of great magnitude; the Hetch-Hetchy water-supply and power scheme was put into service in 1934. Water is obtained in a catchment area in the Yosemite National Park and conveyed to the city through an aqueduct 155 miles long, 82 miles of which consists of tunnels (the remainder is pipelines). Several dams are also included; the largest is the

Fɪɢ. 15.4. The Eagle Mountain Pumping Plant on the Colorado Aqueduct, California, U.S.A., which lifts water 438 ft out of the total lift on the aqueduct of 1,617 ft; the view shows typical terrain traversed by this great water-supply system. (*Photograph by Steve Barrett. Reproduced by permission of the General Manager and Chief Engineer, Metropolitan Water District of Southern California.*)

O'Shaughnessy (impounding) Dam, which is 430 ft high. It is founded on granite which was seen to contain many large and deep potholes when uncovered by excavation. The tunnels were driven through varying rock strata, including granite, slate, and recent sedimentary formations. In these last, much trouble was encountered because of "quicksand" and excessive pressure from chlorites, methane gas, and sulfureted hydrogen; an explosion of methane was the cause of a fatal accident. Despite all difficulties, the tunnels were completed; in some the granite rock was so satisfactory that they are in use without a concrete lining.[15.11]

Brief reference may finally be made to one of the largest of all these projects, the Colorado River Aqueduct of the Metropolitan District of Southern California, which conveys water a distance of 240½ miles from the Colorado River to the Los Angeles district for the use of the 13 cities which constitute the metropolitan district. The aqueduct was designed for a peak flow of 1,605 cfs, or approximately 1,000 million gpd. There are five pumping stations having a total lift of 1,618 ft. The aqueduct consists of 91.9 miles of tunnels, 63.4 miles of open canal, 54.7 miles of conduit, and 28.9 miles of siphons. Excavation in the aqueduct totaled about 25 million cu yd; and concrete, 3½ million cu yd. Of the total tunnel footage, 58 per cent was supported by structural lining; 14 per cent was coated with gunite; and the remainder was unlined. These figures will give some idea of the magnitude of the project, but its unique nature will fully be realized only when it is considered that the eastern part of the aqueduct is located in an arid desert region, construction operations in which could begin only after the building of 148 miles of surfaced highway, 471 miles of power lines, and 180 miles of water-supply lines. The aqueduct passes through the desert as a concrete-lined open canal, and the lining is watertight, as the surface of the ground consists generally of alluvial deposits. It crosses three earthquake faults which are classed as active; flexible pressure pipelines across these locations have been considered desirable. Excavation for the Parker Dam, impounding the reservoir from which the supply of water is obtained, and the construction of the tunnels were affected by unusual geological conditions. It is not possible to describe these works in detail, but as is the case so fortunately with many leading civil engineering projects, full descriptions are available in technical journals to which reference can be made by those interested. In these descriptions repeated references are made to geological features that affected the work.[15.12]

15.6. Water Supply from Wells and Boreholes. Wells and boreholes constitute the principal means of obtaining a supply of water from underground sources. They may be considered together, since they are similar in principle and action. As a matter of convenience, wells are generally used for small depths and boreholes for greater depths. Unless they pass through very stable strata, wells (using this term to denote both types of hole) will be cased in some way throughout the depth of all strata except that from which the supply is to be obtained. Occasionally wire screens are used to protect that part of the well into which the water is being drawn. Another common precaution is to fill the excavated hole with specially selected coarse gravel through which the discharge pipe is led. This may decrease the yield of the well by about 5 per cent, but it will prevent plugging.

In wells that penetrate strata having a low specific yield, it may be necessary to attempt to secure a greater exposed surface in the pervious strata than is given around the perimeter of the well shaft. This is easily effected by driving adits into the strata from suitable locations in the well. It will generally be a wet construction operation; but it has the advantage that as soon as water problems become too troublesome, the object of the adit is achieved. The Romans used adits in wells that they excavated in Great Britain; today, adits are quite common in wells in the chalk of southern England and in the Bunter sandstones. In the Canary Islands adits alone are sometimes used as water-collecting galleries; they are driven into steeply sloping lava beds in order to obtain the water that seeps through this porous rock. The *karez* of northern India and the *keghriz* of Iran (Persia) are primitive types of a special kind of adit of considerable interest but restricted application. The planning and building of these unusual collecting galleries appear to be a matter of intuition rather than calculation, and the work is generally hereditary. Soviet engineers working in the Caucasus have tried to construct *keghriz* scientifically but without success.[15.13]

Fortunately, the usual type of well installation does not call for anything beyond ordinary scientific skill. When the excavation has tapped the water-yielding stratum, a body of relatively free water will be available which can be drawn upon as required. The level of this water may vary from time to time quite apart from the variation due to pumping. When the water table is near the surface, barometric pressure may affect the level, and even temperature has been found to have some effect because the capillary properties of the strata above are affected by a change in temperature. Water levels in adjacent wells may not coincide if there is a marked change in geological conditions between them. A striking example occurred at St. Andrews, Scotland. A farm drew its supply from a borehole 28 ft deep in sands and gravel. An architect sank a well 60 ft from the borehole in order to supply some new cottages; only a trace of water was found, although the well was sunk to a depth of 30 ft in the gravel. This was in all probability due to variation in level of the underlying impervious boulder-clay floor.[15.14]

When pumping is started in a well that has been satisfactorily completed to a free water surface, the water level will naturally fall and continue to do so until the hydraulic gradient in the surrounding material is such that flow will take place in the well to equalize the amount withdrawn. It can be shown theoretically that for uniform material, the curve of the gradient is a parabola. As this will be the same all around the well, the phenomenon known as the "cone of depression" is obtained. The intersection of a cone of depression with the water table will trace out a circle which will mark the range of influence of the pumping operation. It will be clear that the effective yield of any other well located within this range will be interfered with to some extent. Such interference is a critical matter in built-up city areas where ground-water resources are being taxed to the limit. It is surprising to note how wide these ranges of influence may be in pervious strata. In Liverpool, England, the effect of pumping has been noticed as much as 2 miles away from the well in which pumping was taking place; the intervening ground was largely pervious red sandstone.

The wells so far considered have been those which are ordinarily encountered, having no unusual geological features. In addition, not only artesian wells but also a few special types of wells may be noted briefly; although they are not of common occurrence, they are often of great importance in some localities. There are, in the first place, shallow wells which depend for their supply on a *perched water table*, i.e., a body of ground water perched high above the zone of saturation by means of an impermeable stratum overlying the main body of porous material. Some striking examples are found on Long Island, New York, where a thin layer of almost impermeable till separates a pervious surface deposit from the main body of pervious strata, and the main water table is as much as 250 ft below this perched water.[15.15]

Australia provides numerous examples of two other types of unusual wells. *Soak wells* is the name that has been given to the shallow wells used for obtaining ground water that collects, after running off exposed sloping surfaces of impervious weathered granite, in the accumulation of decomposed or disintegrated granite at the foot of these slopes. The products of decomposition vary and often yield quartz grains in a matrix of kaolin; from such a deposit no water supply can be obtained. But if the borehole is continued, a water supply will often be obtained from the body of water trapped between the bottom of this deposit and the top of the completely fresh granite; the transitional space is often open enough to yield water itself and to serve as a drain for the overlying kaolin.

The second type of unusual well encountered in parts of Australia (and elsewhere) is known as a *tray well*. This is really a case of tapping a localized body of perched ground water, a body of water perched not on a continuous impermeable stratum but on a lenticular bed of impervious material often of limited extent. A good example is furnished by a well at Challner, where a saucer-shaped bed of impervious clay with some ironstone nodules about it, located halfway down through a deep stratum of sand which overlies solid granite, collects a small quantity of fresh water as it percolates through from the surface. This supply is tapped by the Challner Well; endeavors were made to increase the supply by boring further, but the bed of clay was pierced and the fresh water started to empty into the sand below. Fortunately, the well was saved by plugging the hole. Ten chains away from this well is another, known as Nugent's Well, the bore of which encountered no water above the thin clay layer, so that it had to be extended to the main body of ground water overlying the granite directly. This second well is also unusual:

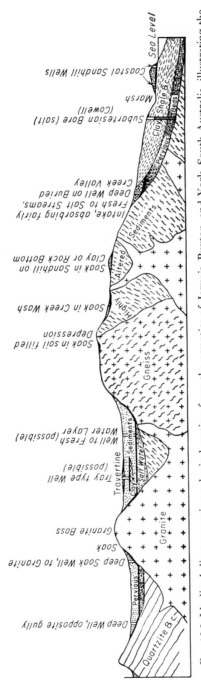

Fig. 15.5. Idealized diagrammatic geological section from the counties of Jervois, Buxton, and York, South Australia, illustrating the formation of tray wells and the dependence of these and other ground-water features upon local geological structure. (*Reproduced by permission of the Director of Mines, South Australia.*)

it cannot be extended right down to rock surface because the water immediately above the rock has a strong saline content, which makes it quite unsuitable for domestic use. Only the thin layer of fresh water that tops this salt-water layer can be tapped for use.[15.16]

The presence of salt water in wells is so important that it calls for attention. Salt water may be present for two general reasons: (1) encroachment of sea water into wells located near the seacoast, and (2) contamination of inland well waters with excessive mineral content. In both cases, as soon as the salt content passes a certain limit, the water ceases to be fit for human use. The following general limits have been suggested, based mainly on Australian practice.[15.17]

Oz per gal (Imp)

$\frac{1}{2}$ (3,125 ppm)........... Can be used domestically.
1   (6,250 ppm).......... Horses can live on this and keep in good condition.
$1\frac{1}{4}$ (7,812 ppm).......... Horses can live on this.
$1\frac{1}{2}$ (9,375 ppm).......... Cattle can live on this.
$2\frac{1}{2}$ (15,625 ppm)......... Sheep can live on this.

The contamination of inland ground-water supplies with excessive salt content, such as is found in parts of Australia and in the Sudan, has in the past been attributed to the leaching out of decomposition products of overlying or adjacent rocks. Consideration of the chlorine content of samples investigated in South Australia disproved this supposition and pointed to the fact that saline content is due to insufficient drainage for carrying off the salts brought down by rain. Continued evaporation of water gradually concentrates these dilute salt solutions, with the results already indicated. (Decomposition products probably contribute to the actual salt content found.) As evidence of what rain water may contain, it may be mentioned that in England the average chlorine content is about 2.2 ppm, equivalent to 3.62 parts of salt. Rain falling at Land's End during strong southwest winds blowing in from the sea has been found to contain one hundred times this amount.[15.18] As can be imagined, the problem is a complex one and is further complicated by varying local conditions. The greatest care must always be taken to avoid driving a well into the salt-water layer; and in the case of correctly driven wells, care must be taken to prevent the possibility of overpumping.

15.7. Some Unusual Sources of Supply. Brief reference may be made to one or two unusual sources of water supply which have been adopted in some parts of the world. The supply to the community living at the foot of the Rock of Gibraltar is one such example. The great rock consists of a hard and compact Jurassic limestone which provides no natural supply of spring water. For strategic reasons, the potable water supply has had to be obtained within the fortress area and so the supply was limited for many years to the rainfall on the surface of the rock itself.

This is steeply sloped on the east side, and the town is located on the west; a catchment area of 24 acres was constructed on the east side, using corrugated iron sheets laid on 40° sand slopes. The sheets were secured by means of timber purlins and piles creosoted under pressure. An additional catchment area of 15 acres was secured by utilizing steep

Fig. 15.6. The "ironclad" catchment area on the Rock of Gibraltar, looking north. (*Photo by N. N. Cumming. Reproduced by permission of the City Engineer, Gibraltar.*)

rock slopes on the west side. Rockfalls frequently damage the east catchment area, but because of the careful watch that is maintained, trouble is quickly located; washouts of considerable areas have nevertheless occurred. An additional supply of potable water was found by means of test borings sunk in the sand of the flat tableland to the north of the rock. Two wells were later dug and these supply about half of the total consumption. The brackish water supply to the town for all purposes other than drinking is obtained from shallow wells in the same area; it is kept separate from the potable supply. All drinking water is stored in reservoirs tunneled out of the rock; these have a total capacity of 14 million gal (Imp); they are generally in the form of galleries, leading off from two main construction adits, driven from west to east at a level of roughly 375 ft above sea level. An additional corrugated-iron catchment area of 10 acres, together with two new reservoirs inside the rock, is being added to supplement the existing water supply for shipping.

This interesting example shows how geological conditions distinctly unfavorable to the type of water-supply system that might have been expected (springs, wells, or other methods of underground extraction) have been adapted to give an almost perfect, although miniature, example of a surface water supply. It is of interest to note that the water thus obtained at Gibraltar is used without treatment, and although it is rather "flat," it is quite palatable and consistently safe.

Another unusual type of surface water supply is provided by the dew ponds that are still found in Sussex and other parts of southern England and probably also in other parts of the world. Some of these dew ponds seem to be natural formations, possibly finished off to some extent by the farmers who use them, but they are occasionally made artificially. The water deposited in them as dew is the result of condensation of the atmospheric moisture on the cold surface provided in the pond. The construction of a pond has been described as follows:[15.19]

A basin-shaped hollow is excavated in an open space, well exposed to damp sea winds. The hollow is covered by a layer of straw and twigs, or other non-conducting material, about 18 inches thick. On this is laid a continuous bed of puddled clay, about 2 feet thick, which in its turn is covered by a layer of broken stone. The object is to provide a surface of stone and clay which rapidly grows cold at night, and the dew thus collected is caught by the layer of puddle clay, and conducted to the central pond. Such a prepared area, about 200 feet in diameter, under favourable conditions, will keep the pond in the centre about 20 feet in diameter, and say 3 feet maximum depth. So far as can be gathered, in default of systematic observations, the yield is about 0.01 inch per night during the summer, over the prepared area.

The geological aspect of this source of supply is concerned with the provision of an impermeable basin, and the surface deposits of clay found in the south of England are well suited to this. The ponds illustrate vividly the direct relation of water supply to atmospheric moisture; the water thus obtained so directly is of admirable quality.

In parts of Australia, "ironclad catchment" areas are sometimes used. These are extensions of the "100 per cent catchment areas" provided by such impermeable surfaces as the roofs of farm buildings. Corrugated iron sheets laid on ground specially graded to give a convenient fall to special storage tanks have provided a large number of ironclad catchments at relatively low cost. All the scanty rainfall in these locations is thus obtained for use; an area of 26,000 sq ft has been found sufficient for the average farm.[15.20]

The use of corrugated iron can hardly be classed as a geological feature; but in other parts of Australia (notably Western Australia), a similar result is achieved by the use of rock catchment areas. At some places outcrops of granite are remarkably solid and so shaped that small concrete walls can be constructed around them in such a way that all rain falling upon them can be led to suitable storage tanks. Sometimes, holes excavated in the granite are used as the storage tanks.[15.21] In areas where no solid rock is available for use in this rather unusual way, Australian engineers have ingeniously waterproofed catchment areas whose surface consists of sandy soils. Attempts to render the ground surface impermeable and to promote full runoff of the sparse rainfall were first made in 1935 in Western Australia; emulsified bitumen was used on carefully graded natural soil. The experiments proved successful, and a small catchment area located at Narrogin in Western Australia was then treated in this way. Two areas of 30 and 18 acres, respectively, were treated by carefully rolling the cleared soil and then sealing the surface with 0.4 gal of emulsified bitumen to the sq yd. Local rainfall averages 18 in. per year of which only about 5 per cent used to run off, to be retained in the previously constructed reservoir. Suitable drains and surface channels now ensure complete runoff from the "water-proofed" catchment to the reservoir where it is retained for public use.[15.22]

15.8. Quality of Surface Waters. Rainfall absorbs gases and floating solid particles from the air before it reaches the ground. Rain water is therefore by no means pure; it is often definitely acidic, especially during thunderstorms when nitric acid may be formed. Small portions of carbon dioxide are always absorbed. Consequently, in flowing over rock formations of various types, rain water has a slight chemical effect on them, and the characteristics of lake and river water can therefore vary considerably. Although the detailed examination of water intended for use as domestic supplies is now a matter for specialist study, more particularly from the bacteriological aspect, it is one with which the civil engineer has to be generally familiar. Knowledge of the geological conditions causing the various impurities in water is a prerequisite for such familiarity.

Many upland gathering grounds, by reason of their topographical arrangement and the underlying geological structure, are covered with a layer of peat for much of their total area. Rain falling on peat deposits and running off to become stream flow inevitably takes with it traces of the peat and of the organic acids found in peat deposits. It thus becomes brackish, often slightly discolored, and usually slightly acidic. If the acidity is pronounced, the water may be slightly plumbosolvent, a grave matter in England and other European countries where lead piping is still used for water-supply purposes. Similarly, such water may have a serious effect on concrete surfaces exposed to it. Investigations in Scotland have shown that the only normal types of open conduit lining that successfully resist the action of moorland water are Staffordshire blue brick (an engineering brick of high quality) and aluminous cement concrete. Ordinary portland cement concrete of varying consistencies is seriously affected.[15.23]

The brackish taste and discoloration are objectionable from the point of view of the user of the water, although they are not usually of serious consequence. Both can be removed by modern filtration and treatment methods. In many cases, recourse has been had to stripping off all the peat from the area to be submerged by impounded water, often at great cost. Thus, a total volume of 4 million cu yd of peat was removed from the site of No. 5 Reservoir of the Boston, Massachusetts, waterworks. The bottom of the reservoir formed by the Silent Valley Dam in Northern Ireland (see page 501) was found to be covered with peat, in some places 30 ft deep. The peat was not removed, but the valley floor was covered with a layer of clean sand 2 to 3 ft in thickness. An area of 342,000 sq yd was covered in this way with sand obtained from local glacial deposits.[15.24] It will be seen, therefore, that thorough examination of the surface condition of any proposed reservoir site is a necessary part of preliminary investigation work.

Hardness, temporary and permanent, is perhaps the most widely recognized of possible impurities. In surface waters, hardness is the result of contact with rocks containing calcium or magnesium carbonate or calcium or magnesium sulfate. If a river is known to flow over limestone or dolomitic deposits, the source of the contamination can easily be found. Sometimes the strata in the bed of the river do not suggest the cause of the salt content. The river Derwent in Derbyshire, England, for example, flows over grit beds, and yet its water is hard. The hardness is due to the fact that the stream flow is fed by tributary streams which come down from mountain limestone deposits. Study of geological features both in river bed and over catchment area will suggest the type of hardness and the necessary treatment. Although generally troublesome, hardness of water is not always a disadvantage, as some beer drinkers may know. It is usually the mineral content of water that gives special local flavor to pale and bitter ales; hard water is desirable for their manufacture. For example, ales brewed at Burton-on-Trent, England, are made from hard water obtained from valley gravels and Keuper sandstones. It was once carefully calculated that in 1 year drinkers of Burton ales consumed 350,000 lb of solid gypsum in the process of assuaging their thirst. Soft water is required, on the contrary, for stout.

Waters used in the north of Scotland and elsewhere for a similar, although stronger, purpose are also dependent on hardness for their peculiar efficiency.

15.9 Some Outstanding Water-supply Systems. So varied are the conditions encountered in the development of public water-supply systems that a review of the importance of geology in this branch of civil engineering work may usefully conclude with brief descriptions of some outstanding examples. The examples have been selected because of their special geological interest and so all relate to the use of ground water in one way or another. Some of the better known systems have been passed over, such as the remarkable supply for the city of London obtained

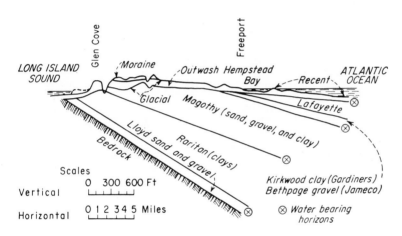

Fig. 15.7. Simplified geological section through Long Island, New York, indicating water-bearing horizons. (*Reproduced by permission of the Division of Water Power and Control, Conservation Dept., State of New York.*)

from the underlying London Basin, in order to invite attention to combinations of geological conditions and outstanding engineering work that may not be so generally familiar.

Long Island, New York. Long Island constitutes the coastal plain of the states of New York and Connecticut, separated from the mainland by Long Island Sound and isolated geologically from it with respect to its water-bearing beds. The island supports a population of several million people, and in recent years a large part of its water supply has been obtained from ground water. Crystalline bedrock outcrops in some of the western parts of the island, and the rock surface dips to the east so that in places it is at least 2,000 ft below the surface. Overlying the rock is a great deposit of stratified Cretaceous sands, clays, and gravels; the dip of the strata decreases toward the surface. At the surface, stratified sand and gravel drift deposits and two terminal moraines give rise to a fairly regular surface topography; the highest ground elevation is about 420 ft above the sea. These unconsolidated deposits constitute the great underground reservoir from which has been drawn probably the greatest concentrated ground-water supply utilized in North America. As the unconsolidated strata do not cross the sound to the mainland, the ground water underlying the island is obtained only from the rain falling on it, and consequently, the relation of this body of fresh water with the surrounding sea water is a delicate one. The rainfall averages about 42 in. per year, of which possibly one-half reaches the zone of saturation.

FIG. 15.8. A part of the area providing Southern California's great underground storage basin; the photograph shows the apex of the detrital cone of the San Gabriel River as it emerges into the South Coastal Plain. (*Photograph by Spence Air Photos.*)

Opinions differ as to how much of this water can be obtained for use; but from the records available, it is known that over 200 million gpd have been pumped for domestic and industrial use. Unfortunately, this pumping has been concentrated in developed areas, and a serious situation with regard to saline contamination has been created. Under the older part of Brooklyn, the water table has dropped to such a depth that most of the water under Brooklyn is now unfit for drinking purposes. The situation is complicated by the fact that as the area has been developed, the construction of paved areas and sewerage systems to carry off the rain water to the sea has been reducing the ground-water recharge. As is sometimes the case, the present problem is more a legislative one than an engineering matter, but the development and use of this great source of water supply still constitutes one of the best examples of ground-water utilization on a large scale.[15.25]

South Coastal Basin of California. Southern California is well known in many parts of the world for reasons other than engineering. What is not so well known is that a large part of the water supply to this area is obtained in a singularly interesting manner from underground sources. The South Coastal Basin of California comprises the Los Angeles metro-politan area and territory to the east, mainly agricultural but including 26 incorporated cities. The area consists essentially of the coastal plain, separated from the desert hinterland by three ranges of mountains gen-erally parallel with the coast. In these mountains rise three major streams: the Los Angeles, the San Gabriel, and the Santa Anna, the valleys of each of which are well defined. Geologically, the area is most complex, with the result that there are 37 fairly distinct basins, although the boundaries of these are not always evident at the surface; many are fault planes. The slope of the valleys is quite steep, but that of the coastal plain is relatively flat; the junctions of valleys and plain provide almost perfect examples of discharge cones, as is well illustrated in Fig. 15.8. Rainfall in the mountains is high but irregular; thus, the discharge of the streams is "flashy." Their courses through the coastal plain are often dry, the dry-weather flow percolating into their beds to replenish the ground water stored in the unconsolidated deposits forming the plain. These are varied in the extreme, although generally coarse. Faulting has complicated their distribution, but the area as a whole constitutes a great underground reservoir. It has been calculated that its capacity, in the 100-ft layer immediately below outflow level, is no less than 7 million acre-ft, of which only about 60 per cent has so far been used. The total surface area of the basins is 1,305 sq miles, and the average specific yield of the unconsolidated strata is 8.4 per cent by volume. Despite the high cost of pumping, the ground water is used not only for domestic purposes but also for agricultural irrigation. So great has been the demand that the water level has dropped very seriously. It is to augment this supply that some of the great aqueducts already mentioned have been con-structed.[15.26]

Nassau, Bahamas, British West Indies. The Bahamas are interesting islands, geologically and in other ways; they are flat and low lying, composed almost entirely of debris derived from corals and calcareous organisms, and resting on a shallow submerged platform which is separated by deep submarine troughs from the neighboring land masses of North America and the West Indies. The sand derived from the corals, together with infiltrated calcium carbonate, has formed as the local rock a very soft and porous limestone which weathers quickly. Many of the low-lying areas contain large brackish ponds whose water level rises and falls with the tides. These ponds are connected to the sea by means of underground passages, the salt and fresh water being in a state of balance. New Providence, the island on which Nassau, the capital city of the Bahamas, is located, is only 21 miles across from west to east and 7 miles from north to south. It has two ranges of low hills which nowhere rise more than 100 ft above sea level. Water supply was obtained solely from shallow wells and the flow from roofs until the year 1933. A serious outbreak of typhoid fever in 1926 and 1927 caused reconsideration of the whole question of the island water supply. After exhaustive surveys, and despite the unfavorable local geological conditions, an area was found that would yield fresh water in quantities sufficient for the

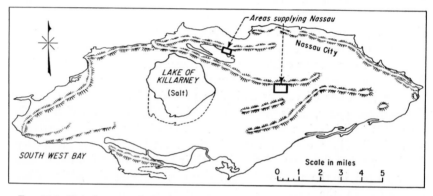

Fig. 15.9. Sketch map of the island of New Providence, Bahamas, showing areas supplying Nassau with fresh water. (*Reproduced by permission of the Director of* (*Public Works, Bahamas.*)

desired supply without danger of overpumping, provided that the wells installed were not carried too low, as they had often been in the past. This area measures about 3,300 by 2,000 ft. Sixty-five wells were sunk to the necessary elevation to reach the fresh-water layer, generally at intervals of about 300 ft, and staggered in plan. The depth to fresh-water level varied up to 40 ft; many of the wells are quite shallow, and pumping arrangements are designed in accordance with the various lifts. The water obtained from this ingenious installation is calculated to be enough to supply a population of 15,000; it is hard (230 ppm) and so has to be softened before use; it is also chlorinated as a safeguard to public health.[15.27]

Vancouver, British Columbia. Brief mention only will be made of the supply system of the Greater Vancouver Water District since it must be the envy of many other water authorities. The district is able to draw a supply of pure water by gravity from three catchment areas in the Coast Range almost within sight of the city of Vancouver; the dams are located 10 miles or less from the city proper. The magnificent geological setting of this western Canadian city is responsible for this good fortune;

the only disadvantage is that, because of the precipitous slopes to the valleys in which the impounding dams are located, their foundation has proved to be an unusually difficult matter, especially in the case of the last dam to be constructed, the Cleveland Dam at the outfall from Capilano Lake.

Ogden Valley, Utah. Possibly the most unusual water-supply system of its kind is that supplying the city of Ogden which, in 1914, started drilling wells in the artesian system of the lower Ogden Valley, created by the existence of silts and gravels beneath an impervious bed of 70 ft of varved clay. By 1933 a total of 51 wells had been drilled in what was called "Artesian Park"; the flowing wells are illustrated in Fig. 15.10. In 1935 and 1936 the U.S. Bureau of Reclamation constructed the Pine-

Fig. 15.10. The flowing artesian wells of the Ogden City water-supply system before they were submerged beneath the water of the Pineview Reservoir; a photograph taken probably about 1925. (*Photograph by the Ogden City Engineer. Reproduced by permission of the Commissioner, U.S. Bureau of Reclamation.*)

view Dam at the lower end of Ogden Valley; the reservoir so formed floods Artesian Park, and is the source of the city's water supply. Before the dam was built, however, a contract was negotiated between the city and the United States government providing for the capping of the artesian wells and the construction of the necessary collecting system, which would naturally be flooded by the water in the reservoir. The city therefore reserved the right to have the reservoir drained if ever there appeared to be trouble with its water system. The reservoir has been drained for this purpose, and repairs have been executed. Some of the damage that has been detected appears to have been due to the consolidation of the clay stratum because of the extra load of the water impounded by the dam. In 1955, therefore, special precautions were taken before the dam was raised by 29 ft to give additional storage. Flexible connections were used to minimize the effects of future ground movement. The system has been described as a "three-layer" water system, an unusual but not inaccurate title for an unusual but successful engineering project.

Honolulu, Hawaii: Maui Wells. The eight inhabited islands that comprise the main part of the state of Hawaii are world-famous for their beauty and their equitable climate. In a more restricted sense, they are known throughout the world by geologists as unusually interesting examples of volcanic-island formation. Since they have been developed for the extensive production of sugar cane and pineapples, for defense, and in more recent years as almost ideal tourist resorts, an increasing amount of engineering work has been necessary. This has included the development of what are some of the most unusual water-supply systems of the world. The volcanic rocks which form so much of the islands

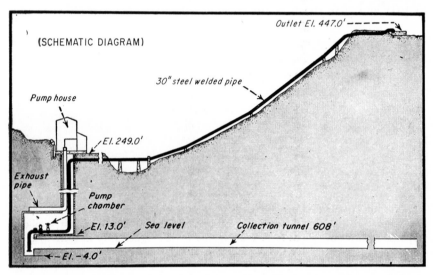

Fig. 15.11. Simplified section through a typical Maui-type well as used in the Hawaiian Islands.

are generally water bearing, particularly the Koolau and Waianae formations, that constitute most of the island of Oahu, upon which is located the city of Honolulu. The islands therefore provide excellent examples of the delicate balance of sea water and fresh water (the latter derived from the heavy rainfall upon parts of the islands) illustrated in Fig. 5-9 (page 15A). In earlier years, fresh-water supplies were obtained either from the artesian flows which occur in some locations, from dug wells, or from deeper drilled wells and boreholes. By 1933 as many as 700 wells had been drilled on the island of Oahu alone; the inevitable contamination by salt water resulted. Conservation measures were essential; these were initiated on a general scale with the establishment of the Board of Water Supply of Honolulu in 1929. In 1959, the board assumed control of all water-supply services in Oahu.

The key to successful conservation of this almost unique water-supply system was the adoption, starting in 1936, of a type of well first used about the turn of the century on the island of Maui for the supply of irrigation water for sugar-cane plantations. Maui wells, as they are now widely known, consist essentially of horizontal tunnels excavated in the local volcanic rock at carefully selected locations, generally just below the known fresh-water level. Access to the tunnels is usually obtained by means of inclined shafts, sometimes by vertical shafts, in which the necessary pumps and discharge mains can be located. By pumping at controlled rates from the supply which accumulates in the tunnels, a water supply is, so to speak, "skimmed off" the reservoir of fresh water so delicately balanced upon the underlying salt water. The surface level of the sea is depressed beneath the island by the overlying fresh water to the extent that for every foot of fresh water that exists in the rock above sea level, almost 40 ft of fresh water are found below sea level. The rapid rise of salt water consequent upon depletion of the fresh-water reservoir will be obvious from these figures. By the use of the horizontal skimming tunnels of the Maui wells, an assured supply is now being obtained for the city of Honolulu and the other rapidly developing communities on Oahu.[15,28]

It would be difficult to imagine a more vivid example than the Maui wells of Hawaii of the constructive application of the fundamentals of an unusual local geological situation for "the use and convenience of man" (to use the famous old phrase again). To stand, as has been the privilege of the writer, in the complete silence at the end of one of the collecting tunnels in Oahu; to watch the crystal-clear water in the lower part of the tunnel, knowing that it is slowly seeping from the surrounding basalt, volcanic rock the character of which is itself geologically interesting; and to think of the delicate balance existing between the clear fresh water thus being collected for use and the great expanse of sea water deep in the porous rock below one's feet is to have one of the most moving experiences possible for one interested in the proper appreciation of geology in all the works of the civil engineer.

Suggestions for Further Reading

Geology is so intimately related to the provision of water supply that there are few treatments of the engineering of water supply that do not touch upon its geological aspects. Geological problems, however, are related either to the structures necessary in water-supply schemes (references to which will be found at the end of other chapters) or to ground-water conditions. Reference may therefore be made to the notes at the end of Chap. 5 (see page 171). Only one volume is known to the author that deals exclusively with the geology of water supply; now more than half a century old, it can still be read with interest and profit:

Woodward, H. B., "The Geology of Water Supply," Edward Arnold & Co., London, 1910.

Chapter 16

TRANSPORTATION ROUTES

> Now in the middle ages, to keep these roads and especially these
> bridges in repair, was one of the first calls on Godly piety—charitable
> concern for all travellers. Turn to your Litany and read: "That it may
> please Thee to preserve all that travel by land or by water."
>
> Sir Arthur Quiller-Couch[16.1]

THE HISTORY of transportation routes presents a vivid picture of the
development of civil engineering—from the first efforts of primitive
man to bridge a stream with a fallen tree trunk to the conception and
construction of modern express highways with all associated works.
Beaten tracks to drinking places were probably the first artificially constructed pathways. Communication between settlements was a natural
development, and thus gradually arose the idea of main transportation
routes. In early historical records, many references to practical road
building are to be found. The road work of the Roman Empire was
the culmination of such development, and some Roman roads are still
in use today. Many centuries had to pass before road construction regained the eminence that it held in Roman times. This last advance has
not yet been halted and continues as the virile construction practice of
today. The nineteenth century saw the road challenged as the main
artery of transport by the railroad. In this present era, the road has more
than answered the challenge, and both now play their part in the general
transportation scene. Many problems, both economic and social, face the
railroads as they adjust themselves to their competitive position. The
advantages they present, however, are still so marked that they will long
continue to play a vital part in general transportation. New railroads
will continue to be built; the 370-mile line going north to Labrador from
Seven Islands, Quebec, for the Iron Ore Company of Canada is just one
example of new lines of the last decade. Railways therefore warrant full
attention here, as do also the airfields which make possible air travel, the
great contribution of the twentieth century to the transportation scene.

Preceding the development of land transport was the steady develop-

592

ment of water transport. Beginning with the primitive local use of rivers and slowly extending into the use of lakes and inland seas, the record of water transport is continuous throughout the whole range of human history. The use of the ocean itself for travel presents one of the most fascinating chapters in the story of man. Even so limited a part of this story as the provision of the necessary marine works is of such importance in the history of engineering that a separate chapter must be devoted to it. It will be convenient to consider the use of rivers as transportation routes in connection with other aspects of river engineering; this branch of water transport will therefore be considered in Chap. 19. There remain for consideration canals, those artificial waterways necessary to join natural waterways or to give access from the sea to inland points. Although the building of new canals is now a rare occurrence, the canals in use today are so vital to the human economy and present such interest from so many points of view, including the geological, that brief reference to them may well preface this discussion of the geology of land transportation routes.

16.2. Canals. The extension of inland waterway systems and the penetration of narrow land barriers between seas by means of canals have attracted the attention of master builders throughout the ages. A canal connecting the Nile and the Red Sea is said to have been begun in the fourteenth century B.C.; work on the project was abandoned by Necho about 610 B.C. after 120,000 men had lost their lives in the excavation work. According to Strabo, it was finished by Ptolemy II, who is said to have constructed in it locks with movable gates. The many canals constructed in what is now Iraq are familiar to students of early history. Xerxes, in his war against the Greeks, constructed a canal across the isthmus of Mount Athos; trouble was encountered because the sides (up to 50 ft deep) were excavated at too steep a slope.[16.2] The isthmus of Corinth was a continuing challenge to the early Greeks, even though the Corinth Canal was not finally completed until as recently as 1893. A crossing of the isthmus is said to have been first conceived by Periander of Corinth, one of the Seven Sages. With the facilities available to him, he could not possibly have constructed a canal, but in order to give the merchants of Corinth an eastward outlet, he built the best alternative to a canal, what might be termed the first marine railway. This was the *dioclos*, a paved roadway upon which vessels could be portaged from the Gulf of Corinth to the Saronic, 4 miles away. A legend to this effect has long persisted; in 1957 Greek archaeologists found undoubted remains of the *dioclos*, still in good condition where it had not been cut away for the modern canal or crossed by railway tracks. It was 13 ft wide and built of heavy rectangular blocks of the local limestone. Evidence that it was built in the time of Periander, probably about 606 B.C., is found in the letters carved into some of the limestone blocks; the letters are from the Corinthian alphabet which was in use in the sixth century B.C. Periander's idea of constructing a canal was taken up by later rulers. One of them, however, Demetrius Poliocretes, was dissuaded from starting the work by his priests, who claimed that the sea level in the Gulf of Corinth was higher than that in the Saronic. Nero came nearest to completing the project in these early years. He himself inaugurated the work in A.D. 67, cutting the first sod with a golden spade. With the aid of 6,000 slaves (sent by Vespasian from Judea) he did complete 2,200 yd on one side of the isthmus and 1,600 yd on the other. Four months later the work was stopped, probably because of the revolt of Vindex, but when modern engineers resumed the work in the nineteenth century, they used exactly the same cuts. The canal is 4 miles long, 70 ft wide, and 26 ft deep. It was seriously damaged during the Second World War but is now back in service.[16.3]

From these very early times, the building of canals has had a fascination for inquiring minds to a degree probably not equaled by other engineering works. It may, therefore, be useful to recall this wide early interest in modern canal building by a quotation from Goethe, the appearance of whose name in this volume is entirely appropriate since, as the "universal scholar," he had a very lively interest in geology. Eckermann reports him to have said in 1827:[16.4]

So much, however, is certain that, if they succeed in cutting a canal that ships of any burden and size can be navigated through it from the Mexican Gulf to the Pacific Ocean, innumerable benefits would result to the whole human race. But I should wonder if the United States were to let an opportunity of getting such a work into their own hands escape . . . it is absolutely indispensable for the United States to effect a passage from the Mexican Gulf to the Pacific Ocean and I am certain they will do it. Would that I might live to see it!—but I shall not. I should like to see another thing— a junction of the Danube and the Rhine. But this undertaking is so gigantic that I have doubts of its completion, particularly when I consider our German resources. And thirdly, and lastly, I should wish to see England in possession of a canal through the Isthmus of Suez. Would I could live to see these three great works! It would be well worth the trouble to last some fifty more years for that purpose.

In this, as in so many other things, Goethe was a man with vision. Others shared his enthusiasm for canals, and many canal works were started in the nineteenth century, although some were abandoned long before actual completion. In most of these cases, it seems to have been a neglect of geology that led to the abandonment of projects that appeared superficially to be practicable. The "pathology of canals" would form an interesting, if sobering, study in engineering geology. Let brief reference to but one example suffice, with corresponding apologies to the Emerald Isle in which so much fine engineering work has been carried out. T. Mellard Reade in a paper presented in 1888 records the following case:[16.5]

> Another well-known piece of stupidity was the attempt to make a canal between Loughs Mask and Corrib in the West of Ireland. This was one of the relief works planned during the great famine, and it is not known who was responsible for it. A canal between the two loughs would have been of some utility, but the strata in which they lie is carboniferous limestone much jointed, and the communication or drainage between the two waters, is by underground channels. The engineers, Royal or otherwise, went bravely to work, the canal was cut in the limestone rock, the water turned in, when lo! it all quickly disappeared. The abandoned cutting may now be seen sparsely overgrown with grass.

This appears to be an unfortunate reference to the work of the Royal Engineers (of Great Britain) since some of their early canal building was notable pioneer civil engineering. Outstanding is the Rideau Canal, built between 1826 and 1832 as a military canal from Ottawa to Kingston in eastern Canada. It is 127 miles long, and its construction involved the canalization of two rivers and several lakes by means of 47 locks and over 50 dams; it was a masterly demonstration of what the Royal Engineers could do in virgin forest. Lt. Col. John By, the engineer in charge, must have had an innate sense of sound geological understanding since both the location of the canal and the selection of masonry for locks and dams could not have been better done today.[16.6]

Superficially, the excavation of a regular water channel along a selected route appears to be a simple operation. It is only when the details of design and construction are considered that the true complexity of the work becomes evident. Canal bed and canal banks should be impermeable; if permeable, the leakage must be predictable with certainty. Canal banks, if necessary, must be stable. Bridge foundations adjacent to the canal must be sound and secure; similarly, the foundation of all lock and control structures must be susceptible to rational design and expeditious construction. Geology is of fundamental importance in all these problems, as can be seen at a glance. Adequate knowledge of all geological features is therefore an essential prerequisite to canal construction.

The foundation of locks is of particular interest because of the varying hydrostatic conditions to which the completed structures will be subjected. When locks are founded upon solid rock, few problems usually arise. Some locks, however, must be founded on soil, and this necessitates special care in design and construction. As an example of somewhat unusual conditions ingeniously utilized, there may be mentioned the main sea lock of the Ijmuiden Canal, Holland, a diagrammatic cross section through which is shown in Fig. 16.1. The local fresh-water supply is obtained from ground water trapped beneath the top clay stratum shown in the diagram. There was grave danger that if construction operations interfered with this underground reservoir, the supply might be affected in quantity and possibly in saline content by ingress of sea water. As a result of thorough subsurface exploration, the conditions shown in Fig. 16.1 were determined, and this permitted the complete enclosure of the space occupied by the lock—1,315 ft long by 161 ft wide—by a wall of steel sheet piling. This course was followed as indicated in the diagram, and the work was successfully completed. It constitutes an outstanding example of the adaptation of local geological features as a definite part of a scheme of construction.[16.7]

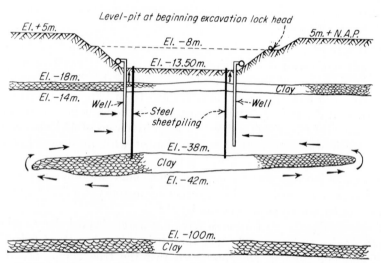

Fig. 16.1. Subsurface conditions at the site of the Ijmuiden Lock of the North Sea Canal, Holland. (*Reproduced by permission of The Editor, Engineering News-Record.*)

Another of the great European canals connects the noted seaport of Antwerp on the river Scheldt with the inland port of Liege on the river Meuse. This is the Albert Canal, a masterpiece of Belgian engineering, completed just before the Second World War; because of its critical location, it was a vital factor in some of the war's most crucial fighting. The purpose of the canal was, indeed, twofold: it served as a defense barrier and as a means of conveying barges with a capacity of 2,600 tons from the sea to the important industrial area around Liege. It is 80 miles long and has only six locks (as compared with 23 in the smaller canal which it replaced); these give a drop of 184 ft from the river Meuse to the Antwerp docks. Excavation amounted to 89 million cu yd. Geology was a determining factor throughout its route; two features only can be mentioned here. Near Lanaye, at the Liege end of the canal, an open cut proved to be necessary ranging from 65 to 212 ft in depth. This had to be carried out through a formation of tufa and chalk, a rock combination which hardens on exposure to the atmosphere. Steep slopes, as shown in Fig. 16.2, were therefore possible because of this rock characteristic. Steam shovels were used to remove clay and gravel overburden and also to remove the rock, which was so soft when first exposed that it could be removed with liquid air cartridges. Pneumatic tools were used for dressing the finished slopes; the good effect can be seen from the illustration.

Fig. 16.2. The cutting at Lanaye on the Albert Canal, Belgium, during construction (above) and as completed (below). (*Reproduced by permission of La Ministere des Travaux Publics et de la Reconstruction, Belgium.*)

Berms, 3 to 6 ft wide, were broken out at intervals of 33 ft. Another of the major cuts on the canal is near Briegden, some miles "downstream" from Lanaye. Here careful preliminary exploration had revealed difficult conditions at a depth of 130 ft, with waterlogged sand and clay; to have avoided these strata would have necessitated two extra locks in order to raise the canal level above them. The bold decision was made to stay with the original concept of a deep cut, using special drainage installations to take care of ground water, special construction methods throughout, and most carefully designed side slopes. The great cut, over 150 ft deep, was successfully completed, and it has continued to perform well.[16.8]

The Welland Canal joining Lakes Erie and Ontario across the Niagara escarpment is an outstanding example from North American practice. It is about 26 miles long; its drop of 326½ ft was achieved by means of only seven locks, each of which has a usable size of 820 by 80 ft. Throughout its course, it crosses 10 distinct geological formations of the

Fig. 16.3. A landslide on the Panama Canal, September 18 and 19, 1915, showing an island formed overnight in 30 ft of water. (*Reproduced by permission of The Governor, Canal Zone.*)

Ordovician and Silurian measures, including dolomites, limestones, sandstones, and shales. Of these, the Medina or Queenston shale gave unusual trouble during excavation, disintegrating as it dried out in the atmosphere. The practice developed, therefore, of so excavating it that a thin cover was left in place until just before concreting began; it was then removed after having thus protected the final excavated surface.

One more canal must be mentioned—a project the completion of which was one of the most notable achievements in the history of civil engineering. The Panama Canal, joining the Atlantic Ocean with the Pacific, is now one of the most important waterways of the world. Located just north of the equator, it crosses the Isthmus of Panama where the great Continental Divide dips to its lowest elevation, about 312 ft above sea level. The route of the canal follows existing river valleys and crosses the divide in the great Gaillard Cut; it is 40.27 miles long. Its history is interesting. First projected in 1529 by Alvaro de Saavedra (a companion of Balboa in the discovery of the Pacific and a lieutenant of "stout Cortez"), it remained for over 300 years no more than an international hope. Construction was started in 1882 by a French company which operated until 1889; a reorganized company started work in 1894 but was eventually bought by the United States of America in 1902, under whose auspices the canal was completed in 1914. The canal was officially opened on July 12, 1920.

Despite the magnitude of its engineering features, attention must here be restricted to the canal's geological interest. This is typified, perhaps, by the following figures of excavation carried out up to June 30, 1959:[16.9]

	Cu yd
Excavated by French	29,908,000
Excavated by Americans	588,181,200
Excavation in Gaillard Cut	189,832,700
Excavation in Gaillard Cut attributed to slides	76,228,000

This last surprising figure is at least a clue to the difficulties encountered in the excavation of the great cut penetrating the Continental Divide. It is 8.75 miles long. The geological formations encountered during the construction of the canal are mainly sedimentary beds of shale and sandstone, irregular masses of intruded basaltic and agglomeritic dikes and plugs, and volcanic tuff. Their distribution is somewhat complicated and is seriously affected by frequent faults. The greater part of the Gaillard Cut is through rock strata; although these strata are variable, slides in them caused little trouble. In the Culebra section of the cut, however, a synclinal trough about 1 mile wide at canal level crosses the cut directly at its deepest portion. The trough is filled with a "fine-grained sandy clayey formation" called *cucaracha;* it is structurally weak, and its repeated failure led to most of the slides that interfered so seriously with the construction of the canal.

These slides began at least as early as 1884, just after the start of excavation by the French, and they continued until long after the completion of the canal. One slide of over 500,000 cu yd happened overnight; others were of considerable duration. They were of varied types and included upheavals of the floor of the cut, described thus by Colonel Gaillard: "Most of the slides of the past year (1911–12) were breaks resulting from the failure of an underlying layer of rock of poor quality due to the pressure of the enormous weight which crushes the underlying layer, forces it laterally and causes it to rise up and heave in the bottom of the cut. The heaving at times is 30 feet." An accompanying photo-

Fig. 16.4. Cross sections through Gaillard Cut, Panama Canal, showing excavation originally proposed and that actually carried out. (*Reproduced by permission of The Governor, Canal Zone.*)

graph (Fig. 16.3) shows such an upheaval in the form of an island which appeared overnight out of a depth of 30 ft of water.

Figure 16.4 represents a cross section through the Gaillard Cut as it exists today and as it was originally projected. From a study of this, coupled with recognition of the structural instability of the *cucaracha* formation, one can appreciate that the slides were due to the inherent weakness of this material in standing up to the loading to which it was subjected by progress of the excavation, intensified in some places by the extra loading of excavated material dumped too near the canal. The unsatisfactory nature of the *cucaracha* formation was reported on in 1898 by the French geologists Bertrand and Zurcher, and it has been suggested that their opinions were not utilized. It is therefore of significance to note that the final report of the Committee of the National Academy of Sciences (of the United States) appointed by the President of the United States to study the Panama Canal slides, following the closing of the canal in September, 1915, due to blockage by slides, included this statement:

The Committee regrets that the United States engineers in charge of the canal excavation have not had the benefit, from the outset, of the best available technical advice in regard to the proper slopes for the canal banks, based on a thorough study of the rocks in the banks, and in regard to the character of the slides. Dr. Howe, who was attached to the canal force under Engineer John F. Stevens, 1906–7, before much progress had been made in excavation, was occupied mainly in the preliminary geological study of the canal route and in special problems which were pressing at that time. Dr. Hayes, the first geologist called upon to examine the Culebra slides, was sent to the canal in 1910, on the request of President Taft, but remained there for a short time only. On his recommendation a geologist [Mr. MacDonald] was attached to the canal corps and for three years rendered valuable assistance, although the great slides were already past control. He was the first to recognize the general character of the deep-seated deformation which characterizes the Culebra slides and explains the upheaval of the bottom of the cut, which was a feature of some movements.

The report of this committee and its valuable appendices constitute a document of great engineering and geological interest and illustrate vividly the necessity of the application of geological study to all problems such as those which the construction of the Gaillard Cut involved.[16.10]

Careful maintenance has naturally been a continuing feature of the operation of the canal. In the course of this work, a surveyor noticed in 1938 a small crack at the top of Contractors' Hill, a dominating feature of this critical part of the canal. The crack was regularly observed; in 1954, it had increased to such an extent that remedial action was clearly necessary. On the recommendation of consultants, a drainage tunnel, 5 by 7 ft, was quickly excavated in order to drain ground water from the vicinity of the main crack, since this was one of its contributory causes. A contract was awarded for the removal of about 2.5 million cu yd of the Pedro Miguel agglomerate forming the hill in order to relieve the pressure on the underlying *cucaracha* shale. Most unusual expedients were necessary in carrying out controlled blasting in order to cause as little disturbance as possible; the work was successfully completed before the end of 1955; the finished appearance of the cut is shown in Fig. 16.5.[16.11] The

Fig. 16.5. Excavation on Contractors' Hill, Panama Canal, required to ensure stabilization of this part of the Culebra Cut (see text). (*Reproduced by permission of The Governor, Canal Zone.*)

Second World War taxed the capacity of the great canal to the limit and much study has been given to possible means of enlarging the facility it provides. Eventually, there will probably be more construction at Panama; canal construction here and elsewhere will continue its challenge to the cooperative efforts of engineers and geologists.

16.3. Route Location. In land transportation, there are two main problems to be faced in the design and construction of both roads and railways: (1) the selection of the route to be followed and (2) the provision of a roadbed and a bearing surface capable of carrying intended traffic and of reasonably permanent stability. The final choice in both will today depend largely on economic aspects, but geology may often have a considerable bearing on the final solutions. In very early days, road location was a matter of adapting for vehicular use older pathways that had been formed by primitive peoples as their tracks through the forests and along riverbanks. Roman road construction marked a significant break from this primitive practice; Roman engineers usually laid out their roads, upon which the greatness of their Empire depended, as straight as possible, a practice that continued in France until the eighteenth century. When changes in direction had to be made, this was generally done on high ground or at station houses; curves were used only infrequently. The Fosse Way in England, to cite one example, is about 200 miles long (joining Lincoln and Axminster), but the greatest departure from a straight line between the two end points is only 6 miles. There has been much discussion of the reason for this almost invariable practice of route selection; one suggestion (not very well founded) is that the Romans could not construct vehicles that could easily negotiate curves. The Romans only rarely used anything but embankments for easing the grades on their roads; there does seem to be some foundation for believing that this was done deliberately to promote snow clearing by the wind, a practice regarded by many as a feature of modern road design.[16.12]

Roman road building, however, for centuries stood alone. It took the coming of the railway to direct attention to the basic problems of economical route selection, of severely limiting grades, and of keeping curvature to a minimum. In flat country, selection was largely a matter of convenience and of land availability; the route chosen was selected to give the shortest possible convenient link between the centers to be joined, although deviations were made if necessary to obtain improved river crossings. In hilly country, however, many alternatives could be considered. The ridge route up a valley, for example, might be chosen in preference to the valley route; the climb to the ridge would more than compensate in convenience for the numerous river crossings usually necessary if a valley route were used. Such selections were inevitably influenced by the underlying geology since it determines the local topography.

The records of railway locations are replete with graphic examples of such geological determinants; to select even one example is not easy. Figure 16.6, however, shows what may perhaps be called a "classical" case. The view shows how the main Gothard line of the Swiss Federal Railways makes its way across Lake Lugano. This lake very effectively bars the direct route that could otherwise have been followed in the direction of Como. The lake is over 900 ft deep opposite the town of Lugano. Swiss engineers found the solution to their location problem, however, by noticing that Melide, a village at the base of Monte San Salvadore, the conical peak that is visible from Lugano, was located on a rather odd-looking promontory in the lake. This suggested that it might be a part of a glacial moraine. Soundings in the lake were therefore taken opposite the village and a ridge was found, running across the lake at quite a shallow depth, clearly the remainder of the suspected moraine. An embankment was, therefore, easy to construct; it is this that is seen in the photograph; the embankment carries not only the railway but also a main highway. The railway line curves sharply at the end of the embankment to follow a winding route along the foot of the mountains until it reaches the border station of Chiasso.[16.13]

Fɪɢ. 16.6. The Melide Causeway across the Lake Lugano, constructed on top of a submerged glacial moraine and carrying the Gothard line of the Swiss Federal Railways on its way to Italy. (*Reproduced by permission of Schweizische Bundesbahnen.*)

In more recent years, the building of superhighways has resulted in similar vivid examples of the effect of local geology upon road location and upon the costs of construction within the limits thus determined. The similarity of modern road location with the long-established practice of railroad location is nowhere better illustrated than by the construction of the Pennsylvania Turnpike, much of the route of which utilized an abandoned railway right of way. New roads will still be built, not only in the less developed parts of the world but also in North America; new railways will also still be built. What techniques are now available for final route selection after a general course has been determined? Here is found change indeed, and current techniques contrast greatly with the laborious work of field location practiced until the 1930s. Today, office study of topographical and geological maps is a first requirement, and almost always a possibility, even though the scales of available maps in more isolated areas are still small. Concurrently, the detailed study of aerial photographs of the area through which the proposed route must run is a relatively new technique that gives a different pattern to route location.

The use of aerial photographs for preliminary site study has been briefly touched upon in Chap. 6. As there noted, the art of aerial-photo interpretation has now developed to such an extent that it has its own voluminous literature to which recourse may be had for detailed account of techniques. There are few applications in which the value of this procedure is more in evidence than in the selection of routes for highways and railways. Field surveys are still necessary, but these can now be restricted to the route selected by means of aerial photographs with the certain knowledge that it is the best of all available. Survey work can thus be speeded up and carried out with more thoroughness than would be desirable if final choice of route depended upon the preliminary surveys themselves. Soil and rock surveys along the route, and in adjacent areas for the provision of necessary fill or roadbed material, must similarly be carried out, but again, the conduct of such surveys will be greatly aided by the preliminary information gained from a study of aerial photographs, especially if this can be done in association with available geological and pedological maps.

Illustrative of the saving in time now possible is the record of the preliminary surveys conducted for the construction of an extension of the Nigerian Railway into Bornu Province in central Africa, a project which was assisted by the World Bank. Here aerial photographs were not available and so had to be specially taken. A total length of 611 miles was covered by aerial strip photography (to include possible alternative routes); the work involved just over 50 hr of flying time and was done in 11 working days. Mapping of the route selected by means of the aerial photographs, a distance of 443 miles, started in July, 1956, and was completed in September, 1957; the only unusual geological feature was the unavoidable use of a section of route over *black cotton* soil, one of the most difficult of tropical soils with which to deal in engineering work. Despite the isolated tropical location of the work, the total cost of aerial photography and ground mapping was approximately £70,000 or £173 per mile of final alignment.[16.14]

Preliminary work for the Ohio Turnpike Project No. 1 may be cited as an excellent example of the application to a modern highway undertaking of the procedure summarized above. This first-class modern dual highway is 241 miles long and cost about $1 million per mile; almost 40 million cu yd of excavation was involved, with a corresponding volume of fill, and over 7 million sq yd of concrete paving. A complete set of consecutive aerial photographs to a scale of 1:10,000 covering a strip of territory 1½ miles wide within which it was known the road would run was first studied. A band 2,000 ft wide was then selected for more detailed study. All available pedological and geological maps and reports relating in any way to the selected route were studied concurrently. Thus all main soil types and soil boundaries, drainage patterns, etc., could be marked upon the photographs; the photographs were viewed stereoscopically and terrain-interpretation techniques were used. The Ohio Geological Survey provided some unpublished material on abandoned glacial shore lines which, when applied to the photographs, proved to be unusually accurate—a good example of the use of unpublished geological information that is sometimes to be found if approach is made to the appropriate authorities. Preliminary correlation of pedological soil characteristics with engineering soil properties, assisted by study of information provided by the Ohio State Highway Testing and Research Laboratory, meant that a good approximation to soil conditions along the route was obtained merely by office work.

Careful check lists were prepared for field study. These greatly facilitated the final surveys in the field, which did not have to be so extensive because of the preliminary correlation of all existing information through the vivid aid of aerial photographs. Before field studies commenced, 34 stream crossings and 114 road and railway crossings were similarly studied in detail in the office, again aided by information from the State Highway Department obtained from adjacent locations. Twenty-two contracts were then awarded to 11 contractors for the requisite test-boring program, the main lines of which had been carefully and accurately determined by means of the office studies. Eventually 60,405 ft of earth borings and 8,812 ft of rock borings were put down at a total cost of $441,785, a figure that may usefully be compared again with the total cost for the entire project of over $200 million. All rock cores and soil samples were passed to the state geologist for safekeeping and public use, a good example of the reciprocal service that now so happily characterizes cooperative geological-engineering investigations.

Some special problems were encountered with glacial tills and with road construction over swamplands, but the only really unusual feature of the project was that part of the route passed through an area well known for coal strip-mining operations. Land of potential value for strip-mining operations had to be carefully surveyed before being preempted for road construction. Forty special prospect borings were put down to supplement surface observations (which included study of adjacent strip-mining operations) in order to provide the necessary information upon which land valuations could be based. It was found that, for the Mahoning County area, the average quantity of coal to be obtained by strip mining could be estimated as 125 tons per acre per in. of seam. It was also found that strip mining of coal could be regarded as economical if a maximum of 2 ft of overburden was removed for every inch thickness of merchantable coal. Although these figures are directly applicable only to this area of Ohio, they may be useful as a general guide. Cash payments for land taken over for the turnpike project were made on the basis of the factual evidence thus assembled, despite the claims made by landowners in the manner usual on such occasions. The full record of these preliminary geological and soil studies for the Ohio Turnpike is a valuable guide to the best of modern practice in route selection.[16.15]

With railways and roads now so commonplace in the more developed countries of the world, it should not be forgotten that the surveys for many of the pioneer routes of the New World in particular (especially for railways) provided the first information about the local geology of the areas traversed. There are fortunately on record many papers giving invaluable geological information as by-products of such preliminary engineering work. A singularly useful paper of this sort was published as early as 1888;[16.16] one of the most recent examples is the record prepared of the geology along the Alaska Highway, a wartime emergency route that penetrated the relatively unknown Canadian Northwest.[16.17] The wheel has now turned full circle, for there have begun to appear handbooks in which geologists (and engineers) explain and interpret the geology of the land adjacent to main highways for the information and enjoyment of those who travel these routes by bus or automobile. One of the best handbooks known to the writer is that issued in 1958 by the West Texas Geological Society. This is a well-produced quarto-sized guidebook to the geology (and also the history) of the country traversed by U.S. Highways 90 and 80 from Del Rio to El Paso. A concise road log is well supplemented by a brief description of the areal geology and notes on the wildlife and plants to be seen along the highway.[16.18] The guide may well serve as a model to other groups who contemplate the same sort of public service.

16.4. Road Construction. "The Story of the Road" is the title of a book (by J. W. Gregory) which traces the broad outlines of highway development through the ages, a book that is mentioned at the outset of this section since so little can here be said about the background of this particular application of geology.[16.19] Roman road building, always carried out with intuitive geological appreciation, has already been mentioned. It may be well to recall, before modern highway construction attracts attention, that at the height of the Roman Empire, over 50,000 miles of first-class highways had been built and were in use by Roman legions. Julius Caesar, of schoolboy memory, was at one time curator of the Via Appia and is said to have expended vast sums of his own money upon its improvement. On the American continents, however, was to be found the greatest of all early roads. This road, built by the Incas, was 4,000 miles long and stretched from Quito in Ecuador to Tucuman in central Chile; it was 25 ft wide, and much of its surface was paved with bitumen. A second road paralleled the main road for almost 2,000 miles along the coast. Much of this great road can be seen today; some of it is still in use. All who are interested in the historical background of modern engineering have a treat in store for them if they have not yet read Prescott's "Conquest of Peru," a volume that can well be termed supplementary reading to any study of the relation between geology and road building.

It was not until the dawn of the industrial era that road building again assumed importance; Britain and France led the way in this early branch of modern civil engineering. John Metcalfe (Blind Jock of Knaresborough) was probably the first of the pioneers: Sir Walter Scott, through the character of Wandering Willie in "Redgauntlet," has shown how this gifted man overcame his blindness even to the extent of appreciating geology in his road-building work. It was not until 60 years later that Thomas Telford and James Loudon McAdam started their notable road work, the results of which are still to be seen in Great Britain today. Although neither of these great men wrote very much, the writings they did leave show clearly that geology (even though not so called) was a vital part of their thinking about roads.[16.20]

North America had its road pioneers also, quite naturally long after those of Europe in view of the differing pace of development between the Old World and the New. It was as early as 1906, for example, that Dr. C. M. Strahan, then county engineer of Clark County, Georgia, started his experiments into the desirable properties of soils for road-building purposes, although his first published statement on this work did not appear until 1914. This pioneer research work of Dr. Strahan paved the way in North America for the more general scientific study of soils for engineering purposes, now so well known as soil mechanics, as was noted in Chap. 4 (see page 107). Just a year after the start of this work in Georgia, the Wisconsin Geological Survey (in 1907) was granted $10,000 by the state legislature for investigations and experimental work in road building.[16.21] Such progress was made in comparable studies in Illinois that in 1927 the Illinois Geological Survey organized its own Areal and Engineering Geology Division, one of the first such units to be established.[16.22] In other states, similar progress was made. In Kansas, for example, the State Highway Commission appointed a chief geologist as early as 1937, a position later occupied by S. E. Horner who made notable contributions to the applications of geology to highway engineering.[16.23]

Today, there is probably no branch of civil engineering in which the potential contributions of geology are more generally appreciated than in the field of road design and construction. In the eastern states, an annual informal forum has been held for some years on this branch of applied geology (the Annual Symposia on Geology as Applied to Highway Engineering, the proceedings of which are valuable contributions) at which those engaged in this type of work willingly share their experiences.[16.24] The importance of geology has long been recognized in the proceedings of the United States Highway Research Board; its famous annual meetings almost always feature several papers with geological content. Possibly the ultimate recognition is given by the fact that the

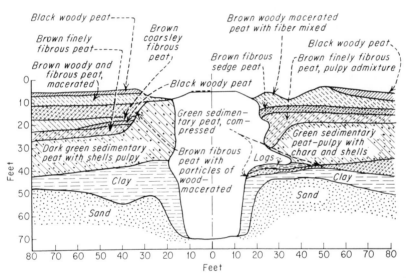

FIG. 16.7. Cross section through an unusually deep fill; preliminary borings would have indicated the local ground condition and so have suggested an alternative location. (*Reproduced by permission of the U.S. Bureau of Public Roads.*)

American Society for Testing and Materials (ASTM) has published a Standard Test Method for Surveying and Sampling Highway Subgrade Soils.[16.25] There are some who dislike seeing any geological procedure reduced (if that be the word) to the status of a standard procedure, but if the ASTM document is taken as a guide, for it is so intended, then it can be of real assistance to those who have to direct the work of others in this field.

With this background of experience available, a full appreciation of geology should be a part of all road design and construction work. It may be helpful to give just one example of what can happen when geology is neglected in preliminary design work. Figure 16.7 shows a cross section through a marsh between two lakes now connected by a small stream. It is clear that the highway could not have been located more unfortunately, since it is directly above the ancient glacial valley that at one time existed between the two lakes. The existence of this could have been determined by a combination of test borings and geological investigation, and about 25 ft of fill over this section of road could have been saved.[16.26]

Fortunately, such cases are now the exception rather than the rule. It will be appreciated that in the actual design of a new highway many of the principal branches of civil engineering work may be involved, such as the construction of bridges, the driving of tunnels, and the stabilizing of slopes, all of which are common to other fields of work and which are herein considered in separate chapters. The design of the roadbed and the procurement of construction materials are, however, two special features of highway engineering. It might be thought that sound and solid rock would provide an admirable roadbed; however, this is not always so, since in many cases solid rock is of varying strength and durability, and the existence of joints often adds a further complication. The softer rocks such as chalk constitute fair roadbeds when dry, but they can be troublesome when wet. Clay is similar; it is extremely unreliable when wet because most clays expand greatly as they increase their moisture content. Probably the best of all roadbeds is provided by well-packed coarse sand and gravel resting on some type of solid substratum. This ideal case is not often met, and the engineer has to contend with actual ground conditions varying from fissured igneous rock to peat bogs.

In practically all cases, drainage is of supreme importance in order to prevent waterlogging of the subgrade and consequent trouble. Drainage methods vary; they must inevitably be suitably related to the nature of the materials to be drained, the physcial properties of which—in the case of unconsolidated materials—can be tested in the same way as can those of other soils. The underlying geological principle of keeping the water table sufficiently low so that gravity flow through the material can take place is applied in various ways: with "self-draining" porous roadbed materials by means of suitable cross-sectional road design, and with impermeable materials by the provision of suitable artificial drainage channels or the use of a layer of sand or gravel.

It is not often that the reverse process has to be undertaken, but this has been necessary in at least one instance. A concrete roadway in Ellis County, Kansas, was found to be settling unevenly and causing high joints between adjacent slabs. Investigations showed that the differential movement was due to changes in the moisture content of the subgrade soil occurring at joints and cracks. This was successfully corrected, and the concrete slabs were releveled by introducing water into the subgrade material through an installation of well points jacked into place about 10 in. below the slab from the roadway shoulder.[16.27]

A procedure that is almost the reverse of that just noted is now widely used for the stabilization of roadbeds that have to be located over swampy ground or over soils with unusually high-moisture contents; this is the adaptation of an old French technique to subsurface drainage through the use of vertical sand drains. These consist essentially of vertical uncased "piles" of sand or other porous material, placed at predetermined spacings in order to provide an adequate drainage system from the stratum through which they pass either down to a pervious stratum beneath or up to the surface. The pressures exerted by fill placed over an

Fig. 16.8. Preliminary fill across sensitive clay soil on new route for main road from Helsinki to Turku, Finland, after treatment with sand drains.

installation of such vertical drains will assist the consolidation of the wet material, and thus hasten the stabilization desired for road construction over the fill. Many notable sand-drain installations are found in North America. The most extensive sand-drain project that the writer has seen was in Finland, installed in preparation for the construction of a new highway from Helsinki to Turku. Figure 16.8 shows the site of the installation which consisted of more than 500,000 m of vertical drains, carried to a maximum depth of 22 m in an unconsolidated marine clay, installed over a portion of road 1 km long. Estimated maximum settlement of the drained clay under the fill designed to carry the road was 4 m. At the time of the writer's visit (1957), 1.15 m settlement had taken place in the 6 weeks since the drains were installed. The new road was completed in 1959 and the fill section over the sand drains has performed quite successfully.[16.28]

Economics will usually dictate the use of material as close as possible to the road location; study of the local geology is an essential prerequisite to deciding what local materials can be thus used. In some cases, unusual materials have been put to good use after necessary laboratory studies of their properties. In Liberty County, Texas, for example, seashells obtained from reefs in Galveston Bay have been successfully used, when mixed with sand, to form a most satisfactory subbase for main road construction.[16.29] More unusual, but of potentially wider application (with supplies of good road-building material steadily decreasing), is the practice of calcining in place the clay which forms the natural ground at or adjacent to a road location. Apparently this idea was first tried out in Australia (an original patent having been granted to L. H. R. Irvine of Sydney, New South Wales), where local adobe clay, as found in parts of New South Wales and Queensland, was successfully treated in this manner. This clay is one that can be satisfactorily calcined by means of wood-fired downdraft furnaces of the air-gas–producer type; the resulting product is bricklike in texture. The untreated clay (which softens quickly when moist) is used as a binder in places where termite mounds (providing *antbed* material) are not available; the resulting road is stable in wet weather even though achieved at such relatively low cost.[16.30] In more recent years, the same technique has been used with the black cotton soils of the tropics. In both the Sudan and Nigeria, experiments have been conducted on the effect of calcining this difficult soil, but this has so far been carried out in kilns specially built adjacent to airfield-construction jobs.[16.31] Further work in this direction would appear to be well justified in view of the potential economies.

These uses of unusual materials involve the association of design with construction methods, a feature commonly called for in the practice of civil engineering, particularly in highway work. Accurate foreknowledge of the materials to be met in excavation for road cuts will not only assist in accurate cost estimating by engineers, but also in the preparation of bids by contractors based on carefully planned construction methods; expenditure of money on careful preliminary work pays good dividends here, as always, Because of the layout of highway-construction jobs, stretched along a reasonably straight alignment, the moving of material from cuts into fills provides opportunity for especially economical earth moving if the nature of the soil is accurately known. The possibilities of sluicing as a means of combined excavation and transportation should not be overlooked when the soil to be moved is sand; gravity is still an efficient servant of the builder.

Correspondingly, because of the spread-out character of road-construction jobs and the fact that they always involve disturbance of natural ground surfaces, they are unusually susceptible to the vagaries of the weather. Even in North America, there are areas in which a working season of only a few months is available each year because of high precipitation in the form of snow and rain. Slow progress on the Trans Canada Highway through the Rocky Mountains, for example, was attributable to this cause. Even in an area such as Michigan, the weather has affected the progress of road construction. During the building

Fig. 16.9. Blasting operations in progress for fill consolidation over swampland near Ha-ha Branch, on U.S. Route 40, Maryland. (*Reproduced by permission of the Chief Engineer, Maryland State Roads Commission.*)

of the Detroit Industrial Expressway, large wide cuts in brown and blue glacial clays were necessary. When the stratum of weathered brown clay was exposed to freezing weather, its laminated character led to its rapid surface disintegration and subsequent sloughing when wet by spring rains; this interfered appreciably with construction progress.[16.32]

More unusual, perhaps, was the effect of heavy rain upon the rock used as the subbase for Florida's Sunshine State Parkway, completed in 1957. Soon after its opening, trouble was experienced between Stuart and Fort Pierce at the northern end of the road due to "alligatoring" of the pavement. This was traced to the fact that, during paving operations, heavy and unseasonable rainfall (up to 21 in.) was experienced. This had the

effect of seriously wetting the *Belle Glade* or *Okeechobee* rock, a somewhat unusual type of lime rock which here formed the base of the road;
it became "greasy" when wet and under load, and this led to the pavement failures. Tests upon this rock, in its dry state, had been quite satisfactory; possibly the proverbial sunshine of Florida contributed to the
apparent neglect of the possibility of change in these properties when the
rock was wet.[16.33] This can be taken as another salutary reminder of the

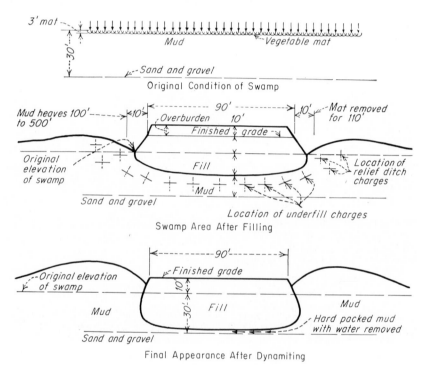

Fig. 16.10. Diagrams illustrating the method followed in consolidating fill material
over swampland during the construction of U.S. Route 40, Maryland. (*Reproduced
by permission of The Editor, Engineering News-Record.*)

importance of climate even in geology. Study of hythergraphs (see page
480) should be an essential part of all preliminary geological investigations.

Water, as is so often the case, is the prime cause of trouble in another
important phase of road building, i.e., when the route selected lies over
terrain that is so unsatisfactory that a road cannot be built directly upon
it. Peat bogs, swamps, marshes, muskeg, and tidal flats are examples of such
a condition; all are relatively new geological deposits which have not
consolidated to any extent and which consequently contain a high percentage of water. Study of the local geology and an adequate program of

test borings will usually reveal the extent of these deposits, since they are not the "limitless sinkholes" sometimes popularly imagined. In early civil engineering work, construction across such materials was generally tackled by dumping solid fill material along the route until it finally stopped settling or, alternatively, by laying down mattresses of brushwood or similar material to serve as artificial foundation beds for solid fill which was then deposited on them. The crossing of Chat Moss in 1827 by the original Liverpool and Manchester Railway in England, with

Fig. 16.11. Vertical cuts in loess on highway just east of Vicksburg, Mississippi, U.S.A., showing how well loess will stand if protected from water, but how quickly it will erode under even small trickles of water. (*Photograph by E. W. Shaw. Reproduced by permission of the Director, U.S. Geological Survey.*)

George Stephenson as the engineer, was one of the earliest notable examples of the use of this device. These ideas are sometimes used today; but with accurate information on the extent of the poor material, other methods can often be applied to better advantage. Replacing the soft material with dry fill by means of jetting is a new method; jetting of peat with pressures up to 100 psi is carried out underneath the dry fill, which is allowed to settle as the disturbed peat is displaced laterally.

Displacement of unstable deposits by blasting is an even more widely used method; blasting with high explosives is carried out either beneath dry fill which has been dumped in place or well down in the soft material in front of the fill deposit. Figure 16.9 is a photograph of a typical example of this work; its dependence on accurate data regarding subsurface conditions will be clear. The work illustrated, on the notable dual highway constructed in 1934 from Baltimore to Havre de Grace, Maryland, was necessitated where the route crossed swamp areas. The surface vegetable mat was first removed by blasting with 50 per cent

Fig. 16.12. Major cut on U.S. Highway 101 in Humboldt County, California, adjacent to the south fork of the Eel River; top of cut 480 ft above road; scale can be gauged by size of automobiles on road. (*Reproduced by permission of the Chief Engineer, Division of Highways, Dept. of Public Works, California.*)

nitroglycerin, and the fill was then advanced and blasted into position; a 40 per cent gelatin explosive which has a slow heaving effect was used.[16.34] This type of construction operation has been considerably developed in North America in recent years.

At the other extreme from swamp conditions is the problem of building roads through loess, from which water must be kept away if its stability is to be maintained. Travelers record that in the interior of China, ancient roads are to be found in the loess country which forms so large a part of that great land. The roads have been worn deep into the dry friable loessal soil by the passage of wagons through the centuries; the wind has blown away the dust formed by the steady disintegration of the loess by wagon wheels. Pumpelly, for example, records having seen such roads worn 50 ft below the general level of the country traversed.[16.35] Widely distributed throughout the world, from New Zealand in the south to the northern parts of the U.S.A. and the U.S.S.R., loess has now been carefully studied in relation to its occurrence on highway routes. Splendid exposures of this interesting soil are to be found on roads in Iowa. During the relocation of U.S. Highway 127 near Magnolia, the Iowa State Highway Commission experimented with a new type of terraced design for deep cuts in the loess, cuts which involved the movement of 800,000 cu yd; some cuts were 80 ft deep. Terraces 15 ft wide were cut between vertical faces each 15 ft high, graded slightly toward their inner edges so that precipitation could be taken care of by a properly installed drainage system. The loess here is typical in texture; it is composed of angular to subangular quartzose and feldspathic silt and fine sand with montmorillonite as the binder. Calcite is also present but not as a binder. Examination of specially prepared thin sections under a microscope shows an open structure with little interlocking of the grains.[16.36]

In contrast with the moderate cuts normally encountered on highway work, Fig. 16.12 shows a rather large cut carried out by the Division of Highways of the Department of Public Works of California on U.S. Highway 101 near Dyerville Bridge over the south fork of the Eel River in Humboldt County. Careful preliminary investigation showed that the cut would be in the Yager formation of Upper Cretaceous age; the material to be encountered would be interbedded sandstone and shale with numerous small zones of conglomerate. The upper 40 to 50 ft were weathered, badly jointed, and fractured. On the basis of this preliminary information, the cut was designed to have a 1:1 slope with 30-ft-wide horizontal berms at 60-ft intervals.[16.37]

16.5. Railway Construction. The building of railways throughout the world has probably provided more vivid examples of the interrelation of geology and civil engineering than has any other type of construction. All the determinants of highway construction are present in railway work, and there are the added imperatives of achieving strictly limited grades and curvature. Only with the most modern type of superhighway is road building coming to approach the same criteria as has railway construction for more than a century. It is interesting to reflect that even the practice in modern highway work of utilizing as much as possible of excavated material was a common feature of early railway construction work, at least once with quite surprising results. George Stephenson, that great figure in early British engineering history, was, among his many assignments, engineer for the North Midland line. He therefore designed and supervised the construction of the Clay Cross Tunnel (north of Nottingham). During the excavation of the tunnel, first-class coal seams were encountered, the potential of which was quickly realized by Stephenson, with his usual acumen. He interested the "Liverpool Party" in his find, and with their help he was able to form the Clay Cross Colliery Company, one of the most successful of British colliery enterprises, which was in continuous operation for over a century. Stephenson erected coke ovens for the processing of some of the coal and became so interested in the local industry that developed around his colliery that he bought Tapton House, a beautiful country residence near Chesterfield, where he died in 1848.[16.38]

All interested in British Railways know that Swindon was for almost a century the headquarters of the justly famous Great Western Railway; what is not so well known is that the stone houses and railway buildings that distinguish the town were all constructed of sandstone excavated from the famous Box Tunnel. The Lockwood Viaduct on the (old) Lancashire and Yorkshire Railway's Huddersfield to Penistone line was built with 30,000 cu yd of stone excavated from the cutting at Berry Brow Station and then quarried by masons at the adjacent site of the viaduct.[16.39] Possibly even more remarkable is the fact that the clay excavated from the long Penge Tunnel of the Southern Railway in the southern outskirts of London was formed into bricks, fired in a brick-making plant specially constructed just outside the tunnel, and then used for local houses and railway buildings. These early British railway engineers knew their local natural building materials and also their engineering economics.

There are few major railway lines that, somewhere along their routes, do not display striking exposures of local bedrock and that do not exhibit the ingenuity of location engineers in circumventing natural geological obstacles. A complete volume could readily be produced containing nothing but summary accounts of such examples. Each reader of these words can probably picture for himself some example well known to him that he would like to see thus recorded. Brief mention of just a few examples must here suffice; they are to be considered against the background of railroad economics and the fact that it is still possible to construct and maintain a main-line railway more economically than a first-class highway. It may also be remembered that there are many railroad lines that penetrate country where there are still no roads. Although this part of the picture is changing, it adds special interest to the geological significance of pioneer railroad construction.

Possibly the most remarkable of all examples is the stretch of the Denver and Rio Grande Western Railway through the Royal Gorge of the Arkansas River in south-central Colorado. The normal limitations of railroad location dictated that the line had to come up this gorge, starting just above river level. The gorge is over 1,000 ft deep, its sides precipitous in the extreme, cutting through upturned Precambrian strata. The character of the granite put tunneling out of the question. The narrow confines of the gorge, coupled with the character of the rock, made

FIG. 16.13. The Royal Gorge on the Arkansas River, Colorado, through which runs a single-track line of the Denver and Rio Grande Western Railroad. (*Reproduced by permission of the Vice President and General Manager, Denver and Rio Grande Western Railroad.*)

bench excavation also impracticable. The responsible engineers therefore took the unusual (and it is believed unique) course of actually suspending a part of the line over the river by means of special steel suspender structures. Figures 16.13 and 16.14 illustrate the result of this bold piece of engineering, now one of the scenic attractions of travel through Colorado.[16.40]

At the other extreme is the use of a natural tunnel by the Bristol-Appalachia section of the Southern Railway System through Powell Mountain in Virginia. The tunnel is 788 ft long and is a natural erosion feature in the local limestone; it was virtually unknown until 1880 when J. H. McCue found it during railway survey work. It was then filled with

Fig. 16.14. The unusual steel suspension structure used to carry the Denver and Rio Grande Western Railroad through the narrowest part of the Royal Gorge of the Arkansas River, Colorado, U.S.A. (*Reproduced by permission of the Vice President and General Manager, Denver and Rio Grande Western Railroad.*)

driftwood, stones, and dirt; when cleaned out, it gave a perfect solution to this particular piece of railroad location; the walls were already smoothed by past water action, and the cross section (120 ft wide and 90 ft high at the east portal) was more than enough to provide easy alignment for the projected rail line, merely by the use of an easy reverse curve within the tunnel. The tunnel is still in use, but no passengers now have the opportunity of passing through this unique tunnel, as the line is now used for freight traffic only.[16.41]

Even in so small a country as England, but undoubtedly because of its unique and varied geology, there are many railway lines of geological significance. The Dore and Chinley line of the old Midland Rail-

Fig. 16.15. A train of the Southern Railway coming out of the Natural Tunnel through Powell Mountain, Virginia, U.S.A. (*Reproduced by permission of The Chief Engineer, Southern Railway System.*)

way (now British Railways) is but one example; it is an important rail link in the Peak district of north-central England. It is unusual in that one-quarter of its entire length is underground, the Totley and Cowburn Tunnels being in part responsible for this unusual feature. These two long tunnels, both of them through limestone, provided great contrast during construction; the Cowburn Tunnel was practically dry but the Totley

Tunnel workings were so wet that there developed a local saying that all the workmen on the job (back in 1892) possessed the miraculous power of Moses. Every time a workman struck a rock, water seemed to spring out of it; a flow of over 5,000 gpm occurred at one heading.[16.42]

It would be very difficult to select any one of the railways of Switzerland for mention here; there are so many that provide classical examples of how geology determines railway location. Attention may rather be directed to one of the several railways of South America that provide some of the most exciting routes now in public use. In Peru, for example, the Peruvian Central line from Callao and Lima to Oroya via the Rimac Valley, was an epic piece of construction; its operation is a continuing masterpiece of railway work. It has a summit of 12,873 ft above sea level, but most of the rise to this elevation takes place in 73 miles. It is not surprising, therefore, that it has grades as steep as 1 in 22, but despite this the line is worked by adhesion. It required 67 tunnels, 62 bridges, and 11 zigzags in order to penetrate to the rich Montana mineral district with its great copper mines at Cerro de Pasco.[16.43]

So the list could continue with reference to such well-known features as the spiral tunnels on the main line of the Canadian Pacific Railway through the Rocky Mountains near Field, British Columbia; the cable-worked inclines up the Serra do Mar of the (old) São Paulo Railway of Brazil, with their elaborate protection works; the famous Rimutaka incline of New Zealand and the great tunnel that now replaces it. No such record as this, however, brief as it must be, would be complete without reference to two northern railways of North America, the White Pass and Yukon Route joining White Horse, Yukon Territory, to the sea at Skagway, and the Alaska Railroad connecting Seward and Fairbanks. On each of these lines are to be found sections that can best be described as illustrations of "geology in the raw."

The White Pass line was built in the closing years of the last century, using the White Pass route to give access to the Klondike gold fields. The pass is crossed at an elevation of 2,900 ft above sea level, only 21 miles from the coast, yet there is only one small tunnel on the line, a fact indicative of the way the railway follows the dictates of local geology. The line passes what used to be Lewes Lake, 81 miles from Skagway. The originally selected location here ran along the shore of this lake but was so broken by coves and bays that the engineers responsible decided to lower the water level of the lake by 14 ft in order to use a shallow underwater bench for their line. A channel was therefore excavated through the ridge that clearly controlled the water level of the lake. It would be too much to have expected those responsible, working as they did under the imperative of the Klondike gold fever and with the Soapy Smith gang continually interfering with construction operations, to have conducted careful preliminary geological studies in that wild and inhospitable area. How were they to know, therefore, that they were excavating through a glacial moraine which, as soon as the natural stream bed through it was disturbed, would be so easily eroded by the increased velocity of the lake discharge that an immense gully would soon be formed, draining the lake to a depth of 70 ft instead of the intended 14 and leaving about a dozen small pools in place of the original lovely lake. These pools can be seen from the train today; in some, lake trout still

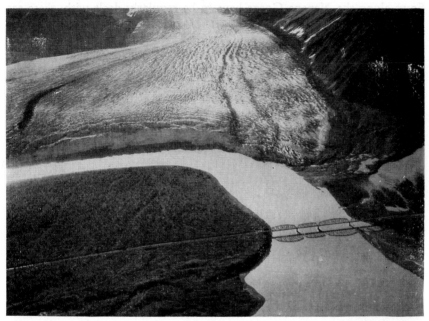

Fig. 16.16. The Copper River railroad bridge, Alaska, showing proximity of an active glacier, now fortunately receding. (*Photograph by Bradford Washburn. Reproduced by permission of the Boston Museum of Natural Science.*)

exist.[16.44] Although this is, admittedly, an unusual case it remains a cautionary tale and a reminder of what *should* be done in the way of preliminary geological investigation—when time and bandits permit.

Because of the route that it follows, the White Pass line is located generally on solid rock. The same cannot be said of the Alaska Railroad, however. Since much of it is over relatively level terrain, it thus runs over permafrost and presents the inevitable maintenance problems. (Even glaciers approach the neighboring Copper River railroad.) Probably the most troublesome part of this truly pioneer line is where it crosses the Alaska Range (miles 322 to 385). The central Alaskan earthquake of October, 1947, triggered a most serious landslide in this area. This disrupted traffic for several days and led to a request to the United States

Geological Survey for assistance with the track troubles in the area. (The report summarizing the results of this study is a memorable document, even though the record it presents makes other railroad engineering problems pale into relative insignificance.)[16.45] Not only does the line have inevitable troubles with thawed ground because of the permafrost used as foundation for the roadbed, but there are corresponding problems with seasonal frost heaving in the frost-susceptible soils beneath the track that have thawed out from their original condition. Slumps and earth flows along the Nenana Gorge have to be regularly dealt with; these are

Fig. 16.17. A train on the Alaska Railroad, showing subsidence of the track due to the thawing of permafrost near mileage 350. (*Photograph by R. F. Black, Reproduced by permission of The Director, U.S. Geological Survey.*)

caused by slow movement of rock debris on the underlying steep slopes as much as a few hundred feet deep. They move the entire railroad down toward the river at rates varying from a few feet per year to a few feet per hour. Near mile 351, an ancient landslide, long ago stabilized by being perennially frozen, is slowly becoming active again as the permafrost thaws out because of the inevitable disturbance of local surface conditions.

At the north end of a tunnel near Garner, the railroad crosses the lower part of a large talus cone which is slowly creeping toward the adjacent river under the increasing load of debris falling from the cliffs above. Large blocks of schist constitute much of this debris; some are at the heads of steep chutes that lead down through the cliffs to the track, and they occasionally break loose. The largest, at the time the USGS study was made, was 100 ft long on its side and was creeping at the rate of 0.2 ft per year toward the edge of a precipice over which it will eventually fall onto the track below. It is not, therefore, altogether surprising that many geologists have recommended that the only thing to do about this part of the Alaska Railroad is to realign the track permanently. Meantime, the engineers responsible for this vitally important rail link continue their really epic work of keeping the traffic moving in the face of geological problems probably without parallel anywhere else in the world.

16.6. Maintenance Problems. "Maintaining lines of communication" is a phrase potent with meaning for both highway and railway engineers. Local failure or obstruction of older transportation routes did not usually involve the safety of travelers, since the trouble could generally be seen in advance and so avoided. In the case of railways and modern highways, however, human lives are often involved if the routes cannot be kept clear and intact. Thus it is that track maintenance and inspection are such important parts of railway work. Bridge foundations constitute a special hazard; in Chap. 17 (page 682) will be found some comments on this matter and a note on two accidents due to bridge failures. Tunnels always require special care in inspection, with due regard to the stability of rock exposed in unlined sections. Embankments always require careful attention, especially in the period just after their completion and in the vicinity of bridge abutments. Cuttings are similarly important, as was shown in Chap. 10. The trouble most readily imagined in cuttings is that due to landslides of adjacent unconsolidated material; all too many occurrences of this kind have taken a toll of human lives. Rockfalls can be just as serious; even minor falls, where solid blocks of rock break off an exposed face, can result in accidents. A train on the Western Pacific Railroad in the United States was derailed on November 11, 1937, with consequent loss of two lives; the train hit a single 3-ton rock boulder which had fallen onto the track in the interval between the arrival of the train and inspection of the track just 30 min previously.[16.46]

These are geological maintenance problems, calling for ceaseless vigilance and regular inspection. Careful observation in the maintenance of the Panama Canal was recorded on page 601. Many railways have stretches of line that require special maintenance procedures, such as multiple tracks of the Pennsylvania Railroad along the Ohio and Monongahela Rivers in the vicinity of Pittsburgh. The alternating strata of sandstones and shales exposed above these tracks (see page 450) constitute a continuing hazard; as a result the railroad has a special team of trackmen who patrol the most critical 6 miles of track day and night. This is naturally an expensive procedure. In many locations, therefore, and where rail traffic is not heavy, mechanical or electrical guard devices have been installed. One of the first of these was on the Callander and Oban line of the (old) Caledonian Railway in the Highlands of Scotland; where the line passes along the north side of the Pass of Brander, it is subject to frequent rockfalls. As long ago as 1881, a special 9-ft wire fence was erected alongside the line, connected to 14 signals located throughout the critical length of 3¼ miles; the fence was so arranged that if a falling rock cleared the fence it should not land on the track, whereas if the rock touched the wires one or more signals would be put in the

Fig. 16.18. Electrical slide-detection fence on the Swan View deviation cutting of Western Australian Government Railways on the down eastern main line in the Darling Range. (*Reproduced by permission of the Chief Engineer, Western Australian Government Railways.*)

danger position. The severance of a wire would also cause an electric bell to ring in the nearest signal box and in the houses of the local track-maintenance men. The speed of the trains is severely restricted, especially at night; it was this fact that minimized the damage done in 1947 when a train was derailed at this location by a large boulder that did land on the track, despite all the precautions described.[16.47]

A more recent example of the same general type of protection is found on the other side of the world, in Australia. On the main line of the Western Australian Government Railways between Perth and Northam, the only remaining section of single line was duplicated in 1944 in order to double-track the entire route. The new line became the down main line. So that its grade might be eased somewhat, it was constructed on a course which deviated a little from the location of the existing line. Construction involved a deep cut in granite, some 1,500 ft long, in which protection from rockfalls was essential in view of the character of the granite exposed after the cut had been excavated. Steel fences were therefore erected on both sides of the cut, 8½ ft high, with supports 33 ft apart. The wires forming the fences are in continuous circuits that are energized; since the line is controlled by automatic track-circuit signaling, a simple but effective system of electrical interlocking was installed which makes the protection system completely automatic. If a wire is broken by falling rock or if a battery or circuit fails, two relays become de-energized and the signal controlling the line in the cut is placed at danger. An indicator in the Swan Valley signal box shows the operator there that a rockfall (or other failure) has occurred; the control signal can only be reset with a special key at the signal itself.[16.48]

The Great Northern Railroad system (of the United States) has to maintain 120,000 ft of protective fencing of this general kind. Peculiar to this system, however, is the fact that this total includes about 41,000 ft of "mud-slide fence" which consists of two wires stretched near the ground so that they will be interfered with if a mud slide should occur, as distinct from a rockfall. Nearly all this fence is installed between Seattle and Vancouver, British Columbia, on the G.N.R. coast line. The system also uses protective fences for detecting snow slides through the Rockies and the Cascade Mountains. The railway experiences unusual difficulties in maintaining its warning fences in the Glacier Park area, not from any of the causes that might normally be expected, but because elk break the wires. "When a big bull comes to the fence on his way up or down the mountain side, he will wind the wires in his horns and then charge, taking the wire with him. It is a #10 copperweld insulated line wire, and he usually has to drag it along with him until the horns fall off in the early spring."[16.49]

Because of the nature of road traffic, the same elaborate precautions against rockfalls do not usually have to be taken on roads, even though inspection of areas in which rockfalls may occur is just as vital. Cautionary signs indicating rockfall areas are familiar along North American highways. The Highway Department of Hawaii had to go further than this on its Nuuanu Pali Highway, which runs between Honolulu and Windward on the island of Oahu. The steel tops of several automobiles using this road had been punctured by sharp falling rocks and some cars had been hit by boulders, although fortunately without serious results. A double row of strong wire fencing was therefore erected along the rock face at the critical curve and this has proved effective. Even at the ancient citadel of Quebec City, where the rock face on Cape Diamond has been exposed to human activity for 3 centuries, rockfalls have given trouble in recent years; the city council of Quebec has installed "rock baskets" to catch falling rocks and so protect those who use a new school at the foot of this historic cliff.

Another unusual source of trouble in connection with railway maintenance is due to what have been described as mud runs—streams of mud and rock debris washed down from the lower slopes of bare mountainsides by the runoff that follows torrential rains. In general, these are confined to tropical countries and are especially severe in sections of

Fɪɢ. 16.19. Arque Bridge on the Antofagasta and Bolivia Railway, showing two of the original 40 spans (which have to be kept open) and the accumulation of rock debris above the original valley floor, about 3 m below track level. (*Reproduced by permission of the Chief Engineer, Ferro-Carril de Antofagasta a Bolivia.*)

South America and in India. The extreme climatic conditions promote rapid disintegration of exposures of relatively weak rocks such as shales, and the concentrated rainfall acts as an efficient transporting agent. If mud runs reach bridge openings under a railroad designed to take normal stream flow, the consequent restriction of movement will block the openings, and thereafter control of the runs will be difficult. It is reported that several sections of the Bolivia Railway have had to be relocated because of this; in one place a town adjacent to the railway had to be completely relocated because the original site was buried deep under the unusual detrital cone formed by blockage of a large mud run at a bridge opening. This bridge, originally 10 ft above stream-bed level, is now located in a cutting.[16.50]

Even more serious is the danger of damage to transportation routes, railways in particular, by avalanches. Snow may not usually be thought of as a geological agent but all who have seen an avalanche or examined the results of one, will know that moving snow has quite remarkable power for terrain modification. Here Switzerland must be mentioned,

FIG. 16.20. Avalanche deflection structure of the Schintigraben in the Lonza ravine on the Lötschberg Railway, Switzerland. (*Reproduced by permission of Berner Alpenbahn-Gesellschaft.*)

for the Swiss have led the world not only in the development of avalanche-protection works but, in more recent years, in avalanche research at the Swiss Institute for Snow and Avalanche Research at the head of the Passern funicular Railway at Davos. From the start of railway construction in Switzerland, avalanches have been of constant concern to Swiss engineers. The building of the great Alpine Tunnels, with their portals necessarily located at the heads of steep valleys, merely served to intensify the need of avalanche-protection works. The case of the Lötschberg Railway may be cited as an example.

This line, which includes the Lötschberg Tunnel, gives a convenient short route between Berne and the Simplon Tunnel to the south. For almost the entire stretch of line from Goppenstein (where the line emerges from the tunnel) down to Brigue, the line is carried high up on the rocky sides of the Lonza and Rhone Valleys, where avalanches are frequent. Fortunately, the paths of regular avalanches can readily be detected on wooded slopes, for they will strip off all major vegetation in their paths. Engineers responsible for the Lötschberg line were therefore able to design protection works, mainly deflecting walls but with some notable snowsheds also, in conjunction with the construction of the railway line itself. In the Lonza Valley, in particular, there must be a record number of avalanche works in relation to the length of line protected. More than 1,000 protection walls have been constructed along this route; some are 40 ft high and located as much 8,500 ft above sea level. More than 10 million trees have also been planted as natural protection up mountain slopes as high as 6,500 ft. The value of all this work is shown by the fact that the Lötschberg Railway has never been closed for any appreciable length of time since it was first opened in 1913, despite the fact that its route lies across the paths of so large a number of well-recognized avalanches.[16.51]

A little to the east of the line just described runs the Furka-Oberalp Railway. Since it runs through a relatively uninhabited part of the country, its owners do not attempt to keep open that part of the line from Oberwald up to the Furka Tunnel and then downhill to Realp near Andermatt during the winter season. On its way down from the Furka Tunnel, this line passes through a very deep valley much subject to avalanches. During the first winter after completion of the line, a bridge that had been constructed here across the Steffenbach Gorge was swept away by an avalanche. Study showed that the bottom of the gorge was a regular path for avalanches of unusual intensity. With typical Swiss ingenuity, therefore, a new bridge was designed that would not be so destroyed when not in use in the winter. Its three deck spans are designed in such a way that the central span can be hinged on the end of one of the side spans, and the three spans, with their steel supporting trestles, can then be swung into positions of rest against the two abutments of the bridge, to stay there out of danger throughout the winter. When the line has to be opened in the spring, the sections of the bridge are unfolded, swung back, and secured together in place. This entire operation (as well as the corresponding dismantling in the fall) takes no more than 1 working day with a trained group of workers if the weather is favorable.[16.52]

(a)

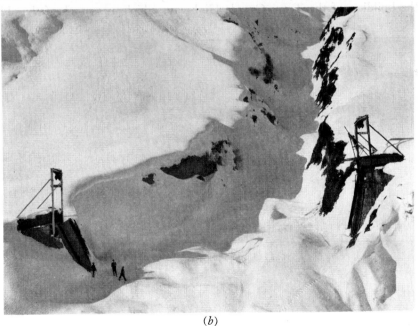

(b)

FIG. 16.21. The Steffenbach Bridge of the Furka-Oberalp Railway, Switzerland: (a) as erected for use in summer, and (b) as folded up during the winter closure of the line to facilitate the passage of avalanches. (*Reproduced by permission of the Furka-Oberalp Railway.*)

These are but two examples of Swiss railway engineering; they are typical of the boldness in location and design that has produced in this little mountainous country (only 226 by 137 miles in size) over 3,500 route miles of railway. Snowsheds for avalanche protection are almost a commonplace on the lines at higher altitudes; one of the longest serves both highway and the Furka-Oberalp Railway at the head of the Oberalp Pass, 6,670 ft above the sea. Even more impressive, however, are the long series of snowsheds, in places almost continuous, that protect the railway line that now joins Oslo and central Norway with Bergen on the western coast, probably the most remarkable of all European railway lines outside Switzerland. Snowsheds are called for also in North American railway practice. One of the most extensive installations was on the old route of the Canadian Pacific Railway where it penetrated the Selkirk Mountains through Rogers Pass. So troublesome were the avalanches in this area that, when the time came to renew the original snowsheds, it was decided to relocate the line even though this meant building the 5-mile-long Connaught Tunnel. It now seems probable that much of the early trouble with avalanches in the pass was due to the indiscriminate burning off of almost all vegetation by the early railway builders. Avalanches still occur in the pass; they have been intensively studied in connection with the building of the Trans Canada Highway, which uses much of the old

Fig. 16.22. Stages in the dismantling of the Steffenbach Bridge on the Furka-Oberalp Railway, Switzerland, an operation carried out at the end of each summer's operating season. (*Reproduced by permission of the Furka-Oberalp Railway.*)

Fig. 16.22. (*Continued*).

railroad right of way through the pass, and for which a special series of avalanche-protection works has been designed.

Finally, mention must be made of the danger due to floods. Protection against floods is largely a civil engineering matter, depending on the accuracy with which preliminary flood predictions can be made for the design of necessary waterways beneath roads or railways. In Chap. 17 mention is made of the scouring of bridge foundations and the precautions to be taken against this hazard. Reference will here be made to a case which is of such special geological significance and which involved one of the most tragic of all accidents in the history of railroading. Late on Christmas Eve, 1953, the main part of the Wellington to Auckland Express in New Zealand was swept away when it plunged into the swirling waters of Whangaehu River at the site of what had been the Tangiwai Bridge. In this accident, 151 persons were killed; 20 bodies were never found. The main finding of the official board of inquiry was that:

> The accident was caused by the sudden release from the Crater Lake on Mount Ruapehu through an outlet cave beneath the Whangaehu Glacier of a huge mass of water which was channeled down the Whangaehu River carrying with it a high content of ash from the 1945 eruption and blocks of ice due to the collapse of large volumes of the glacier. This flood, which can properly be called a "lahar," proceeded down the mountain as a wave, uplifting huge quantities of sand, silt and boulders. It was most violent and turbulent and of great destructive effect. It destroyed portions of the railway bridge at Tangiwai before the arrival of train No. 626, which was engulfed when proceeding across the bridge.

No blame was attached to the engineers or to the train personnel involved; the tragedy was one of those that can only be described, with reverence, as an "Act of God."[16.53]

It is impossible to summarize the technical aspects of the accident; those interested are referred to the unusually complete report of the board of inquiry and to an associated publication. It must be admitted that the combination of an active volcano and a nearby glacier, the discharge from which led directly down a relatively short river crossed by the railway, is unusual, but it would appear that similar damage to communication routes has been done in a few other locations from similar discharges, although, fortunately, without such dreadful loss of life. The board suggested that the geological term *lahar* should be better known by civil engineers. It is defined thus in their report:

> A lahar is a type of mudflow that occurs in volcanic areas. Lahars may be formed by the waters of crater lakes being released by the collapse of the crater wall or by volcanic eruption, by the melting of snow and ice by volcanic heat, or by the action of rain on volcanic ash deposited on the steep

FIG. 16.23. Tangiwai Bridge over the Whangaehu River, North Island, New Zealand, carrying an express passenger train on the day before the disaster shown in Fig. 16.24. (*Photograph by Derek Cross.*)

FIG. 16.24. The scene of disaster following the destruction of the Tangiwai Bridge, North Island, New Zealand, on Christmas Eve, 1953, while carrying a crowded passenger train of New Zealand Government Railways. (*Reproduced by permission of The Dominion, Wellington, New Zealand.*)

slopes of volcanoes. They usually pick up large quantities of volcanic ash and other debris, and form a thick slurry that on account of its high density may carry even enormous boulders for many miles across fairly flat country once the initial momentum has been gained.

The potential danger of lahars in all volcanic areas, therefore, is an added hazard to be carefully considered by those responsible for the design of transportation routes. Similar floods are known in the mountains of British Columbia; they are caused by melting ice, without volcanic action.

The original Tangiwai Bridge consisted of three deck plate girder steel spans supported on concrete piers. Figure 16.23 (which, by chance, was taken on the day before the accident) shows its general appearance. It has since been completely replaced by a new bridge consisting of two 120-ft steel through truss spans, with one mid-river concrete pier. New Zealand engineers have designed and installed a warning system against any future floods that, in some respects, must be unique. It consists of a 20-ft-high concrete pier located in the river 8 miles above the bridge. A series of lead electrodes are exposed, at progressively increasing heights, spirally around the pier; the electrodes are suitably connected to five separate circuits with a somewhat elaborate system of warnings that includes even a device that displays a warning signal actuated by the *speed* of a sudden rise in the water level in the river, since it is the danger of sudden flash floods that is regarded as unusually serious. The lead electrodes were selected for use after it was found that the water of the Whangaehu River was highly acidic; its low pH value permits the design of a warning system that is as close to perfection as engineering design can achieve. If, for example, power is cut off for any reason, the system can still operate for more than 24 hr from its own battery system. The warning panel is located at Waiouru station, 6½ miles away from the river pier and 8 miles from the bridge site.[16.54]

16.7. Airfields. So phenomenal has been the growth in civil aviation all over the world in the last quarter of a century, especially since the end of the Second World War, that there is probably no branch of civil engineering work about which the public is so impatient and responsible officials so frustrated as the construction of airfields—the building of new fields where necessary and the enlargement and improvement of existing facilities. Singapore has had to build a completely new airport within 20 years of the opening of the former one; Washington, D.C., is in almost the same position. Cities such as Chicago are having to construct duplicate fields. And all too many fine landing facilities, built apparently for the foreseeable future but a few years ago, are proving to be inadequate and incapable of expansion to meet the needs of jet propulsion in regular commercial use. In all this rather frantic design and construction work, involving extraordinary sums of money judged by any standards, geology is not the determinant that it usually is in other kinds of construction. Modern airfields have to provide very large reasonably level areas without serious impediments to flying in the vicinity; they must be capable of being thoroughly drained at all times; and above all, they must be as conveniently situated with respect to the cities they serve as is possible.

Fig. 16.25. Special river-level warning tower on the Whangaehu River, 8 miles above the Tangiwai Bridge, erected following the disaster of 1953. (*Reproduced by permission of the Chief Civil Engineer, New Zealand Government Railways.*)

In view of these requirements, the geology of potential sites usually has to be accepted; convenience of access and economic availability of reasonably level ground are the basic determinants. In only one case that has come to the author's attention has a location, otherwise suitable, had to be turned down because of unfavorable geological conditions; in this location, the presence of an extremely sensitive marine clay gave promise of unavoidable settlements of long duration that were quite unacceptable.

Some airfields have had to use sites involving construction over filled ground; examples include the La Guardia Airport at New York and the airport at Baltimore. In such cases, serious design problems have to be met and solved, but they are more in the nature of difficulties in soil mechanics rather than in the field of geology.[16.55]

Despite this over-all situation, the geology of airports is still of great importance. It is imperative that preliminary geological and subsurface investigational work be well done and that it take into account adequately all the area upon which construction is to take place together with any adjacent areas which may influence drainage of the field. In the first place, determination of the amounts of cut and fill material and its exact character will be necessary for the preparation of estimated costs, of tentative time schedules, and ultimately, of contract documents for actual construction. Correspondingly, accurate subsurface information is essential for the proper design of pavements, especially because of the large wheel loads now becoming commonplace in design standards, and for the foundations of the structures that will serve the port. Finally, and perhaps of greatest importance, adequate drainage facilities can only be properly designed and installed if the soils to be encountered, their drainage characteristics, and the local ground-water conditions are known with accuracy. These are not "exciting" applications of geology; they are, nonetheless, vital and call for the same degree of careful attention as the most spectacular service provided by geology for tunnels, dam foundations, or landslide correction.

Landing-field areas have to be graded to a given level, drained, and provided with suitable runways. Design of the latter is comparable to highway design; similar materials are used with similar design requirements. When turf is used to surface a field, special attention must be given to the type of grass and to the spreading of a good top layer of soil if the local material is unsuitable for good growth. Drainage is the counterpart of all such work; it will often prove to be the most difficult part of airport work. The fact that the landing field has to be practically level constitutes a leading problem and necessitates the closest attention to the gradients adopted for drains in order to keep trench excavation to a minimum. A soil survey is therefore essential. This can often be carried out with the aid of hand-boring outfits. Once this information is available, the type of drainage system necessary can be decided upon. If porous materials underlie the site, the system can be simple; if clay or similar material is found, an elaborate system of field drains and main drains may be necessary. Installation of drains must be undertaken with great care; backfilling (of selected porous material) up to within 6 in. of the surface is essential. Surface material should be uniform over the field and therefore should cover all drains and refilled soft spots, the discovery of which in preliminary test borings can be one of the most important contributions of the civil engineer to this phase of transportation engineering. American figures suggest that one accident out of every eight in aviation is due to landing-field defects; even in this branch of work, therefore, adequate preliminary investigation of ground conditions can be of real avail.

It is not within the province of this book to deal with the design of drainage systems, vital as they are in all airport work; reference may be made to standard civil engineering texts. Brief mention, however, may be made of one example in which careful preliminary work yielded unexpected dividends. During the war years, a small airport was constructed at Bowling Green, Kentucky. With an area of only 265 acres, providing four 3,900-ft runways, it was not a large project, but its design was carried out with the usual care exercised by the United States Corps of Engineers, the constructing agency. It was found that the site was located in what was known locally as "sinkhole country"; the bedrock was a cavernous limestone (the upper stratum of which was known locally as "Cathedral rock"), overlain at the airport site by 15 to 20 ft of dense red clay. Existing sinkholes were located and other potential downward drainage channels were surveyed; it was thus possible to grade the field so that 12 manholes, leading directly into the underlying limestone, would take care of all surface drainage. Manholes were connected to precast concrete pipe lengths which led down to the Cathedral rock, through which 12-in.-diameter holes were drilled to the deeper and more cavernous limestone. Surface grading toward the manholes sufficed for most of the surface drainage but some 2,000 ft of French drains were used in flatter areas in order to conduct drainage to the nearest manholes. The airport has now been in use for over 15 years and the unusual drainage system has worked quite satisfactorily. It illustrates what can be done by utilizing constructively a local geological condition that is ordinarily regarded as undesirable.[16.56]

After drainage, the estimating of quantities for cut and fill and the planning and execution of such work probably reveal the necessity of adequate geological study more than anything else in airfield work. Much of what was said about open excavation in Chap. 10 applies directly to airport construction; since excavation does not usually extend to great depths, even though large quantities are often involved, few additional comments are called for. One example may usefully be cited, however, to illustrate the extent to which airfield excavation may have to proceed. Admittedly the case is an extreme one, but there are not a few airfields in North America now in regular use that called for construction operations on an almost comparable scale. One of the many smaller airfields constructed in the United States as the war came to a close, with civil aviation looming large as an important postwar development, was that built to serve the metropolitan district around Charleston, the county seat of Kanawha County and the state capital of West Virginia. Kanawha Airport was constructed for the Kanawha County Court; it is located in the rugged hilly country northeast of Charleston. The severity of the local terrain necessitated moving slightly more than 9.7 million cu yd of material in order to give the necessary level area to accommodate the

Fig. 16.26. Grading work in progress at Kanawha Airport, Charleston, West Virginia, U.S.A. (*Photograph by Caterpillar Tractor Co.*)

main runway, which is 6,000 ft long, and subsidiary runways of 5,800 and 5,200 ft, respectively. The maximum difference in elevation between the highest point in a cut section and the toe of the deepest fill was 450 ft; one fill alone extended 230 ft from its toe to runway level. Alternating layers of shale and sandstone were encountered, and the absence of ground water eliminated any real problems with excavation. Benches filled with rock from 1 to 8 cu yd in size were used to support all slopes steeper than 1 in 3. About one-half of all excavation had to be drilled and blasted, but good fragmentation was obtained; drop weights were used for reducing large rock fragments to manageable size for handling. The Harrison Construction Company of Pittsburgh used a grand total of 226 pieces of earth-moving equipment in carrying out this mammoth piece of "terrain reconstruction."[16.57]

Since flying provides lines of communication all over the globe, it calls for the construction of airports in many of the far places of the world. Frequently, airport construction projects have given rise to unusual experiences with geological conditions not normally encountered in the general run of civil engineering work. Some of those who served during the Second World War with the Seabees will long remember the unusual airfield construction on Iwo Jima. This small Pacific island, measuring only $5\frac{1}{2}$ by 3 miles, is of recent volcanic origin. An active volcano provides the main outcrop of solid rock on the island (Mount Suribachi); the general plateau constituting the main part of the island, at an elevation of 340 ft above the sea, consists of volcanic ash in two main forms—a loose black cinder commonly called "black sand" (which was found to be magnetic) and a consolidated buff-colored ash known as "sandrock." The black sand was easy to handle and formed inexpensive and stable fill material. The buff sandrock was similarly well suited for use as a "stabilized" surfacing for airstrips and roadways for initial construction requirements. This latter material was found to have an *in situ* moisture content greater than that required for optimum compaction, compaction that gave field densities of only 72 lb per cu ft. Modern earth-moving equipment proved quite satisfactory for military airfield construction. Possibly the most unusual features of this isolated wartime job were that the temperature of the volcanic soils exposed in borrow pits ranged from 110 to 208°F and that the temperature of ground water was about 135°F; these were vivid reminders of the proximity of recent volcanic action.[16.58]

In the steady development of her remaining colonial territories, Great Britain has pioneered in the building of airfields in a variety of terrains, notably in tropical regions. An unusually comprehensive group of papers summarizing some of this experience with the construction of airfields in the tropics was presented in London in 1957 to the Institution of Civil Engineers.[16.59] Since the six papers are in themselves condensed in form, they cannot readily be summarized. Suffice it to say that they provide a most useful introduction to some of the construction problems encountered with the tropical black and red soils, lateritic soils, and alluvial sands and silts found in tropical regions, with some reference to construction methods that have been found satisfactory with these most difficult of materials. The 129 references presented with the papers are in themselves an excellent guide to available recent literature on residual soil formation, treatment, and use. The entire presentation is a fine example of the sharing of experience and information that is at once so striking and so valuable a part of professional civil engineering practice.

Suggestions for Further Reading

The references cited in this chapter, listed on pages 849 to 851, contain titles of volumes that provide useful background information. Particular attention is invited to the Proceedings of the itinerant Annual Symposium on Geology as Applied in Highway Engineering; mimeographed volumes are usually issued by the institution that acts as host to these annual meetings, so there is no central publication address. Mention must also be made, once again, of the singularly useful publications of the United States Highway Research Board, a complete listing of which is conveniently available from the offices of the board at 2101 Constitution Ave., Washington, D.C.

Chapter 17

THE FOUNDATION OF BRIDGES AND COFFERDAM PROBLEMS

> Of alle werkys in this worlde that ever were wrought Holy Chirche
> is chefe. . . . Another blessed besines is brigges to make.
>
> Richard Forman, about A.D. 1458, in an old MS, now
> in Christ's Hospital, Abingdon, England (rhyme
> on the building of Abingdon and Culham Bridges)

IN THE discussion of transportation routes, considerations were limited to normal sections of roadways and other traffic arteries. Where such routes meet natural obstacles that cannot be circumvented, tunnels or cuttings are necessary. In a similar way, bridges form a necessary component part of most land transportation routes. If for no other reason than this, their foundation would call for individual treatment to the extent possible within the limits of this book. The founding of bridge piers and abutments, however, is at once so special and so important a part of civil engineering work that of itself it calls for detailed consideration. Bridge construction is, moreover, such a widespread operation, falling at some time to the lot of most practicing civil engineers, that it merits more detailed study than some other specialized types of work.

Schoolboy memories (not perhaps too pleasant) of the piled foundation of a Roman bridge across the Rhine must not be allowed to deflect attention from a subject even the history of which is full of interest. Of the many famous early bridges, London Bridge, over the Thames in England, is one of the best known. According to a third-century Roman writer, there was a bridge across the river just above its mouth as early as A.D. 43, and records indicate the continuous existence thereafter of a river crossing of some type at this location. A reference of peculiar interest in this book is that which tells of King Olaf, "The Saint," coming in A.D. 1014 to aid King Ethelred of England against the Danes who held London. His fleet "rowed quite up under the bridge and then rowed off with all the ships as hard as they could down stream [having secured ropes to the piles supporting the bridge]. The piles were then shaken at the bottom and were loosened under the bridge" which gave way, throwing all the defenders ranged upon it into the river[17.1]

Although such a barbaric use of bridge foundations fortunately has few modern applications, the further history of London Bridge is of special significance in this study. The structure known so well through illustrations in history books appears to have been completed in the early part of the thirteenth century. Fynes Morrison, writing in 1671, states that it was founded on "pakkes of wool most durable against the force of water," but this is probably a garbled reference to the tax on wool which enabled the king to pay his share of the cost. Since the waterway of the river was reduced by this multiarched structure to a width of 195 ft, such swift rapids developed between the arches that many persons lost their lives in passing through; the old saying is that "London Bridge was made for wise men to go over and fools to go under." An act of Parliament passed in 1756 ordered all the buildings on the bridge to be removed and the two central arches rebuilt into one arch; this work inevitably diverted the main flow through the opening and set up serious scouring, which eventually led to the necessity of demolishing the bridge altogether. A modern structure now occupies a site parallel to and adjacent to this famous crossing.[17.2]

This is but one of the ancient bridges the piers of which have given rise to trouble. Records are extremely scarce, unfortunately, but it can safely be said that scouring out of the foundation beds adjacent to bridge piers has been, in the past, a major cause of trouble. The piers of ancient bridges rarely failed because of excessive loading on the foundation beds, if only because of the limitation of span length imposed by the structural materials available. The two defects mentioned can be regarded as the two main possibilities of failure to be investigated in the design of bridge piers. Both are essentially geological in character.

17.2. The Importance of Bridge Foundations. As a necessary preliminary, the fundamental importance of geology in the founding of bridges must be stressed. However scientifically a bridge pier may be designed, the whole weight of the bridge itself and of the loads that it supports must be carried ultimately by the underlying foundation bed. The piers and abutments of a bridge are relatively "uninteresting" to the keen structural engineer. Herein should lie, however, more than passing interest, for all too often the design of the foundations is left to the structural engineer responsible for the design of the superstructure. Many structural engineers appreciate the difference between the two types of design work and their relative importance. Some, however, may not—perhaps naturally, since the careful consideration of the materials available as foundation beds and the forecasting of the forces that may in time affect them are different from the determinate mathematical calculations relating to the

**Table 17.1. Some Typical Bridge Costs, Illustrating the Relative Costs of
Superstructure and Substructure**

Bridge	Type	Cost of		Ratio $a:b$	Reference
		Super-structure (a)	Sub-structure (b)		
Cherry St. Bridge, Toledo, Ohio	7 concrete arches + bascule	$545,482	$531,103	1.02:1	*Am. Soc. Civil Eng. Trans.*, vol. 80, 789 (1916)
Hell Gate Bridge, New York	Steel arch, 977.5-ft span	$2,000,000	$1,700,000	1.18:1	*Am. Soc. Civil Eng. Trans.*, vol. 82, 882 (1918)
Sydney Bridge, Australia	Steel arch, 1,650-ft span	£3,202,000	£1,046,000	3.06:1	*Inst. Civil Eng. Min. Proc.*, vol. 238, 193 (1935)
Iskandar Bridge, Fed. Malay States	7 steel arches, 160- to 148-ft span	£51,217	£76,883	0.67:1	*Inst. Civil Eng. Min. Proc.*, vol. 240, 363 (1937)
Tees (Newport) Bridge, Middlesbrough, England	Steel lift bridge, 259-ft 6-in. span	£201,302 (excluding) approaches)	£65,688 (2 piers)	3.06:1	*Inst. Civil Eng. Min. Proc.*, vol. 240, 598 (1937)
Chelsea Bridge, London	Self-anchored suspension bridge	£149,000	£75,000	1.98:1	*Jour. Inst. Civil Eng.*, vol. 7, 420 (1938)
Thousand Islands Bridge, Canada-United States	Group of structures, including 2 suspension spans, steel arch, etc.	An extreme case, in view of unusually favorable foundation-bed conditions:→		5:1	*Civil Eng.* (New York), vol. 8, 408 (1938)
Bridge across the Tigris, Amara, Iraq	Steel girder and cantilevers	$303,454	$232,879	1.3:1	*Proc. Inst. Civil Eng.*, vol. 16, 46 (1960)
Hindiya Bridge, India	10 46-ft reinforced-concrete spans and 1 102-ft steel arch	$147,000	$173,000	0.85:1	*Proc. Inst. Civil Eng.*, vol. 8, 15 (1957)
Clifton Bridge, Nottingham, England	See p. 666	£224,175	£87,652	2.56:1	*Proc. Inst. Civil Eng.*, vol. 14, 465 (1957)

arrangement of steel, reinforced concrete, or timber to be used for the superstructure.

It may be that in some cases an assumption regarding the relatively small cost of foundations compared with the total cost of a bridge may militate against giving sufficient attention to their design. Actual cost records, however, show that the cost of foundations (piers and abutments) often almost equals the cost of superstructure, even on large bridges, as the typical figures presented in Table 17.1 clearly demonstrate. Whatever may have been the cause, it cannot be denied that the importance of bridge-foundation design has not always been fully recognized, thus betraying on occasion the basic assumption of the superstructure designer—that his pier- and abutment-bearing surfaces will provide him with fixed and solid pedestals on which he can support the structure he conceives and that he need not fear any serious movement.

17.3. Special Preliminary Work. The first considerations in bridge location are generally those of convenience and economy; foundation-bed conditions usually take a subsidiary place, for the prime requirement of a transportation route is that it shall connect its terminal points by the shortest convenient route consistent with topographical configuration. When crossings of any natural defile have to be made, considerations of cost usually limit the choice of site to that calling for the shortest possible structure. The bridge engineer is therefore not usually given much choice of location; in consequence, he often has to accept the foundation-bed conditions at a site so determined and, if it is possible to do so, design for them a suitable foundation structure.

This limitation of site necessitates the most complete information possible with regard to the geological conditions at the site. A still more potent reason for obtaining full geological information is that once the construction of bridge piers is started, their respective locations cannot be changed except in most unusual circumstances. More than the usual degree of certainty must therefore be attached to the design and anticipated performance of bridge piers and abutments. There is yet a further reason for this special care in preliminary investigations. Bridges, as a rule, are constructed to cross river or other valleys—depressions below the normal level of the ground which by their existence suggest some departure from normal geological structure. In districts that in past ages have been subjected to glacial action, an older river bed or other depression now completely hidden by subsequent glacial or river deposits may be found well below the existing river bed. Such a condition, even if known in advance, can have a serious effect on design. If the existence of a buried valley is not discovered before construction begins, it can lead to untold difficulties. Again, river beds are likely to contain many types of deposits, including boulders; and if preliminary work is not carefully done and correlated with geological considerations, an extensive boulder deposit can easily be mistaken for solid rock. For example, a bridge near Cornwall, Ontario, Canada, failed in 1898, with the loss of 15 lives, because a pier was founded on a boulder occurring in a layer of "hardpan" which had not previously been explored by borings and which proved to be only about 2 ft thick. Scouring in the vicinity of one of the bridge piers disclosed the clay beneath; the pier eventually tipped over and dropped two of the bridge spans into the

St. Lawrence which it crossed.[17.3] The wreckage of the original super-structure was salvaged in 1958 in connection with the building of the great St. Lawrence international power project. (It was the same glacial till which led to this bridge failure that caused such trouble in excavation work for the power project.)

Another example is given by the construction of the George's River Bridge, New South Wales, Australia. George's River flows into Botany Bay, 12 miles south of the city of Sydney. Work toward the construction of a toll highway bridge to replace existing vehicular ferries was begun in 1923. Borings were put down at three possible sites for the bridge by an experienced foreman; the borings at the site finally selected disclosed solid rock at depths below bed level, varying between 35 and 47 ft at regular intervals across a river section about 1,500 ft wide, the rock at the sides of which was known to dip steeply. On the basis of this information, a through-truss bridge of six main spans, supported on cylinder piers, was designed, and a lump-sum contract was awarded. During construction, it was found that rock existed, as expected, at only two of the seven main piers; additional borings taken to depths up to 130 ft failed to disclose any solid rock at all at the other pier sites, and what is even more strange, they disclosed no stratum harder than "indurated sand." Construction had to be stopped and designs changed; in consequence, the bridge took 5 years to build instead of 2 and cost 27.6 per cent more than the contract price. Discussion of the paper in which this work was reported to the Institution of Civil Engineers naturally emphasized the rigid necessity of having borings most carefully watched by a trained observer. The absence of geological references in both paper and discussion suggests that neglect of geological features may have been a contributory cause of the trouble that was experienced.[17.4] Although this is an unusual and possibly exceptional example, the construction of the George's River Bridge is a most telling reminder of the supreme importance of preliminary geological information in bridge design.

Another reason for devoting unusual care to the study of the geological conditions at bridge sites in all cases of river crossings is the fact that so much of the ground surface involved is hidden below water. Dependence has thus to be placed on the results of the underwater borings obtained, correlated with geological information secured on the adjacent shores. Where solid rock is encountered, this calls for no unusual attention, provided that the exposed surfaces of the rock show no signs of disintegration or weathering; but if any part of the foundation bed consists either wholly or partially of clay, then it is desirable—in some cases imperative—to obtain samples of the clay in as undisturbed a condition as possible. Suitable test-boring devices have been developed with which undisturbed samples of clay and other unconsolidated materials

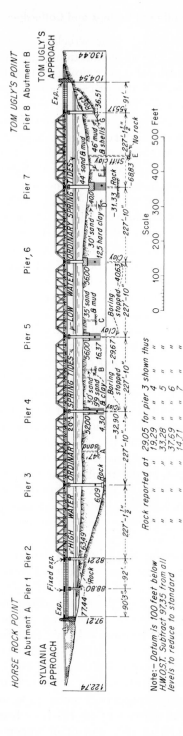

Fig. 17.1. Elevation of the George's River Bridge, New South Wales, Australia, and section through foundation strata, showing results of original borings and strata as revealed during construction. (*Reproduced by permission of the Institution of Civil Engineers.*)

648

can be obtained even through great depths of water. One such piece of equipment was developed especially for investigating underwater soil conditions at a bridge site—that of the San Francisco–Oakland Bay Bridge in California. This project is one of the largest yet undertaken; it will long remain one of the outstanding bridges of the world. Since the design and construction of all piers were determined only after the most thorough preliminary investigations, the subsurface conditions will be briefly described.

San Francisco is separated from the district of Oakland by the entrance to San Francisco Harbor. Yerba Buena Island stands in the center of the harbor and divides it into the East Bay and the West Bay. For many years transportation across the harbor was maintained by ferryboats, but a long-projected bridge scheme finally reached the construction stage in 1933 and was officially opened on November 12, 1936. Early in the planning of the scheme, the engineers in charge decided upon a program of borings and soil tests to determine the nature of the subsurface materials and to enable them (1) to ascertain the most desirable location for the center line of the bridge, (2) to determine the best location for individual piers, and (3) to select a logical basis for the design of the piers. Preliminary jet borings enabled the engineers to prepare a contour map of the underlying solid-rock surface of the harbor, including the West Bay Bridge area. With the aid of additional wash-pipe borings and diamond-drill core borings into the rock, they prepared a final design for the West Bay crossing. Piers were located and designed; all were founded on solid rock and constructed by means of caissons, the behavior of which could be accurately foretold.

The East Bay crossing presented quite distinct problems, since rock was not found by borings at practicable depths, and it became necessary to determine the nature of the overlying unconsolidated material. Cores were obtained and hermetically sealed without removal from the sampling tube on reaching the deck of the drill barge; they were tested later at the University of California. When the containers were opened, perfect cores were generally found, although in some cases a slight swelling was noticed, possibly due to the change in internal pressure in the sample as it came from its deep river bed. Material was obtained in this way from depths up to 273 ft below water level. The section on the final center line of the bridge as finally disclosed by the subsequent tests is shown in Fig. 17.2, from which the completeness of the subsurface survey will be evident; the use of such information in the design of pier foundations will be to some degree self-evident.[17.5]

The example just described is in some ways unique, although many features of the preliminary investigations have general application. Adequate test borings, not only along the line of the selected bridge site but on either side of it; careful study of core specimens so obtained; and

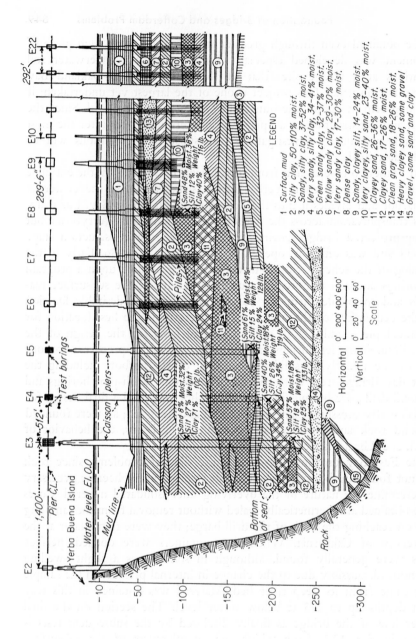

Fig. 17.2. San Francisco–Oakland Bay Bridge; geological section along east channel section, showing results of subsurface exploration and the location of piers. (*Reproduced by permission of The Editor, Engineering News-Record.*)

the correlation of this information with the geological structure of the adjoining dry ground should present a reasonably accurate structural picture of the foundation beds which will enable the designing engineer accurately to locate and to design the bridge abutments and piers. Finally, the necessity of taking all test borings deep enough below the surface of solid material (and especially of unconsolidated material) must be stressed. Loadings from bridge sup-ports are always relatively con-centrated and often inclined to the vertical. It is therefore doubly neces-sary to be sure that no underlying stratum may fail to support the loads transmitted to it, even in-directly, by the strata above.

An interesting example of trouble due to this cause is furnished by the failure of a highway bridge over the La Salle River at St. Nor-bert, Manitoba, Canada, on October 31, 1920. The bridge was a single reinforced-concrete arch, with a clear span of 100 ft; the spandrels were earth filled. The roadway was about 30 ft above the bottom of the river, and the height of the fill placed in each approach was about 20 ft. The bridge abutments were founded on piles driven into the stiff blue clay exposed at the site and thought to overlie limestone bed-rock, as the results of preliminary auger borings and the record of an adjacent well seemed to indicate. Failure occurred by excessive settle-ment; the north abutment dropped 4 ft, and bearing piles were bent and broken. Subsequent investigations

Fig. 17.3. Central anchorage pier of San Francisco–Oakland Bay Bridge, anchoring two suspension spans; a pic-torial representation showing subsur-face conditions and construction details. (*Reproduced by permission of the Chief Engineer, California Dept. of Public Works.*)

disclosed the existence of a stratum of "slippery white mud" (actually bentonite) about 25 ft below the original surface; failure of this material to carry the superimposed load resulted in the bridge collapse. Local soils are sediments from an ancient glacial lake and usually overlie com-pacted glacial till, under which is limestone carrying subartesian water. The existence of this water complicated the underpinning of the bridge foundation, but the work was successfully completed, and the bridge was restored to use. The existence of the bentonite was previously unknown in the vicinity; it illustrates the uncertainty of glacial deposition. The occurrence has a special interest for engineers: although the bearing piles were driven into the compacted till ("hardpan"), settlement of the abutment occurred as the result of failure of soft material overlying this.[17.6]

17.4. The Design of Bridge Piers. Although this chapter is not meant to be an introduction to bridge-pier design, some attention to design requirements is necessary in order to obtain an adequate appreciation of the relation of geological conditions to this design work. Generally speaking, there are four types of loading, one or more of which may have to be provided for in design: (1) vertical loads, possibly of varying intensity, from truss or girder spans or suspension-bridge towers; (2) inclined loads, again of varying intensity and possibly varying direction, from arched spans; (3) inclined tensions, from the cables of suspension bridges; and (4) horizontal thrusts due to the pressure of ice, possible debris, and the flow of water impinging on the piers and also due to wind acting on the bridge superstructure and piers. In earthquake regions, allowance must also be made for seismic forces that may act upon the piers. Combinations of these several loads will give rise to certain maximum and minimum unit pressures to be taken on foundation beds; from considerations of these results and of the nature of the strata to be encountered, the type of foundation can be determined.

The estimation of the load that the foundation strata at the site of a bridge pier will safely support is generally similar to the same operation for ordinary foundation work. The usual precautions must be observed with regard to strata below the surface that might fail under load. There are two unusual features to be noted, and both are reductions which may be applied, under certain circumstances, to the calculated net load on the base area. The first is the allowance that can be made for the displacement by the pier of water and the natural material excavated; the second is the reduction that can be allowed for the skin friction on the sides of the pier because of the usually large surface area exposed as compared with the base area. These two factors are obviously dependent on the nature of the strata penetrated. The estimation of the first is straightforward, but that of the second is generally a matter of past experience or of experiment during pier sinking, coupled with use of the results of careful laboratory tests upon soil samples from the bridge site.

Throughout all determinations of safe foundation loads, the nature of the local strata does play an important part; it may even dictate the use of hollow piers to reduce unit loads or of such unusual structures as the open reinforced-concrete framework abutment supports adopted for the Mortimer E. Cooley Bridge across the Manistee River in Michigan. This singularly beautiful bridge, consisting of two 125-ft deck truss-steel cantilever arms, supporting a 50-ft suspended span and balanced

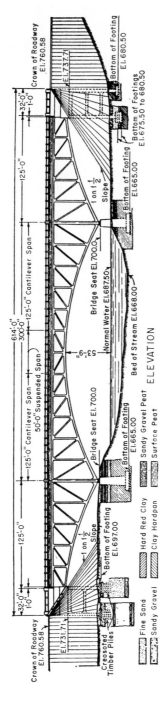

FIG. 17.4. Elevation of the Mortimer E. Cooley Bridge over the Manistee River, Michigan, U.S.A., showing foundation strata and special abutment structures. (*Reproduced by permission of The American Society of Civil Engineers.*)

by two 125-ft anchor arms, has its deck level about 60 ft above the level of the ground on either side of the river; the ground consists of varying strata of unconsolidated materials which were accurately explored. In order to keep foundation loading on this material to a minimum, the open framework design shown in Fig. 17.4 was adopted and successfully used.[17.7]

When preliminary investigations have shown that the foundation-bed material will have poor bearing capacity, consideration may be given to the use of artificial methods of consolidating such material to improve its bearing capacity. That this is no new expedient is shown by some of the older records of bridge building, e.g., the account given by Leland (antiquary to King Henry VIIII), who wrote in 1538 concerning the Wade Bridge in England, that "the foundations of certain of th' arches was first sette on so quick sandy ground that Lovebone (Vicar of Wadebridge) almost despaired to perform the bridge ontyl such tyme as he layed pakkes of wolle for foundation." Although this use of wool has been disputed, the record is interesting as demonstrating that some artificial means was used to improve bearing capacity. Modern methods are described elsewhere in this book. Grouting is naturally the most common method, but chemical consolidation has been suggested for some bridgeworks. Another approach to the problem is to consider leaving the steel piling of the pier cofferdam in place in order to confine the foundation-bed material and thus prevent lateral displacement; in this way bearing capacity will be increased to some extent.

The foundations for the Tappan Zee Bridge that carries the New York Thruway across the Hudson River for a distance of 2.8 miles between Nyack and Tarrytown provide an even more unusual approach to the problem of minimizing loads on strata that are deficient in bearing capacity. Here was a case in which the site of the bridge, selected on the basis of most careful location studies, had to be accepted even though the bedrock that is so dominant a feature of the local landscape drops off under the bridge to depths as great as 1,400 ft below water level; rock elevation throughout the whole length of the bridge is too low to be reached by normal bearing piles. The approach spans are therefore carried on friction bearing piles, driven into the silt and sand and gravel that form the river bed. For the large piers carrying the 1,212-ft-cantilever main-channel span, however, and for the immediately flanking piers, other methods had to be considered. The design finally adopted was to use buoyant reinforced-concrete box foundations to take about two-thirds of the dead load of the superstructure; the remaining part of the dead load, and the live load are taken by 30-in. concrete-filled pipe piles for the four main piers, and by 14-in. steel H piles for the four other buoyant boxes; in each case piles and boxes are ingeniously connected together. The steel piles had to be driven to depths up to 175 ft, but the concrete pipe piles went as deep as 340 ft below water level, being driven through clay and then gravelly clay after the sand and gravel had been penetrated. The hollow piles were mucked out to full depth by water-jet and airlift techniques, and then concreted by a special intrusion method by which grout was forced into preplaced aggregate. The grouting technique also had the effect of consolidating the seamy gneiss and decomposed sandstone, which constitute the underlying bedrock, so as to give the necessary bearing capacity. Boulders added to the complications but all foundations were successfully completed as

FIG. 17.5. The Tappan Zee Bridge over the Hudson River, New York, looking east, showing the main spans supported by the special piers described in the text. (*Reproduced by permission of the Chief Engineer, New York State Thruway Authority.*)

planned and on schedule. Details of the piers are admittedly an engineering matter, but it was the geology of the site that dictated such a bold design.[17.8]

Among the special problems to be faced in bridge-pier design in the solution of which geological information can usefully be applied is that of predicting possible settlement of piers when loaded; unequal settlement can have a serious effect on certain types of bridge structures, notably continuous-truss spans, vertical-lift bridges, and fixed arches. An accurate knowledge of foundation-bed conditions and the probable behavior under load of the material in these strata will usually permit accurate predictions of settlement. What happens when uneven settlement does take place is well illustrated by the failure of piers 4 and 8 of Waterloo Bridge, London; the whole bridge had to be taken down and a new structure erected. Described by Canova as "the noblest bridge in the world worth a visit from the remotest corner of the earth," Waterloo Bridge was constructed from 1811 to 1817 to the designs of John Rennie, who took especial care to protect all his pier foundations—timber rafts on timber piles, bearing on gravel—against scour. Progressive settlement of the two piers mentioned became serious in 1923; the total settlement of pier 4 exceeded 2½ ft and naturally caused an arching action between piers 3 and 5.[17.9]

This case is cited mainly because of its general interest; as an example it can hardly be called typical, since the conditions encountered were relatively unusual. In a general way, settlement may occur from one or another of the following causes: (1) displacement of part of the bed by scour; (2) lateral displacement of the foundation bed due to lack of restraint; (3) consolidation of the underlying material; or (4) failure of an underlying stratum. Only the settlement caused by condition 3 can be called controlled settlement; the other three types are of a nature that may cause serious trouble to the structure. All types can be foretold, in the majority of cases, provided adequate preliminary information is obtained. Dangerous possibilities can therefore be avoided, and the controlled settlement accurately predicted, as in the case of the San Francisco–Oakland Bridge foundations described above.

Provision against unequal settlement of piers in the case of relatively small-span bridges has assumed considerable importance in recent years owing to the development of the rigid-frame type of structure, an essential feature of which is that the abutments are unyielding; this means that any settlement of piers must be almost uniform. For rigid-frame structures founded on clay, the difficulties of which as a foundation bed will later be fully stressed, some interesting expedients have been adopted. One such expedient (employed at a Canadian National Railways bridge at Vaudreuil in Quebec, Canada) is to isolate the bridge foundation from the bearing piles and to transmit the load through a specially tamped layer of crushed rock.[17.10] This is an interesting return to an old practice (although for a new reason); the foundations of the present London Bridge over the Thames in England bear on clay through a similar layer of crushed rock and timber piles; they were installed almost a century ago.

Stresses set up in foundation beds during the bridge construction, especially those which may be set up during unbalanced loading caused by irregular construction scheduling, must also be carefully considered in design. During the construction of the Broadway Bridge, Saskatchewan, Canada, in 1932, a three-span reinforced-concrete arch structure, the concreting of the arches proceeded in varying stages; as a result the piers tilted when carrying the dead load of only one adjacent arch rib (even though this was supported on centering). Careful records were taken, and a maximum deflection of 0.60 in. was recorded. In this instance, the result was not unexpected.[17.11]

The inclined tensions, mentioned as the third type of loading possible, are generally transmitted to anchorages in solid rock, in which case design resolves itself into providing for shearing resistance in the rock, which, together with allowance for the dead weight of the anchorage, will be sufficient to balance the tensile forces in the bridge cables. Sometimes the inclined tension in bridge cables has to be taken up wholly by concrete piers. The Ile d'Orléans (suspension) Bridge, in Quebec, Canada, is one such example. The suspension span of this bridge is flanked by long approaches from the shores; the main cables are secured in anchor piers, one of which is founded on rock but the other on sand. Naturally, the stability calculations for these piers had to take into consideration all stabilizing factors, while keeping the unit toe and heel pressures within the limit of the foundation-bed material. Friction between concrete and rock and concrete and sand, therefore, had to be considered as well as the shearing value of both strata. As a result of these studies, inclined H-beam piles were driven into the sand underlying one of the anchor piers and were left so as to project into the concrete of the finished pier in order to give the necessary increase in stability.[17.12]

Another unusual example is provided by the double suspension spans of the West Bay crossing of the San Francisco–Oakland Bridge; the two 2,210-ft suspension spans join and are anchored into a central anchorage pier 500 ft high above rock level. The engineering design of this structure is of unusual interest; its peculiar relevance to this discussion is that, under one of the most severe combinations of loading considered, a unit pressure on the rock of 79 tons per sq ft may occur, a figure that could be contemplated with safety only after completion of the very thorough preliminary studies made for this bridge project and already described (see Fig. 17.3).

As a final example, there may be mentioned the building of the Burford Bridge as part of a bypass road across the river Mole in Surrey, England, which is one of the most unusual contacts of special geological features with the design of bridges known to the author. The bridge is a single reinforced-concrete arch span of 80 ft, 100 ft wide between parapets with specially selected brick facing. Many who know the lovely valley of this small stream, located some 25 miles to the south of London, will know also that its valley is as geologically interesting as it is scenically beautiful. The river flows over the local chalk formation which has been so eroded in places by the action of the dissolved carbon dioxide in the river water as to have underground cavities large enough to receive the whole normal flow of the stream. Trial borings were put down at the site of the new bridge and carefully checked to see if any such swallow holes in the chalk were revealed. Two soft spots were located, and these proved to be solution channels of this kind, having almost vertical sides and filled up with alluvial matter. It was at first intended to secure adequate bearing for the road and abutments over the holes by driving reinforced-concrete bearing piles into the material found in them, but further studies led to a more unusual solution which could be adopted with more certainty. Concrete domes were constructed over each of the

Fig. 17.6. Foundations for the Burford Bridge on the Mickleham bypass road, Surrey, England. Reinforced-concrete domes over swallow holes under construction. (*Reproduced by permission of the County Engineer, Surrey, through the courtesy of the Ministry of Transport.*)

holes, founded on circular ledges cut in the chalk around the top of the holes; the largest is 58 ft in diameter with a rise of 8 ft. The holes were filled up to the undersides of the domes, and the filling was then covered with waterproof paper and used as the lower form for concreting the domes. Each dome was furnished with an access shaft connecting to a manhole at road level by means of which the engineers may inspect the swallow holes from time to time to see that no dangerous undercutting or further erosion of the chalk is taking place.[17.13]

17.5. The Design of Bridge Abutments. In addition to having to support, at least partially, loads that the piers of a bridge have to carry, the abutments of a bridge may and often do have to resist another load, that of earth pressure against the face and wing walls of the abutment structure. Design may therefore be a complicated matter, combining the difficulties of both bridge-pier and retaining-wall construction. In the case of abutments retaining artificially formed fills such as those of approach embankments, difficulties of design and construction can generally be foreseen and so guarded against. The careful placing of fill material, working away from the abutments; adequate provision for drainage by the installation of cross drains along the lower part of the inner faces of abutment structures, connected to suitable weep holes which cannot become plugged up; and the supervision of all fill settlement are perhaps the leading matters for attention in this type of work.

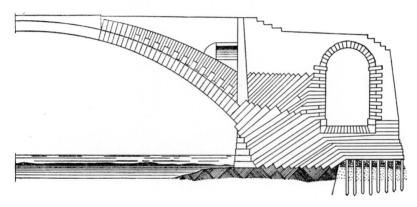

Fig. 17.7. Cross section through the abutment of the Grosvenor Bridge, Chester, England, showing variation of structure with changes in foundation strata. (*Reproduced by permission of The Institution of Structural Engineers.*)

Abutments located on sloping ground, as so many of them have to be, may present different problems; for in addition to having to retain the pressure of earth backing, often with considerable surcharge, they may be subjected to forces set up by the instability of the whole hillside slope; or, alternatively, their foundations may be made insecure by earth movement on slopes below. Again, the forces acting on them are far from symmetrical, so that balancing (especially during construction) is a matter which often calls for great ingenuity in design. A few examples will illustrate the type of problem presented and the dependence of abutment design on foundation-bed conditions.

Bridges for which solid rock provides abutment support will be familiar to almost all engineers, since this is an ideal condition and one which is essential for certain types of arch designs. A famous English bridge illustrates in an interesting way a slight variation from the ideal case; one of the abutments of the Grosvenor Bridge across the river Dee at Chester is founded partially on rock and partially on sand. The bridge, built in the year 1833, has a clear span of 200 ft and a rise of 40 ft. Figure 17.7 illustrates the construction that had to be adopted at the north abutment, because the outcrop of solid rock suddenly terminated and was succeeded by a deep stratum of loose sand to which the arch thrust was transmitted by means of timber piles.[17.14]

Fig. 17.8. Combined pier, anchorage, and abutment structure for viaduct (overhead), suspension span, and steel arch—all component parts of the Thousand Islands International Bridge over the St. Lawrence River at Ivy Lea, Ontario, Canada.

It is naturally with arch bridges that abutments are such critical parts of bridge design. Figure 17.8 shows an unusual example, demonstrating the possibilities in design when rock conditions are excellent. The view shows one of the supporting structures for the Ivy Lea International Bridge that crosses the St. Lawrence River in the lovely Thousand Islands region between Ontario and New York State. Here gneiss bedrock was at the surface; the Thousand Islands are exposures of the "Frontenac Axis," the projection of the Precambrian shield extending into New York and forming the Adirondack Mountains. With such sound rock available the engineers were able to combine in this one structure a main abutment for a long steel arch, an anchorage for cables from one of the main suspension spans, and the necessary support for vertical columns under that part of the bridge joining the arch and the suspended span.

Fɪɢ. 17.9. The Volta River Bridge, Ghana, West Africa, looking toward the west abutment. (*Reproduced by permission of Sir William Halcrow & Partners, Consulting Engineers.*)

Figure 17.9 shows a graceful steel-arch bridge which spans the Volta River in the new African country of Ghana; it is a two-hinged structure with a clear span of 865 ft, making it the seventh longest such bridge in the world. Eight months were spent on preliminary geological studies; rocks at the site were metamorphosed Paleozoic sediments (indurated shales and quartzites). The quartzites form most of the bedrock in the area; they are highly folded. Even with this advance knowledge, however, more difficulty was experienced than had been anticipated when the rock was exposed for the abutment on the west bank. Interbedded shale and quartzites were found to a degree unexpected; the saw-tooth design prepared for the rock excavation had to be modified to take into account the actual dip and strike of the rock, the level of which was not quite as expected since some of the few auger borings used had suggested bedrock where only boulders were found. With modification of the design, however, the west abutment was successfully completed and this fine bridge is now serving to link two major parts of this new and virile country.[17.15]

When no rock is available, abutment designs must follow methods suggested in the case of pier design; subsoil conditions must be thoroughly investigated, and the foundation-structure design determined after a full consideration of test results. In many cases of abutment designs on unconsolidated material of low bearing capacity, bearing piles will have to be employed to provide for the anticipated load. Such piles, unless driven at a batter, will offer small resistance to lateral movement; and for this reason, quite a few abutments have been moved inward from their original positions by the excess of earth pressure behind them over the stabilizing forces. Earth pressures and, similarly, the frictional resistance between foundation and foundation bed must receive the most careful attention in all such designs. In some cases, the only solution possible is to brace one abutment against the other by means of underwater struts. One example of this type was the Summit Street bascule bridge across Swan Creek in Toledo, Ohio, in which a series of braced concrete struts, supported on piles, 4 ft thick and each 9 ft wide, placed in 16 ft of water, had to be installed after abutment movements had seriously affected the bridge operation.[17.16] Many similar cases could be cited; another well-known, for example, one is Bridge No. 16 over the new Welland Canal in Canada.

A strange case which may be mentioned as a matter of some interest concerns the third of a series of three hinged concrete single-span arch bridges constructed in Holland across the Meuse-Waal Canal about 1925, each of which had a span of about 212 ft. All were founded on strata of sand and gravel, apparently identical in character, and the maximum pressure to be exerted on the ground was the same in each case. When the centering of the third bridge was removed, it was found that the abutments were moving backward, horizontally, rotating about a horizontal axis and with some settlement. By means of jacks under the arches, half the movement was removed. As no reason could be found for the movement, the engineers had to design and construct a secondary friction abutment. This successfully prevented further movement, and the bridge has since maintained its correct position with no sign of movement. But the cause of the movement has never been discovered.[17.17]

Not only the design of abutments but even that of bridge super-structures may be affected by the geological structure of the abutment site. Nowhere else has this been better demonstrated, perhaps, than in the case of the Kohala Bridge carrying the Rawalpindi–Kashmir Road across the Jhelum River on the rugged mountainous boundary of the Punjab and Kashmir. Originally constructed as a three-span girder bridge (130-ft center span and two 90-ft approach spans), the unstable condition of the hillside at the Punjab abutment caused movement of the girders

Fig. 17.10. The Kohala Bridge across the Jhelum River on the Rawalpindi–Kashmir Road (Pakistan). The "floating span" may be seen on the right, leading from the abutment on the sloping riverbank that has caused much trouble. (*Photograph originally provided by the Chief Engineer of the (old) North Western Railway of India.*)

toward the Kashmir side; the Punjab approach span was seriously damaged in 1929 and finally wrecked in 1931 through serious landslides occasioned by heavy rains. W. T. Everall, then deputy chief engineer, North Western Railway of India, discovered a large fissure in the hill-side about 200 ft above the level of the bridge; this fissure occurred in a slope of loose soil and rock detritus, which was indicative of future move-ment. In consequence, after the failure of the Punjab approach span, Mr. Everall had a special design for reconstruction accepted and carried into effect, cantilevering a 70-ft span back from the first main river pier and connecting it by means of a light suspended span to the hillside road level. Suitable drainage work and stone pitching were also carried out. Although future earth movement has been well guarded against, the intent is that, should a landslide occur, it shall displace the suspended span which can safely ride up and over the end of the cantilever span. Thus little damage will be done to the main bridge structure, and the

FIG. 17.11. Abutment of Bridge No. 14 on Pemberton Loop line near Wigan, England, showing timber supporting trestle in place on steel box pile foundation. Successive capstones in the masonry abutment show the progressive settlement that has taken place. (*Reproduced by permission of the British Steel Piling Co., Ltd., and the Chief Civil Engineer, London Midland Region, British Railways.*)

span can be easily replaced after movement has stopped. The accompanying photograph shows this feature clearly. Engineering ingenuity has here accepted geological forebodings and anticipated trouble in a particularly imaginative manner.[17.18]

An unusual and extreme case of settlement may next be mentioned. The Pemberton Loop line of the old London Midland and Scottish Railway crosses the Leeds and Liverpool Canal by Bridge No. 14 near Wigan, England. The ground adjacent to the bridge site consists of alluvial and glacial deposits overlying the Middle Coal Measures of the carboniferous formation; the ground surface was originally a few feet above water level in the canal. Owing to extraction of coal from the strata immediately under the bridge site and the adjacent area, continual subsidence took place, and the fields around gradually became an extensive lake. Correspondingly, the plate-web girders of the bridge had to be jacked

Fɪɢ. 17.12. The Clifton Bridge over the river Trent, Nottingham, England, during construction. (*Reproduced by permission of the City Engineer and Surveyor, Nottingham, England.*)

up, and the abutments built up under them to compensate for the settlement. By the beginning of 1935, the headstones on which the girders had originally rested had sunk 13 ft and were barely visible above the canal water level. Subsidence was continuing and its final extent could not be ascertained. The engineers therefore decided to construct timber trestles to replace the abutments (although they were to be left in place); the trestles were supported on two series of special boxes constructed of steel sheet piling, all piles being driven as deeply as possible. Jacking up could then easily be done from the trestles which are intended to serve until subsidence has ceased, when the brick abutments can be permanently rebuilt. The building of the steel pile boxes was carried out without interference to traffic and constituted a most interesting piece of construction.[17.19]

If settlements due to future mining operations are known to be a possibility at a bridge site, superstructure designs can be prepared accordingly. A notable example of this type of "controlled" design is that of the Clifton Bridge at Nottingham, England, across the river Trent. Coal mining is an important local activity; preliminary studies showed that some valuable coal seams, as yet unworked, ran directly under the bridge location. The structure was therefore designed to take account of possible settlement, should mining take place. The resulting structure is a pre-stressed-concrete main span of 275 ft with two end spans of 125 ft, and three 90-ft end viaducts, all built on a skew of 24°. Structural engineers will appreciate the complication that this feature introduced to the design; the aesthetic appeal of the resulting 800-ft river crossing can, however, be generally appreciated. The main span had to be designed as two cantilevers with a central suspended span, all statically determinate because of the anticipated settlement; arrangements were included in the design for the spans to be jacked up off the tops of the main piers whenever this became necessary. The piers are founded on the Keuper marl, which extends to depths of over 500 ft at the bridge site. The marl was badly weathered to a depth of 27 ft, but below this level it was hard and durable, containing bands of siltstone and very stiff clay; the formation is one of the many soil horizons in Britain that are not of geologically recent formation. Consolidation tests showed that the marl, so well known to geologists, was really a highly overconsolidated clay so that it would swell if exposed and deteriorate if unprotected from water.

It remains to add only that, just as the complex design for the bridge was complete, it was found that a geological fault between the colliery and the bridge site made profitable working of the coal seams unlikely. The local city council therefore bought out the rights for the working of the coal seams beneath the bridge for a nominal sum, and thus eliminated all possibility of settlement from this cause. It was too late to change the design so the bridge was built as planned and as here described, except for minor alterations such as the permanent covering in of the jacking pockets left in the piers.[17.20]

17.6. Earthquakes and Bridge Design. In regions susceptible to earthquake shocks, seismic forces have to be carefully considered in bridge design; when bridge piers are high, they must accordingly have full allowance made in their design for seismic forces. Among the highest bridge piers yet built were those for the Pit River Bridge that carries the Southern Pacific Railroad and U.S. Highway 99 over a part of the reservoir formed by the Shasta Dam. The piers have a maximum height of 360 ft, of which over 300 ft is now submerged beneath the waters of the Shasta Reservoir. Because of the location, the possibility of earthquakes had to be considered. A detailed study of this unusual case was therefore carried out by the U.S. Bureau of Reclamation, as a result of which it was shown that, under earthquake shocks and when submerged, these piers would no longer act as elastic structures fixed at their bases but would act as rigid structures, rotating at their bases. This conclusion led to design criteria which can be summarized in the requirement to design the piers for all ordinary loads without considering earthquake effects, and then to design them for anticipated earthquake forces so that the resultant force would be just at the edge of the pier base.[17.21]

FIG. 17.13. A detailed view of the Pajaro River Bridge of the Southern Pacific Railroad, showing the concrete projection above the main pier designed to catch the plate girder spans if ever they are displaced by earthquake action. (*Reproduced by permission of The Editor, Engineering News-Record.*)

The Pajaro River Bridge that carries the Southern Pacific coast line to Los Angeles, 92 miles south from San Francisco, once provided vivid evidence of what an earthquake shock can do to a bridge. A new structure at the same location now demonstrates the best in modern bridge design to take account of the fact that the bridge spans not only the Pajaro River but also the well-known San Andreas fault which here follows the river channel for some distance. At the time of the earthquake of April 18, 1906, the bridge consisted of five simple-deck girder spans with a total length of 460 ft. All five spans were moved by the earthquake vertically and all but one horizontally. In some cases the motion was enough to throw the spans off their supports; one span was left hanging precariously over the edge of one of its piers. When the bridge was reconstructed in 1944, advantage was taken of the opportunity to redesign it as a three-span continuous-deck girder which, with the addition of one 86-ft side span, gave a total length of 450 ft. In this case, the continuity over the central supports in the river bed was deemed to be advantageous in case of any serious movement of the piers. Clearance has been left at the free end of the continuous girder for a reasonable amount of longitudinal movement. Instead of the usual type of support, special rockers were designed, permitting more movement than usual. Concrete projections above the rocker shoes will support the girder should it be moved off its supports. A heavy pendulum has been mounted on a special fitting on one of the piers, so arranged that movement of the center of the bridge in excess of ¾ in. will cause movement of the pendulum to open a circuit, deenergize a relay, and cause the automatic block signals controlling access to the bridge to be set at danger. Abutments and the ends of the girders are similarly connected; they will set the signals at danger for any movement in excess of 1 in. A recording device attached to the pendulum has recorded movements due to seismic shocks up to ⅝ in., but as yet no tremor has been so great as to actuate the tripping of the approach signals.[17.22]

17.7. Scouring around Bridge Piers. The consequences of bridge construction across a waterway involve three main effects which may generally be foreseen: (1) the construction of piers and abutments will generally decrease the effective cross-sectional area of the stream, and thus inevitably increase the velocity and raise the water level (usually very slightly) above the bridge; (2) the existence of piers as obstructions to the stream flow will set up eddies around the piers and may possibly institute crosscurrents in the stream, tending to change it from its normal course below the bridge site; and (3) the combined effect of increased average velocity and eddies may disturb the equilibrium of the bed material between piers and so lead to scouring. All these results represent interference with natural conditions and therefore call for the application of geological information in the engineering solution of the many problems they bring up. An example of the serious effect of a change in permanent water level, almost classical in nature, is the scouring around the pier foundations of the old Westminster and Vauxhall Bridges over the Thames, London, in the early years of the nineteenth century following the removal of old London Bridge and the consequent lowering of the water level in the stretch of the river immediately upstream. This opening of the river channel restored normal flow conditions at the sites of the bridges mentioned; since the foundations had not been designed for these conditions, both structures in course of time had to be completely rebuilt.[17.23]

Geological factors may affect runoff calculations appreciably, and it is from such calculations that estimates can be prepared showing what hydraulic conditions a bridge will have to withstand. On many tropical rivers with low-lying banks, bridges have to be designed on the assumption that they will be completely submerged in flood periods; naturally, therefore, the geological stability of the foundation bed for piers, abutments, and approaches must be assured before a submergible design can be entertained. An interesting and unusual example has been described; this is the bridge across the Nerbudda River near Jubbulpore in India. It is 1,222 ft long, consisting of six 98-ft and eight 46-ft spans, all reinforced-concrete arches; it is founded throughout on basalt. At flood periods, the bridge is completely submerged.[17.24]

The second and third suggestions are both related to that branch of civil engineering known as river-training work. Work of this nature frequently has to be carried out in connection with bridge-construction projects on rivers with relatively unstable beds, for the reasons covered by the suggestions mentioned above. If the river approaches toward such bridges have not been suitably trained, the volumes of water passing between the several piers may not be the same; the flow between pairs of piers has actually been reversed in some cases. It is not only on the great rivers flowing through alluvial plains that river-training and associated problems occur. Scouring of a river bed may happen on even the smallest stream if its normal state is interfered with, as by the construction of bridge piers in midstream. It is safe to say that scouring of bed materials from around the foundation structures supporting bridge spans has been responsible for more bridge failures in the past than has any other cause. In olden days, there was more tendency to set up scouring action under bridge spans because of the relatively small spans and consequent relatively large cross-sectional pier area as compared with water area; a contributory factor was that construction methods then possible did not permit foundations other than timber piling much below low-water level. Construction methods today suffer from no such limitations, and the general use of longer spans does not cause constriction of waterway areas. The problem still remains, however, and even in the records of modern bridge building, there are cases of serious scouring of foundation-bed material; two of these are mentioned in the last section of this chapter. Despite the relative simplicity of the problem, scouring of river beds around bridge piers still takes far too great a toll of property and, occasionally, of lives. It has been estimated that in one 10-year period $15 million worth of damage was done to highway bridges in the United States by this one cause.[17.25]

17.8. Some Construction Requirements. The design of bridge-foundation structures can rarely be considered without specific relation to the problems of constructing the piers so designed. Limitations in the re-

striction of a watercourse during construction, requirements of navigation, requirements of traffic across the bridge in the case of reconstruction work, depths of water and tidal range, and the depth below
water to foundation-bed level are all features that must be considered
in relation not only to structural stability but also to construction
methods. Here, too, the geological nature of the underlying strata must
be correlated with other design factors.

Construction of piers will generally be carried out by one of three
main methods: the use of open cofferdams (working either in the dry
or in water), the use of open dredging caissons, or the use of compressed-
air caissons. There are, of course, other special methods available. The
general arrangement of foundation strata will be a potent factor in
determining which of these construction methods shall be followed. In
the case of cofferdam work, for example, subsurface conditions will indicate fairly accurately the length of the piles required and will at least
suggest what resistance to penetration will have to be overcome in
driving. Further notes on cofferdams will be found in the next section
of this chapter. Should varying strata be encountered, possibly a combination of two of the methods will be advisable, especially of the second
and third, but such a possibility can be considered only if the details of
the strata are accurately known.

The development in recent years of modern construction techniques
has opened up new possibilities for bridge-pier design that can sometimes
prove much more economical than the older and more conventional
methods in some cases of poor foundation conditions. By the use of long
steel H piles driven to rock, possibly encased between bed and water
level with sheet-pile cofferdams in which aggregate can easily be placed
and converted into solid concrete by specialized grouting techniques,
bridge piers can readily be constructed that give all necessary support
above water level, provide requisite protection down to river-bed level,
and derive their bearing capacity from the column action of deeply
buried steel piles transferring loads to bedrock. There are now quite a
number of bridges in Canada successfully supported by long steel piles;
one of the most notable is that which carries the line of the Canadian
National Railways from Noranda to Senneterre in northwestern Quebec
over the Kinojevis River. Steel piles up to 175 ft long were used to form
bridge piers in material that could best be described as "soup."[17.26]

When subsurface conditions at bridge sites are bad, therefore, there are
now available to the designing engineer a variety of approaches to pier
design. By way of contrast, there may be mentioned the dilemma facing
Isambard Kingdom Brunel, another of the noted early British railway
engineers, when he came to design the Royal Albert Bridge at Saltash
over the river Tamar on the Great Western line to Penzance. Divers first
revealed the poor foundation conditions in 1847; Brunel decided that he

must know more about the river bed. A wrought-iron cylinder, 6 ft in diameter and 85 ft long, was therefore fabricated, towed out to the site of the necessary central pier between two barges, and sunk through the water and mud to bedrock. From this cylinder 175 borings were made into the rock, and its profile was plotted; a column of masonry was even built on the rock and carried up to the level of the river bed. Only then was Brunel satisfied; but he knew that unusual construction methods would be necessary to give him the satisfactory pier he required. Caissons had been used as early as 1720 by Gabriel but the caisson designed by Brunel for the Saltash Bridge must surely be one of the pioneer structures of construction practice. It measured 37 ft in diameter, 90 ft high, weighed 300 tons, was floated out into place, and fitted with an inner cylinder to give access to the "diving-bell" compartment that eventually extended to rock level. Dense beds of oyster shells in the river were only part of the troubles that had to be overcome before the pier was well founded, but overcome they were. They were recalled appreciatively by British engineers on the occasion of the centenary of the opening of the bridge in 1959.[17.27]

If caissons are used, one of the first problems to be faced is the skin friction which must be overcome in sinking the caisson through the foundation-bed material. Preliminary estimates of the skin friction to be overcome may be guided to some extent by knowledge of the strata which will be passed through, although the determining factors are so variable that only actual experience can be relied upon to give an accurate estimate of the resistance to movement. Overcoming the resistance can sometimes be facilitated by the use of jetting pipes around the cutting edge of the caisson, discharging water under pressure, but this course can be followed only when it is known with certainty that it will not seriously disturb the surrounding foundation-bed material.

Trouble with caissons is often experienced because of uneven settlement. This may be due to purely mechanical causes, but often it is due to variations in the underlying strata. In a general way, these may be foretold if a full soil survey has previously been carried out. So many factors are involved that it must be added that information on soil properties can be only a contributory source of information relative to possible movements, and that it must be considered in conjunction with other relevant information. Study of the tilting of bridge-pier caissons (several cases of which are on record) shows that such occurrences are generally due to a combination of causes; ground conditions are usually the most important either because of uneven settlement due to varying strata or because the soil material does not "break down" under the cutting edges of caissons, as had been anticipated. The tilting (through 42°) of the 19,000-ton reinforced-concrete open caisson for the east pier of the Mid-Hudson Bridge, at Poughkeepsie, New York, seemed to be due to this latter cause; a stiff stratum of clay and sand, in association with the design of the dredging pockets, resulted in excavation extending more than 10 ft below the cutting edge. Sudden collapse of the unsupported wall of the bed material seems to have been the cause of the serious tilting that occurred, the righting of which constituted a construction operation of unusual interest and ingenuity.[17.28]

Knowledge of subsurface conditions in advance of the start of actual work will always be of assistance in the selection of construction methods and may even suggest new methods. This seems to have been the case with what is now known as the "sand-island method," which was apparently originally evolved by M. R. Hornibrook, Ltd., for their contract for the construction of the Grey Street Bridge, Brisbane, Australia, in November, 1927. The main part of the structure consists of three reinforced-concrete arch spans, each 238 ft from center to center of piers. The river pier had to be founded in depths of water up to 50 ft, with rock varying from 83 to 107 ft below high-tide level; reinforced-concrete cylinders were to be used for the two central piers, and two caissons for the main pier on the south bank. Preliminary information revealed mud as the surface stratum, and this, together with other information, led to the construction of artificial "islands" at each pier site, formed of cylinders of steel sheet piling filled up to above water level with sand. Thus, the cutting edges could be set up in the dry and the sinking of the cylinders and caissons could be carried out under constant control. The steel piling was salvaged after the foundation structure was well founded in the river bed.[17.29] A similar method has been successfully applied to other leading bridge contracts in various parts of the world, notably the Suisan Bay Bridge of the Southern Pacific Railroad in California (1930) and the Mississippi River Bridge at New Orleans, Louisiana (1934). An outstanding example of more recent date is the Philadelphia–Gloucester suspension bridge (1957).

A further construction requirement of design is that some means must usually be provided for thoroughly inspecting and, if necessary, cleaning the surface of the foundation bed on which the bridge pier or abutment is to be founded. In the case of bridges to be founded on unconsolidated materials using low unit-bearing pressures, such inspection is not so important as it is in the case of solid-rock foundation beds. Personal inspection of rock surfaces is always a necessary supplement to even the best preliminary core drillings; the engineer must check on the structure of the rock stratum and possible surface disintegration; he must also be sure that it has been properly cleaned of all unconsolidated material so that good bond may be obtained between concrete and rock. There is on record at least one case, that of a bridge over the Colorado River of the Union Pacific Railroad in the United States, in which the piers had to be rebuilt only 15 years after the date of their original construction (1925) because the rock-bearing surface had not been properly cleaned before concreting was carried out.[17.30]

17.9. Cofferdam Construction. Consideration of the essentially geological aspects of cofferdam construction has been left for discussion in this separate section as a matter of convenience because cofferdams are used for much general foundation work in addition to providing facilities for the construction of bridge piers and abutments. They are now so common a feature of construction work that they are generally accepted without much thought being given to their development. It is sometimes believed that they are a relatively modern innovation; frequent reference is made to their "early" use on the river Thames in England for the construction of Waterloo Bridge (from 1809 to 1817), to which extended reference has already been made. The following extract from Vitruvius, dated probably about 20 B.C., is therefore of special interest:[17.31]

Then, in the place previously determined, a cofferdam, with its sides formed of oaken stakes with ties between them, is to be driven down into the water and firmly propped there; then, the lower surface, inside, under the water, must be levelled off and dredged, working from beams laid across; and finally, concrete from the mortar trough—the stuff having been mixed as prescribed above—must be heaped up until the empty space which was within the cofferdam is filled up by the wall. . . . A cofferdam with double sides, composed of charred stakes fastened together with ties, should be constructed in the appointed place, and clay in wicker baskets made of swamp rushes should be packed in among the props. After this has been well packed down and filled in as closely as possible, set up your water screws, wheels, and drums, and let the space now bounded by the enclosure be emptied and dried. Then dig out the bottom within the enclosure.

Cofferdams designed to be pumped dry (as distinct from those used merely to provide a still-water area) perform one main function, that of retaining the surrounding water and unconsolidated materials and thus providing an exposed dry area of river, lake, or sea bed on which construction operations can be carried out. The retention of sand, clay, or other foundation-bed material, e.g., after excavation has proceeded inside a cofferdam lower than the bed level outside, is not a difficult matter; it is a special case of the retaining structures already considered. The retention of water above bed level is also a relatively simple matter provided that the piling used to form the cofferdam has watertight joints; calculations for the necessary bracing to support the water pressures are straightforward. One main problem remains, that of preventing the ingress of water around the lower edge of the piling—in other words, that of preventing blows.

The usual cofferdam structure consists of a single continuous wall of interlocking piling, driven into the foundation strata for a distance sometimes determined by the resistance offered to pile driving, sometimes merely on the basis of previous work, but almost always in an empirical manner. Experience must ever be a guide in such matters, and the actual evidence presented by the driving of the sheet piling into the strata to be met with will be a telling indication of the underground conditions encountered. Cofferdams generally have to be designed prior to construction; materials have to be ordered before they can be used. Estimates of piling penetration necessary are therefore an essential preliminary;

Fig. 17.14. A general view of excavation proceeding behind the river section of the main cofferdam at the Grand Coulee Dam on the Columbia River, Washington. (*Reproduced by permission of the Commissioner, U.S. Bureau of Reclamation.*)

and in this estimating work, accurate information on the strata to be encountered will be of value.

Permeability is naturally a soil characteristic of leading importance in such considerations, but it cannot be considered alone. Sands and gravels, when revealed by test borings, will naturally suggest the necessity of deep penetration, and if sufficiently permeable, they may even dictate the use of a clay blanket all around the outer face of a cofferdam as a means of sealing the direct path that would be taken by water when pumping inside began. Clays, on the other hand, will generally provide an impermeable barrier to the seepage of water, provided the piling is driven below any influence from surface disturbance. In cofferdams constructed in tidal water, or in any watercourse liable to fluctuation of water level, the greatest care must be exercised with all cofferdam structures in clay. Under certain maximum water-level conditions, the clay will be compressed by one face of the piling and may possibly deform permanently, leaving a gap between piling and clay when the water level changes to the other extreme. This type of water passage is a far easier course for the flow of water to follow than even the pores in sand and gravel; and if this condition is allowed to develop unobserved, serious damage may result, and a bad blow occur.

These notes indicate the importance that subsurface conditions occupy even in this detail of construction; they emphasize, above all else, the necessity of knowing as accurately as possible the nature of the material to be penetrated. Again, careful tests are necessary to distinguish various soil types. The author knows of at least one case in which a material that to the untrained eye appeared to be clay actually proved to be compacted limestone flour (with practically no clay content at all). It was assumed to be clay in cofferdam design, and yet it proved in practice to be "as porous as a sieve," leading to most serious trouble with blows.

Another type of cofferdam sometimes used for larger structures is that known as "cellular"; steel sheet piling is driven in the form of large cell structures which are then filled with sand and which are stable as gravity structures. One of the most extensive cofferdam operations utilizing steel sheet pile cell units was that carried out during the construction of the Grand Coulee Dam in Washington. The Columbia River was diverted first into one-half of its original bed and then into the other by cofferdams which were about 3,000 ft long. The piles were driven generally into a consolidated glacial deposit which was difficult to penetrate, resulting in splitting and deformation of the steel piling. When excavation was carried out within the cofferdams, a sand seam 4 to 10 in. thick was encountered exposed across the excavation at an

Table 17.2. Grout "Prescription" Developed at Grand Coulee Dam

Sawdust.	8 cu ft
Shavings (thin and wispy, from refinishing machines, measured loose).	10 to 16 cu ft
Portland cement (two sacks).	2 cu ft
Sand.	6 cu ft
Lump bentonite.	50 lb
Mix the foregoing ingredients, dry, in a concrete mixer for about half a minute, and then add:	
Water.	8 to 10 cu ft
Pulverized bentonite (5 per cent by weight, of water).	30 lb
After adding second part of the batch, mix 1½ min more.	
Product will be a 14-cu ft batch resembling wet cement plaster.	

SOURCE: *Eng. News-Record* (New York), **119:**15 (1937).

elevation just below the general elevation of the bottoms of the steel piles. In the west cofferdam, no trouble was caused by this seam; but in the east cofferdam, owing to some complicating factors, including the deformation of the bottoms of steel piles, a leak developed through the seam and reached a flow of 35,000 gpm. Much trouble resulted, including the wrecking of a small part of the cellular dam; some of the steel piles were split from top to bottom. The emergency was met by a combination of engineering skill and construction ingenuity, the record of which is of great interest to all engineers; the leak was finally stopped without serious interruption of the main dam-construction operations. The only feature of this emergency work that can here be mentioned is that 4-in. well drills were used to locate the main passage through the sand seam that the leak was taking, and cavities were found from 1 to 3 ft deep. This passage was successfully plugged, despite the great flow through it, by the use of a special grout; ordinary cement grout washed out before it could set. The type of grout finally evolved is of interest in view of the frequent necessity of plugging leaks in cofferdam work, and its "prescription" is therefore given in Table 17.2. Four hundred batches of this grout were used to plug the leak described; the grout was pumped through a 7-in. concrete pipeline and forced into the passage under a pressure of 35 psi.[17.32]

Another way in which geological advice can be of appreciable assistance in cofferdam work is in foretelling, with some degree of accuracy, the presence of boulders in the strata through which piles have to be driven. The presence of even one boulder can on occasion cause as much trouble in constructing and pumping out a cofferdam as all the rest of the work put together, as all engineers who have had such an experience will know. Test borings may possibly show the existence of boulders; but unless the boulder formation is closely packed, it is quite probable that the few test borings put down on the actual site of a bridge pier may miss any boulders that may be present. On the other hand, knowledge of the nature of the geological strata to be encountered in foundation work will at least suggest whether or not boulders are to be expected, e.g., as in glacial deposits, in which case extra care must be exercised in the preliminary test-boring work. Foundation records for neighboring works have often been found to be of great value in an application of geological considerations; their value has already been generally stressed but may be specially emphasized for this case.

Some cofferdam construction which encountered unusual difficulties with boulders was an important part of the building of three new bridges across the Cape Cod Canal in Massachusetts in 1934 and 1935. Wash borings had disclosed the existence of glacial deposits of sand and granitic gravel containing numerous granite boulders. Specifications were drawn up calling for foundations to be constructed inside steel sheet-pile cofferdams driven to predetermined depths. What was not known and was revealed only by the foundation operations was the variable amount of boulders, their relatively large size, and their varying distribution. The contractor for the work estimated that 10 per cent of the piling might strike boulders that would have to be removed; actually, as much as 40 per cent of the piling in one cofferdam was so obstructed; and at all the main cofferdams for the three bridges, serious difficulties were encountered. It was found, for example, that the disturbance caused by pile driving and the operations for removing the boulders so disturbed the sand that it went "quick" and thus resulted in large and frequent boils. Ordinary pumping methods failed to keep pace with the flow of water into the cofferdams to facilitate the removal of the boulders; and

Fig. 17.15. Cofferdam for the Bourne south channel pier, Cape Cod Highway Bridges, showing irregular driving of steel sheet piling due to the presence of boulders, some of which may be seen between the tracks and the cofferdam. (*Reproduced by permission of Fay, Spofford and Thorndyke, Consulting Engineers.*)

eventually an extensive well-point installation had to be used both inside and outside the sheeting. The presence of boulders had been revealed during the original construction of the canal 20 years before, but whether or not this earlier construction indicated the presence of boulders in the amount encountered at the bridge piers was a matter of controversy.[17.33]

Cavernous limestone comes up again for mention when attention is directed to an unusual bridge construction job of the Kentucky State Highway Department across the Barren River at Bowling Green; the structure was a four-span continuous-plate girder with each span 110 ft long. The bedrock across the river bed was limestone, extensively honeycombed below its surface for several feet and filled with mud pockets. Up to 10 ft of the cavernous limestone had to be excavated over the sites of the two river piers, constructed within sheet-pile cofferdams. The steel piling could not be driven into the limestone, so pile driving and excavation had to be carried out concurrently. The necessary blasting disturbed the natural sealing of the rock and strong flows of water into the cofferdams commenced. Various expedients were tried in attempts to cut off the water, but eventually very extensive grouting programs had to be carried out; as many as 9,000 bags of cement were used for this purpose around the two relatively small cofferdams.[17.34]

An entirely different sort of ground-water problem was encountered by the Illinois Division of Highways during the construction of a 4,745-ft bridge over the Illinois River at Peoria. The Peoria Water Works Co., a private utility that supplies water in the city, obtains its supplies from wells extending into a sand and gravel stratum, separated from the river bed by layers of clay and shale of varying thickness. Some of the H bearing piles for the main piers supporting the three-span continuous-through bridge over the main channel were designed to pass through this water-bearing stratum; the water company was naturally concerned over the possibility of pollution of its supply. Extensive studies were made, and an unusual schedule was worked out for the control of water level in the cofferdams from which the steel piles were to be driven; the level was held down to river-bed level while pile driving was in progress, and allowed to rise only when pile driving was complete and thick concrete seals had been placed.[17.35]

17.10. Inspection and Maintenance. The regular and thorough inspection of all civil engineering structures is a matter that can hardly be over-emphasized. It is always important but nowhere more so than in such features as bridge piers, the underwater parts of which are not seen from day to day and yet are most prone to periodic damage. In the case of piers and abutments founded on dry land, inspection of the structures and regular checks on their positions and levels are the main requirements of inspection. Should any movement of the pier be detected, and no deterioration of the constituent material be evident, then inevitably some feature of the underlying geological strata is responsible for the trouble; and in consequence, foundation-bed conditions must be investigated anew.

An outstanding example of the benefits to be derived from inspection work is given by the famous Lethbridge Viaduct of the Canadian Pacific Railway, a steel-trestle structure 5,327 ft long carrying track 312 ft high above the bed of the Belly River of Alberta, Canada. The trestle bents were founded on concrete pedestals supported on concrete piles driven into the clay which overlies the whole site. Completed in 1909, the deck of the bridge soon showed signs of settlement; a line of check levels run in 1913 disclosed a subsidence of $2\frac{1}{2}$ in. at pedestal 53 south. Cracks and gopher holes in the clay below were plugged with clay, and drainage arrangements improved, but settlement continued; eventually, the pedestal had to be underpinned by caissons carried to shale rock 50 ft below ground level, and a drainage tunnel had to be constructed; as a result of these measures, subsidence was arrested.[17.36]

Similar vigilance in track maintenance was responsible for the first detection of trouble with one of Robert Maillart's justly famous slender reinforced-concrete bridges in Switzerland. This bridge is located at Klosters, a well-known skiing center near the eastern border. The bridge carries the meter gauge Rhaetian Railway running from a junction with

Fig. 17.16. Lethbridge Viaduct, Canadian Pacific Railway, Alberta Canada, seen from the northwest. (*Reproduced by permission of the Chief Engineer, Canadian Pacific Railway Co.*)

the Swiss Federal Railways at Landquart to Davos and St. Moritz. Built upon a sharp curve, the bridge is characterized by its main arch of 30 m span; its total length is 75m. The arch rests upon mass-concrete abutments; one of these is located on a relatively steep hillside, which the railway tunnel passes through; the portal of the tunnel is close to the end of the bridge. Soon after the bridge was placed in service, one of the track-maintenance men noticed a slight rise in the track at the center of the span; this was corrected in the roadbed formation, but it was soon noticed again. This led to detailed study of the situation and it was then found that the soffit of the arch was slowly rising. In turn, this was traced to a slow but progressive movement toward the river of the hillside abutment. Extensive borings were taken and it was found that the movement was widespread on the sloping ground, since the underlying rock talus was in unstable equilibrium. After much study it was decided that the only possible solution was to brace one abutment against the other,

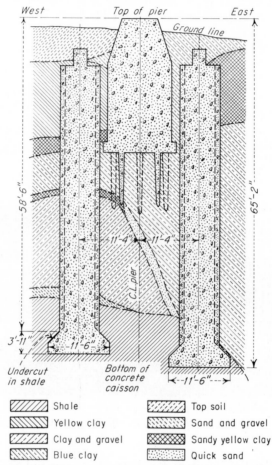

Fɪɢ. 17.17. Pier No. 59S of the Lethbridge Viaduct, Canadian Pacific Railway, Alberta, Canada; a geological section of foundation strata, showing the pier as reconstructed. (*Reproduced by permission of the Chief Engineer, Canadian Pacific Railway Co.*)

even though this would interfere with the general appearance of the bridge. Therefore, a heavily reinforced concrete strut was built across the river at haunch level; the strut was of U section with a width of 2.5 m between the insides of the webs, or walls, as they appear to be to the uninformed visitor. (At the time of the writer's visit, the local villagers were still enjoying to the full the access across the river thus given to them by what some of them took to be a footpath constructed for their special benefit.) Embedded within the strut are strain gauges, regular observations upon which have enabled the responsible engineers to check on the adequacy of their design and, incidentally, to accumulate information, which they are making publicly available, on the magnitude of the pressures developed in this unusual way.[17.37]

Fig. 17.18. Reinforced-concrete bridge at Klosters, Switzerland, carrying the narrow-gauge Rhaetian Railway to Davos and St. Moritz, showing the special reinforced-concrete strut between abutments.

The inspection of piers founded below normal water levels is a more extensive operation, involving underwater work and also the regular sounding of the river bed or watercourse between piers and for some distance on either side of the bridge site. Underwater inspection from a diving suit, although generally a matter for the field inspecting staff, is something that should regularly be undertaken also by the bridge engineering staff. It is not necessary to stress here the value of diving experience to engineers, but the importance to an engineer of being able to see the effect of his bridge structure on river-bed stability is a special feature which may fittingly be mentioned. Examination of the pier structure is a part of underwater work, but equally so is the study of actual bed conditions, especially around the pier bases. This inspection, coupled with soundings over the whole water area adjacent to the bridge, if performed regularly will be a constant check on the dangerous possibility of river-bed scouring. The regular nature of this inspection work must be stressed. Naturally, inspections should be timed in accordance with periodic danger periods, e.g., those caused by regular spring-flood discharges in rivers. They must also be supplemented by special surveys if any new structures are built in a waterway near enough to the existing bridge to affect it even to a slight degree. Interesting records are available of the methods and programs adopted for bridge-inspection work by leading railways. It may perhaps be mentioned that in order to speed up the inspection of bridge piers in shallow water, Canadian National Railways employed on one of its inspection crews an expert high diver who carried out underwater inspection without the use of a cumbersome diving suit. Skin divers are now regularly used for this vital inspection work.

The importance of these and other features of bridge-inspection work is well illustrated by two bridge failures that occurred in the United States in the late summer of 1933, both of which caused loss of life, injuries, and serious damage to stock and structures. The first occurred at the Anacostia River Bridge of the Pennsylvania Railroad near Washington, D.C., a four-span deck plate-girder structure, which, owing to the failure of the center pier, collapsed when a train was passing over it. Subsequent investigation showed that the gravel stratum on which the piers were founded had been seriously eroded; the culmination of the erosion process was probably caused by a tropical storm which was abating when the collapse occurred. The railroad company had no record of soundings or underwater inspection from the time the bridge was built in 1904 until the date of failure, stating that as no settlements or cracks had developed, unsafe conditions underwater had not been indicated. Some dredging had been done downstream after the completion of the bridge, but at the investigation it was stated that, even if this had not affected the river bed at the bridge, "it was the duty of the railroad company to keep informed concerning changes that might have any effect on the safety of the bridge."[17.38]

The second accident, which also occurred in August, 1933, was on the Southern Pacific Line between Hargis and Tucumcari, New Mexico. It, too, was due to unusual floodwaters which undermined the east abutment of the deck plate-girder structure and thus caused the collapse of the bridge as a train was crossing. The Bureau of Safety of the Interstate

Commerce Commission, in its report on the accident, attributed the failure to the fact that the embankment had not been protected against erosion and to heavy rains which had caused excessive floodwater; the position of a highway bridge (constructed 150 ft upstream) had increased the current velocity and probably had diverted it against the railroad-approach embankments.[17.38]

Mention of such illustrative examples prompts the thought that it is always easy to be wise after the event. This cannot be disputed; and yet at the same time, it must be recalled that one of the surest ways of learning constructive methods is to study past mistakes and errors. Bridge inspection can provide information of general value only by records of the discovery of features unsuspected and of serious consequence; and if some of these have been discovered too late, they may still serve as a reminder of the supreme importance of the regular examination by the engineer of the foundation strata in which he places such confidence for the sure and certain support of his bridge structures.

Suggestions for Further Reading

In addition to standard texts on bridge design and the descriptions of individual bridge projects in engineering journals and the records of professional societies, the Proceedings of the International Association for Bridge and Structural Engineering (Office of the Secretary, Care of Ecole Polytechnique, Zurich, Switzerland) provide useful information on the geology of bridge foundations in occasional papers.

Chapter 18

MARINE WORKS

The congeries of rocks called Edystone appear to me to be all of the same kind of stone, and of a kind so peculiar that I have not seen any stone exactly like it in Cornwall or Devonshire. . . . It differs from the Moorstone in this; instead of being composed of grains or small fragments, united by a strong cement, interspersed with a shining talky substance, as the Cornish moorstone appears to be; it is composed of the like matter formed into laminae commonly from one twentieth to one sixth part of an inch in thickness . . . and is nearly one foot dip to the westward, in two feet horizontal, that is, in an angle of about 26 degrees with the horizon.

John Smeaton, Civil Engineer, F.R.S.
(in his account of the building of the
Eddystone Lighthouse, published in
1791)[18.1]

"THE SEA AROUND US" is not only the title of a beautifully written and most interesting book by Rachel Carson but it is also a literal description of the place that the ocean occupies in the life of man.[18.2] When it is remembered that almost three-quarters of the surface of the globe is covered by the sea, the fact that it does surround all the lands on which men live will be the better appreciated, even though it may be difficult to realize this when in mid-continent almost 2,000 miles from the nearest coast line. On the other hand, no resident of the British Isles lives more than 70 miles from the sea; residents of smaller islands frequently see the sea every day of their lives. It was along seacoasts that some of the first human settlements developed in the dawn of history. The first long-distance travel was by sea. For many centuries, ocean and coastal travel was the only means of mass transport. The Mediterranean Sea, in particular, may be regarded in many ways as one of the cradles of human history. Along its shores some of the earliest of man-made harbors were constructed. Some still remain. Others have long since disappeared, vivid reminders that the construction of marine work is always a battle between man and nature, requiring for success a singularly careful appreciation of the natural forces that have to be contended with and knowledge as accurate as is possible of the site conditions and of the local geology.

Sea water has a high salt content, but it is "salt" in a peculiar way; the composition of the solid materials that the sea water contains differs appreciably from the average salt content of the fresh water entering the sea from rivers. The difference is accounted for biologically—the animal life of the sea uses some dissolved salts but not others. The Red Sea is the saltiest part of the ocean; its mineral content reaches 40 parts per thousand. Along the Atlantic Coast of North America the salt content of sea water varies from 33 to 36 parts per thousand; these are typical limits for most of the oceans. The temperature of sea water varies from a low of 28°F in polar seas to a high of 98°F in the Persian Gulf. Only when the temperature of the sea is over 70°F can coral reefs, the most commonly recognized type of marine growth, develop. These remarkable formations, which are the result of the gradual accumulation of the skeletal remains of organisms with a high content of calcium carbonate, are thus generally confined between latitudes 30°S and 30°N.

18.2. The Tide, Waves, and Currents. The movement of the sea is more important to the civil engineer than the specific properties of sea water. Never does one see the ocean at rest. In motion, as at the height of a great storm, it presents one of the most majestic of all natural phenomena. The wind is the chief factor in the formation of waves and currents, but the regular movement of the tides is perhaps the greater determinant in the design and construction of the marine works of the civil engineer. These three types of motion constitute some of the "great forces of nature" that it is the task of the civil engineer to tame, even as down through the ages they have been amongst the more important agencies of physical geology, molding the shape and form of the earth along all its borders on the sea.

Local currents, near harbors and in estuaries, will affect the layout and siting of marine works, but when once determined by hydrographic surveying, they must usually be accepted as a part of the natural order and integrated into design. Wave action, however, is of far more serious consequence. In general, waves are of two types: swell waves and storm waves. Both are generated by the action of the wind on the surface of the sea, the latter more directly than the former. Much study has been given in recent years to the mechanics of wave motion. There are many convenient references, but again the civil engineer will usually be more concerned with the effects of wave action than with its detailed character. Of major importance is the maximum force that is to be expected from wave action at the location of any proposed works. This problem appears to have been first studied by Thomas Stevenson (the father, incidentally, of Robert Louis Stevenson) in connection with the design of harbor works in Scotland. He propounded the first empirical rules for determinating the probable forces of waves, based upon the length of the "fetch" at a particular location—the distance of uninterrupted open sea in the direction of prevailing wind.

Those who have never seen the sea, particularly at the height of a great storm, find it difficult to imagine the force that the sea can exert. Even well-authenticated figures tend to seem unrealistic. As an indication of what waves can be and do it may be noted that, although ocean waves do not normally exceed 25 ft in height in mid-ocean, there is a well-established record of a storm wave in the Pacific with a height of 112 ft.[18.3] The writer has witnessed storm waves in the Atlantic over 50 ft high. Approaching a coast line, waves will naturally be reduced in size, but the potential force of breaking waves is remarkable. One of the stormiest parts of all the oceans is the Pentland Firth, a stretch of water separating the northern coast of Scotland from the Orkney Islands. Close to the eastern end lies the town of Wick with its small harbor, famous in the annals of civil engineering. When its breakwater was destroyed in 1872 there was clear proof that blocks of masonry weighing up to 1,350 (long) tons had been moved intact by the sea. A new pier was constructed, but in 1877 it was also destroyed by a great storm; accurate observations showed that a block of masonry weighing 2,600 (long) tons had been carried away from its original location.[18.4] One of the lighthouses guarding this stormy Scottish coast (at the western end of the Firth) is at Dunnet Head; the windows around the light of this high structure, which stands atop a 300-ft cliff, are frequently broken by stones tossed aloft by storm waves breaking on the coast below. A door near the top of the lighthouse at Unst, the most northerly of the Shetland Islands, 195 ft above the sea, has been broken open at the height of a storm. So the tall but true tales of the force of the sea can be continued. It is small wonder that the design and construction of marine works provide some of the supreme examples of the art of the civil engineer.

The movement of the tide is a natural phenomenon of an entirely different but equally majestic character, involving the simultaneous movement of all the water in the oceans. Under the combined attraction of the moon and the sun, but chiefly the moon, the waters of the oceans tend to move away from the earth; this movement when combined with the rotational movement of the three celestial bodies results in the rhythmical movements known as the tide. Normal tides have a dual cycle of about 24 hr and 50 min (the extra 50 min are most significant for the scheduling of marine-construction operations). As the moon waxes and wanes each lunar month, so do the tides vary from neap (or low) tides, twice a month when the pull of the sun and the moon are opposed, to spring (or high) tides, also twice a month when the two bodies are in line and so pulling together on the waters of the sea. In almost all countries of the world which have tidal coast lines, there are now regularly published tide tables that give particulars of tidal ranges and times for many months ahead; such publications are naturally of vital importance to marine constructors.

With so simple a basic explanation for the movement of the tides, it is surprising to find so great a variation in tidal ranges along the coasts of the world. Possibly the most remarkable variation is that along the coast line of the northeastern part of North America. At Nantucket, near Boston, the range is less than 1 ft. As one goes north into Canada, the

FIG. 18.1. Slipway in the harbor of Saint John, New Brunswick, Canada (on the Bay of Fundy) at high tide. (*Photograph by the New Brunswick Travel Bureau.*)

FIG. 18.2. Slipway in the harbor of Saint John, New Brunswick, Canada (on the Bay of Fundy) at low tide; the same location as shown in Fig. 18.1. (*Photograph by the New Brunswick Travel Bureau.*)

range steadily increases until, in the Bay of Fundy, which separates New Brunswick from Nova Scotia, some of the highest tidal ranges of the world are experienced; on spring tides, they reach a height of 54 ft in Minas Basin. This lovely spot is only about 400 miles from Nantucket. Tides almost as high as the famous Fundy tides have been observed in the Canadian Arctic on the Ungava Coast. Such strange variation as the fact that many coast lines have almost negligible tides, that some locations have only one tide each day instead of two, and that other locations have a tidal period of an even 12 hr can be explained only after meticulous oceanographic study. This is a branch of learning that attracts the interest of many civil engineers, but in the practice of civil engineering what is essential for all marine work is accurate knowledge of local tidal conditions. This is to be obtained directly from published title tables for locations listed in such tables and by interpolation from the tables for other points, always with a check (by means of a correlation of readings from a local tide gauge with those for a listed port) for the location of any new marine works of any magnitude.

There are no tides in the ordinary sense on the large lakes of the world; civil engineering works upon such lakes may properly be called "marine works" even though they are in fresh water. On certain very large shallow lakes, however, mass movements of water occur that may be more troublesome than the tide. These movements are known as *seiches*. Lake Erie, the shallowest of the Great Lakes, is renowned for the seiches that distinguish it. These movements of water, resulting in rapid changes in water level, may be caused by changes in barometric pressure or, more commonly, by changes in the wind. The free water surface is subject to a shearing force as the wind moves over it; the transfer of energy results in water displacement, the magnitude of which depends on the depth of the lake, the wind speed, and the fetch over which it blows. Differences of 13.5 ft have been observed between the levels of the two ends of Lake Erie, at Buffalo and Toledo, with wind "setups" (as they have come to be known) of as much as 8.4 ft in the harbor of Buffalo. The effects upon harbor structures can well be imagined. One indirect result is the development of currents at intermediate points along the lake; the harbor of Conneaut experiences currents as high as 1 ft per sec at its entrance in response to a major seiche.[18.5]

18.3. The Earth beneath the Sea. It is difficult to refrain from using the title of yet another book to describe this short treatment of some features of the geology of the ocean bed of importance to civil engineers in the prosecution of their work. "The Earth beneath the Sea" is the title of a recent volume by F. P. Shepard, one of the leaders in the relatively new study of submarine geology.[18.6] Not only does this title describe a graphically written account of current knowledge of the sea bed and of modern methods of underwater investigation, but it is also a telling reminder that there does exist "solid ground" (for want of a better term) beneath the surface of the sea. To see a stretch of wide beach at low tide, as in the Bay of Fundy, helps one appreciate the fact that the solid crust of the earth is continuous over the entire globe even though large parts of it are shielded from view by the waters of the sea. Since there was little tide around the shores of those countries in which civilization took root, it is not surprising that strange and misleading ideas about the sea bed persisted for so long. Only in the last few decades has even a general impression of the character of the ocean bed been obtained, a statement well supported by the fact that only about 15,000 deep soundings had been taken over the entire globe when echo sounding was introduced on a general scale immediately following the First World War.

The first deep-sea sounding, to a depth of 2,425 fathoms, was obtained by Sir James Clark Ross in 1840 during one of the early voyages of exploration to the Antarctic. He used a weight on the end of a manila line, and this crude method had to suffice until 1870 when Lord Kelvin used piano wire for this purpose, and so extended appreciably the depths that could be plumbed. Prior to this development, fewer than 200 soundings had been made throughout the entire Atlantic area. The 15,000 soundings, already noted as having been taken by mechanical means, represented about one sounding for every 6,000 sq miles of sea; thus it has been only through the medium of indirect depth determinations, notably the use of echo-sounding devices, that a real beginning has been possible at determining the over-all configuration of the bottom of the sea. Immense mountain ranges, correspondingly great "deeps," and gigantic submarine canyons, the dimensions of which surpass any to be seen on dry land, have now been located. The irregularity of the sea bed is well recognized, but perhaps the most unusual underwater physiographic feature of all is the wide extent of the *continental shelf*.

This remarkable area has been defined officially as the "zone around the continents, extending from low-water line to the depth at which there is a marked increase of slope to greater depth"; this outer slope is called the *continental slope*. The average depth to the shelf is 72 fathoms, the greatest depth about 200 fathoms. The widest parts of the shelf are those bordering glaciated lands; the Arctic coasts have the widest examples of all. The average width is about 42 miles; the average slope is about 10 ft to the mile. Vividly demonstrated on all small-scale ocean charts, the continental shelf is clearly of great practical significance to fishermen, to mariners, to those concerned with cable laying, and in relatively recent years, to those in search of petroleum. Civil engineering structures for both oil drilling and defense purposes now stand upon the shelf at selected locations off the American coast. North American lightships are now being replaced by tower-type structures founded on the shelf.

It requires but the most general appreciation of geology to realize that this submarine shelf must bear some relation to geological phenomena of the recent period. Changes in the level of the sea have already been mentioned (see page 221). There is an almost certain connection between such changes and the continental shelf as it exists today. The latest determinations suggest that the level of the sea rose from about 260 ft below present level to possibly 20 ft below it between 17,000 and 6,000 years ago. Movements of the sea level in the last 6,000 years are not so well defined, but it is almost certain that the level is rising today very slowly; there is good evidence to suggest that the level rose about 4 in.

along the Atlantic Coast of the United States between 1930 and 1948. Those who find it difficult to visualize a concept of the changing level of the sea might refer to the many examples of "raised beaches" to be found in all parts of the world; these are vivid evidence of a much higher sea level in the past.[18.7] The reverse process appears to be closely related to the existence of the continental shelf that is today such an important feature of submarine geology. Correspondingly, fragments of peat and artifacts of Stone Age man which have been brought up in nets from the Dogger Bank in the North Sea by fishermen show clearly that this famous fishing ground was once dry land.

Interesting and scientifically significant as such geological considerations are, they are of only indirect importance to the civil engineer, since he works to a different time scale. Explanation of the formation of the shelf, however, is a prerequisite for study of its composition; its surface characteristics, particularly, constitute a matter of real importance for the engineer. Following in the trail of underwater depth determinations has been the start of a study of the sediments that constitute the sea bed. Already it is known, in a general way, that the sediments on the shelf consist predominantly of sand, some mud, and a small percentage of gravel, whereas the percentage of mud is much increased in the deposits on the continental slope. The different types of mud that constitute so much of the deep ocean bottom have already been delineated in a general way; more information about them is steadily being accumulated. They raise some interesting questions, such as why sediments in the Atlantic Ocean reach a depth of 12,000 ft whereas those in the Pacific and Indian Oceans are never more than 1,000 ft deep. The existence of manganese nodules on the sea floor has been known since the time of the pioneer expedition of H.M.S. "Challenger" but their presence is still unexplained. Also unexplained is the fact that no fossils have been found in deep-sea deposits any older than the Cretaceous; this presents most penetrating questions about the age of the oceans.

It was during the "Challenger" expedition that the first advance was made in the study of the nature of the sea bed. It had been traditional for mariners to have a lump of tallow on the underside of their sounding leads, to which samples of bottom sediments would adhere and thus be brought to the surface for study. The scientists of the "Challenger," however, were able to obtain short cores of the material forming the sea bed. The practice of undersea core boring, although fraught with many mechanical difficulties, has steadily progressed since then, and cores up to 10 ft in length can now be obtained from great depths. Study of the sediments so retrieved from the bottom of the ocean is opening up new phases of geological study. Concurrently, there has been steady advance in personal inspections of the sea bottom—first by means of diving equipment, with the most complicated of which depths of 500 ft can be reached by a diver; then with special units, such as William Beebe's bathysphere, with which a depth of 3,028 ft beneath the surface was reached in 1934; and finally by the use of the U.S. Navy's bathyscape, the "Trieste," in which Jacques Picard and Lt. Don Walsh reached a depth of 35,780 ft at the bottom of the "Challenger Deep" on January 23, 1960.[18.8]

Investigations at such great depths are of only academic interest to the civil engineer, but methods of submarine investigation at shallower depths are of great practical importance. The standard diving suit will long remain the chief aid to such personal inspection; depths of about 50 ft can be readily penetrated with only a minimum of training when expert supervision is available, as it must be for all such underwater inspection. The value to the civil engineer of seeing for himself what the geology of the sea bed is at the site of works for which he is responsible is inestimable. On one job the writer was told that the dredging contractor was being hampered by the presence of "boulders as big as cottages." It required only a short survey in a diving suit, once the contractor had recovered from the shock of being asked to permit the writer to use his diving outfit, to see that the expression "cottages" was a poetic exaggeration; the efficacy of the dredging that had been done was, however, similarly demonstrated by this personal inspection. The modern practice of skin diving naturally presents great possibilities for use in connection with the marine work of the civil engineer. The extension of its use can be a significant factor in giving all engineers who are involved in marine work a better appreciation of the physiography and the geology of the earth beneath the sea.

18.4. The Coast of England and Wales. So wide is the range of civil engineering works that come within the general title of marine works and so varied are the coastal conditions with which the engineer has to deal in his practice that it is impossible in a short chapter such as this to do more than touch upon the geological background, aided by reference to a few examples. Even the most carefully selected cases cannot be called typical since there is no such thing as a typical marine civil engineering undertaking; every job has some unique features. Accordingly, to give greater emphasis to this almost bewildering variety and at the same time to demonstrate the results of engineering through the centuries, the reader is invited to glance at one of the most historical and famous coast lines of the world, that of England and Wales; Scotland is omitted only because the most cursory mention of the Scottish coast would require equally lengthy treatment.

Earlier references have demonstrated that there are few, if any, parts of the world where such varied geology is found in so confined an area as Great Britain. This geological showcase is nowhere better on view than around the coast line of the British Isles. Under study for many centuries, the coast has been well documented; the fact that at least two books have been published since the Second World War dealing with the coast line of England and Wales is testimony to its perennial interest.[18.9] In 1911, the third (and final) report of the British Royal Commission on

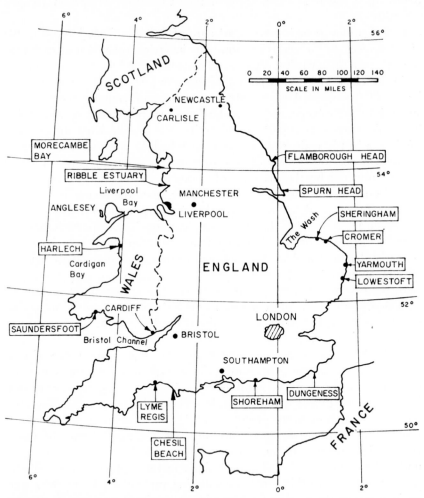

Fig. 18.3. Sketch map of England and Wales, showing some locations mentioned in the text.

Coast-Erosion was published, one of the most notable of all publications in this field and a starting point even today for studies of coastal engineering.[18.10] One of the many historical lessons underlined by this masterly study was that, without the most careful planning and design, engineering works on one stretch of coast may cause serious trouble on adjacent sections, a lesson that has unfortunately had to be learned anew on all too many occasions since the report of the Royal Commission appeared.

Morecambe Bay is a leading feature of the coast line of northwestern England; its present form is the result of ice action and silting from the rivers and streams that flow into it. At low tide, much of the bay consists of fairly level stretches of sand, generally firm but containing some "quick" sections. Since about a 5-hr period is available for the crossing on each tide, the bay has long been used as a convenient roadway at low tide; it was crossed by Robert Bruce and his soldiers in 1322 when they invaded England. In 1837 George Stephenson proposed the construction of a great wall across part of the bay that would have enclosed and reclaimed 40,000 acres, but it was never built. Stage coaches, however, ran regularly across the bay between tides until the Furness Railway was constructed in 1857 along the northern shore of the bay. Cutting across many of the small estuaries leading into the bay, this railway permitted the easy reclamation of about 1,000 acres but it also had the effect of changing the character of the sands in the bay. Although there were many serious accidents, local guides continued to be available for those who wished to make the crossing, and a troop of cavalry succeeded in doing so during the First World War. The Vikings used at least one of the old ports on the bay, but progressive silting has now made them all useless.

The estuary of the river Ribble is the next major feature to the south; it is characterized by thick peat beds, relics of vegetation of an earlier age, and by extensive sand dunes. These have been stabilized to a degree by plants which are not native to Great Britain but which, it has been shown, originated in the sweepings from ships that brought grain from the United States to assist in the rearing of poultry in this area during the First World War. Approaching the great port of Liverpool, one sees evidence of the works of the engineer in a continuing battle with the great sandbanks that distinguish Liverpool Bay; further reference to these works will shortly be made. Turning along the coast of North Wales, one sees the dubious results of running a main road and a main railway line in close juxtaposition to an exposed coast line; the striking coastal scenery as the island of Anglesea is approached leaves no doubt that this engineering location was dictated by geology, but it has led to ceaseless maintenance work along almost all the coast.

Great banks of sand and shingle distinguished much of the northern part of Cardigan Bay. Harlech Castle is but one of the many historical spots on this coast; it was built by King Edward I in 1286. Now more than half a mile from the sea, the castle must almost certainly have been built with access to the sea, but silting and the possible change of the course of a small river have made it difficult to realize this today. "Sarns," unusual causeways, are a feature of this bay somewhat farther to the south; they are related to the legend of the lost land of Cantref-y-Gwaelod, a large area once said to have been utilized for settlement but lost when it was flooded, owing to the neglect of the controlling sluices by a renowned drunkard. Even the best of engineering works cannot withstand such mistreatment.

Leaving the bay and turning into the Bristol Channel, one reaches a most important industrial coast of Britain; ports such as Cardiff and Swansea are but the largest of a series of man-developed natural harbors. One of the ports not now used was at Saundersfoot. There are here the remains of a fine shingle beach, now denuded; it was formed in the nineteenth century by the dumping of stone ballast overboard from the vessels that came to load coal at the little port. One of the new harbors is at Port Talbot; when excavation was in progress here in 1928 a stone was found in an upright position bearing the date 1626; the fact that the stone was 20 ft below the surface provides interesting proof of the sand movement on this coast. Even more remarkable is the history of the church at Penard; built about 1270, church and neighboring castle were inundated by advancing sand in 1528 and remained covered until rediscovered in 1861.

Much of the coast of southwestern England is formed of high rock cliffs which provide a great scenic attraction. Only when the rocks so exposed are of weaker varieties such as marls and sandstones, as near the mouth of the river Exe, is erosion a problem; here the construction of the Great Western Railway right along the coast provided excellent protection, and natural erosion was halted. Further to the east, some of the spectacular landslips that distinguish parts of the south coast of England (see page 427) are to be seen near Lyme Regis. On Christmas night, 1839, a great slip occurred after only a few hours warning and precipitated 8 million tons of rock into the sea; the resulting scar is known today as Dowland's Chasm.

Chesil Beach, one of the unique beaches of the world, leads to the Isle of Portland, famous itself for the building stone that it has so long supplied for southern England. The beach is 18 miles long; for 6 miles it is in contact with the coast, but for the remainder of its length it is separated by a narrow stretch of water known as the Fleet. It is only about 600 ft wide at its maximum, but its most remarkable feature is that the shingle of which it consists is graded consistently from pea size at its northwestern end to coarse gravel size (2 to 3 in. in diameter) at the Portland end. The first, and still notable, scientific paper on this unusual natural phenomenon was presented by Sir John Coode, a leading civil engineer, to the Institution of Civil Engineers in 1852. The force of the sea was well illustrated by his statement that, after the great onshore storm of 1852, the slope of the entire beach was flattened from 1 to $3\frac{1}{2}$ or 4 units (during offshore winds) to 1 to 9 or $9\frac{1}{2}$ units.[18.11]

The harbor works at Shoreham, farther to the east, provide a classical example of the development of harbor engineering throughout 10 centuries; Shoreham was a fishing port in Norman times, and its harbor was reconstructed as recently as 1955. Protective works have had to be changed and extended almost regularly throughout the centuries, and their design has always been aided by the long-term records of actual experience accumulated through the years.[18.12] Dungeness, still farther to the east, is the largest shingle foreland in Great Britain; the accompany-

Fig. 18.4. An aerial view of Dungeness on the south coast of England, showing the trend of the shingle ridges. (*Photograph by J. K. St. Joseph. Crown Copyright Reserved. Reproduced by permission of the British Air Ministry and the Committee for Aerial Photography, University of Cambridge.*)

ing photograph speaks for itself in showing the progressive stages of the formation of this great accumulation of shingle that started, almost certainly, in Neolithic times. Ninety-eight per cent of the shingle in Dungeness is flint; its seaward growth has averaged about 16 ft a year throughout the last 4 centuries.

Passing by the white cliffs of Dover (see page 437) and turning up the east coast, one finds that East Anglia is generally low lying and that coastal erosion is a major problem. It is now known that the direction of littoral drift changes at or near Sheringham; this will be mentioned again shortly. Erosion is no new thing on this coast; records exist showing that it had become so serious as early as 1391 in the vicinity of the modern town of Cromer that a jetty had to be built for the protection of the local fishing boats. This did not stop the erosion, and protective works have been necessary ever since. William Smith was consulted on the problem, as were many noted British civil engineers of the nineteenth century; the records of their studies and works constitute one of the most valuable repositories of practical experience in the annals of civil engineering. Control of the tidal marshes, which are a dominant feature of parts of the coast, has long been a matter for debate; an official commission reported upon them as early as 1846. Many years before this, John Smeaton (often referred to as the first civil engineer) had made a careful analysis of the development of the marshes and their drainage; his explanation has a modern ring to it today, almost two centuries later.

Moving northward, noting in passing that the "twin" ports of Yarmouth and Lowestoft provide an excellent example of the interaction of marine works at one location upon the stability of the adjacent coast, one is reminded by the great inlet from the sea known as The Wash that around much of the southeastern part of the British coast, and notably here, there are clear evidences of Roman engineering works. A fascinating field for archaeological study, these Roman works are a salutary reminder to civil engineers of today that they follow in a tradition many centuries old. Immediately north of the estuary of the Humber, between Spurn Head and Flamborough Head, there is what is perhaps the most famous example in the world of an eroding coast line. The coast consists mainly of boulder clay in cliffs that reach 100 ft in height. Despite this, the entire stretch of coast south of the resort town of Bridlington has been eroding steadily since Roman times, with a general average loss of almost 6 ft per year. It has been estimated that the equivalent of a strip of land 2½ miles wide along this entire coast has been washed into the sea since the Romans left England. "The Lost Towns of the Yorkshire Coast" is the melancholy title of a volume that presents a detailed review of this extreme case of coastal erosion.[18.13] The material so eroded accumulates at Spurn Head where it provides the inverse problem of steady extension of this headland at a rate of about 40 ft per year; this land growth has already necessitated many moves of the lighthouse that stands on the point guarding the entrance to the Humber.

The instability of this section of coast was well shown by the attempt in the late nineteenth century to construct a new dock at Sutton Bridge, a venture in which the Great Northern Railway had a substantial financial interest, since it would have provided a most convenient port connection for that important rail line. The dock was completed and opened with due ceremony on May 14, 1881, but it was discovered on the very next day that leakage was taking place from the entrance lock. A thorough inspection of the site was made, and expert advice taken, but the consensus was that the site was so unsuitable that reconstruction was impossible. It is said that the only ship which entered the dock on its one day of operation brought a load of timber from Norway and sailed the next day with a cargo of coal. The entire project was abandoned. The Sutton Bridge golf course now occupies the site; a side of the abandoned dock forms one of the bunkers for the course. It is not unreasonable to imagine that consultation with a Roman engineer who worked at this location many centuries before might have obviated one of the few really complete failures in the history of modern civil engineering.[18.14]

18.5. Docks and Harbors. Dock and harbor engineering has always been a leading branch of civil engineering; its history goes back to the very earliest of all civil engineering works. Because of the inevitable interference with natural processes caused by dock construction and the natural lack of knowledge of such processes on the part of early constructors, many ancient harbors, although initially successful, eventually proved unsuccessful for reasons that can only be classed as geological. One of the most famous of all ancient ports was that at Tyre, a city often mentioned in the Bible, second port of the Phoenician empire; it was founded on an island and included two harbors protected by rock-fill breakwaters. In 332 B.C., Alexander the Great destroyed the city after building a solid causeway to the island. This interfered with the local movement of coastal sand, and the channel soon filled up; the site of Tyre is now on a peninsula. The great Roman harbor of Ostia, having marine structures which even today command respect, finally was silted up by sediment brought down by the Tiber despite the ingenuity of the Roman engineers in designing structures to offset this sedimentation; its site is now $1\frac{1}{2}$ miles from the sea.[18.15] Throughout the intervening 2,000 years, engineers have had to wage ceaseless effort in overcoming similar difficulties. If today the abandonment of a harbor is almost unheard of, this indicates no modification of the action of natural processes along seacoasts but only the availability of dredging equipment and other devices capable of dealing with the great volume of sediment carried to sea by rivers or moved along the coast by the sea.

Modern dock and harbor practice has included some of the most notable civil engineering works of recent years. The extensive dock system of Liverpool, England; the steady development of the port of New York; and the many and varied engineering works in the gulf and tidal portion of the St. Lawrence, Canada—these and many similar developments testify to the magnitude of dock and harbor works. Geological features affect all construction of this kind to some degree, although usually in one or more of the ways described in the other chapters of this book. Thus a notable underwater geophysical survey was carried out in the harbor of Algiers, using an electrical method, in order to obtain information on the position of a rock surface covered by superficial deposits.[18.16] For the construction of the rock-fill breakwater at the new harbor of Haifa, Israel, a large quarry had to be opened up—a striking reminder of the similar construction methods adopted at the adjacent harbors, Tyre and Alexandria, over 2,000 years before.[18,17]

The ports on both sides of the English Channel form a particularly interesting group of harbors, catering for one of the busiest international exchanges of traffic to be found anywhere. The long-discussed channel tunnel will have, as its main objective, the improvement of this cross-channel traffic. One of the major reports upon this tunnel project was completed in 1930, but the British government decided, shortly there-after, not to proceed with the project, not for technical reasons but be-cause of national policy. The Southern Railway Company of England thereupon decided to proceed with a train-ferry scheme connecting Dover with the other side of the channel. The ferry terminal at Dover was designed as an enclosed and watertight dock in which the train-ferry vessels could berth at all stages of the 25-ft tide, the water level being raised or lowered by pumps to the berthing level. The geological forma-tion of the sea bed at the site consists of the Lower Chalk Measures. Work and borings previously carried out in the vicinity and the ex-istence of the underwater headings for the proposed tunnel which were within a distance of a few hundred yards and which had been practically dry for 50 years suggested that the chalk would be of a solid and homo-geneous nature. It was therefore proposed that the work should be car-ried out in the dry within a cofferdam constructed of steel piling driven into the chalk.

This did not prove possible, as the hardness of the chalk limited the penetration of the piles, but a slight modification of the design per-mitted the work to go ahead. When pumping of the enclosed area was started, it was "found that, although a head of from 10 to 20 feet could be sustained, the difference in pressure . . . caused an inflow of water through the sea-bed in the immediate vicinity of the works greater than the pumps could discharge." Usual methods of sealing were tried, but all proved unsuccessful. Small bags filled with permanganate of potash were placed by divers in fissures in the sea bed outside the cofferdam, and the color showed up all over the enclosed area. Further consideration showed that increased pumping might enlarge the fissures and make matters worse. Special methods such as the use of freezing were contemplated, but eventually the entire project had to be carried out in the wet instead of in the dry; the placing of large quantities of underwater concrete proved to be a notable construction operation. Various explanations of the unusual state of the chalk were advanced, the most interesting of which was that the chalk encountered consisted not of solid chalk but of ancient rockfalls from adjacent chalk cliffs, consolidated by the passage above it, over a long period of time, of the littoral drift of gravel for which the adjacent coast is noted. A drill hole put down some miles away

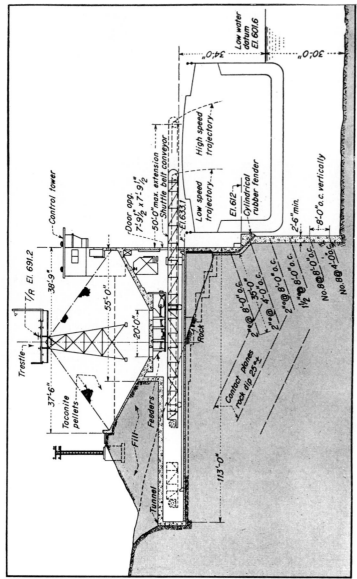

Fig. 18.5. Section through the main wharf of Taconite Harbor, Lake Superior, U.S.A., showing the use of rock anchors. (*Reproduced by permission of The Editor, Engineering News-Record.*)

for the construction of the Beachy Head Lighthouse showed solid chalk, although similar difficulties were encountered during construction.[18.18]

The construction of the Dover ferry terminal was one of the most difficult marine undertakings of recent years. Almost at the other extreme, from the geological point of view, was the building between 1953 and 1956 of a port on the Great Lakes to serve a new taconite (low-grade iron ore) mining development. (Civil engineering works on major lakes of the world, particularly on the Great Lakes, are marine works in every

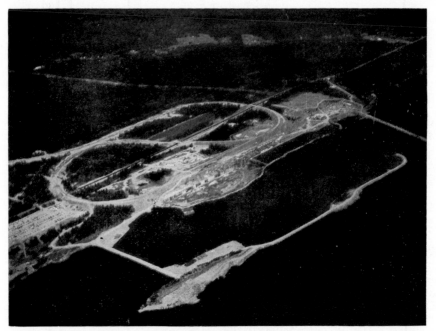

Fig. 18.6. An aerial view of Taconite Harbor, Lake Superior, U.S.A., showing the breakwater formed by two offshore islands. (*Reproduced by permission of the Erie Mining Company.*)

sense except that the water to be built in is fresh and not salt.) Taconite Harbor is located on the northern shore of Lake Superior, 80 miles northeast of Duluth and 75 miles due east of the new taconite plant at Hoyt Lake. Two islands were conveniently located in the lake at this point, about 1,500 ft offshore. When the islands were connected and extended, it was possible to construct a large enough breakwater to give complete protection to the area planned for the loading facilities. The local bedrock is a fairly good amygdaloidal basalt, laid down in successive surface flows, with a strike parallel to the shore line and a dip of about 25° toward the lake. After careful study it was decided to take advantage of this favorable geological formation and excavate the rock to the shape required for the finished wharf, covering the excavated rock face with a relatively thin wall of reinforced concrete after anchoring the rock with long steel dowels against possible movement on the dip toward the lake. Figure 18.5 shows the finished cross section, and Fig. 18.6 is an aerial view of the work under construction; the rock excavation was carried out within the area enclosed by a cellular cofferdam. Almost 1 million cu yd of rock was removed, excavation starting with line drilling at 1-ft centers. Some evidence of contact planes was noticed as rock was removed from the vertical face; some of the planes were water bearing, and some contained fragmented material. Extensive grouting was carried out both before and after excavation, and all anchor rods (the arrangement of which was designed after detailed geological study) were carefully grouted into place.[18.19]

It is only very infrequently that local rock conditions can be adapted for harbor design so effectively as at Taconite Harbor, but it is similarly only seldom that a harbor has to be developed from scratch, so to speak, without taking advantage of some natural feature that requires only modification to form the harbor desired. Most of the major harbors of the world have developed from the initial use of a natural harbor. Some of the most famous—such as Sydney Harbor in Australia, that of St. John's, Newfoundland, the shelter provided by San Francisco Bay, and the dock facilities of London and New York, which are supreme examples—these and many other harbors seem to fit quite naturally into "shelter provided by nature." This old expression is really another way of saying "because of local geological conditions." A study of the geological factors responsible for major American harbors was published (by the United States Geological Survey) as early as 1893.[18.20] In most cases, it has been the flooding of land by the rise of the sea (see page 689) that has led to the natural sea-filled depressions that today form such splendid harbors as those mentioned and many other world-wide ports.

There is probably only one harbor in the world that engineers formed by imitating nature in this way, i.e., by flooding a natural depression that could thus be connected to the sea. This unique example is in the Mediterranean, on the north coast of the little island of Ischia (described by Ludwig Bemelmans as his "Cinderella Island"), lying immediately to the west of Naples. Porto d'Ischia is today one of the safest harbors on the Gulf of Naples, but until the 1850s it was a landlocked crater lake, separated from the sea by a narrow neck of land. Italian engineers spent two years excavating an opening through this neck. The resulting harbor is seen in all its beauty in Fig. 18.7, filled as usual with the colored sails of local boats carrying cargoes of wine, fruit, and vegetables.[18.21] In this case, it required relatively little work to convert a natural feature into a perfect harbor, but usually major civil engineering work is necessary to form a new harbor. Possibly the greatest challenge to the civil engineer engaged in dock and harbor engineering comes when natural conditions do not provide all the shelter needed, and protective works, such as breakwaters, have to be constructed almost in defiance of the elements.

18.6. Breakwaters. From the very earliest times attempts have been made to develop harbors of refuge by the construction of protective breakwaters in locations that provide no natural shelter for shipping. One of the very earliest examples of the potential dangers in this branch of

Fig. 18.7. The beautiful harbor of Ischia in the Gulf of Naples, Italy, showing the artificially formed entrance. (*Photograph by Ente Provinciale per il Turismo di Napoli.*)

civil engineering is provided by the history of port works in the Gulf of Ephesus. Strabo has recorded the history of this early harbor construction, going back for·many centuries B.C. Under King Attalus Philadelphius of Pergamon, engineers constructed a breakwater across the end of the gulf in an attempt to provide a protected harbor, but the breakwater interfered with the natural channel and accelerated silting so greatly that the main objective of the work was not achieved. Many years later, Roman engineers attempted to rectify the mistake, but it was too late and the natural harbor was ruined. Today, it is difficult to imagine that the sea once extended 15 miles into the Gulf of Ephesus.[18.22] Similar examples, extending in time throughout the intervening 3,000 years, could be quoted, but all would demonstrate that in the construction of breakwaters the greatest possible care must be taken to investigate fully all possible interference with natural geological conditions *before* construction is started. As recently as 1939, a small breakwater was constructed at Redonda Beach, California, that soon revealed itself to be a serious impediment to the natural littoral drift along the adjacent stretch of coast, and expensive remedial measures have been necessary since that time. This is but one example of many that could be cited, all of which would give solid support to the suggestion of J. B. Schijf, a leading Netherlands coastal engineer, that in all coastal engineering one should *"Be sure to put off to tomorrow what you do not absolutely have to do today."*[18.23]

This is a cryptic way of pointing out that in the design and construction of breakwaters, unusually careful preliminary study *must* be made of all phases of the local geology, static and dynamic, before designs are finalized and construction begins. Not only must the sea bed be investigated fully with respect to its stability, bearing capacity, and ease of removal if dredging is involved, but the adjacent stretches of coast must be studied in order to determine local currents, littoral drifts, and any features that may in any way be affected by the proposed structure. This is a procedure that can take years, even for a small harbor. The writer has published a summary account of one such investigation for which he was responsible at Forestville in the Gulf of St. Lawrence. The investigation was for an initial harbor development on a small scale (although since greatly enlarged); despite this, the preliminary field studies extended over a period of more than 2 years. Methods of investigation are but little different from those treated generally in Chap. 6; the added difficulty of working in tidal waters is often the main variation.[18.24]

The associated problems of coastal erosion and littoral drift are so important that they call for special mention in the sections that follow. The character of the sea bed at the site of proposed breakwaters does not usually present unusual problems; the action of the sea itself generally results in satisfactory bed conditions, at least in relatively shallow water, although these must always be carefully investigated. The main problem of design is to ensure stability against the anticipated action of the waves that will strike the proposed structure. With modern knowledge of wave mechanics, the availability of model studies as a guide to design, and the abundance of meteorological records now on hand for most coastal regions where construction may be anticipated, design is today rather more determinate than it was in the early years of modern civil engineering practice. Often, however, the old empirical design rules still have their use.

The provision of large blocks of suitable rock is usually a major construction problem, which frequently leads to quarrying operations on a large scale; this work also calls for full and careful preliminary geological investigation. Where no suitable rock is economically available, structures of mass concrete may have to be used, leading to critical structural design requirements. Alternatively, artificial "rocks" may be used such as the patented "tetrapods," successfully developed in the first instance by French engineers for use at harbors in North Africa, but now used in such widely spaced locations as Kahului Harbor on the Hawaiian island of Maui, at Crescent City, California, and at another Pacific Coast location shortly to be mentioned. Still another alternative for locations where rocks of only limited size can be obtained is to construct the breakwater to the usual mound form with grout pipes embedded in it. Through these,

Fig. 18.8. Start of the construction of a breakwater in the Gulf of St. Lawrence, at Forestville, Quebec, Canada.

special cement grout can be forced as soon as the rock is stabilized, thus reversing the usual procedure of fragmenting large masses of rock into smaller pieces for handling by recementing small pieces into a solid mass of artificial conglomerate large enough to withstand all anticipated seas. This procedure was successfully followed at the small Quebec harbor of Forestville already mentioned.

Geological processes have to be remembered and kept ceaselessly under observation throughout construction and long afterward in all breakwater work, as the records of civil engineering make clear. One of the largest and most important "artificial" harbors formed by large breakwaters is that at Valparaiso in Chile, South America. The base for one of the main breakwater extensions here was formed by depositing sand from dredgers in water up to 160 ft deep onto a sea bed consisting of black clayey silt. Slides of the deposited material occurred owing to deformation of the entire sea bed in the vicinity of the work, and over 50 per cent of the material deposited was "lost" as compared to theoretical quantities. It was found, during deposition of the sand, that everything of a light character —"shells, mud and things of that sort"—was washed out of it; the sand that reached the bottom was so dense that an anchor fluke would not enter it; this provides an interesting example of the principles of sedimentation in operation on a major scale.[18.25]

Fig. 18.9. The Eddystone Lighthouse in the English Channel, off Plymouth, England; the "stump" of John Smeaton's pioneer structure of 1759 may be seen on the right. (*Photograph by Kemsley Picture Service.*)

18.7. Offshore Structures. Even more hazardous than the construction of breakwaters is the building of marine structures in the sea at some distance from shore. Lighthouses come immediately to mind, as the most common type of offshore structure. All who have sailed the seas will be familiar with some well-known "light" in its isolation on a hidden shoal or rocky islet, a mere glance at which will show how dependent is the stability of the structure upon the geology of the location it has been built to indicate. The Pharos of Alexandria, built by Sustratus of Cnidus in the reign of Ptolemy II between 283 and 247 b.c., was probably the most famous of all early lighthouses. Built on a small island near the mouth of the Nile, it served until demolished by an earthquake in the thirteenth century. Of lighthouses in use today, that at Cordonan, near the mouth of the Gironde River in the Bay of Biscay, is the oldest. The first light at this location was constructed as early as 805 A.D., the second by the Black Prince; the present structure was built between 1584 and 1611. With more recent additions it is now 207 ft high. (It is of some interest to note that the light it showed was produced until the eighteenth century by a fire of oak logs; a coal fire was used for many years after that; this is a reminder of the relative youth of modern technology such as is now used in illumination.)

Possibly the most famous of all lighthouses is that guarding the Eddystone Rocks, 14 miles off the coast near Plymouth, England, a landmark (seamark?) in the English Channel familiar to all who have sailed up this historic seaway. The first light on the rocks was a timber structure built between 1695 and 1698 by Henry Winstanley but tragically washed away by a great storm in 1705. It was replaced by "Rudyard's Tower," built of oak but destroyed by fire in 1755. Then John Smeaton undertook one of his outstanding works, the construction of the first stone Eddystone Lighthouse, one of the truly pioneer structures of civil engineering. Not only did Smeaton study the geology of the rock upon which he had to build, and of the quarry from which he obtained his finished masonry, but he also studied carefully the records of Roman civil engineering. He followed Roman practice in the use of wooden wedges to fasten together the dovetails by which he interconnected each course of masonry and, possibly of more significance, in the use of pozzolan cement. Smeaton actually sent to Italy for the ingredients of the cement so that he could be sure he was using the material so well proved by the Romans. Started in 1756, the tower was first lit in 1759; it served continually until 1882 when it, in turn, was replaced by the structure to be seen today. This was built by J. N. Douglas and is located 120 ft south-southeast of Smeaton's tower; one reason for constructing the new tower was that Smeaton's had been undermined somewhat by the sea.[18.26]

The story of almost every lighthouse, certainly those located offshore, has its geological interest. Even those founded on sand shoals instead of on bedrock are of interest. Perhaps the most famous of these guards the entrance to the river Weser in Germany; it was built between 1881 and 1885 and exemplifies one of the first uses of iron caissons. Studies of the sea bed suggested the necessary use of a mattress covered by loose rock rubble in order to eliminate dangers of possible erosion; the sand within the caisson was removed by pumping and replaced with concrete. Fortunately, there are available interesting records of lighthouse building, study of which is a very sobering experience for all who are to be concerned with marine construction. There are many illustrative cases, but attention will be directed to an offshore structure which is a lighthouse in a very modern sense. The same natural forces had to be withstood, but new techniques made the preliminary studies for the Texas Towers rather more certain than they could possibly have been for any offshore construction until very recent years.

Off the east coast of North America now stand two steel structures, each with twin decks, triangular in plan, equipped for the safe and comfortable living of eighty men who man them in order to operate the radar installations which they support. Constructed between 1955 and 1957, the Texas Towers were designed only after a most thorough investigation of the rather scanty information then available concerning maximum wind and wave conditions in the open ocean. The towers were designed for the forces of 60-ft waves, but the platforms were set at a height to clear the crests of 90-ft waves. They were designed for depths of water from 55 to 180 ft (a reminder of the existence of the continental shelf, even as far off shore as the George's Bank Tower about 100 miles from the nearest land). To investigate the sea bed at the selected locations, borings were put down from a patented barge arrangement, spudded to the sea bed—an arrangement which was workable for water depths up to 80 ft. Soil conditions were determined to depths of 150 ft beneath the sea floor. Generally, about ten ft of loose sand was found underlain by compact sand as far as the borings went, but borings at two locations encountered strata of medium to stiff clay interbedded with the sand at depths of 60 to 80 ft below ocean bottom. Towers were not placed at locations where clay was encountered. At a possible location on Brown's Bank, off the southern tip of Nova Scotia, the water depth of 140 ft made boring impracticable. The sea floor was investigated, therefore, by means of underwater photography, undertaken by the Woods Hole Oceanographic Institute; this technique showed that the surface of the ocean bottom consisted of sand and gravel with boulders up to 4 ft in diameter. Design and construction of the Towers was a masterly piece of modern civil engineering. From them, for the first time, measurements of ocean storm waves from a fixed point of reference have been possible, and valuable oceanographic data have been obtained. Their service amid the storms of the western Atlantic is another reminder of the value of complete preliminary site investigation.[18.27]

On the other side of North America, off the Pacific Coast of the United States between Santa Barbara and Ventura, there now stands one of the very few man-made islands of any magnitude that have been constructed in the open ocean. Rincon Island was constructed for the Richfield Oil Corporation as an alternative to an open tower of the type just described, other examples of which have been built in the Gulf of Mexico for supporting oil-drilling rigs. The island will permit the owner-company to explore, with modern "slant" drilling techniques, a large proportion of an offshore oil lease granted to it by the state of California. At the island site, water varies from 41 to 48 ft in depth. Extensive site investigation, carried out by a variety of methods, revealed that the bottom consisted of a silty sand grading into sandy silt, increasing in thickness with increasing depth of water varying at the island site from 14 to 25 ft. Slope of the ocean floor was found to be 3 per cent. Recent shale or silt stone underlies the sediment. Sand movement on the sea floor at the site was found to be negligible; thus, the construction of a solid island structure was a feasible proposition. The completed island has an area of 6.3 acres on the ocean bed, with a working area of 1.1 acres out

Fig. 18.10. One of the Texas Towers used in coastal waters off the east coast of North America as described in the text. (Photograph by Long Lines Div., A. T. and T. Co. Reproduced by permission of Moran, Proctor, Mueser and Rutledge, and Anderson–Nichols and Co., Design Engineers to the U.S. Air Force.)

of a total area at elevation 16 of 2.2 acres. The island was formed by means of rock embankments enclosing sand fill; the rock faces are protected from the action of the sea by 1,130 tetrapods having a total weight of 35,000 tons. Rock was obtained from a quarry on Santa Cruz Island, previously used for the construction of the Santa Barbara breakwater; it is Eocene sandstone of the Cold Water formation. It proved to be variable as quarried, but a satisfactory supply was obtained that passed all requisite tests. The island was completed in less than 2 years in 1957 and 1958.[18.28]

18.8. Coastal Erosion. There can be few engineers who are not familiar with a stretch of coast on ocean, lake, or inland sea that is being eroded at a rate noticeable in the course of a few years or possibly months. Although sandspits and bars give some evidence of corresponding accretion, the balance always appears to be against the land in this constant battle with the sea. Rock-bound coasts and cliffs are similarly affected, although their increased resistance as compared with that of unconsolidated beach deposits usually renders erosion on rocky shore lines of

Fig. 18.11. Rincon Island, man-made for the support of oil-exploration installations, off the coast of California, U.S.A. (*Reproduced by permission of Richfield Oil Corporation.*)

small consequence. This relative unimportance is emphasized by the fact that coast lines distinguished by continuous rock outcrops are not so favorably placed for development, either for pleasure or for commerce, as are coast lines formed of unconsolidated material. Although the process of erosion is similar for all types of shore and although the erosion of rock cliffs often presents geological features of unusual interest, attention will be devoted more particularly to the erosion of low-lying coastal lands.

Despite the fact that the erosion of coast lines is a part of the natural geological cycle, the protection of coast lines against erosion has become a world-wide problem. Steady increase in land values, development of large industrial estates on coastal lands, the natural desire of home owners to have building sites "near the water"—these and other factors make the problem of steadily increasing economic importance every year. All around the coasts of Great Britain are to be seen substantial coastal-protection works. The same picture is developing on many North American coasts; American concern is indicated by the existence of the Beach Erosion Board as a special agency of the American government. In Japan, with its long coast line of 16,214 miles for a land area of only 142,338 sq miles, the problem is equally serious. From Australia, South America, India, and from many other lands come reports of engineering studies of how to protect valuable coastal lands from the erosive force of the waters of the sea or of great lakes.

Even the crudest estimate of the cost of coastal-protection works would be so astronomical as to defy belief. The following are typical figures for individual projects: $26 million for works on the coast of Long Island, $1.5 million to protect merely about 2,000 ft of the tracks of the Pere Marquette Railroad along the shore of Lake Michigan, $250,000 for studies alone to investigate what Rio de Janeiro should do to preserve its beaches. Such figures could be duplicated hundreds of times over and would still fail to indicate the full magnitude of this branch of civil engineering work that depends so completely upon a full appreciation of the geological conditions of the coast that has to be protected.

To those unfamiliar with the shore lines of inland lakes, the fact that coastal erosion is also a serious problem on lake shores may be surprising. The natural forces that have to be contended with, however, are just the same as those along the seacoast. In the case of the Great Lakes, storm damage can equal that on many of the seacoasts of the world. Because of the intensive industrial and residential development around the shores of Lakes Ontario, Erie, Huron, and Michigan, coastal erosion on these lakes is probably as serious today as anywhere in the world. Intensive studies are in progress by American and Canadian agencies, designed to limit the damage to the (literally) billions of dollars worth of property fronting on these lakes. It has been estimated that the loss of land and of property on the Lake Erie shore in the state of Ohio alone, during a period of merely 20 years, amounted to almost $9 million. All that is involved in this major branch of remedial civil engineering work is one of the simplest of geological processes, but exercised on a grand scale.[18.29]

The erosive action of pounding waves and swirling water is always obvious, so that the cause of coastal erosion need not be discussed in detail. Generally, it may be said that the essentials of the action are now understood, since the direct hydrodynamic forces exerted by waves have been successfully measured and the erosive effect of eddies is at least generally appreciated. When the nature of a beach is such that waves carry with them sand or gravel in suspension, the resulting intensified action in eroding the standing beach will readily be appreciated. Wave action is only one factor in erosion; the determining factor is the geological formation of the coast line exposed to wave action. On rock-bound coasts characterized by regular strata of appreciable thickness, erosion will generally be uniform. When strata of varying types are exposed having differing resistance to abrasion and solution, differential erosion will result, often with somewhat fantastic effects, such as the formation

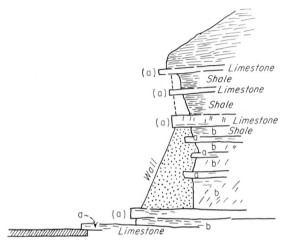

Fig. 18.12. Simplified geological section of the sea cliff at Lyme Regis, England, showing protection wall constructed to halt erosion. (*Reproduced from "Sixty Three Years of Engineering" by Sir Francis Fox by permission of the publisher, John Murray, London.*)

of "natural arches." Only when erosion threatens a stretch of rocky coast that has been developed right up to the edge of cliffs is the civil engineer called upon to exercise his skill and ingenuity. The cause of erosion will usually be obvious after even a preliminary survey, but only provided that this has been made with due regard to the geological formation of the coast line.

A section similar to that shown in Fig. 18.12 might be found in many places. The section is through a small cliff close to the famous old church of Lyme Regis in Dorset, England. The sketch is based on one included in "Sixty Three Years of Engineering," an entertaining volume of reminiscences by Sir Francis Fox, who carried out the necessary remedial works. The alternating layers of shale, being much softer than the limestone beds, were easily eroded by the sea waves, and the alternate limestone beds were left overhanging. When the overhanging became too great, a fracture of the limestone bed resulted, and renewed erosion of the shale took place. Other forces at work in completing the disintegration were the action of heavy seas, which lifted the projecting layers of limestone and so loosened them from their beds, and slips in the upper layers of unconsolidated materials due to seepage of ground water along the face of the receding cliff. The remedy successfully adopted was the construction of a continuous wall protecting the underlying layers of shale from further erosion and thus stabilizing the entire cliff face.

Shores consisting of unconsolidated material can rarely be regarded as stable; even prevailing winds sometimes affect their stability. If any development work is to be carried out adjacent to the high-water line on such beaches, consideration of general beach conditions is essential. Protection walls will be a frequent recourse, especially if the works are to project below the high-water mark. Foundation-bed conditions for these retaining structures must be given unusual attention. Scour at the foot of protection walls will always be a possibility to be seriously considered; allowance must be made for every change in beach regime that can be visualized. Cutoff walls of steel sheet piling below reinforced-concrete superstructures provide a convenient and effective method of construction, ensuring protection against scouring. Provided that the wall structure does not encroach far below high-water mark, the existence of this wall should not affect the stability of the beach. If a bulkhead wall has to be constructed either within the tidal range on the beach or below the low-water line, then study must be made of the possible consequences of construction.

This leads to the study of beach formation—an extensive branch of physical geology and a perennial subject for debate among engineers responsible for coastal works. Of necessity, study must be largely empirical, since local conditions are of unusual significance. In general, two leading types of coast lines may be recognized: the shore line of emergence and the shore line of submergence, the names being descriptive. The first is the result of a gradual uplift of the sea bed; the floor of the sea emerges to form a flat coastal plain consisting of unconsolidated deposits. Wave action will then erode the edge of the emergent land mass, carrying this away from the water line to form an offshore barrier beach which will gradually work nearer to the original shore line until ultimately the two will merge.

Shore lines of submergence are the result of a gradual depression of a coast line; the original coastal area is submerged beneath the sea, which will thus stretch far inland and be in contact with an eroded land surface. The initial characteristic is extreme irregularity of outline; features such as fiords and deep bays are indicative of submerged valleys. Erosion by the sea will continue, and its first effect will be a tendency to straighten the shore line, a process in which strata that are harder than the surrounding beds will offer greater resistance and consequently give rise to special features such as stacks, arches, and small offshore islands. The products of erosion will be rapidly washed into deep water in initial stages of development, but eventually a small beach will form at the foot of the cliffs. If littoral currents exist, they will tend to sweep these beach deposits along the coast past headlands to be deposited in the deeper water of bays, forming what are, in effect, submarine embankments. With continued action, these formations will reach water level; they become spits or hooks and in some cases are of so great an extent that they almost completely block a whole bay. Eventually, a submergent shore line will lose its irregularities and acquire a beach formation. After this has reached equilibrium its development will be identical with that of a shore line of emergence. When a shore line has reached this stage of stability, erosion

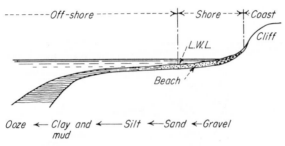

Fig. 18.13. Diagrammatic section of a developed shore.

of the coast or cliff will tend to proceed regularly. Movement of the eroded materials will be caused by currents and waves; the general tendency will be for the finer material to be carried into deeper water and for the coarser material to form the main beach deposit. The nature of beaches may vary considerably from place to place; but as a general rule, gravels will be found within 1 mile from shore in depths of not more than 30 ft of water; sand rarely extends beyond a depth of 300 ft. Figure 18.13 illustrates diagrammatically an ideal beach formation which has become reasonably stable. Studies have shown that the size of sand grains or gravel is related to the slope of a beach—the larger the sand grain the steeper the slope.

The shores of the Great Lakes provide striking examples of coastal features, some classical in form. Two of the most notable are the *compound recurved spits* that provide the harbors of Toronto, Ontario, and of Erie, Pennsylvania. They are shown in outline form in Fig. 18.14. It requires but little imagination to visualize that these two major projections from the normal lake shore have been caused by the interaction of movement of material along the shore (but in opposite directions in the two cases) and the flow from a river, deflecting this material away from its mouth. Nature has thus provided two of the finest harbors on the Great Lakes, although much work has had to be done to maintain and develop them, especially at Presque Isle (a most descriptive name). At Toronto, the eastern entrance was artificially formed; it has to be maintained by dredging. Knowledge of the drift coming from the Scarborough Cliffs to the east was put to good effect by a contractor for one

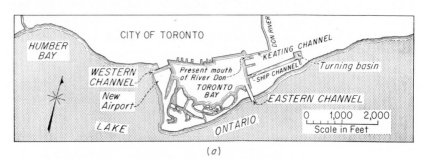

(a)

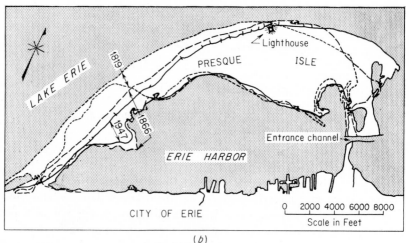

(b)

FIG. 18.14. The harbors of Toronto, Ontario, on Lake Ontario, Canada, and Erie, Pennsylvania, on Lake Erie, illustrating shore-line formations utilized to form well-protected harbors. (*Reproduced by permission of the Toronto Harbour Commissioners and the American Society of Civil Engineers, respectively.*)

of the great coal docks in the harbor. This required a large quantity of sand fill. The low tenderer for the work reckoned on dredging this from a point just outside the east entrance with the anticipation that he would have a continually replenished supply, necessitating little if any moving of his dredge. His geological knowledge paid off; once his dredge had made its initial cut, it did not have to be moved again, but was provided by the orderly process of "geology in action" with all the fill required for the job.

Erie Harbor is notable in that it was the first harbor project ever undertaken by the United States Corps of Engineers, the original act authorizing its improvement having been passed as early as March 3, 1823. The shape of the peninsula has changed appreciably through the intervening years; there is now a continuous record of the civil engineering works that have been necessary to keep the narrow connecting neck of land unbroken as a convenient access to the great park that has been developed on the spit proper. Many surveys have been made and many measurements of erosion taken. Eventually, it was decided that natural replenishment of the beaches that were being so regularly eroded was insufficient, despite all that had been done in the way of constructing groynes and other protective works (at an expenditure of several million dollars). In 1955 tenders were received for the dredging of over 4 million cu yd of sand to form an artificial beach; this work was carried out in 1955 and 1956 at a total cost of about $2.5 million.[18.30]

The maintenance of the Presque Isle shore line is a fine example of cooperative effort in the careful study of the natural forces involved; even with this sound approach, some idea of the costs involved is to be gained from the two figures quoted. As an example of what costs may be involved without due initial consideration of the geological implications of engineering work, there may be mentioned the destruction of more than one-half of U.S. Highway 90 between Pass Christian and Biloxi in 1915, involving damage estimated at $13 million. After the highway had been replaced, the local country authority constructed a sea wall 24 miles long adjacent to the road at a cost of $3.4 million. The beach disappeared completely in a very short time; fill behind the wall escaped, and the highway was again threatened. The United States Corps of Engineers was asked to help in the restoration work, but before it could provide its expert assistance, another hurricane occurred and did more damage. The estimated cost of the repair work eventually carried out was about one-third of the original total cost of the wall. The beach was replaced by pumping. It is estimated that 32,500 cu yd is lost from the beach every year, but routine maintenance has been sufficient to keep it in good condition in view of the large amount of pumped fill placed in 1951.[18.31]

18.9. Littoral Drift. It is not necessary to see the works of the civil engineer to appreciate the existence of the extensive movement of sand in regular and steady manner along many stretches of coast, generally known as *littoral drift*. Its existence is obvious, owing to the regular accretion of products of erosion in not a few coastal locations. At river mouths, conditions are especially favorable for its observation; one peculiar result of the interaction of drift and estuarine conditions is the *barachois* (a French word meaning sand and gravel bars) which are a prominent feature of certain parts of the Atlantic Coast of Canada. The records of physical geology contain many examples of great interest based on observations of coastal conditions and development. Valuable information is also presented in studies undertaken in conjunction with engineering works, such as the extension of Rockaway Point, Long Island, a sandspit near New York. The point of this spit has advanced at an average rate (at least between 1835 and 1927) of more than 200 ft per year. When

Fig. 18.15. Accumulation of sand at the east jetty, Rockaway Point, Long Island, New York. (*Reproduced by permission of The Director, U.S. Coast and Geodetic Survey.*)

the progression of the point was halted by a rock-mound jetty, 300,000 cu yd of sand was found to have accumulated behind it in the course of little more than a year.[18.32]

With the advent of man-made structures projecting out into the sea, littoral drift has come to be of great practical importance, usually as a difficult problem to be faced but occasionally as a factor beneficial to coastal development. On any section of coast where there is appreciable drift (and this includes most sand beaches), the projection of any solid structure below mean tide level will result in the building up of sand or other drift material on one side of the structure and a corresponding, although not necessarily equal, erosion of material from the other side. If the drift is of any magnitude, the serious effects of the action will be readily apparent, especially in the case of works protecting harbor entrances. The possibility of trapping drifting sand by deliberately stopping littoral drift in order to build up a good beach section will be equally clear.

Fig. 18.16. Protective breakwater (formed of two scuttled steamships) at Vizagapatam Harbor, India, the purpose of which is explained in the text. (*Reproduced by permission of the Deputy Administrative Officer, Vizagapatam Port.*)

The coasts and major harbors of India have provided some of the most valuable information yet available on this important matter, much having been obtained as the result of bitter experience which has been faithfully recorded for the benefit of the profession generally. Thus it has been found that at Madras on the east coast of India, where the sand travels from north to south, approximately 1 million tons of sand passes any given spot on the coast each year. Similar conditions exist on the east coast of South Africa; at Durban, in particular, great difficulties have been experienced in maintaining the harbor entrance.

Much of this accumulated experience was applied to the design of the harbor of Vizagapatam between Madras and Calcutta on the east coast of

India. Initial studies suggested that no trouble would be encountered with drift, but the start of dredging operations at the harbor entrance soon demonstrated that conditions similar to those at Madras existed. Eventually, it was found that (1) the volume of sand traveling along the coast amounted to 1 million tons per year; (2) the travel took place largely in shallow water and was generally confined to a zone 600 ft wide; and (3) the travel was primarily the result of wave action although sometimes it was accentuated by shore currents. At Madras and Durban, erosion corresponding to the drift deflected by harbor works had occurred, and hundreds of acres of agricultural land had been lost in this way. At Durban, 700,000 cu yd of sand was required to restore an eroded foreshore

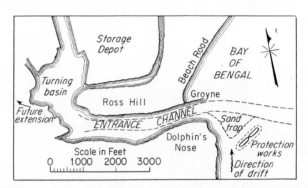

Fig. 18.17. Sketch map of the entrance to Vizagapatam Harbor, India, showing arrangement made to deal with littoral drift. (*Reproduced by permission of The Institution of Civil Engineers.*)

to its original state. This aspect of littoral drift also had to be considered in connection with the Vizagapatam Harbor entrance. Eventually, a scale model was constructed by means of which the action of waves of varying degree on the coastal section was noted. This gave valuable indications of what protective works could be effectively carried out; the final solution is shown in Fig. 18.17

The breakwater (consisting, incidentally, of two scuttled ships loaded with rubble) ensures deflection of the littoral drift between it and the coast line; therefore, the drift has to fall into the dredged sand trap on the inner side of the entrance channel from which the sand is excavated by a dredge working under the lee of the protective breakwater. This discharges the sand onto the other side of the entrance channel, whence it is gradually moved away by the erosive drift action.[18.33]

This example from engineering experience in India has been cited not only because of its intrinsic interest but because it illustrates a rather perplexing but certainly unfortunate break in communication between civil engineers of different countries. British engineers working in India for more than a century after the start of the development of that great sub-continent recorded in a quite remarkable way their varied experience, generally in Indian and British publications. Their papers on coastal engineering were notable, but only rarely does one see reference to them in North American publications. As recently as 1959, a paper to the American Society of Civil Engineers (ASCE) contained the statement that "by-passing . . . was suggested for the first time at the Navigation Congress at Brussels in 1935." There cannot have been anyone at that conference who had heard of Vizagapatam.

In another recent ASCE paper, however, the following quotation from a paper to the (British) Institution of Civil Engineers given by Sir Francis Spring in 1912 is cited with appreciation.[18.34] It is worthy of repeated study by all concerned with coastal engineering work:

> The chief lesson to be learned from a study of sand-travel at Madras ap-pears to be that it is absolutely necessary, when an engineer is called on to advise about a work situation on a coast where there is any suspicion of travelling sand, mud, or shingle, that he should be allowed adequate time to make observations, conducted with due precautions, of the directions and causes of travel; and that if he should arrive at the conclusion that such travel is likely to affect the proposed works in the near or distant future, he ought at least to acquaint his employers with what he conceives to be the broad general facts of the case and their probable financial effects, whether on the proposed works or on other works or interests.

This sound advice of half a century ago could have saved untold trouble and expense if it had been more widely known and heeded.

The hydrodynamic aspects of littoral drift have now been carefully studied and the general character of the movement is well understood. The influence of the wind has been shown to be dominant. This is well illustrated on stretches of coast where the direction of drift is found to change, generally at a well-defined location. In the case of the north shore of Lake Ontario (in the vicinity of Whitby), this location can be linked directly with the direction of the prevailing wind on the lake and the corresponding fetches on the Ontario shore. In the case of the west shore of Lake Michigan, the change appears to occur in the vicinity of 55th Street, Chicago. The source of the material constituting the drift always provides a geological problem of interest and significance. If there are cliffs that are obviously being eroded in the vicinity of the area of accretion and in the direction from which the drift is coming, they will clearly be a first source. Not so obvious, but probably more important, is the sediment brought down by rivers and streams discharging near the area under study. It has been estimated, for example, that the streams and rivers discharging into the Pacific Ocean between Point Conception and the Ventura River amounts to almost 2 million cu yd annually, and much of this moves steadily along the coast. If the supply from either of these sources is interfered with, as can so easily be done by a misplaced engineering structure built on the beach, trouble may soon develop at beaches that have been thus maintained.

Fig. 18.18. Coastal protection works at Sherringham, Norfolk, England. (*Photograph by Photoflight, Ltd. Reproduced by permission of J. Duvivier, Consulting Engineer.*)

There are many stretches of sand beach the progressive erosion of which will interfere with either recreational facilities or developed property and that must therefore be conserved as much as possible. When erosion is the result of continued littoral drift, the use of groynes is often the most satisfactory solution. Groynes are wall structures generally built at right angles to the shore line and extending below low-water line; their action interferes to such an extent with the travel of drift that the sand is trapped against the walls and then gradually accumulates until a stable beach is formed. The shores of many parts of the British Isles have been protected in this way, as also has much of the low-lying eastern seaboard of the United States; erosion of the coasts of Florida and New Jersey in particular has been severe. Records of the New Jersey coast line show an average recession of about 2 ft per year (153 ft between 1840 and 1920); and figures for Florida are similar. Problems arising on these coasts were among those considered and investigated by the United States Beach Erosion Board; as a result, specific recommendations regarding groyne location were drawn up. It was found, for example, that groynes need not extend higher than the level of uprush at high water; construction at right angles to the coast line was found to be beneficial. A spacing tentatively suggested was 1½ to 4 times the length from the bulkhead or shore line, the longer spacing being successful when the volume of drift was large, and vice versa.

Almost all older installations of groynes used walls that were solid in construction, providing a complete barrier to material coming into contact with them. In more recent years, the practice has developed in some locations of constructing groynes with "windows" in them, short sections of wall constructed to a lesser height than the main section of the groyne, with the intention of allowing some of the drift to pass the groyne while retaining sufficient to maintain the beach. Another method of achieving the same objective is to use permeable groynes, of which there are a number of types now available, some patented. A notable installation of this type of groyne is at Sheridan Park, Wisconsin, on the west coast of Lake Michigan where erosion was taking place at the rate of 2 ft per year until corrective measures were undertaken in 1933. The groyne installation then constructed has served well in the intervening years.[18.35] It is illustrated in Fig. 18.19.

It must be emphasized, however, that the solution to each individual coastal problem is to be found only by making the most exhaustive field studies at the site and by comparing the situation thus determined with the experience of others who have had to deal with similar problems. No two coastal-protection problems will be exactly similar; possible local variations must continually be kept in view. Careful study of available records is, however, as useful in this branch of applied geology as anywhere. The Beach Erosion Board of the United States has an impressive record of publications now available for consultation. The experience of other nations should not be forgotten, particularly the records of British engineers, since they have now documented experience extending back well over a century for protection works along a coast line presenting most varied geological conditions. Figure 18.18 is included to show a recent example of British coastal-protection work; the paper in which it was first reproduced can be commended as a guide to modern British practice.[18.36]

British engineers have also suggested the use of what may be called "littoral drift in reverse." Disposal of fly ash from modern steam power stations is becoming an important economic problem. Despite the progress made in using fly ash as a component in building materials (see Chap. 8), most large steam power stations still have an appreciable amount of fly ash that must be disposed of economically. One such station is that at Blyth in northern England which, by 1970, will have to dispose of 500,000 tons of fly ash per year. The station is located close to the coast, adjacent to

Fig. 18.19. Reinforced-concrete permeable groynes at Sheridan Park, Wisconsin, on the shore of Lake Michigan. (*Reproduced by permission of the Regional Planning Dept., Milwaukee County, Wisconsin.*)

Blyth Harbor. Study of the character of the fly ash showed that 80 per cent of it consisted of particles finer than the No. 100 sieve. Engineers studying the disposal problem found that material finer than No. 100 sieve was never a constituent of the material on a number of British beaches; the same thing has been found in a study of 400 American beaches. It was therefore concluded that 80 per cent of the Blyth fly ash would be removed by the normal action of the sea if discharged with the waste water from the plant. Study showed that one other power station—that at Casablanca—used this system, but there the discharge was only 50 tons per day. Colliery wastes have been dumped into the sea, as at the Cambois Colliery, without any of the material staying on the adjacent beach. This unusual proposal has yet to be tried on the scale contemplated, but it presents interesting possibilities that should be economically more valid with every passing year.[18.37]

With this vivid reminder of the dynamic character of ocean and lake beaches, attention may finally be directed to more recent applications of the bypassing principle for protecting the entrances to harbors, usually artificially constructed, from littoral drift that tends to cross them. Examples are now available from several countries on scales varying from that at Vizagapatam to those designed to protect small inlets on the Florida coast.

As one example, the bypassing of the entrance to Lake Worth may be briefly described. The inlet gives access to the harbor of Palm Beach, some 70 miles north of Miami; it was constructed by private interests in 1945; its 300-ft navigable channel is protected by rock-mound jetties. Sand started to accumulate against the north jetty soon after completion, and beaches between the Lake Worth Inlet and that at South Lake Worth Inlet (15½ miles to the south) were correspondingly depleted; naturally, the effect was serious in view of the popularity of this area. Various studies were made, and large quantities of sand were pumped into stock piles on the beach on several occasions. Observations showed that the beaches could be replenished, at least in part, by periodic nourishment at the rate of about 200,000 cu yd a year. Successful operation of a small bypassing sand-pumping plant at the south inlet, with a capacity of 80,000 cu yd per year, installed in 1937, focused attention upon the possibility of using a larger pumping installation. Studies proved the suitability of this solution, but local difficulties (such as not drawing any sand from that already built up around the north jetty and making sure that local residents would not hear any noise from the sand movement in the suction or discharge pipes) made the task of the consulting engineers somewhat difficult. A monolithic concrete pump house was constructed, equipped with a 400 hp electric motor-pump installation with a 12-in. suction inlet and 10-in.-diameter discharge, all protected by an L-shaped groyne. The plant was completed in 1958; its total cost of about $500,000 is an indication of the intrinsic value of the beaches that the plant is designed to maintain by merely pumping sand from one side of a 900-ft-wide inlet to the other—vivid evidence of the dynamics of coastal protection and of the ceaseless action of the sea on the coast.[18.38]

18.10. Maintenance of Tidal Estuaries. The formation and persistence of bars at the entrance to many tidal river estuaries has long been a matter of keen debate and investigation. Bars may be said to have been the object of some of the earliest hydraulic research of which record exists; the Abbot Castelli included them in the subjects that he investigated in the years around 1660. Other early Italian and French engineers devoted considerable attention to them, and many explanations of their existence have been advanced in the intervening years. Bars in tidal estuaries and river mouths may be divided into two general classes: (1) those consisting of hard material not affected by the scouring action of normal currents passing over them, and (2) those of sand, shingle, or other unconsolidated material which, while retaining their general features, are constantly subject to alteration from effects caused by winds, waves, and varying currents. In addition, temporary bars of sand or shingle are occasionally heaped up by the action of waves in heavy gales and afterward displaced by currents such as the famous Chesil Bank (see page 694).

An example of the first type of bar is that which existed at the entrance to Aberdeen Harbor, Scotland. It consisted of boulder clay and when removed by dredging was formed again by the piling up of sea sand from the neighboring shore. Continued dredging finally gave a permanent channel by the removal of all the sand exposed in the vicinity as it filled into the bar channel, thus leaving exposed only boulder clay which was not eroded to any appreciable degree by tidal currents.[18.39] Many examples of the second type of bar could be given, since details of such bars have been presented in connection with the many discussions of the general subject before technical societies. These discussions would appear to have reduced to a certainty the cause of the formation of such bars from out of the wealth of controversy that has raged about the question. It seems almost certain that sand and shingle bars across the mouths of tidal estuaries are formed by the interaction of tidal and other shore currents, although local topographical detail has considerable indirect effect. The influence of the discharge of river water into these estuaries appears to be small. An interesting fact is that, although the exact location of a river discharge channel in the sandbanks of its estuary may change appreciably, a sand bar will always exist at the entrance to any new channel if such was the case in the original channel.

It may be fitting to describe what is at once one of the most remarkable and one of the best known of these natural impediments to navigation, that at the entrance to the river Mersey in England, on which stands Liverpool, one of the world's greatest ports. The river is relatively small—only 56 miles long and draining only 1,724 sq miles. It has a high tidal range (up to 32 ft), and the lower part of the river is therefore swept by large volumes of water on every tide. The actual mouth is located in what may be called the "corner" of Liverpool Bay, in which there are certain well-defined sandbanks, some of which are high and dry at low water. Through these, the river maintains a regular channel with a depth of between 30 and 50 ft below low-water level. The lower section of the channel has undergone considerable change of position in the last 100 years, limiting positions being 3 miles apart. In every case, the channel finished in a large sand bar; that which existed before dredging started rose directly out of 53 and 46 ft of water at low tide in the landward and seaward directions, respectively, giving a depth at the bar itself between 7 and 17 ft. Flood conditions in the upper reaches of the river appear to have the effect of increasing the available depth of water. The interference which this obstruction meant to navigation can well be appreciated; but it was only in 1890, after exhaustive studies, that dredging across the bar was started experimentally. The success obtained in deepening the bar brought into prominence other shoals in the main approach channel, and it was foreseen that if the depth of this channel

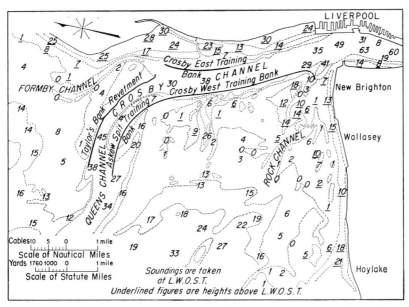

Fig. 18.20. Liverpool Bay and the estuary of the river Mersey, England, showing ship channel and training walls. (*Reproduced by permission of the Engineer-in-Chief, Mersey Docks and Harbor Board.*)

throughout its length was to be commensurate with the deepening that had been effected on the bar, considerable further dredging would be necessary. For some years, therefore, extensive and systematic dredging was practiced; and since the desired depth in the main channel was achieved, the natural tendency to deposit on the former site of the bar has been easily countered by occasional dredging. Inside the bar, the channel has been stabilized by the construction of large rock revetments or training walls.[18.40]

Although dredging is often an essential part of improvement work, it deals only with an effect, whereas the training walls involve an attempt to modify a cause of silting or shoal formation. The general function of training walls is to train a river in a permanent course in which its own velocity will have the necessary scouring action. The use of training works is a more hazardous operation than the initiation of dredging since it involves large expenditures and is liable to make matters worse instead of better if it is not successful. As an illustration, the development of the entrance to New York Harbor may be mentioned. Four long shoals obstructed the main ship channel and Gedney Channel in providing access into the lower bay from the ocean. One proposed form of improvement was by dredging, maintaining this channel, should it be necessary, either by periodic dredging or by contracting the entrance by the construction of a dike running across the shoals from the Coney Island side. The estimated cost for obtaining the dredged channel was almost $1.5 million, with a total cost of improvement, should the contraction works be necessary, estimated at between $5 million and $6 million. Between 1884 and 1890, after much discussion and some trials of dredging, the proposal for the dike was discarded and the channel dredged to 30 ft, saving approximately $4 million. Since that time a new channel 2,000 ft wide and 45 ft deep has been dredged from the main entrance to New York Harbor. Practically no maintenance is required on this channel owing to the normal scour action of the lower section of the Hudson River.[18.41]

A sidelight on the second point mentioned, and an incident of general interest in connection with tidal rivers, is provided by some observations made of the river Garonne, France, at the end of the last century. A steamer was sunk by collision at the mouth of the river opposite Verdon and rested with her keel at the bottom of the channel; masts and funnel alone showed at low water. On examination, it was found that the vessel was completely buried in sand and that the sandbank extended 300 ft fore and aft and 150 ft on either side. Subsequently, a second examination showed that the sandbank had completely disappeared; the hull was unsupported at the ends and rested on sand only in the central section. Further study showed that the sandbank formed and disappeared with every tide; the first examination had been made at the end of the ebb tide and the second at the end of the flood; the ebb deposited the sand, and the flood removed it. No more striking evidence of sand travel with tidal currents can be imagined; it serves also to illustrate what troubles can be invoked by a training wall not correctly located.[18.42]

Many rivers and river entrance channels have been successfully developed and deepened by the judicious use of training works. Liverpool is a case in point, but of more importance (since regular dredging is not involved) is the mouth of the Mississippi River, improved during the period from 1875 to 1879 by Gen. James B. Eads at his own expense until the improvement had definitely satisfied governmental requirements. The method adopted by this distinguished American engineer was to concentrate the scour of the current in one of the "passes" of the river mouth by two parallel jetties of fascine work, and thus to make the water the agent

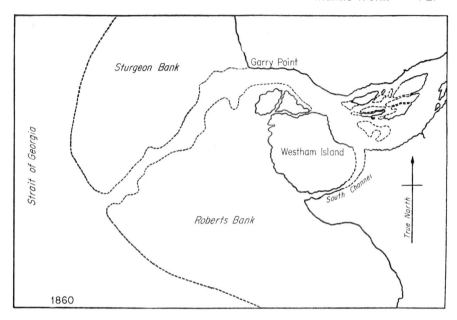

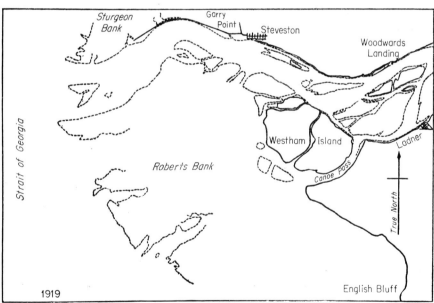

FIG. 18.21. Sketch maps showing the development of the Fraser River Delta, British Columbia, Canada, and the changes in river channels between 1860 and 1919. (*Reproduced by permission of the Director, Geological Survey of Canada.*)

for effecting the improvement of its own course. A full account of this important example of river-training work is available in a volume that has long been of value and interest to engineers.[18.43]

There may also be mentioned the case of the Fraser River in British Columbia which, although not perhaps so important commercially as some rivers mentioned, is yet one of the great rivers of the Pacific Coast of North America. It has a length of 790 miles and drains an area of 91,700 sq miles; the average yearly flood discharge is 380,000 cfs. The river passes through drift deposits and is therefore fairly heavily charged with sediment. This has resulted in the formation of an unusual delta, the outbuilding of which occurs because the river currents dominate the tidal currents and because the wave action is not great. The tides and tidal currents have had the effect of giving an unusual form to the seaward part of the delta and of introducing unusual and complex problems into the successful training of the estuary of the river. Borings have disclosed the depth of the deltaic formation as at least 800 ft, and evidence has also been found of the formation of calcareous sandstone in relatively recent years in the delta. The main navigation channel is maintained by extensive training walls and by dredging; in dredging a bar at the mouth of one of the arms of the delta, a deposit of this sandstone had to be cut through by the dredge. The training works are in the charge of engineers of the Department of Public Works, Canada. In connection with their work, the engineers have cooperated with the Geological Survey of Canada; a most useful report was one early result of this cooperation.[18.44]

Local conditions affecting tidal estuaries are so variable that detailed study of each case is usually required. In recent years, specially constructed scale models have been used in many such studies; this is one of the most interesting and important branches of civil engineering in which models have proved of assistance. By the use of the principles of hydraulic similarity, it is possible to construct a model of an estuary to such a distorted linear scale that observation in a vertical direction can accurately be made without the use of a model too large in plan. By extension of the similarity to the scale of time, tidal effects occurring over long periods of years can be reproduced in a matter of days. This branch of model work appears to have been first used in France in 1875 when a model was constructed to study the action of certain proposals for improving the river Garonne between Bordeaux and the sea. The first real attempt to apply scientific principles in the design of models was made in 1885 by Prof. Osborne Reynolds at the University of Manchester, and his work is being continued today in leading hydraulic-research laboratories throughout the world. It must be emphasized, however, that even the best of model studies are only a supplement to the most meticulous field investigations; nature always has to be observed with the greatest care before any change of her natural order is contemplated.

18.11. Some Submarine Problems. Marine works designed and constructed by civil engineers are almost always close to or on the shore; even those few isolated structures built offshore are necessarily in relatively shallow water. Just as engineers are now beginning to study the details of the land beneath the sea, so also are they beginning to consider what may properly be called "submarine problems." Mining operations, such as those in the Cape Breton coal field of Nova Scotia, have been conducted beneath the sea bed for many years. Tunnels beneath the sea or under tidal rivers, although still not numerous, are not now the novelty they were when the Brunels, father and son, succeeded in completing the first underwater tunnel under the river Thames at Wapping in 1843. A more recent underwater tunneling operation was carried out for an entirely different purpose; this was for placing the explosive charge necessary for the removal of Ripple Rock in the coastal waters of British Columbia.

Ripple Rock was the name given to the dual hump-shaped summit of a well-rounded "hogsback" located near the south end of Seymour Narrows in the beautiful Inland Passage between Vancouver Island and the mainland of Canada. Long an impediment to navigation, the rock became a hazard of increasing danger since its peaks reached to within 9 and 20 ft of low water in a navigable channel marked by strong tidal currents and difficult to navigate even without the added problem of avoiding Ripple Rock. Elaborate test drilling showed that the rock underlying the adjoining channels, and forming Ripple Rock itself, was generally fresh basalt, with some andesite and a few bands of breccia. After much study, the engineers in charge decided to remove the rock by tunneling out to it from an adjacent island and then placing a suitable charge of explosive, large enough to blast off the entire twin peaks. A shaft was first sunk on Maud Island, 7 by 18 ft and 570 ft deep. From this a 7- by 8-ft tunnel was driven under the channel to a point under the center of the rock. Two 7- by 15-ft raises, each about 300 ft long, were then driven up to within 40 ft of each summit. Finally, about 3,220 ft of coyote workings were driven under the rock, 5 by 4 ft in section. A total charge of 2,736,324 lb of "Nitramex 2H" was then placed throughout the workings and detonated on the morning of April 5, 1958; the charge represented 4.1 lb of explosive per lb of rock and water to be moved. The operation was entirely successful, and the hazard to navigation was completely removed at a cost somewhat in excess of $2.5 million. Scientists from a number of Canadian research and scientific organizations took many geophysical observations at the time of the blast, over a wide area, so that this largest of man-made explosions was very fully documented.[18.45]

This was a carefully planned and premeditated earth movement beneath the sea. Other submarine earth movements completely unplanned and quite unexpected have made their occurrence felt by their effects upon enginering structures. Many underwater slides have been noted by Dutch engineers in connection with their extensive coastal engineering work. Koppejan reported 224 major slides in a 65-year period involving the mass movement of about 3 million cu yd. Dr. Terzaghi has reported upon a slide in clean sand and gravel forming an underwater delta in Howe Sound, British Columbia, which took out part of a wharf and warehouse. More serious, however, have been major submarine slides in some of the fiords of western Norway, even though the physical damage they have

Fig. 18.22. The destruction of Ripple Rock, Inner Channel, British Columbia, Canada, on Apr. 5, 1958. (*Photograph by the National Film Board, Canada.*)

done is relatively small. Damage of a very serious nature occurred on November 18, 1929, when more than 20 breaks developed in trans-Atlantic cables south of Newfoundland on the edge of and down the continental slope from the Grand Banks. The breaks occurred very shortly after a serious earthquake. The times and locations of the breaks followed an orderly sequence down the continental slope, suggesting a speed of about 60 mph gradually decreasing along the 350 miles over which breaks occurred, but giving an over-all average velocity of about 25 mph. Kuenan has suggested that the breaks were caused by turbidity currents, but Terzaghi suggests rather that they were the result of temporary liquefaction of sediments forming the sea bed.[18.46] Figure 18.23 is a simplified section along the route of one of the trans-Atlantic cables. Even allowing for the distorted scale, it typifies the remarkable configuration of this particular part of the ocean floor so that the hazards of cable laying and maintenance can well be imagined.

Cable laying may not strictly be classified as civil engineering, but the importance of the geology of the ocean floor in relation to cable laying will be obvious. A new application of oceanographic studies has therefore developed in which even such a modern aid as underwater photography is playing a part.[18.47] The significance of the movements of the sea bed, already mentioned, in all such work is clearly shown by the experience on record of undersea slides at the mouth of the Magdalena River, Colombia, South America, in August, 1935. The slide carried away

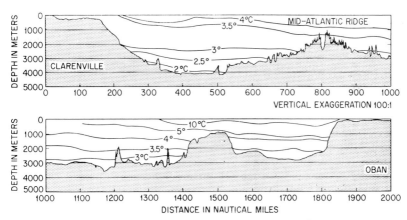

Fig. 18.23. Profile across the North Atlantic Ocean from Clarenville, Newfoundland, Canada, to Oban, Scotland, showing isotherms of mean sea temperature. (*Reproduced by permission of The Editor, The Bell System Journal and of C. H. Elmendorf and B. C. Heezen.*)

480 m of the western end of a breakwater and most of the long-term river bar; that same night, several hours later, tension breaks occurred in the submarine cable located 15 miles offshore in 700 fathoms of water. When the cable was brought up for repair, grass of the type that grew near the jetties was brought up with it.[18.47] Clearly, the geology of the sea bed is of vital concern to civil engineers engaged upon marine works.

Suggestions for Further Reading

In addition to the volumes cited as references, two others dealing with the latest developments in the study of shore lines may be noted:

Guilcher, A., "Coastal and Submarine Morphology" (a translation), John Wiley & Sons, Inc., New York, 1958.

King, C. A. M, "Beaches and Coasts," Edward Arnold & Co., London, 1959.

One of the earliest volumes in this field, to which reference is still made, is:

Johnson, D. W., "Shore Processes and Shoreline Development," John Wiley & Sons, Inc., New York, 1919; even at this date, it was possible for the author of this volume to include quite an extensive bibliography.

The publications of the United States Beach Erosion Board of the United States Corps of Engineers (Washington, D.C.) and the Proceedings of the regular conferences on coastal engineering sponsored by the Wave Research Council of the Engineering Foundation, held in various American cities, contain a fund of valuable information on coastal-protection work.

Chapter 19

EROSION AND SILTING

We see water washing away the earth and running down from the mountains carrying the rocks along with it, filling up the valleys and raising the level of the plains. On the other hand, we see water cutting into the land and making valleys, and the valleys thus being made, high land remains on either side. And we see water taking earth from one place and depositing it in another place.

Ristoro d'Arazzo
About A.D. 1282[19.1]

THE PHENOMENON of erosion and the complementary action of sedimentation can probably be regarded as the geological processes of most importance in civil engineering work, even when considered only in so far as they are operating at present. If the past is considered and even cursory thought is given to the difficulties introduced into construction work by the existence of underground eroded valleys and by the variation of unconsolidated sediments and glacial deposits, the significance of these processes will be considerably increased. They constitute a vital part of the geological cycle. By the glaciation now taking place in arctic regions, just as by the cutting of solid rock by the wind-driven sand of tropical deserts, parts of the earth's crust are steadily being eroded. Other parts are similarly being built up. In combination, these processes disturb the static equilibrium of the earth's crust, with the result that the erosion and sedimentation of today are probably contributing to earth movements of the future.

The civil engineer is repeatedly faced with problems caused by erosion: on the seacoast the action of the sea may be destroying valuable developed property; at bends in rivers the current steadily encroaches upon bankside property or adjacent transportation routes; and in other areas the combined action of wind and rain erodes fertile topsoil. Similarly, the deposition of silt behind many artificially constructed barriers to river flow, the silting up of slow-flowing rivers, and the formation of bars in tidal estuaries present special problems in the solution of which the

733

engineer is called upon to play a leading part. Even in this brief introductory note civil engineering works of such important types as river-training work, coastal protection, and soil conservation have already been suggested. All have a common feature, since in them the work of the engineer is concerned with an attempt to conserve or develop physical features that are constantly exposed to natural forces tending to alter them in some way. These forces will persist despite all the efforts of the engineer. Hence, in civil engineering work connected with erosion or silting, not only must the engineer face structural problems, but he must also consider the effect that the resulting structures will have on the future action of these natural forces. In all these considerations, a knowledge of the fundamental geological processes at work is essential; their neglect may result in the failure of works structurally quite sound.

19.2. River-training Work. For more than 3,000 years men have been trying to "tame" some of the great rivers of the world. The first civil engineering works of any magnitude were in all probability river-training works. Today, the training of rivers is still an important branch of civil engineering, so diverse in its character, so widespread in its practice, and so specialized for each individual river that brief reference only can be made to it here, despite the fact that the meandering of rivers, which river-training works are designed to control, is a part of the natural order, one phenomenon in the broad field of physical geology. Decisions regarding design must necessarily be empirical; and as no two rivers are alike in all particulars, the local application of the results of experience elsewhere is often fraught with uncertainty and is liable to misinterpretation.

River-control work is essentially the control of a natural river flow within a certain well-defined course, usually that which the stream normally occupies. Since deviations from this course will be most likely to occur during periods of flood flow, control work is often a matter of flood regulation. In addition to this, the prevention of erosion of riverbanks during periods of normal flow constitutes another important branch of control work. Finally, the improvement of rivers in connection with civic or industrial development, such as the straightening of a river bed in connection with town planning and the canalization of a stretch of river to facilitate navigation, is another type of river regulation that is often of importance. In undertaking work of this nature, an engineer is dealing with a fundamental geological process, and all his designs must be based on an acceptance of the natural characteristics of river flow. In the past, a rigid restriction of this work to assumed natural conditions has led to major controversy, especially with regard to the control of the Mississippi River, one of the outstanding river-control projects of the world; special attention is given to it in the next section.

Four of the major river systems of the world have well-developed flood plains long occupied by human settlements; it is natural that they should have been prominent in the long history of river-training work. They are the Mississippi, the Nile, and the Yellow (or Hwang Ho) and the Yangtze Rivers of China. Other rivers of comparable size are the Amazon, the Congo, the Lena, and the Bramhaputra, but only the last of these has seen development comparable to that which has been carried out on the two great rivers of China for 30 centuries or more. The Yangtze River is 3,200 miles in length; it is navigable for a longer distance than any other river in the world. Its flow on July 19, 1915, was recorded as 2,531,692 cfs, the greatest flow ever recorded for one river channel, much in excess of the maximum flood flow on the Mississippi. In 1871, its level rose to the phenomenal height of 275 ft above normal in the Wind Box Gorge, 1,100 miles from its mouth. About 180 million people live in its watershed. Its floods have caused untold tragedies in loss of life down through the ages. Dikes have been manfully built in attempts to control its channel; the word "manfully" is used in its literal sense, since 50,000 people were at work on one dike alone in repairing flood damage after an inundation in April, 1927. Today, the Yangtze is one of the most completely diked rivers of the world.[19.2]

Even more remarkable is the Yellow River, "China's Sorrow," 2,500 miles long, with at least 100 million people living in its basin; its name is derived from the high content of loess that it carries to the sea and out into the sea, sediment being visible far from its mouth. At one time the river ran north by Tientsin and at another it emptied in central China, into the Yangtze River, near Chekiang, several hundred miles to the south. For 700 years it discharged eastward into the Yellow Sea, but in 1852 it broke its banks at a point more than 300 miles from its mouth, formed a new channel across the province of Shantung, and finally a new mouth in the Gulf of Chihli, almost 300 miles from its old mouth; it occupies this position today. The silt that it carries is unusually fine so that if the velocity, which averages 8 fps, drops below 3 fps, silt is deposited rapidly, the waters overtop the existing dikes, and a new page of sorrow starts. It was an old Chinese tradition that restless dragons stirred the mud in the rivers, causing great calamities. Until early in this century, foreign engineers working in China often had their work delayed while the river dragons were propitiated.[19.3]

Chinese manpower, coupled with expert engineering advice, controlled the Yellow River when it broke its banks again in 1935 near the towns of Tung Chuang and Lin Pao Chi. Four million people were affected by the resulting flood through a breach in the dike system 1½ miles long. The ancient Chinese contraction method was used to close the gap; the ends of the breach were first built up strongly, new dike structures were then built out gradually from both ends, and the final closure was made with the aid of immense wire stone-filled sausages and willow-fascine mattresses. As many as 25,000 men were employed at the peak of the work, but almost every operation was by hand, even the tamping of the soil placed in the dike; ingenious stone "flappers" lifted by eight men with attached ropes suggested that the Chinese had a good appreciation of the necessity of soil compaction long before it became a well-established technique in modern soil mechanics.[19.4] This recent case illustrates a development of the Chinese river-training work that has an unbroken record through the centuries of controlling two of the most unruly rivers of the world.

India has also had its share of sorrows caused by rivers on the rampage, particularly the Bramhaputra. This great river left its normal course spectacularly toward the end of the eighteenth century, seriously affecting the ancient city of Mymensingh. With the development of irrigation works of magnitude by British engineers in the nineteenth century, river-training works became an established part of Indian engineering. It was in 1887 that J. H. Bell advanced new proposals for training the Chenab River at Sher Shah where a large new bridge was proposed. He suggested concentrating the low river flow in a relatively deep channel by means of low embankments, soon known far beyond India as "Bell's bunds." The same idea was further developed by Sir Francis Spring and has since been amended and improved. The record of the gradual evolution of satisfactory methods of river control for the rivers of India, with their low low-water flows and erodible beds, is an unusually important chapter in the written records of civil engineering.

The importance of bank-protection work must be emphasized, since it enters into so many phases of river-control work. Methods of protection range from the construction of permanent retaining walls in front of natural soil slopes for preventing the initial formation of soil gullies to the use of expedients such as mattresses of brushwood, dumped rock, and even sandbags in cases of emergency. In the evolution of the many successful types of protection, due consideration has inevitably had to be given to the nature of the river action at the location. For example, on many sharp bends, the use of a wall of deep-driven interlocking steel sheet piling has often proved successful where other expedients have failed because it enabled additional scour of the river bed to take place in front of the wall until a condition of equilibrium was attained. In the case of levee protection, many ingenious designs of flexible mattresses built of different materials, including reinforced concrete, take up initial variations of the river bed and also any alteration caused by further minor erosion at the edge of the mattress. Flexibility is also the keynote of the "wire-sausage" type of protection adopted so successfully in India and China; cages of wire are filled with loose stones and so placed that in the failure of one sausage the superimposed cages will automatically move down to take its place. Another idea has been the planting of low-growing willow trees at or about normal water line, so that the foilage may impede the flow at flood periods and therefore reduce its eroding power. Throughout all this work, however, as in all satisfactory river-training work, the basic concept has been to cooperate as closely as possible with the natural process of river flow, to control it within necessary limits without attempting to usurp the place of nature.

19.3. The Mississippi River. Nowhere, perhaps, has this precept been better illustrated than in the history of the control of the "Father of Waters," America's greatest river, and its lusty tributary, the Missouri,

FIG. 19.1. Aerial view of the Missouri River, looking upstream from mile 440 in Buchanan County, Missouri, U.S.A., showing channel-stabilization works along both banks. (*Reproduced by permission of the Chief of Engineers, U.S. Army.*)

so commonly known as "Big Muddy." The Mississippi is fed by a drainage area of 1,243,000 sq miles and has a total length of about 2,400 miles. Its average discharge at Vicksburg is about 500,000 cfs; flood discharge is as high as 2 million cfs. In general profile, it is flat and slow moving for the greater part of its length. The valley of the Mississippi follows the general form for such river valleys. The flood waters, before confinement by levees was effected, covered a much greater area than the normal stream bed, at times as much as 30,000 sq miles. The first attempts were made in the early nineteenth century to confine the river during flood periods by raising the natural levees with artificial embankments, thus raising the next flood water level and promoting deepening of the channel through this restriction. In consequence, no local addition to a levee could really be made without all levees being raised similarly. The first levee, built at New Orleans in 1717, was 4 ft high. In 1932, the average height was more than 13 ft, and 2,500 miles of artificial levees were being maintained on the river. All this work, up to 1932, was based on the idea of maintaining the existing channel of the river.

In June, 1932, after years of discussion, a new policy was inaugurated under the direction of Gen. H. B. Ferguson, newly appointed president

Fig. 19.2. The site of the Sarah Island cutoff on the Mississippi River, U.S.A., when right of way had been cleared and the first dredge cut started. The main river flows from right to left at top and from left to right at bottom of photograph. (*Reproduced by permission of the Mississippi River Commission.*)

of the Mississippi River Commission. Another characteristic of the river was adopted for use; the natural process whereby the river makes cutoffs at narrow necks between bends, at long intervals of time, was expedited by making artificial cutoffs with the aid of powerful dredges. These cutoffs have materially reduced the length of the river and have lowered its flood stages. Supplementary dredging is done in the reaches between cutoffs to assist the river in restoring the steepened gradients to normal. A famous example of a natural cutoff is at Vicksburg, Mississippi, where in 1863 during the Civil War, General Grant tried to isolate the city from the river by cutting a canal through a narrow neck of land. This attempt was not successful; but in 1876, the river made the change for itself. Fortunately, the town of Vicksburg was able to maintain contact with the main river through the diversion of another stream; it is now well known to engineers as the location of the large-scale model of the river on which most valuable experiments have been made. This shortening of the river was started, initially, at 12 sharp bends. When all these cutoffs were fully developed, the total shortening effected by them amounted to nearly 116 miles in a stretch of 330 miles. Associated with

Fɪɢ. 19.3. The Sarah Island cutoff on the Mississippi River, U.S.A., in initial operation; some of the river discharge still uses the old river bed, although this has started to silt up. (*Reproduced by permission of the Mississippi River Commission.*)

this work, relief floodways were provided, designed to allow floodwaters to spill over the natural banks but only under control and in specially selected locations. Reservoirs have been created on tributary streams by the construction of some important dams; and although this work is of relatively minor importance on a river as large as the Mississippi, regulation by this means on smaller streams is often extremely valuable. Finally, continued bank-protection work has been carried out, involving mattress designs of much engineering ingenuity.[19.5]

This great program of river training, to a new plan, had just got well under way when there occurred the remarkable flood of 1936 and 1937, the greatest ever to flow down the Mississippi to the sea without any break in the levees. With the engineering organization for the river-training work already in the field and at strategic offices in the great valley, it was possible to make a detailed study of the entire flood to a degree that had not previously been attempted. This gave much invaluable new information about the Mississippi, all recorded conveniently for future use. The flood directed attention to gaps in available knowledge, and a major program of investigation, particularly into the geological features of the valley dependent on the great river, was started shortly afterward. This work resulted in one of the most comprehensive engineering-geological studies ever made, taking in the entire valley not only by means of surface observations but with the aid of the most complete collection of boring records that could be assembled. At least 16,000 boring records were made available by engineering organizations operating in the valley; more recently the results of the extensive test-boring programs carried out in the search for oil near the Mississippi Delta have added more valuable information to this steadily growing fund of knowledge. The results have been summarized in a number of papers and in a comprehensive volume by H. N. Fisk who was directly responsible for much of the geological part of this notable undertaking.[19.6]

As with all such studies, the results have proved of mutual benefit—to engineering, in providing the essential background for the continuing improvement of the great system of training works for the Mississippi, and to geology, in revealing hitherto unsuspected aspects of the Pleistocene history of the valley sediments. It has been shown, for example, that there has been considerable subsidence of the earth's surface in the delta area under the increasing weight of the deposited sediment; this fact accounts for the limited extension of the delta deposits within recent decades. Jetties constructed at the mouths of the Mississippi in 1875, for example, have not had to be extended since then. Corresponding elevation of adjacent areas on dry land appears to have occurred. The investigation continues but it already constitutes one of the most fascinating of all interrelations of geology and engineering.

Of the many aspects of Mississippian geology, one more only can be mentioned; this is the most dangerous, potentially, of all. For some time the future of the lower 300 miles of the Mississippi River has been threatened by the possibility of the "capture" of its flow by the Atchafalaya River through what has long been known as the "Old River diversion." The Atchafalaya River, although only a minor waterway in comparison with the Mississippi, is still the third largest American river that flows into the sea. The Old River connection is 6 miles long; its location is shown in Fig. 19.5. In 1956, the Old River took 23.5 per cent of the main river flow, diverting it into the Atchafalaya; it has been estimated that in the absence of any control measures, this diversion could reach 40 per cent by 1975. At that stage it would constitute a real threat to the lower section of the main river since the lower flow would

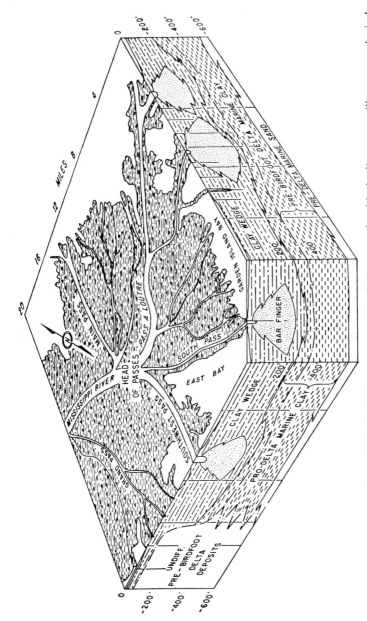

Fig. 19.4. The delta of the Mississippi River; an example of the use of a block diagram to illustrate geological features. (*Reproduced by permission of American Association of Petroleum Geologists and of H. N. Fisk, E. Mc-Farlan, C. R. Kolb, and L. J. Wilbert.*)

promote the silting up of the main channel, with probably disastrous effects upon the major port of New Orleans. A master control plan has been prepared by the United States Corps of Engineers and the first stages of it are already complete. The total plan will take from 8 to 10 years to complete and will cost about $47 million. The essential parts of the plan are shown in Fig. 19.5. Two control structures are to be built on the west bank of the Mississippi, upstream from Old River, a navigation lock connecting the two rivers, with the corresponding connecting

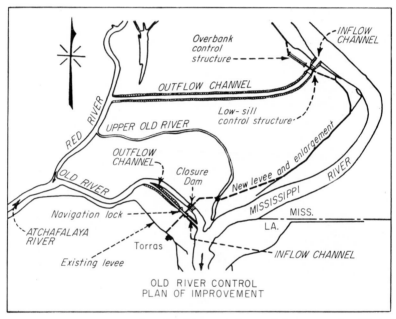

Fig. 19.5. Sketch plan of the Old River works carried out on the Mississippi River for the control of the Atchafalaya River. (*Reproduced by permission of The Editor, Engineering News-Record.*)

channels. Additional levee work is involved, and the Old River itself will eventually be sealed off when all the new works are functioning as planned. This vast project, so critical in its conception, planning, design, and construction, is necessitated merely to control the further development of a relatively simple, if unusually large, case of natural "river capture."[19.7]

Brief reference has been made to the main tributary of the Mississippi, the Missouri River. For more than 100 years, the Missouri has been a troublesome river to those who live near its banks; its floods sometimes reach catastrophic proportions. It is the chief source of the silt load of the Mississippi which, although often talked about, is minor in degree compared to that of its tributary. In flood flow, the silt content of the

Mississippi rises to 5,000 ppm. That of the Missouri, by comparison, may rise as high as 20,000 ppm, a figure exceeded only by such rivers as the Colorado and the Rio Grande that may reach as high as 40,000 ppm at times of high flood. Two plans for the amelioration of Missouri floods were prepared, one by the United States Corps of Engineers submitted in 1943, and one by the U.S. Bureau of Reclamation released in 1944. Although having the same objective, the approaches were somewhat different; reservoirs on the main stream were a prime factor in the first scheme, and "upriver" works a leading feature of the second. The two schemes were combined; the Missouri Basin Inter-Agency Committee was formed in 1945 to implement the policies of the Federal Inter-Agency River Basin Committee. The former committee consists of four representatives of the American government and four from the states in the Missouri Basin. Steady progress has been made with many parts of the over-all valley plan, and reference to some of the major engineering works appears elsewhere in this book.[19.8]

As typical of the troubles that the Missouri can cause, there may be mentioned just one example, its change to a new course in the vicinity of Decatur, Nebraska, in 1946. A new $2 million bridge had been located at a site on the deserted bed; it was decided to take advantage of the absence of the river to build the new bridge in the dry with considerable economy. It was estimated that $400,000 would be saved in this way, with the river to be returned to its old course when the bridge was built. But the Missouri, as so often in the past, did not cooperate, and major construction work had to be undertaken in order to get the river back into its old channel and to keep it there; much of the anticipated saving was thus lost. But the task was completed in 1956 and the bridge that was once on dry land is now serving as was intended with water flowing between its piers.[19.9]

19.4. Deltas and Estuaries. The valley of the Nile provides annually a vivid example of the silt-bearing function of rivers, as a result of which the fertility of that cradle of civilization has been long renowned. Records taken at the famous Roda gauge near Cairo (which has been maintained for many hundreds of years) show that the average silt deposit over the valley is about 10 cm per century. The corresponding formation of deltas at the mouths of several of the major rivers of the world, for example, the Ganges and the Mississippi in addition to the Nile, is one of the most obvious and generally appreciated demonstrations of the silt-transporting power of rivers. The somewhat similar phenomenon of the existence of bars at the entrances to tidal estuaries into which quite small rivers may discharge is a telling reminder of the great transporting power of the sea. Both natural features introduce engineering problems of the greatest magnitude which, although simple in essence, are extremely complicated in detail, having provided a fertile field for discussion for at least 3,000 years. The building up of large areas of new land in deltas provides land for development work of various kinds, and this involves structural foundation problems, often of unusual complexity. It is estimated that the delta of the Rhone in France (under observation since 400 B.C.) has been growing at the rate of 36 ft yearly; the corresponding rate for both the Danube and the Nile is 10 ft per year.[19.10] It may be noted that the physiography of the mouth of a river is a factor of great importance in determining the existence of

Fɪɢ. 19.6. New bed for the Missouri River under a highway bridge at Decatur, Nebraska, U.S.A.; the river has now been diverted under the bridge, and the new highway has been constructed on an embankment across the old river bed. (*Reproduced by permission of the Chief of Engineers, U.S. Army.*)

deltaic conditions, for rivers such as the Severn in England and the Amazon in South America, although they carry large quantities of silt, exhibit no special deltaic features; the funnel-shaped estuaries promote self-maintenance of the main channels. One of the largest deltas in the world is also one of the most unusual; this is the delta at the mouth of the Mackenzie River in Arctic Canada. It is 150 miles long and up to 50 miles wide, and is enclosed by high land to east and west; the main load of silt in the river is deposited in a great underwater delta in the Behring Sea.

The geological conditions affecting the formation of deltas are well recognized; the load of the stream is deposited on the river bed because the velocity, and therefore the carrying capacity, is reduced when the stream flow merges with the water of the sea or lake. Part of the load which might still be held in suspension may be deposited by flocculation of the colloidal material by the salt solution provided by the sea water. As a result, deposits are formed in regular beds, and they constitute some of the newest of sedimentary deposits. These may reach surprising depths; for example, a boring put down in Venice on the delta of the river Po in Italy reached a depth of 500 ft without penetrating the bottom of the deltaic beds. It will be appreciated that, although a delta

Fig. 19.7. A typical view of the delta of the Mackenzie River, Northwest Territories, Canada; all the ground seen is perennially frozen silt (permafrost). (*Photograph by G. H. Johnston, D.B.R., N.R.C., Canada.*)

is popularly imagined to be above water level, a deltaic formation is essentially an underwater geological structure, a fact influencing its engineering significance. It may also be emphasized that, although a delta may be the formation of a single stream, breakages of the natural levees above the river mouth may possibly cause the main stream to branch out into numerous distributaries through which the river finally discharges into the sea. The Nile Delta and that of the Ganges are two excellent examples of this special feature.

The magnitude of the engineering problem created by the deposition of the silt load of rivers in estuarial waters is well illustrated by the experience of the port of Baltimore, Maryland, the only one of the original group of towns on Chesapeake Bay that has developed into an ocean port. Designated a port by the General Assembly of Maryland as early as 1706, it has developed into one of the greatest of American ports; the harbor proper is the parent estuary of the Petapsco River and the arms formed by its minor tributaries. In the course of 200 years, the head of navigation has been pushed steadily seaward for a distance of 7 miles; depth at low water at one well-defined location decreased from 17 ft in 1845 to about 6 in. in 1924. It is not surprising to find that dredging was first started (by the Federal government) as early as 1836. It is said that Baltimore in 1783 saw the development of the first "mud machine," a simple type of drag dredge operated by horsepower. In the course of a century, the American government spent about $17 million in dredging 111 million cu yd of sediment from Baltimore harbor, and the work of maintenance dredging still continues. There is no doubt about the origin of the material deposited in the harbor and then removed at such expense by dredging. Soil erosion in the watershed of the Petapsco River is well recognized; measurements taken of the corresponding silt load carried by this small river agree reasonably well with the amount of material known to be deposited in the harbor.[19.11] If only for strictly economic reasons, therefore, civil engineers must take cognizance of the menace of soil erosion.

19.5. Erosion by Stream Flow. The flow of water in rivers and streams is perhaps the best recognized of the major causes of erosion. As the material eroded must be carried away by stream flow, complementary problems of silt deposition arise whenever the flow of a silt-laden river is interfered with in any way. Many and diverse engineering problems are thus created; the correct solution of these problems requires an appreciation of the general geological characteristics of river flow as a necessary background. The life history of rivers, although essentially a study in physical geology, is therefore a matter that should be familiar, at least in general outline, to all engineers engaged on river works.

Rainfall is the main source of all water reaching the surface of the earth. That portion which passes over the surface to become the runoff must naturally take a definite course and will at first gravitate into small gullies. These will lead, in turn, to larger gullies which will give place eventually to valleys down which a definite stream will flow on its way to lake or sea. Visualizing a complete profile of a river from source to mouth, one can imagine the river gradually decreasing in slope as it nears its mouth, increasing in volume and cross section on its way. This theoretical profile is not universal, although many of the large rivers of the world, such as the Amazon and the Ganges, conform to it. Rivers rising in mountainous country near the sea may be steeply graded from source to mouth, whereas other rivers which have their sources in relatively low-lying ground will have a flat profile throughout and corresponding characteristics.

The curved profile is one that a river will constantly tend to produce, and therefore it is a fundamental concept underlying all river studies; changes in gradient are achieved through the erosive power of running water and of the debris that it transports. Thus the steepest part of the theoretical profile may be regarded as the youthful stage of a river, the central section its middle-age period, and the flat gradient at the lower end its old age; the meandering of slow-flowing streams across surrounding plains is another characteristic of this last stage. All references to time apply to the geological time scale; but despite this, rivers in all stages of development may be seen today, and many show clearly their immediate past history. The canyons of the Colorado River in the United States, the Cheddar Gorge through which the river Avon flows in the south of England, and similar scenic river features present vivid evidence of progressive deepening due to erosion.

The main interest of the civil engineer in river history is in connection with the erosive processes that have been and still are at work. Weathering of the exposed rock surfaces can be regarded as the starting point in the train of erosion that eventually finishes in the depths of the sea or of an inland lake. Gravity and the wind will have the effect of bringing the products of weathering down from the hillsides. After rainstorms, the flows in even the smallest gullies will start the work of transporting this debris downward with the stream. The erosive action of streams, although starting in this way, can be generally classified as three separate processes: (1) transportation, (2) corrasion, and (3) solution. The start of the transportation of material by a stream has just been described. This is a process easy to visualize and in some cases to watch, and it is one the general nature of which can be readily appreciated. Solution is also a type of action easy to understand.

The term "corrasion" is used to denote the combined erosive action, mechanical in nature, of the flow of water and of the material that it is transporting along the bed of a stream. The action has been likened to the passing of a continually moving file over the stream bottom. A direct analogy can be seen in the practice of cutting solid rock with wire saws, quartz grains being usually introduced beneath the moving wire rope, to be carried along by it as it passes over the rock. The wire rope is similar in action to the river flow, and the quartz grains to the material being transported by the stream. Corrasion will clearly depend on the velocity of the stream flow, on the amount and nature of the load that the stream is transporting, on the plan and profile of the stream course, and on the geological nature of the stream bed. The direct influence of stream velocity on erosive action is a feature that needs no elaboration. The load of a stream is also of great importance, since the erosive action of water itself flowing in a straight and regular course over solid rock is small indeed. When it is carrying along sand and gravel, that portion of the load which travels on the bed of the stream will be con-

stantly in irregular movement, bumping against the bottom and intensify-
ing eddies. In this way, the resistance of the bed material to movement
will be broken down, and erosion will gradually take place. A striking
although rather localized example of this action is provided by the potholes which are often found in the beds of swift-flowing streams; the

Fig. 19.8. Typical gully erosion on Scarborough bluffs near Toronto, Ontario,
Canada. (The visitors are some of the Friends of the Pleistocene on one of their
annual field trips.)

presence of pebbles or even boulders at the bottom of such holes is a telling reminder of their mode of formation. During the construction of the
Assuan Dam in Egypt, potholes were found in the unwatered river-bed
area, 4 to 5 ft in diameter and up to 20 ft deep eroded out of the hardest
granite.[19.12]

The plan and profile of a stream naturally affect its flow and so inevitably are related to its corrasive action. Bed profiles have been discussed in a general way; the increased erosion liable to take place in the

more steeply graded section of a stream bed will be easily appreciated, especially since the erosive power of a stream depends not directly on the velocity but on some power of the velocity higher than the square. Another feature of a stream profile may be the existence of waterfalls. These will often be due to geological conditions influencing bed erosion.

Fig. 19.9. An unusual example of a deep pothole exposed by rock excavation for railway construction in northern Quebec, Canada.

No better example can be quoted than that provided by Niagara Falls, where the Niagara River drops over the Niagara escarpment in two waterfalls, 167 ft high, world famous for their majestic beauty and of peculiar interest to engineers in view of the water-power developments associated with them. A typical cross section through the falls is shown in Fig. 19.10, from which it will be seen that above the falls the river flows over an outcropping bed of Niagara limestone, a relatively hard rock below which occur beds of shale with a thin bed of Clinton limestone interposed. The shale is affected by the action of water more quickly than is the limestone; thus, even under the lip of the falls it is gradually eroded; this action leads eventually to an unstable projection of the limestone bed which then breaks off. Such rockfalls are periodically reported, and the recession of the lip is proceeding at a rate averaging 3 ft per year. It is suggested by geological studies that the falls were originally near Lewiston, several miles below the present site. The erosion of this great gorge, which is known to have taken place in the present era, is therefore a vivid reminder of the potentiality of rivers

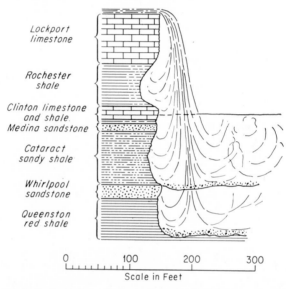

Lockport limestone
Rochester shale
Clinton limestone and shale
Medina sandstone
Cataract sandy shale
Whirlpool sandstone
Queenston red shale

0   100   200   300
Scale in Feet

Fig. 19.10. Geological section through Niagara Falls, illustrating the alternation of strata which assists erosion. (*Reproduced by permission of The Director, Geological Survey of Canada.*)

as a cause of erosion. So important have the falls at Niagara become, from the scenic point of view for tourists in both the United States and Canada but more particularly because of their vast power potential, that a Special International Niagara Board was appointed by the governments of the two countries in 1926. The board's report showed that the crest had receded at a rate of 3.8 ft per year from 1842 to 1905 and 2.3 ft per year between 1905 and 1927. The board recommended certain remedial works on either side of the river above the falls as a means of preserving their beauty and at the same time permitting abstraction of water by both countries in the amounts internationally agreed upon for power-generation purposes. These works, which include a notable submerged weir, have been constructed. Two great new power plants now utilize the full amount of power available in the authorized diverted water and the beauty of the falls is preserved, if not for all time—for the power of erosion cannot be eliminated but only controlled —at least for a reasonable period.[19.13]

19.6. Erosion below Dams. Natural erosion at so famous a location as Niagara Falls can be serious enough to warrant the expenditure of many millions of dollars upon remedial works, but erosion that is induced by man's interference with natural river flow by the construction of dams can have consequences that go beyond recognition in terms of money. The concentration of water flow and the high head under which it may take place render the hydraulic design of spillway channels always a delicate matter, and the proportioning of the artificial structure must be most carefully done. Unfortunate experiences have led engineers to undertake comprehensive research work in connection with studies, and there now exists in engineering literature a series of most valuable papers dealing with the hydraulic solution of the problems thus raised; many of these are based on the use of model structures.

A typical example is a paper by Butcher and Atkinson which describes extensive research work on models undertaken as a result of certain problems of erosion that had arisen in Sudan at the Sennar Dam controlling the Blue Nile, located about 200 miles south of Khartoum.[19.14] The dam is founded on a ridge of solid rock, but the river bed immediately below the dam consists of boulders and rock of doubtful quality. No masonry aprons were originally provided; and after the first year's operation, it was found that considerable erosion had taken place in this part of the river bed. A glass-sided observation tank with models of dam cross sections was employed in a way similar to that used by Dr. Rehbock in his original experiments on this problem carried out in 1905 and 1909 at the Technical University of Karlsruhe. The necessity of using some type of sill at the foot of the outfall apron of a dam was demonstrated in Butcher's and Atkinson's experiments, as it had been previously during Dr. Rehbock's experiments when the patented dentated sill that now bears his name was evolved. This detail of spillway design is mentioned because of its importance when geological studies show that the rock immediately below the overflow apron is liable to be affected by the intensity of direct flow; the use of some type of sill often reduces the eroding effect of the discharge flow. The experiments described also led to the conclusion that symmetry of flow and therefore of design is essential if scour is to be minimized, a feature that can usefully be applied to any cuttings in natural rock that have to be made immediately below an overflow structure.

In the discussion of this paper, some interesting examples were cited of erosion in New Red sandstone and in clay and shale beds adjacent to sluices at some of the locks of the Manchester Ship Canal. Since these openings did not have to pass large volumes of water, they illustrate how this problem of erosion may be of extreme importance even in relatively small structures. At least one major structure, the Islam Weir of the Sutlej Valley project, has failed from this cause. The weir is one of four similar structures on the Sutlej River in the Punjab which constitute diversion dams for a large irrigation project. Consisting of 24 openings, each of 60-ft span, it is a floating type of dam which rests on a sand foundation and is protected by upstream and downstream aprons. Although the head on the dam was only 18 ft, downstream scour in 2

Fig. 19.11. The Islam Weir, Sutlej Valley irrigation project, Punjab, as seen from upstream following the failure of six bays on Sept. 19, 1929. (*Photograph originally provided by the Secretary of the (then) Central Board of Irrigation, Simla, India.*)

years had amounted to 6½ ft; and in 1929, six bays of the structure collapsed. The official report of this accident is a most valuable publication.[19.15]

Numerous examples of the erosion of rock below dam spillways could be cited; in most instances the erosion developed only after the dam structure had been in use for some time. In some cases, although admittedly not in all, trouble of this kind can be foreseen if a detailed geological survey of the area immediately downstream from a spillway is made before construction begins. Careful study must be made not only of the effect of water and of concentrated flow on the rock but also of the structure of the rock. Besides the more usual erosion processes which will operate with increased intensity below a spillway discharge, there always exists the possibility that concentrated flow will loosen blocks of the rock at its more definite joints and bedding planes, especially if these contain any disintegrated material or product such as clay. This loosening would not normally be serious, but the velocities that occur in a spillway discharge may be so high that blocks of rock of great size will thus be transported downstream bodily. They provide a dangerous "tool" for the stream flow to use in further erosion and leave exposed a further area of bedrock

Fig. 9.12. Calderwood Dam on the Little Tennessee River, Tennessee, U.S.A., showing the special overflow pool which "cushions" the fall of spillway discharge and thus controls erosion. (*Reproduced by permission of the Aluminum Company of America.*)

on which the concentrated flow will impinge. Such a condition existed on the Susquehanna River in Maryland, in the case of the fissured granite below the Conowingo Dam, the joints of which were filled with clay. Remedial measures include aprons and protective works, as already mentioned, and also the provision of deep stilling pools, as in the case of the Calderwood Dam.

Erosion below spillways is no "respecter of persons" or even of the importance of dams; many of the best known dam structures in North America and elsewhere have had to have remedial works carried out after erosion was detected below their spillways. The spillway at Grand Coulee Dam had a carefully designed spillway bucket, formed of concrete, and designed to provide a cushion of water at the foot of the spillway proper. First flooded in 1937, the bucket was examined by divers in 1943. Variable erosion even in the surface of the first-class concrete used for construction averaged about 2 in. throughout the length of the spillway and included potholes (in the concrete) formed by the action of boulders that had got into the bucket; one of granite had a diameter of 24 in. Remedial action served to correct the erosion thus discovered which, although surprising, did not affect in any way the stability of the great structure.[19.16]

The erosive power of swiftly moving water was well illustrated by the damage done to the spillway of the Bonneville Dam on the Columbia River, the repair of which cost $750,000. The spillway has a dentated sill which was designed after most careful study; the concrete baffles are protected by steel armor plates. Cavitation around the baffles had completely removed some of the steel plates and eroded the concrete to depths up to 22 in.[19.17] Erosion of shale bedrock to a depth of 22 ft and the necessary placement of 50,000 cu yd of concrete to replace eroded concrete and shale provide further evidence of this aspect of erosion from experience with the Lake Waco Dam in Texas. More than $1 million had to be expended in finally replacing the old timber apron and rock-filled cribs used for many years to protect the historic St. Anthony Falls on the Mississippi River at Minneapolis after serious erosion had been caused by an unprecedented flood in 1952. A new reinforced-concrete apron was designed following hydraulic model studies and installed before erosion had proceeded too far into the soft St. Peter sandstone which constitutes the bedrock at the famous falls and which is mentioned elsewhere in this book (see page 489).[19.18]

Finally, as a typical example of another interrelation of dam construction and erosional processes, there may be mentioned the Wilder Dam on the Connecticut River completed in November, 1950, by the New England Power Company. The dam was built at a famous site on this historic river known in earlier years as "White River Falls" where the Rogers Rangers saw their raft broken by the turbulent rapids. Integral with the dam is a powerhouse equipped with two 16,500-kw generators operating under a head of 51 ft. The dam is a mass concrete structure 2,100 ft long. The necessary excavation revealed a deep pothole 15 ft below the bottom of the river. Amid the debris filling this pothole an old piece of iron rail was found. Those responsible for the work had the rail analyzed by the Carnegie–Illinois Steel Corporation, and the analysis suggested that the rail had been made between the years 1845 and 1850. At that time the first railway was under construction up the west side of the river; this suggests the origin of the rail, but its location so far below the river bed only a century later provides vivid evidence of the erosional power of swift water.[19.19]

19.7. Transportation of Solid Material by Stream Flow. When rivers reach the state described as that of old age, they will have a bed profile that approaches the minimum possible if the discharge of the river is to reach the sea through the cross section of the natural waterway. This hydraulic criterion is related to the critical velocity for silt and scour, since there is one particular condition at which a regulated stream will neither erode the exposed material in its bed nor deposit the silt that it carries in suspension. This silt and scour criterion is a condition of delicate hydraulic balance, and many problems of river engineering, especially those connected with river-development work involving some alteration of natural features, may be seriously complicated by the continued presence in a river bed of solid material being transported down the river as a product of erosion. The matter has been the object of much engineering research work; records of detailed investigations by engineers go back at least to 1851 and recur in increasing numbers in engineering publications since that time. Concurrently, the approach to what was originally a relatively simple geological process has changed from that of generalized observation to a detailed and sometimes complicated analytical mathematical investigation. The quantitative study of transportation by running water is now rightly regarded as an important branch of the science of hydraulics, with which this book is not directly concerned, but the basis of all such analytical study is the fundamental geological process of erosion.

As an extreme example of how serious the matter may become, an observation of the San Juan River in Colorado may be mentioned; in flood the river appears to be a moving stream of red mud and proves on test, to be 75 per cent by volume composed of silt and red sand. Admittedly, this is an extreme case, but the fact that careful estimates suggest that as much as 250 million tons of silt annually pass the lower end of the canyon section of the Colorado River and that the Mississippi River carries almost twice this amount of silt into its delta each year will show that silt transportation is a process of magnitude. In many parts of the world, the regular deposition of silt so transported is beneficial to fertile areas; the Nile Valley of Egypt is perhaps the best known example. In other parts of the world, deposition of silt transported by river flow during flood periods can be injurious; New Zealand, South Africa, and the Malay Peninsula are countries seriously affected in this way. As an example of what may result from this cause the town of Kuala Kubo in Malaya may be mentioned: the town had to be completely abandoned in 1929 and reestablished on a new site some miles away, because the original site was buried many feet deep in river-deposited silt.[19.20]

The source of the material transported by river flow is usually confined to the catchment area of the particular river. The quantity of material transported and the regularity of its movement are therefore dependent on the geological characteristics of the catchment basin. In preliminary studies of a river prior to the prosecution of development or remedial work, a rough survey of the geology of the drainage area is therefore an essential requirement. Coupled with the complementary topographical survey, this will indicate the stage of development that the river has reached above the point considered, the natural or initial causes of erosion (such as disintegration of steep rock slopes, wind action, surface soil erosion), and probably the main source of material transported by the river. This information is useful mainly as a guide to further studies, since the effect of transportation by water is to reduce practically all material, whatever its initial state, to particles fine enough to be classified as either fine sand or silt. For example, the vast quantity of silt transported by the Colorado River is actually rock flour mixed with some organic matter and ground so fine by water action that in grain size it is truly described as silt.

A more detailed study and one of immediate value to the engineer is the securing of samples of river water together with the silt they carry and the quantitative analysis of these in order to obtain an estimate of the average quantity of material being transported. For this purpose, one of the several types of silt sampler now available may be used. Most silt samplers consist essentially of a closed container to which river water can be admitted at some determinate point in the cross section of the river. Results given by sampling present only a partial picture, since transportation is not a simple matter of suspension but a threefold process. Described in the simplest way, the means of transportation may be said to be a rolling along the river bed of the heaviest particles, an intermittent bumping up and rolling of the next grade of particles, and finally the transportation in suspension of the finest particles of the river's load. The total load is therefore divisible into two parts: the bed load is that transported by the first two types of movement, and the suspended load is that moved by the third. The suspended load is capable of accurate measurement by means of samples, but no really satisfactory method of measuring bed load has yet been devised for general application.

The study of the several types of movement is what has naturally attracted the attention of investigators, and the correlation of the results of mathematical analysis with experimental results has provided engineering literature with many notable papers. The engineer is interested primarily in the results of theoretical investigations; he is especially interested in the way in which they may be applied to his specific problems. He will not usually be concerned with the transport of material in normal river sections; but whenever a river section has to be artificially enlarged or reduced, with consequent changes in velocity, he should be able to calculate in advance how these changes will affect the transportation of material, especially in relation to the scouring out of bed material if this is unconsolidated. An associated problem is that faced by engineers engaged on irrigation work who have to design their canal systems so that the bulk of the transported load in the irrigation water shall be deposited before the water reaches the final feeder systems. The deposition of river silt on irrigated farm land has in some instances been found to have injurious effects on fertility. Elaborate precautions have therefore to be taken in order to remove silt before river water is admitted to a canal system.

One installation of this type is at the entrance to the All-American Canal which takes off from the Colorado River about 300 miles below Hoover Dam and serves the Imperial Irrigation District. Although Hoover Dam naturally holds up practically all the material transported by the Colorado River as far down as the dam site, the scouring action of the river is such that in the 12 miles immediately downstream from the dam, the river bed scoured out to an average depth of about 3 ft in the first 5 months following the closure of the gates at the head of the diversion tunnels at the Hoover Dam site. This was not an unexpected result, since preliminary design work for the canal intake works had been based on an assumed total load of 120 million lb of silt per day in the maximum anticipated diversion of 15,000 cfs of water. Estimates suggested that the cost of removing this amount of silt from the irrigation system if deposited in the canals would amount to $1 million per year; a desilting installation at the canal intake proved therefore to be an economic possibility. The installation eventually provided consists essentially of six settling basins, 269 by 769 ft, with a rated capacity of 2,000 cfs; the maximum velocity in the basins is 0.24 fps; and the deposited silt is removed by power-operated rotary scrapers. The efficiency of desilting at normal flow has been found to be 80 per cent by the engineering staff of the U.S. Bureau of Reclamation, which is responsible for the installation.[19.21]

In India, the main problem faced by irrigation engineers is sometimes the reverse of that indicated by the American example just cited, since the silt transported by Indian rivers is not always injurious to agriculture. It is present in such quantities that the general practice has developed of designing Indian irrigation works so that the silt and sand are deposited in the channels on individual farms where they can easily be cleared out by the peasant farmers. Thus a main canal will be so "designed as to its section and slope that it will be able to carry forward its full quota of sand silt without either deposition or erosion".[19.22] These words are quoted from a publication of the well-known irrigation engineer, R. G. Kennedy; as a result of prolonged investigation, Kennedy developed a formula for the conditions of flow described, a formula that now bears his name and is widely used. Kennedy's work was but one step in a large series of studies carried out in many parts of India devoted to the problem of so-called "stable flow" and closely related to river-training work.

In this work, hydraulic studies come into close contact with the geological background; the grain size of the silt is an all-important factor. An appreciation of the geological origin of the silt considered will go far toward assisting in the correct application of the results of such hydraulic research.

The more usual problem faced by civil engineers in connection with the material transported by running water, however, is the removal of the solid material. Not only must silt be removed in some cases, as at the

Fig. 19.13. Aerial view of the Imperial Dam on the Colorado River, U.S.A., and the intake of the All-American Canal on the California bank, including the extensive desilting works (seen before the admission of river water). (*Reproduced by permission of The Commissioner, U.S. Bureau of Reclamation.*)

Imperial Dam desilting works, but coarser debris must sometimes be removed for the protection of machinery through which the debris-laden water is to pass, such as the turbines in water-power plants. It is only in mountainous areas with streams of occasional high velocity that this becomes a serious problem. A notable desanding installation is a part of the Marlengo hydroelectric station on the river Adige in the southern Alps where the mountainous terrain necessitated building the installation underground; at the adjacent Tel station, there is a corresponding installation. The building of these two special plants led to an immediate decrease in the cost of maintenance and a corresponding increase in the amount of power generated.[19.23]

The debris carried by streams and rivers in flood is a familiar sight in almost all parts of the world. Excessive floods sometimes necessitate debris-removal operations in their wake but only rarely do engineering works have to be specially constructed to take care of flood debris. One important area where such works are necessary is that around the city of Los Angeles. The Los Angeles County Flood Control District has developed an extensive series of debris-collecting basins which serve to protect the lives of residents in the great metropolitan district of Los

FIG. 19.14. Sluicing operations in progress upstream of the Santa Anita Dam, removing flood debris retained by this constant-angle arched concrete dam of the Los Angeles County Flood Control District, California, U.S.A. (*Reproduced by permission of the Chief Engineer, Los Angeles County Flood Control District.*)

Angeles and the valuable property that now lies in this vast developed area so close to the foothills of the San Gabriel Mountains. Some of the basins are relatively shallow, formed by low-lying dikes; others are located in narrow valleys, formed by dams some of which are notable in size and design. Flood debris has to be removed regularly from the collecting basins; this is usually done by sluicing into the normal stream flow but in some cases it is done by excavation with earth-moving equipment. Because of the character of the watershed and the heavy flood flows that occur in this area, an average amount of debris (soil, gravel, and boulders) of 60,000 cu yd per sq mile for one flood has been found to collect; occasional measurements register twice this amount. Actual observations of flood flows have disclosed flows of 85 per cent solid material, the consistency of sloppy concrete. These figures for material eroded from steeply sloped mountain watersheds may be contrasted with the silt content of the Mississippi River that rarely exceeds 0.5 per cent (5,000 ppm). Even that of the Missouri River, "Big Muddy," rarely exceeds 20,000 ppm or about 2 per cent. [19.24]

The economic significance of desilting, desanding, and flood-debris collecting works will be clear. It is so obvious a drain on the public purse

Fig. 19.15. Dredge No. 117 of the Pennsylvania Power and Light Company at work dredging coal in the Susquehanna River, Pennsylvania, U.S.A., as an integral unit of the Manor coal plant. (*Reproduced by permission of the General Superintendent, Pennsylvania Power and Light Company.*)

that it may be surprising to find that there are locations where the existence of silt has been not unwelcome. Notable amongst these are places on some of the rivers of Pennsylvania which run through areas marked by outcrops of the famous Pennsylvania coal seams. In the early days of coal mining, only desirable coarse coal was sold; the finer "river coal" was dumped directly into adjacent streams or it eroded from spoil dumps in which it was piled. The wet process of preparing anthracite is another source of fine coal particles washed into waterways; the ordinary coal-washing process has had similar effect. It has been estimated that collieries in the Schuylkill Valley have been responsible for as much as 1 million tons of silt and coal washed into the river in one year. As a part of the operations of the Interstate Commission on the Delaware River Basin, a $35 million dredging program was initiated in 1944 to remove the accumulated silt and fine coal ("culm") that had been steadily spoiling the Schuylkill River; much of the project is self-liquidating because some of the coal content of the dredged material is recovered in special plants.[19.25]

More recently, the Pennsylvania Power and Light Company has built a special plant for the reclamation of 500,000 tons of coal annually from the bed of the Susquehanna River. This followed the successful operation since 1938 of the 30,000-kw steam plant at Holtwood using only reclaimed river coal as fuel. Over 3 million tons of coal have been used in this plant in its first 20 years of operation. The Holtwood plant was increased by the installation of a 66,000-kw steam generator to serve which the new coal-reclaiming plant was started in 1951; studies showed that the known reserve of submerged coal would last approximately 35 years. The Safe Harbor Dam, built to create the necessary head for the associated water-power plant, had resulted in the accumulation of vast quantities of the river coal in the bed of the reservoir so formed. The new coal plant was therefore located just above the dam. Coal and silt are dredged out by a 14-in. hydraulic rotary cutter dredge, transported by barge to an unloading wharf, and then pumped through a 12-in. line to the coal-washing plant, located on a convenient site 275 ft above river level. The finished product is transported 8 miles by rail to the Holtwood steam plant and there stored until required for use. The entire plant was designed in full conformity with the clean-streams program of the Commonwealth of Pennsylvania. The fact that an investment of $6 million for this unusual plant was warranted is further indication of the economic significance of the process of erosion by river flow, even though in this case the entry is on the right side of the balance sheet.[19.26]

19.8. Silting Up of Reservoirs. In all but exceptional cases, the construction of a dam or weir across a stream bed will raise the water level above the line of the dam, and thus increase the cross-sectional area of the stream and decrease the average velocity. This will automatically eliminate a part of the suspended load of the stream, which will fall to the bottom of the stream or reservoir. Although all the bed load may move down toward the dam, it will eventually be caught in the basin formed by the dam structure. There exist all too many records of large dams rendered either ineffective or useless by the unscheduled and rapid filling of the reservoir behind them with transported material. To mention but a few of these, reference may be made to the so-called New Lake Austin on the Colorado River in Texas, which lost 95.6 per cent of its capacity in 13 years; La Grange Reservoir on the Tuolumne River in California, which lost 83 per cent in 36 years; and the Habra Reservoir on the Habra

River in Algeria, which lost 58 per cent in 22 years. These figures are quoted from an extensive list of silted reservoirs compiled by J. C. Stevens.[19.27] Reference is also made in this paper to the unusual siltation record for the Lake Macmillan Reservoir of the Pecos Irrigation District in the United States, which lost 55.5 per cent of its capacity between 1894 and 1920. Since the latter year, no further accumulation of silt has taken place, because an extensive growth of tamarisk (salt cedar) in the flatlands immediately above the reservoir has so reduced the stream velocity that the main part of the silt load is deposited before the reservoir is reached.

An essential part of preliminary work in connection with the construction of all dam structures is consequently an investigation of the amount of silt normally transported by the stream to be dammed. It may often be found that the quantity of material carried is negligible; but in other cases, further and more detailed studies will be necessary. These will inevitably include a careful correlation of information on the quantity of debris transported and its geological origin, so that the nature of the resulting deposit may be anticipated. This information is necessary in view of the engineering problems involved. These may be classified into two groups: (1) possible methods of removal of the transported material either before it is deposited in the reservoir or after it has come to rest behind the dam; and (2) the effect that deposits of material, if they cannot be avoided, will have on the stability and on the utility of the structure being planned.

Detailed discussion of these problems is mainly an engineering matter, but their essential dependence upon geological conditions will be apparent. The second problem relates mainly to the effect of silt and other retained debris upon mechanical and other moving parts integral with a dam structure, since under normal circumstances the deposition of silt against the face of a dam does not increase the normal pressure upon it. The possibility of removing silt that is trapped in a reservoir is, however, a matter of much wider significance. For very large mass concrete structures, it may be practically impossible to include in the design any means for passing silt through the dam after retention; the problem then becomes one of economics with relation to the anticipated useful life of the reservoir. For smaller structures that are known in advance of construction to be so located that they will retain silt, bypass arrangements can sometimes be incorporated into the design of the dam for occasional sluicing of the retained material. Alternatively, arrangements can be contemplated, or even made after construction when necessary, for the removal of retained silt by sluicing or dredging. And in extreme cases, when silt is unexpectedly retained by a dam, the structure may be breached in order to make the reservoir again serviceable.

Reference has already been made to the high silt content of the Rio Grande and the Colorado Rivers; examples of major dams upon these two rivers may therefore appropriately be cited. Elephant Butte Dam is on the Rio Grande River a short distance north of the junction of Mexico and the states of Texas and New Mexico. It was completed in 1916; its drainage basin has an area of 25,923 sq miles. Probably because of the international character of the river, it has been continuously under measured observation for many years and so there are available records of the silt load coming into Elephant Butte reservoir that can be correlated with the measured deposition of silt on a scale probably unequaled for any other major reservoir. Estimates based upon these observations suggest that the useful life of the reservoir after its first filling will be about 150 years unless some unanticipated change in river regime or other natural conditions should take place.[19.28]

On the Colorado River, Hoover Dam has created one of the largest of man-made lakes, Lake Mead, already mentioned several times in this book because of its outstanding geological significance. All the silt load of the Colorado River is naturally held up as the water of the river passes the great dam, so that studies of sedimentation have been actively pursued ever since the dam first began to retain water. Estimates of the useful life of the reservoir have naturally varied, but one of the most recent suggests that the reservoir will not be filled with silt to its crest level until about 445 years after the first closing of the gates controlling the bypass tunnels on February 1, 1935.[19.29] When the magnitude of Hoover Dam is recalled, this estimate of 445 years is still a sobering figure, even though human thinking is not normally accustomed to look ahead beyond the current century. The estimate is in keeping with the suggestion that the useful life of the reservoirs constructed in North America in the second quarter of this century, which probably exceed in number all those built previously, averages about 200 years.

The cleaning out of filled reservoirs is a normal part of the operation of flood-control dams, such as those of the Los Angeles County Flood Control District already mentioned. Reservoirs for water supply, however, experience the same sort of problem, although usually at a slower rate. The San Fernando reservoir of the Los Angeles Bureau of Waterworks and Supply, for example, lost 24 per cent of its capacity in about 20 years. Arrangements were made for dewatering the reservoir for a period of 38 days, during which a major sluicing operation was undertaken; about 20,000 cu yd of silt was sluiced out of the reservoir into a specially constructed debris basin; it was found that about 90 cu yd could be moved in this way per man-day.[19.30] Philadelphia faced a similar problem with its Queen Lane sedimentation basin in which 500,000 cu yd of silt had accumulated during its first 50 years of operation. The basin had to be kept in operation, and so on the basis of satisfactory experience with the same problem at the city's Torresdale plant, it was decided to remove the silt by an electrically operated floating dredge. The dredge had to be assembled at the site and launched into the basin (that used at Torresdale was floated in from the Delaware River). The large accumulation of silt is accounted for by the fact that the Schuylkill River water, with its high silt content that has already been mentioned, is treated in the Queen Lane plant by chemical coagulation so that, to some extent, the silt deposition here is premeditated although still derived from river flow.[19.31]

Fig. 19.16. Reservoir of the old Furnish Dam, Umatilla River, Oregon, completely silted up after only 16 years of use. After purchasing the entire reservoir site, the Union Pacific Railway destroyed the dam (center of photograph) to obviate damage by high water to one of its tunnels, just off the left. Alfalfa is now being grown on the silt beds formed in the old reservoir; the beds are irrigated by means of sprinklers. (*Reproduced by permission of the U.S. Soil Conservation Service.*)

More unusual was the experience with a 120-ft arched-concrete dam spanning the narrow Cat Creek Canyon in an isolated part of Nevada, constructed in 1931 by the U.S. Bureau of Reclamation to serve the water supply needs of the Naval Ammunition Depot at Hawthorne, with an impounded volume of 50 million gal. On July 21, 1955, a half-hour thunderstorm caused a flash flood in Cat Creek so intense that it cleaned off all erodible material from the catchment area above the dam, depositing it behind the dam and almost completely filling the reservoir. After 35,000 cu yd had been removed by excavation, with some difficulty, the reservoir was again filled with debris and silt after heavy rains. The decision was made to breach it at its lowest point since no sluiceway had been considered necessary in the original design. This difficult operation was successfully completed early in 1956 and a 4- by 4-ft hole was blasted through the concrete, close to the bed of the canyon. For half an hour after the breach was made, little came through the hole, but then the mud plug shot out with a roar and in the course of a few hours, 50,000 cu yd of silt and water rushed through; the water effectively washed the silt downstream. Sluicing then completed the job. A sluice gate was attached to the face of the dam, utilizing the hole as the sluiceway, so that future deposits of silt (unless of a phenomenal character) can readily be removed.[19.32]

The deposition of silt in reservoirs is so obvious a result of dam construction that there remains little more to be said about it. Silt contents of streams and rivers can be determined at the time of design; predictions can be made of the probable continuation of this amount of silt reaching the dam after its construction; the effect of the dam upon the river bed downstream can be estimated and the possible effects of the degradation of the stream bed investigated; and finally the economics of the entire project, based on a probable finite useful length of life for the reservoir as a key factor in the study, can be evaluated as a basis for the final decision regarding building. Behind all such mundane proceedings, however, is the tragic significance of the origin of most of the silt that is to be trapped in the reservoir. To some extent, this may be derived by normal river flow from the bed of the streams and rivers that bring it to the dam site. In almost all cases, however, most of the silt load will represent topsoil that has been washed off the surface of the land in the watershed above the dam. No civil engineer should be able to look upon a silt-laden stream without being disturbed by the critical problem of soil erosion.

19.9. Soil Erosion and Conservation. The silt in streams, in rivers, retained behind dams, and that which builds the great deltas of the world or slowly fills up river estuaries until removed by costly dredging—all this is not just "silt." Almost all of it has once been topsoil, gracing the land served by the river or stream, the soil in which vegetation large and small has had its roots. The possible erosive action of surface flow over rock is negligible during a period of relatively few years; but erosive action on unconsolidated materials may be far from negligible. When vegetation covers the ground on which rain falls, the binding effect of plant-root systems, in addition to the protection afforded by foliage, will generally result in the rain reaching the actual ground strata gradually. Alternatively, after heavy rains the rain may flow over the surface vegetation at such a speed and in such a manner that little erosion of the ground will take place. It is only when vegetation is lacking that erosion can become serious. And vegetation can so easily be disturbed by the hand of man, by uncontrolled tree felling, improper cultivation practices, abuse of the land instead of its nurture, and by regarding crops both large and small as something to be "mined" without regard for the future.

Although the widespread effects of soil erosion have attracted public attention in North America (as in other Western countries) in relatively recent years only, soil erosion is no new thing. The deserts of North China, of Iran, of Iraq, and of North Africa were not always deserts; this is clear from the records of history. They have become deserts within the span of recorded history because of the gradual but steady depletion of the topsoil which once covered them as the demands

Fig. 19.17. The beginnings of soil erosion in a grainfield in Pickering Township, Ontario, Canada. (*Reproduced by permission of the Ontario Department of Commerce and Development, Conservation Branch.*)

upon the soil by expanding civilizations increased. The glory that was Carthage is now a waste of sand, caused by soil exhaustion, crop failures, land abandonment, and the encroachment of the desert, and not merely as a result of warfare. Vast areas of China resemble gigantic battlefields, scarred deep in a way not seen on the scenes of man's mortal fights but as a result of man's battle with nature in the great loessal region, nature making short work of carving deep channels into any land that was abandoned in the unequal fight. And of all the countries of the world most in need of the conservation measures that it is now receiving, none comes before present-day Israel, the land "flowing with milk and honey" so familiar as a pleasant place and fertile as recently as when the words of Holy Writ were penned.

In the world today, there are few "developed" countries that have not felt the effects of soil erosion to some degree, although the effects have been less profound in older countries with well-established agricultural practices and equitable temperate climates, such as France and Great Britain. In South Africa, soil erosion was described by Field Marshal Smuts as a scourge second only to war. Even in so pleasant a land as New Zealand, large areas have been eroded. In South Australia, to take just one of the Australian states, it has been said that over 1,000 sq miles that were once pastoral country are now desert. In Canada, the first soil erosion was noticed at Indian Head, Saskatchewan as early as 1875; since then all too much land has been lost to agriculture. The Magdalen Islands, once a fertile group in the center of the Gulf of St. Lawrence, have had all their topsoil removed; only sand, not a stick of timber, now remains on the islands. And in the United States, it has been estimated that 50 million acres of good cropland has been ruined almost permanently, with another 50 million acres almost as seriously depleted, and an equivalent total area affected to some degree. Over-all figures are so astronomical as to be almost unbelievable; two, however, may be noted. It has been estimated that 5.4 billion tons of topsoil have been lost in 1 year in the United States; the total cost of the soil erosion itself and associated damage to engineering structures is said to be well over $3.8 billion.[19,33]

It is the damage done to engineering structures by soil erosion that usually first attracts the attention of the civil engineer to this widespread public problem. There may be some who, like the writer, have been forced to think of the matter because of participation in the design and construction of engineering works necessitated by the effects of soil erosion. The writer was privileged to be associated with the design of the Shand Dam on the Grand River in central Ontario (an earth dam formed of compacted glacial till); its purpose was to regulate the flow of the Grand River in order to reduce flooding but more particularly to give a minimum low-water flow in order to remove unsanitary conditions resulting from an almost negligible summer flow. When one sees more than $1 million thus spent to counteract the misuse of land, "soil erosion" becomes very much more than a mere name; the engineering significance of soil erosion is at once apparent.

Full discussion of the cause of soil erosion and of the best methods to be followed in soil conservation is complex since so many factors are involved. Fortunately, there are now in most countries active agencies whose responsibility it is to deal with the problem. The United States Soil Conservation Service is perhaps the pioneer and an acknowledged leader in this vital field. Conservation measures necessarily vary widely, but a fundamental feature is that all designs shall aid natural processes. Thus it is that the labor of the engineer on such work is closely allied with geological considerations and that the construction of small dams across gullies in order to check flood flows and reduce flood velocities, and therefore erosion, is a leading type of work and one demanding cooperative endeavor. This sort of small-scale engineering is often called "upstream engineering"; the term has sometimes been used in a somewhat derogatory manner. If it were only remembered that all such soil conservation work has as a prime objective the conservation of invaluable topsoil, the reducing of floods being secondary although of unusual

Fig. 19.18. Small masonry dam for stream and erosion control; Contra Costa County, California. (*Reproduced by permission of the U.S. Soil Conservation Service.*)

significance and value, much of the fruitless discussion between the proponents of "big dams" and "little dams" could be avoided. Both measures are needed; applied intelligently and cooperatively, they can do much to conserve soil and reduce floods.

19.10. Erosion by the Wind. The importance of the wind in structural engineering is self-evident; sometimes wind loads on structures are the maximum loads to be considered in design. Wind is also important to the civil engineer, however, as an agent of erosion; its natural role in the work of erosion is speedily evident on any unprotected land. Some of the main evidences of its work are drifting sand dunes. Although these are prominent in desert regions, they often present troublesome local problems on seacoasts with sandy beaches. The travel of coastal sand has wrought great damage in Europe, especially on the shores of the Bay of Biscay. At Liege in France, for example, sand dunes have been moving for 2 centuries at the rate of 81 ft per year, necessitating two successive reconstructions of the local church. The geologist can but observe this phenomenon. The botanist, however, is here of assistance, and much has been done in the development of plants, grasses, and shrubs that will take root in sand and provide a matting of root material which will effectively bind the surface together. In a few places, these wind-formed dunes have an economic value where they serve as a storage ground for rain water; in western Texas, for example, rangers get their water supplies from wells put down at the summits of large dunes.

Reference to sand dunes in the west of Texas will be puzzling to those who associate dunes only with seacoasts. It is here that they are most in evidence, but large areas of dunes—generally of recent origin, unfortunately, the result of improper land practices—are now to be found in much of the Great Plains area and especially in New Mexico, Colorado, Texas, Kansas, Wyoming, and the Dakotas. On the Pacific Coast, dunes are found all the way from Baja California to southern Alaska. The ravages of forest fire, which removes all humus from the ground surface and leaves it open to the action of the wind, and the uncontrolled grazing of cattle are two prime causes of many modern dune areas. In open country, the presence of dunes may not be a menace, but in all too many areas they have encroached upon valuable land or tend to do so. Thus, the need of expert control measures can be seen. Although "mechanical" means of control, such as fences and brush mats, have their uses, their effect is temporary only. The use of vegetation is essential for the complete control of drifting sands; when properly used, vegetation has succeeded in solving some of the most serious problems of wind erosion.

An inland example of such control was provided when the U.S. Army Engineers constructed the John Martin Dam across the Arkansas River in southeastern Colorado. Flooding of the reservoir so formed was going to submerge many miles of the main line of the Santa Fe Railroad. On the south side of the river was an area of 1,200 acres of sand dunes which everyone wished to avoid if possible. On the other side of the river, however, purchase of 17 miles of right of way through valuable irrigated farm land, as well as the construction of two large bridges, would have been necessary. The Soil Conservation Service was asked to assist; it did, and to such good effect that the dune area was stabilized so well that the crack trains of the Santa Fe have been safely using the relocated track, running right through the dunes, without any trouble at all; a substantial saving of money from the public purse was achieved in the process. The principal grasses used were little and big bluestem, sand reed grass, blue grama, switch grass, sand dropseed, and sand love grass. Some trees were also planted after the grass had taken root.[19.34]

Although the control of sand dunes is the most obvious form of erosion control necessary because of the wind, the construction of major airports has led to another and more artificial hazard of the same kind. When an airport is graded, all vegetation may be so disturbed as to leave a bare soil surface. If this is not immediately protected, erosion by the wind may speedily follow. It is clear that only by vegetation can

Fig. 19.19. Rehabilitated sand dunes on the south side of the Arkansas River near the reservoir formed by the John Martin Dam, Colorado, U.S.A., showing the effective use of specially selected grasses. (*Reproduced by permission of the U.S. Soil Conservation Service.*)

such control effectively and economically be achieved. New York's Idlewild Airport provides a good example of what can be done in this way. The original marsh and meadowland at the airport site was completely covered by the 65 million cu yd of sand pumped from Jamaica Bay. The area of 4,900 acres thus formed was vulnerable to the winds that almost continually sweep this coastal location. Fortunately, because of the experience gained in controlling neighboring beach areas, especially at Jones Beach, engineers were able to meet the problem at the airport. They sowed a mixture of 10 per cent poverty grass and 90 per cent beach grass all over the airport. By means of a machine planter 20,000 grass roots could be planted on 1 acre in 2 hr; if the job had been done by hand, this would have been a full day's work for 20 men.[19.35] It is of interest to note that an attempt was made at Idlewild to control the sand by spraying with oil. As soon as the volatile content of the oil evaporated, however, the residual bitumen dried out, cracked, flaked, and blew away. Repeated treatments of even the most satisfactory oil are always necessary if the more certain control given when the aid of nature is recruited cannot be achieved.

19.11. Biology and Civil Engineering. Poverty grass and common beach grass have just been mentioned; they should more properly have been

Fɪɢ. 19.20. Geology and engineering "in the raw." The Alaska Highway crossing a large alluvial fan, the result of erosion, British Columbia, Canada, near Muncho Lake, mileage 467. (*Photograph by H. W. Richardson.*)

referred to as *Ammophila arenaria* with *Ammophila breviligulata* and *Andropogon virginicus* var *littoralis*, since here the civil engineer is using the results of the work of the botanist, to whom such semantic exactitude is as common as corresponding engineering terminology is to the engineer. There may be some engineers to whom reference to botanical terms in a book such as this may appear out of place, but not to those who have seen for themselves the immense value of the use of living agencies in engineering work. To speak of biology and civil engineering is not, therefore, to link the names of mutually exclusive disciplines but to suggest one of the most potent of all scientific combinations in the practice of civil engineering. In fact, it is not going too far to say that if nature can be so utilized as to restore natural conditions that have been disturbed by engineering works, the best possible remedy will have been achieved and, in some cases, the only practicable solution.

The use of grasses and shrubs in controlling erosion is perhaps the most obvious and quite the most widespread application of biology to the geological aspects of civil engineering. But it is not the only one, as the existence of many notable publications makes clear. Possibly even more striking is the fact that, under the auspices of the oldest of all civil engineering bodies, the Institution of Civil Engineers, this newest of interdisciplinary liaisons was the subject of a full 3-day conference held in London, England, in September, 1948.[19.36] The published volume of the proceedings of this unusual and valuable meeting constitutes a most useful guide to the aid that the civil engineer can obtain through close cooperation with biologists, particularly with botanists, with reference to the selection of the best type of vegetation with which to restore the damaged surface of land. It has been well said that "there are many similarities between the methods of Nature in healing damage to the earth and to the skin of any living animal. If a man cuts his hand, Nature immediately begins to restore the protective layer . . . when man damages the surface of the earth in a comparatively small way, Nature steps in and creates a protective layer, first of grasses, then shrubs, and finally trees." This is normally a very slow process, but with the aid of biological advice, the engineer can speed up the process by careful surface preparation and by the selection of appropriate species for planting. The results can be quite astonishing, given only a minimum of time, as all who have seen the results of such scientific horticultural practice can testify.

Reference has already been made to the use of vegetation in stabilizing slopes. Its use in controlling the new surfaces of airfields has just been discussed. Perhaps the most important and also the most spectacular use of vegetation has been in the stabilization of sand dunes both inland and on the seacoast. In many parts of the world, notably in New Zealand, Great Britain, and the Netherlands, extensive areas of unstable dune sand have been brought under control merely by the proper use of vegetation. Names of the plants used could be given but since the best species to be used in any location depends on the local climate and environment, it is perhaps advisable to suggest alternatively that local biologists should be consulted, since the use of the wrong types of vegetation can be frustrating, time consuming, and very costly.

In all this work, the engineer is merely imitating and assisting nature. It is not only in engineering that nature can provide so useful an example, but certainly in engineering there is a great deal to be learned from the careful study of living things. The spider's web, for example, must have given early man ideas from which rope suspension bridges were developed. Correspondingly, the internal structure of the bamboo is a masterpiece of structural design, explaining, in part at least, how this organic material can be successfully used as reinforcing in concrete structures.

The beaver has sometimes been called nature's own engineer. To all who have studied the construction of a large beaver dam, this suggestion is no mere poetic fancy. The way in which the beaver regularly dams up the flow of swift-flowing streams has been almost exactly followed in many check-dam projects for the control of stream erosion. Notable examples of this type of work were used in soil-conservation work in Utah by L. M. Winsor, district engineer of the U.S. Department of Agriculture at Salt Lake City who freely acknowledged his debt to the beavers he had seen at work in his area.[19.37] In some districts, beavers have been too efficient in their work. In northern Ontario, for example, engineers of Canadian National Railways regularly have to blast away beaver dams on streams adjacent to their main line, dams constructed with no regard, unfortunately for the C.N.R., to the relation of the crest level of the dams and the elevation of the rail right of way. Flooding is a regular occurrence; since beavers are persistent workers, with unlimited patience, the struggle has been a long one.

The construction of golf courses may not normally classify as civil engineering work in the fullest sense, but there is on record an example that may finally be cited as a real "cautionary tale for engineers." Off the coast of Australia, in a location that shall be nameless, there is a small island on which an attractive 9-hole golf course has been laid out. The club decided some years after the course was opened to extend it to 18 holes by using adjacent dunes and sandy land between the island and the coast. Grading started in the winter with the filling in of a network of burrows excavated by a colony of muttonbirds (shearwaters) which had just left on their annual migration. The new fairway was almost ready for official opening in the late spring when the muttonbirds returned, to be most annoyed by the disturbance of their traditional burrows. Being creatures of habit, they proceeded to excavate them again in exactly the same locations, despite the change in appearance of their habitat. This played havoc with the new course, but with speedy work the mess created by the birds was rectified the next day after they had left for their daily fishing flights. At dusk, the birds returned, and methodically redug their burrows. The battle proceeded for some days, but the birds finally won. The course still has only 9 holes.[19.38]

Suggestions for Further Reading

The problems associated with the Mississippi River are so vast and so complex, and also of such interest, that they have generated an extensive literature, only one or two examples of which are herein cited as references. The Waterways Experiment Station of the United States Corps of Engineers at Vicksburg, Mississippi, in association with the Mississippi River Commission, has published many notable papers and volumes on the technical aspects of the Mississippi work.

Correspondingly, now that soil erosion has been widely recognized for the scourge that it is, many books and even more papers have been written on its various aspects, and the necessary measures for soil conservation. Outstanding in this work has been the Soil Conservation Service of the U.S. Department of Agriculture, to which application can be made for lists of its extensive publications. Still the standard reference work in this field is:

Bennett, H. H., "Soil Conservation," McGraw-Hill Book Company, Inc., New York, 1939.

So long neglected has been the assistance that biology can be to civil engineers that special attention is invited to the proceedings of the first conference to be held on this subject:

"Biology and Engineering," Proceedings of the conference held at the Institution of Civil Engineers, London S.W. 1, September, 1948.

Chapter 20

THE CIVIL ENGINEER AS GEOLOGICAL AGENT

Accuse not Nature, she hath done her part; do thou but thine.

John Milton

"ONE TENTH of the land surface of England and Wales is covered with buildings, railways, roads and the like. In the past twenty years about 650,000 acres have been lost to farming."[20.1] Similar statements, but with amended figures, could be made for most of the countries of the Western world. Even in so large a land as the United States, more than 1 per cent of the total land area has been utilized for streets and roads alone, making no allowance for developed urban areas apart from the space used for streets.[20.2] Only when viewed in this broad perspective does the significant change that man has caused in the character of the surface of the earth become clear. And much of this change is the direct result of the works of the civil engineer.

Indirectly, by providing the surfaces upon which can operate the products of mechanical engineering, the civil engineer is responsible for one of the most significant of all changes in the physical state of the Western world until quite recent years, the steady increase in the amount of carbon dioxide in the atmosphere. It has long been known that this contamination of the atmosphere affects the amount of solar radiation reaching the surface of the earth.[20.3] Recent climatic changes are held by some to be directly related to the products of combustion; their effect upon the atmospheric conditions in the many city areas are, unfortunately, all too well known. The incidence of radioactive material in the atmosphere due to atomic developments has now created greater and more immediate problems the full significance of which is still uncertain. Both effects, however, are the result of the work of engineers.

Vitally important as are these atmospheric aspects of the results of engineering work, the operations of the civil engineer of themselves have enough direct effect upon the surface of the earth to give cause for serious thought. In preceding chapters reference has been made to the large open excavations made necessary by some engineering projects, to

775

tunneling through the depths of mountains, to execution of major works on seacoasts that interfere with the action of the sea, to the draining of lakes, to the construction of water-retaining dams and so the formation of artificial reservoirs. All these are activities that affect the surface of the earth, and so they are, in effect, geological operations. In their local setting, the projects may appear immense in scope and significant in their effect upon natural conditions. Even the greatest of civil engineering projects has only to be viewed from the air, however, to be put in perspective; it will then appear to be a relatively small thing when compared with the unaided operations of nature. Viewed in such perspective, civil engineering projects can be seen merely to "scratch the surface."

The remarkable achievements of civil engineering are not to be belittled; all that is suggested is that the scale of comparison being used must always be kept in mind. The catacombs of Rome, for example, originally developed as quarries, have a length of 550 miles, yet a visitor to this ancient city may never realize that such excavations are so close at hand. The catacombs of Paris, not so well known, required the excavation of 13 million cu yd, about four times the volume of the Great Pyramid. Excavation of the "wet docks" of the port of Liverpool, England, still the greatest continuous area of enclosed dock space in the world, required the excavation of 6 million cu yd of soil from which, incidentally, 30 million bricks were manufactured for use in local buildings.[20.4] Typical of more general figures that can be cited in this connection is the volume of about 40 billion cu yd of soil and rock that is estimated to have been excavated in Great Britain for all purposes prior to the start of the First World War, a figure that has today been greatly exceeded.

These are impressive figures when considered in the light of the volumes normally dealt with in engineering work. When such excavations are considered in broader context, however, then their effect in a geological sense is seen to be almost negligible. The materials excavated are inert and their removal from their original location has normally no indirect effects. It can be argued, in fact, that the effects of the disposal of waste excavated material has been more serious than the process of excavation, since the formation of large waste dumps and the destruction of topsoil in open-pit mining (even when surface materials have been replaced) have all too often destroyed large areas of valuable agricultural land. Fortunately this is one aspect of engineering operations that is now being controlled. In general, disposal of waste material, such as that from mining operations, is now strictly circumscribed so that interference with usable land will be minimized. Great strides have been made in the immediate reclamation of land used for open-pit mining; some schemes have resulted in an actual improvement over local conditions existing before the mining operation was carried out. In this sphere of action, at least, man is learning that he is "steward of the land" and not its despoiler.[20.5]

There is one type of excavation work that can have a very serious effect upon natural conditions. Fortunately, it is restricted in location and so is somewhat remote from the practice of ordinary civil engineering. This is the task of excavating in areas of perennially frozen clays and silts, that is, in what is commonly called "permafrost." Only in Alaska, in the northern parts of the U.S.S.R., and in northern Canada is permafrost a major problem in civil engineering operations. Frequently, the frozen soil is protected by a covering of organic material (muskeg in North American terminology). Through its association with water and because of its own fibrous character, this material has an insulating effect, protecting frozen material from melting for all but a few inches beneath the organic cover, even at the end of the short Arctic summer. Accordingly, one of the basic rules for northern construction work is to disturb the muskeg as little as possible, and thus to preserve natural conditions to the maximum extent. If, however, the muskeg is disturbed, then material that has been frozen probably since the last Ice Age will thaw; as its excess moisture content is released, it will quickly turn to the consistency of soup. This happened frequently in the early days of the Second World War, e.g., on the Alaska Highway, when experience in such work was being gained the hard way, and it may happen even today if inexperienced construction men are not well advised about northern work. Once thawed, the material will never return to the same frozen state; thus, the work of a few hours by a bulldozer can result in a soil condition that will give trouble for many summers thereafter as drainage of excess water very gradually takes place. Solid material will eventually result even in summer, but the thermal regime of the ground will have been permanently changed; this will also be the case to some extent for all ground disturbed by construction work in the north, though not always with such disastrous effects as are illustrated in Fig. 20.1.[20.6]

The construction of large dams does interfere with previously existing natural conditions, having indirect as well as direct and clearly visible results. Ground-water conditions will be immediately changed upstream, and possibly downstream, from the dam. The reservoir area lying beneath the elevation of the crest level of the dam will be flooded and removed, more or less permanently, from human sight and use. All vegetation in the flooded area will be changed; trees are now almost always removed before flooding. Animal and insect life will be displaced from the reservoir area. And a new load, the weight of the retained water, will be placed upon the rocks that form the bed of the reservoir.

These factors might appear to be of slight importance until they are considered in relation to very large structures. Hoover Dam, for example, is 726.4 ft high; the new lake which it formed, Lake Mead, is 115 miles long with an area of 163,000 acres and an estimated volume of 31 million acre-ft. Interference with biological conditions was not here an important matter because of the character of the country that was flooded. But some surprising effects have been observed in the operation of the reservoir, such as the discharge of muddy water through the outlet gates within 8 months of the start of filling by the closure of the same gates. This demonstrated clearly the existence of density currents

Fig. 20.1. The effect of disturbing the muskeg cover on perennially frozen coarse silt ("bull's liver" when thawed), near Uranium City, Saskatchewan, Canada.

in the waters of the new lake and pointed the way to a new appreciation of sedimentation processes. Silting of the reservoir was naturally anticipated and had been allowed for in the design of the dam; it has been referred to on page 763. Somewhat unexpected, however, was the change in the chemical balance of the water within the reservoir. It has been found that large quantities of salts, particularly gypsum, are going into solution at a rate of more than 1.5 million tons per year. On the other hand, it is estimated that as much as 800,000 tons of salts, mainly calcium carbonate, are being deposited on the floor of the reservoir every year.[20.7] One effect of the weight of water in the reservoir has been a subsidence of the land around the lake, as determined by precise leveling, of up to 7 in. in less than 20 years. And several hundred small, but observable, earthquakes noted by the seismographs installed at Boulder City early in 1938 have been a direct result of the change in the state of stress in the rocks beneath the reservoir.[20.8] Epicenters were located generally along known or suspected faults on the southern margins of the lower basin of Lake Mead; observations have been taken regularly not only at the permanent seismological station but also at temporary stations around the lake.

Drastic interference with biological conditions was the first major effect of the closing in 1959 of the discharge gates of the Kariba Dam

Fig. 20.2. The Kariba Dam, Rhodesia, with its vast reservoir filling for the first time. [*Reproduced by permission of the Joint Civil Consulting Engineers, Gibb, Coyne, Soqei (Kariba) (Pvt), Ltd., and the Federal Power Board.*]

on the Zambesi River in Rhodesia; this is a 420-ft-high arched concrete dam across the Kariba Gorge. In an underground power station, fifteen 100,000-kw generators, of which six were initially installed, will develop power for use throughout the Federation of Rhodesia and Nyasaland. This outstanding civil engineering project is further distinguished in that the dam has created the largest of all man-made lakes, Lake Kariba, 175 miles long, impounding 130 million acre-ft. Much of the flooded area was covered with lush tropical vegetation and inhabited by singularly varied wildlife. Operations to rescue wild animals trapped on artificially formed islands as the water gradually rose constituted an epic zoological adventure. More permanent effects upon local fauna and flora are anticipated as well as some effect upon the equilibrium of the adjacent country. Unusually complete arrangements have been made for careful scientific observation of the continuing effects of this great dam upon the country around it.[20.9]

In connection with providing more water for storage by large dams, some very real interferences with natural conditions have been effected by civil engineers. The Big Thompson scheme of the U.S. Bureau of Reclamation diverts water from the Pacific to the Atlantic watersheds in the vicinity of Denver, Colorado. In northern Ontario, Canada, the Long Lac project diverts water from the Arctic watershed of the Nelson River into Lake Superior and the St. Lawrence watershed; the water thus gained from Hudson Bay flows through powerhouses at Sault Ste. Marie, Niagara Falls, and Cornwall before reaching sea level below Montreal. In northern British Columbia, another large Canadian power project takes water from the upper reaches of the Fraser River and by means of an impounding dam and long tunnel brings it quickly to the sea through the Coast Range by way of the great Kemano power-house (see page 308). And in Australia, as explained in Chap. 1, (see page 18), the Snowy Mountains project diverts water through the Great Dividing Range so that it may usefully generate power before being made available for irrigation purposes in one of the great fruit-growing districts of the world.

These are water-diversion schemes of vision and great extent, the design and construction of which called for civil engineering skills of high order. Although they affect the flows in the rivers from which water is abstracted, they have all been so designed that there will be no permanent injury to the depleted watersheds and but little interference with local natural conditions. Far different are some civil engineering projects that have been long under discussion but have as yet failed to come to realization. Prominent among such schemes is the plan to divert water from the Mediterranean Sea into the Qattara Depression of the Western Desert of Egypt. This 90- by 190-mile depressed section of the earth's crust lies between the Egyptian-Libyan border and the Nile Valley, less than 200 miles from Cairo. Its lowest point is 436 ft below sea level. The project, under discussion for many years, depends essentially upon excavating a 50-mile-long channel from the coast near El Alamein in order to admit sea water to the depression. A power installation of 225,000 kw is anticipated, but it is also hoped that sea water in the depression will change fresh-water conditions and so permit farming in the area. Key to the ultimate economic feasibility of the scheme is the excavation of 380 million cu yd of soil and rock. If and when the project is undertaken, it will indeed be a civil engineering job with geological overtones, changing the entire character of a singularly interesting, if unusual, part of this historical section of northern Africa.[20.10]

Civil engineering projects have had similar diversionary effects in the sea, where embankments have been constructed to connect mainland to islands or islands to one another, because the normal pattern of tidal currents is thus interfered with to some extent. Most of the projects of this kind are small and so perhaps may not be significant in a geological sense, although (as related on page 697) some have had serious effects in causing accumulations of moving sand. One of the largest of such

Fig. 20.3. The Canso Causeway across the Strait of Canso, Nova Scotia, Canada, looking toward Cape Breton Island. (*Photograph by the National Film Board, Canada.*)

projects was the construction of a rock-fill embankment to form a causeway between Cape Breton Island and the mainland of Nova Scotia in northeastern Canada. The chief purpose of this work was to give better rail and road access to Cape Breton than was possible with the previously existing ferry service. A bridge could have achieved the same purpose, even though its piers would have had to be unusually deep, but a $23 million embankment was built by direct tipping of rock working from the shores, with a navigation lock at one end to take care of the shipping that had regularly used the Strait of Canso. Currents through this strait were quite strong. These have now been stopped, since the embankment provides a complete barrier to flow. It will be many years before the possible effects of the causeway upon marine conditions and upon the climate can be evaluated. That there will probably be some such effects is suggested by the fact that two much greater marine barriers have been proposed specifically in order to ameliorate local climatic conditions. These are the proposal to block off the Strait of Belle Isle (between Labrador and the mainland of Newfoundland) to influence conditions in the Gulf of St. Lawrence, and the far greater project to block off Behring Strait between Alaska and the U.S.S.R. Visionary as these schemes may still seem to be, they have been seriously discussed, a fact which shows that there are some who do not flinch from contemplating serious interference with long-standing natural conditions through the works of the engineer.

It is in connection with marine works, particularly the protection of coast lines from erosion by the sea, that the operations of the civil engineer are perhaps most obviously linked with geological processes— in this case in opposition to the natural order by attempting to halt erosive forces that have been operating without interruption for many centuries. In many places success has been achieved, often at great cost, but the total length of coast line so protected artificially is small indeed in comparison with the full extent of unprotected eroding shore lines. But even as the sea carries on its inexorable work of wearing away the land, engineers have been winning from the sea other areas that they have reclaimed for human use. Examples of land reclamation from the sea are to be found in many countries. The Back Bay reclamation scheme in Bombay, India, is a notable case; the new airport runway at Hong Kong provides a dramatic example. Airports in the United States and Canada have been similarly extended over land that was recently under water. Many dock and harbor projects have included the reclamation of land for port service areas, often utilizing material obtained from dredging approach channels to the dock facilities. (An example is noted on page 714.) Interesting and significant as are all such works, they pale into insignificance when compared with the work of Dutch engineers in the protection and extension of their native country.

Forty per cent of the Netherlands, known throughout history as part of the Low Countries, lies below mean sea level. Some 1,200 miles of dikes protect this lovely and gracious land from the inroads of the sea, dikes built up over the centuries and the subject of many stories. Steady lowering of the level of the land, combined with a corresponding rise in the level of the North Sea, has given rise to a continuing battle against the encroachment of the sea into the fertile low-lying plains of Holland. Roman records mention a small fresh-water lake in the area known through recent history as the Zuider Zee. Historical records of the struggle go back for at least 1,000 years, when the first dikes were built between high mounds that had been constructed as safety measures for use in times of high water. Poldering, or the reclaiming of land from the sea, started as early as A.D. 1200. Windmills, for pumping out areas so reclaimed, came into use about A.D. 1600. But the battle has been a losing one until very recent years. It is estimated that, from A.D. 1200 until quite recently, the sea claimed 1.4 million acres whereas reclamation on the coast and by pumping won back less than 1.3 million acres. In the year 1421 a dreadful storm destroyed 65 villages through inundation and took the lives of 10,000 people.

In 1918 the Dutch government passed an act setting in motion the greatest land-reclamation project that the world has yet seen: the reclama-

FIG. 20.4. Reclamation of the Zuider Zee, Holland; circular dike of Eastern Flevo-land, before the polder was dried, with temporary Lelystad on right. (*Aerial photograph KLM Aerocarto n.v., the Netherlands.*)

tion of 550,000 acres in the Zuider Zee and the transformation of this great bay into a fresh-water lake with an area of almost 1 million acres. The incidence of nine major floods in the course of the previous 40 years and the loss of over 600,000 acres spurred the Dutch nation to this great effort. When the project is complete, as it will be well before the end of the present century, the area of arable land in Holland will have been increased by 10 per cent, the total area of the country by 7 per cent. Of the land thus far reclaimed, 85 per cent has proven to be high-quality agricultural soil. The task is being carried out in stages. The Wieringer-meer Polder, the first to be drained, was put into use in 1930; it has an area of 49,000 acres. The North Eastern Polder, 119,000 acres, was dried out in 1942; and Eastern Flevoland, 133,000 acres, in 1957. The Marker-waard and Southern Flevoland, having 150,000 and 100,000 acres, respectively, are scheduled for future draining.

The entire project is being carried out along lines first proposed by a great civil engineer, Dr. Ing. C. Lely, a fine monument to whom is seen

Fig. 20.5. Reclamation of the Zuider Zee, Holland: pumping the sand core of a major dike by dredging. Deposition is between two impervious dikes of boulder clay. (*Aerial photograph KLM Aerocarto n.v., the Netherlands.*)

by all who visit the Zuider Zee works. Key to the entire scheme was the construction of the great Enclosing Dam across the northern end of the Zuider Zee. About 20 miles long and 300 ft wide at its crest, this earth embankment, built with the aid of fascine matresses for protection of the sea floor, was constructed between 1927 and 1932 in the open sea. Pumping started immediately upon its completion and the enclosed water was soon converted into the Ysselmeer, a vast fresh-water lake. Within this, further dikes were then built so that the areas they enclosed could be pumped out and the land now known as the "polders" could be reclaimed for cultivation. The Enclosing Dam had the effect of pushing the sea back 53 miles from the southern end of the old Zuider Zee; the shore line of the country was thus reduced by 186 miles. The freshening of the water enclosed soon had the effect of leaching out much of the salt content of the soils to be drained. Samples of water showed salt contents of 1.39 grams per liter in 1943 and 0.82 grams per liter in 1955. Draining, cultivation, and settlement of the polders followed as quickly as possible after the drying out was complete. Today there are thriving communities, lovely buildings, tree-lined roads, and many comfortable and happy homes where but a few years ago there was the sea. Excavation carried out in connection with the work of settlement has yielded many archaeological treasures dating back many centuries and fossil relics dating from the last glacial period; these are indirect geological results of a great geological-engineering undertaking.[20.11]

The first day of February, 1953, is a date that will long be remembered by the Dutch people and, indeed, by many in other countries bordering on the North Sea, for on that day occurred a storm coupled with high-water levels that rivaled the great storm of 1421 in the havoc it wrought. In the Netherlands, 133 villages were seriously damaged by inundation and 1,800 people died. The cost of physical damage amounted to at least $400 million. Many dikes were breached. Reacting characteristically, the Dutch people put into effect, through legislation passed just 20 days after the flood, another great reclamation scheme known as the Delta Plan. This is a 25-year plan, the aim of which is to block off by permanent barrages, with all necessary ancillary structures, sluice gates, and pumping stations, four of the main channels of the Schelde estuary. Two main channels will be left open to serve the ports of Rotterdam and Antwerp, but these will be isolated by suitable structures from the impounded area, the water in which will gradually become fresh as the existing salt water is pumped out and replaced from the rivers that feed into the estuary. No new land will be won, but existing fertile land will be protected and future danger from flooding averted.

Strengthening and raising existing dikes is naturally a major part of the plan; one of the islands upon which work is already being carried out is Walcheren, which achieved such ill fame as a battleground in the Second World War. In repairing the Walcheren dikes blasted by Allied bombing, Dutch engineers tried a new method, making use of some floating concrete caissons, left over (so to speak) from the Normandy landing operations of the war. Put to this constructive use, these wartime units proved serviceable (as they have frequently proved to be in North American harbor construction). The use of similar units is being followed in the implementation of the Delta Plan. No final estimate of the cost for this great scheme is yet available, but it appears that expenditures may exceed $600 million, putting it among the most expensive as well as the greatest civil engineering works yet executed.[20.12] And Dutch and German engineers already have their eyes upon an even greater reclamation scheme,

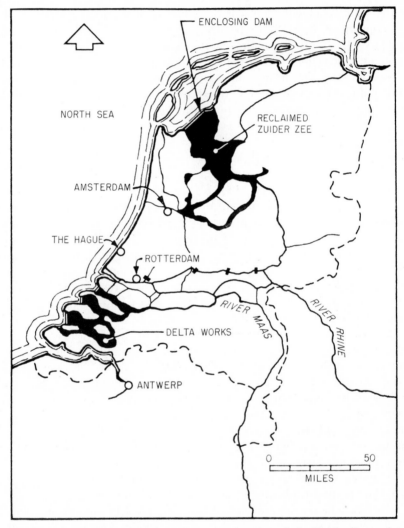

Fɪɢ. 20-6. Sketch plan showing generally the location of the Zuider Zee reclamation project and the area to be enclosed by the delta works in Holland.

this time for the winning of new land, impounding the northern part of the Zuider Zee by using the Frisian Islands as the basis for an immense enclosing dam that will far exceed the existing dam in the Zuider Zee in size and daring of conception.

One of the most remarkable features of both the Zuider Zee reclamation work and the Delta Plan has yet to be mentioned. Although land reclamation is an important element in the Zuider Zee work and shore protection a vital part of both schemes, another common feature of the greatest importance is the conversion of great areas of salt water into corresponding areas of fresh water—the Ysselmeer and the new lake that will be formed in the Schelde estuary. The necessity of this arises from the difficulties already being experienced in Holland, despite its annual rainfall of 27 in., in meeting the demands for water of the growing population of this heavily populated little country. To think that there is a water shortage in a land in which it is almost impossible to walk more than a few miles without being in sight of some body of water is, perhaps, as dramatic a piece of evidence as can be found to emphasize the critical place that water has already come to occupy in the world. Here, indeed, is where the works of the civil engineer have sometimes seriously affected geological features in relation to ground water, where the works of the civil engineer must be planned and constructed with the most careful attention to the proper conservation of this most vital of natural resources.

"Water," as Izaak Walton wrote so many years ago, "is the eldest daughter of creation, the element upon which the Spirit of God did first move. The water is more productive than the earth. Nay, the earth hath no fruitfulness without showers or dews, for all the herbs and flowers and fruits are produced and thrive by water." The civil engineer knows well the place of water in the natural order, but he may not always appreciate to the full that the uses to which man has been putting water have seriously depleted many of the most extensive supplies of ground water in all parts of the world. The engineer cannot be blamed for the overpumping that has characterized so many water-supply systems, even though he inherits the problems that overpumping creates and has to face the challenge of designing and carrying out necessary remedial works. Brief reference to serious lowering of ground-water levels was made in Chaps. 5 and 15 (see pages 153 and 586). Unfortunately, all too many examples could be cited of the sometimes disastrous results of uncontrolled pumping from natural ground-water reservoirs. In recent years a start has been made at controlling this abuse of one of the greatest of natural resources. To illustrate what has taken place in the past in many countries, however, some older figures may be quoted as typical:

1. Records obtained from the area of the Great Australian Artesian Basin disclosed that the discharge of 233 bores in New South Wales (taken as examples) decreased by 39.92 per cent between 1914 and 1928, i.e., from 83,543,586 to 50,192,429 gpd (Imp).

2. In the case of the Great Dakota Artesian Basin in the United States, the artesian pressure at Woonsocket, South Dakota, dropped from 250 psi in 1892 to 35 psi in 1923.

3. In the Paris syncline, France, the level of the water table dropped about 250 ft in 93 years.

4. In the Chicago district in the United States, the drop in the level of the ground-water surface has averaged about 4 ft per year.

5. In the London Basin, England, the underground water level is known to have dropped since about 1878 at the rate of about 18 in. per year.[20.13]

The importance of this depletion of ground-water supplies in populated areas can hardly be overemphasized. The reduction in the quantity of water available in storage is the most obvious and probably the most serious result. Associated with it is the increase in the lift for all such water which has to be pumped and the corresponding drop in pressure of artesian waters. As the level of the water table drops, flow conditions from the surface are altered, and there is a possibility that contaminated waters, previously discharging safely into streams, will reach the main body of ground water and have serious consequences. This has actually been found to happen in some areas in England. Flow of ground water to rivers may be interfered with, and the vitally important dry-weather flow of such streams seriously affected. Finally—as has already been noted (page 461)—a lowering of the ground-water level in unconsolidated strata that are being utilized as the foundation beds for large structures may have most serious and disastrous results if in this way the bearing value of the strata is reduced.

Fortunately, a public awareness of the serious nature of ground-water depletion has at last arisen. Public regulations about overpumping are now well accepted in many areas and are not regarded as "unwarranted interference with the freedom of the individual." But irreparable damage has been done in some places. Replacement of ground water, however, is possible and is being practiced on an ever-increasing scale. Basically, ground-water recharging is a simple operation. Water is spread over the ground surface in locations where geological conditions are such that it can seep into the ground and percolate down until it joins the main body of permanent ground water. This natural filtration has had a beneficial effect, especially in sandy soils. In actual practice there are some difficulties to be faced, such as keeping the surface of the spreading basins clean, but these are of minor significance when one considers that in this way water can be conserved and depletion of ground water corrected at least to some extent. Here the civil engineer is working with nature rather than against the natural order; such work is the more satisfying for this reason.

It would appear that the first attempts to replenish ground water were made in 1881 at Northampton in England; water was fed back in this case into the Lias limestone. Experiments were conducted in the London Basin by the East London Water Company as early as 1890. In North America, the Denver Union Water Company started spreading water over the gravel cone of the South Platte River near the mouth of its canyon in 1889.[20.14] It was not until well into the present century, however, that the need for replenishment of ground water became so urgent that major schemes were investigated and ultimately put into operation. Los Angeles, with its great concentration of population, has been the center of much activity in this field. Experiments were first started in the San Fernando Valley as early as 1931, and spreading grounds were gradually developed that could affect one-third of the ground-water supply for the city of Los Angeles. After 5 years' successful operation, the system took on a definite character. At the end of this period, 47 out of a possible 180 acres were in use for this purpose, through which 106 cfs of water were fed to the valley bed. Basins 100 by 400 ft are separated by dikes 4 ft high and 15 ft wide. To each basin a 6-in. pipe supplied water to a depth of 6 in. during filling operations. The water was then left to stand and seep into the ground; this took between 8 and 24 hr, depending on the state of the beds which had to be harrowed and cleaned of silt at intervals of 10 days. Percolation goes on at the rate of between 3 and 10 fpd, depending on the state of the beds. The water reaches the North Hollywood Pumping Station, some distance down the valley, 1 year later, and is there pumped out for use through eighteen 20-in. wells 400 ft deep.[20.15] Since this early work, great progress has been made; today the Los Angeles area probably has more examples of ground-water recharge than any other area in the world. Because of the continuing serious depletion of ground-water supplies, estimated to amount to 700,000 acre-ft, a special water-replenishment district has now been created to coordinate many local efforts. The area includes 29 cities with a combined population of 2.5 million people. Costs will be met by levying pumping assessments on water companies and large water users. Between 50 and 75 new wells are to be drilled for recharging purposes along 11 miles of coast line as part of the "Barrier Project" designed to limit further encroachment of sea water into this valuable area.[20.16] Some progress has been made also in the Los Angeles area, on an experimental basis, in the use of reclaimed sewage-plant effluent for recharging ground-water supplies; naturally this operation is under strict control.[20.17]

The city of Amarillo, Texas, has similarly improved its ground-water situation by recharging from the surface. The practice is, however, not restricted to the United States. In Europe, too, falling ground-water levels have created similar needs. In Sweden there are 20 municipalities that obtain their water supply from underground sources now supplemented by surface recharging. And in London, England, the Metropolitan Water Board has used old shafts and adits to put water back into the Chalk that serves as such a useful underground reservoir for the great metropolitan area. In this particular case, it was possible to measure the amount of the recharged water that was obtained by later pumping. Only about 40 per cent was so reclaimed, although in other recorded cases full return of all recharged water has been obtained. Interesting administrative questions are raised by the missing 60 per cent of the London water but they may be left for disentanglement by legal authorities.[20.18] The important thing is that man is at last beginning to repay some of the debt he has incurred by a too profligate use of one of nature's great bounties.

Fig. 20.7. Restoring water to the land. The Rio Hondo spreading grounds for ground-water recharge of the Los Angeles County Flood Control District, located mainly in the city of Pico Rivers, California, U.S.A. (*Reproduced by permission of the Chief Engineer, Los Angeles County Flood Control District.*)

What of surface waters? Here the tale is a different one—the same amount of water flowing down rivers, not at the same rate as in times past, but with increasingly great variations between flood flow and low flow. Reference to Roman writings shows clearly that, for certain European rivers, such as the Durance and the Seine in France, it can be stated with certainty that their flow was much more uniform 2,000 years ago than it is today. And there can be little doubt of the reason for the change: the cutting down of forests with the consequent removal of the forest litter that acts as such a regulator of runoff, followed by the erosion of topsoil, all constituting nature's own regulator of runoff.[20.19] This is no new idea; many writers, with vision ahead of their times, have warned of the serious effects that would follow the indiscriminate removal of forest cover; Bernard Palissy among others wrote on this subject in the sixteenth century.

Lest it be thought that this is a situation peculiar to Europe, consideration may well be given to this quotation:

> If the summer floods in the United States are attended by less pecuniary
> damage than those of the Loire and other rivers of France, the Po and its
> tributaries in Italy . . . it is partly because the banks of American rivers are
> not yet lined with towns, their shores and bottoms which skirt them not yet
> covered with improvements whose cost is counted by millions and, conse-
> quently, a smaller amount of property is exposed to injury by inundation. But
> the comparative exemption of the American people from the terrible calam-
> ities which the overflow of rivers has brought on some of the fairest portions
> of the Old World, is, in a still greater degree, to be ascribed to the fact that,
> with all our thoughtless improvidence, we have not yet bared all the sources
> of our streams, not yet overthrown all the barriers which nature has created
> to restrain her own destructive energies. Let us be wise in time, and profit by
> the errors of our elder brethren!

These words were written in 1863 by George P. Marsh in a notable
book first called "Man and Nature," later reissued as "The Earth as
Modified by Human Action," long since forgotten, unfortunately, but
containing much information and sage advice of great value still today
(even though couched in typically involved Victorian prose).[20.20]

Of the floods on American rivers in recent decades and of the immense
and varied engineering works undertaken to combat them, there is no
need to write here. Nor need words be wasted in ascribing blame for
what has happened to the land—of the United States and of Canada, in
particular, although many of the countries of the Old World have their
problems also with floods and the companion scourge, soil erosion, while
countries like South Africa, New Zealand, and to a limited extent
Australia, know well how too speedy development of a new land can
bring its train of troubles in uncontrolled water and loss of soil.[20.21] The
engineer has not been any more responsible for this rape of the land than
any other citizen, but he should be more appreciative of what it has
meant and of what must be done to remedy its dire results. Any civil
engineer who has been engaged upon construction works the purpose of
which was to put water back into its natural surroundings because of
earlier man-made works that had disturbed the natural balance is forced
to ask himself why such things can happen, why the serious effects of the
original work—such as indiscriminate land clearing—were not realized
at the time. If he knows his Shakespeare, he will find an ancient answer,
possibly with surprise, in these words from *Much Ado about Nothing*:

> For it so falls out
> That what we have, we prize not to the worth
> Whiles we enjoy it; but, being lack'd and lost,
> Why, then we rack the value, then we find
> The virtue that possession would not show us.

Fig. 20.8. The rape of the land: soil erosion by wind and water on morainal land once well forested in the watershed of the Ganaraska River, Ontario, Canada. (*Reproduced by permission of the Ontario Dept. of Commerce and Development, Conservation Branch.*)

Fig. 20.9. Restoring the land: the start of reforestation on morainal land in the watershed of the Ganaraska River, Ontario, Canada. (*Reproduced by permission of the Ontario Dept. of Commerce and Development, Conservation Branch.*)

792

The sight of silt being deposited in a reservoir may well call these words to mind, for the "silt" was once topsoil, and in all too many cases it was topsoil on good agricultural land. Again, the civil engineer has to deal with the results of the erosion of this soil, in the management of his reservoirs, the training of rivers, the dredging of harbors. As in the case of floods, this is no new phenomenon, although North America has seen possibly the most accelerated erosion of soil ever to take place in history. But in Europe there are silted reservoirs, and there are cities that were

Fɪɢ. 20.10. The land preserved: rice paddies in Kanagawa Prefecture, Japan, showing soil conservation practices long followed by the Japanese. (*Reproduced by permission of the Embassy of Japan, Ottawa, Canada.*)

once great ports now far from the sea. The Adriatic, for example, took its name from the ancient port of Adria, located between the Po and the Adige, accessible to large vessels in the time of Caesar Augustus, but now 14 miles inland; the coast has been silted up by soil washed down the two rivers. No such disaster should overtake any modern port, if only because man is now well aware of the forces of nature, their power, their inter-relation, and the necessity of their proper control in the interests of human development. And in the hands of the civil engineer rests the responsibility for doing all that he can to conserve all renewable natural resources through the medium of his undertakings; while accepting with-out recrimination against the past the state of the land in which he works, he must, so far as is possible, act in conformity with the operation of natural forces, and he must always act in accord with all that the processes of geology can show him in his work.[20.22]

The civil engineer should, therefore, be in the forefront of supporters of soil-conservation measures, knowing that every bit of soil retained on the ground is soil kept out of his reservoirs, rivers, or harbors; he should be the first to encourage sound reforestation projects, knowing that they are one further means of controlling runoff and so assist him in his river- and flood-control work; in his own excavation work, he should see that bare soil is never left to the mercies of the elements but is protected as quickly as possible by the natural cover that vegetation can so fully provide; in his studies of ground water, he should always remember the natural balance that he may be tempted to disturb and see to it that his works do not permanently impair this condition; in the construction of his dams, he should appreciate that they are only a partial answer to river control, an essential part in many cases, but fully effective only in association with what has been called "upstream engineering"; in his river-training schemes, he must let nature "have her head" under his control, remembering again that there is a natural balance even of stream regimes that must not be too seriously disturbed; and in his bank- and shore-protection work, not attempting the impossible, he must fit his protection works, in so far as is possible, into the natural order. In all his operations, he should be working with nature and not against her, remembering that "nature never deceives you, if you watch her long enough"; and so, never hesitating to be an imitator of natural processes as he carries out his works for the use and convenience of his fellow men, he is, in fact, a geological agent in the very best sense. And he may well recall that he has the support of great men of all ages, from many of whom appropriate words could be quoted to bring this volume to a close. Let Thomas Carlyle, in his own inimitable crusty style, have the last word: "*Nature keeps silently a most exact Savings Bank and official register correct to the most evanescent item. . . . and at the end of the account, you will have it all to pay, my friend, there's the rub.*"

APPENDIX A

A SHORT GLOSSARY OF GEOLOGICAL TERMS COMMONLY ENCOUNTERED

This glossary is merely an introduction to geological terminology. Compound names such as *gabbro-syenite* are not generally included, and no mention is made of the names of minerals—whether used to describe minerals only or, as in such cases as *serpentine*, rocks as well. Reference may be made to Table 2.1 on page 43 for particulars of the more common minerals. Names in the geological "time table" are not included (see page 61) nor are terms explained diagrammatically in the text, such as *anticline* (see page 56). Many words in normal use have been adopted literally for geological use, such as *analogy*, and there are naturally many commonly used words, such as *avalanche*, that would appear in a complete glossary of geology but which are not included here. An attempt has been made to provide the engineer with a guide to the unfamiliar terms that he may encounter in his geological reading.

The letters in parentheses refer to the list of references at the end of the appendix.

Aa. A Hawaiian term for basaltic lava flows typified by a rough, jagged, spinose, clinkery surface (G).

Accessory. A term applied to minerals occurring in small quantities in a rock, and whose presence or absence does not affect its diagnosis (H).

Acidic. A descriptive term applied to those igneous rocks that contain more than 66 per cent SiO_2 as contrasted with intermediate and basic (G).

Adobe. A name applied to clayey and silty deposits found in the desert basins of southwestern North America and in Mexico where the material is extensively used for making sun-dried brick (G).

Aeolian. A term applied to deposits whose constituents have been carried by, and laid down from, the wind (H).

Agglomerate. Contemporaneous pyroclastic rocks containing a predominance of rounded or subangular fragments greater than 32 mm in diameter, lying in an ash or tuff matrix and usually localized in volcanic necks. The form of the fragments is in no way determined by the action of running water (N).

Alluvium. The deposits made by streams in their channels and over their flood plains and deltas. The materials are usually uncemented and are of many kinds and dimensions (N).

Andesite. A volcanic rock, generally porphyritic, composed essentially of plagioclase, together with one or more of the mafic minerals, biotite, hornblende, and pyroxene (H).

Anorthosite. A plutonic rock composed almost wholly of plagioclase (G).

795

Aphanitic (Rock). Refers to rocks that are so fine grained that the individual minerals cannot be distinguished by the naked eye (R).

Arenaceous. Like or pertaining to sand. An example is arenaceous limestone or a sandy limestone (R).

Argillaceous. An adjective meaning clayey and applied to rocks containing clay (N).

Ash (Volcanic). Uncemented pyroclastic debris consisting of fragments mostly under 4 mm in diameter (N).

Basalt. A microlithic or porphyritic igneous rock of a lava flow or minor intrusion, having an aphanitic texture as a whole or in the groundmass and composed essentially of plagioclase and pyroxene, with or without interstitial glass (H).

Basic. A term applied to igneous rocks having a relatively low percentage of silica; the limit below which they are regarded as basic is about 52 per cent (H).

Batholith. A huge intrusive body of igneous rock, without a known floor—in contrast to a laccolith, which rests on a floor. Like other intrusive bodies, batholiths become accessible to human observation only as a result of their exposure by erosion (L).

Bedding Plane (of Rock). Refers to the plane of junction between different beds or layers of rock (R).

Bentonite. The plastic residue from the devitrification and attendant chemical alteration of glassy igneous material, usually volcanic tuff or ash. It swells greatly with the addition of water and forms a milky suspension (after N and R).

Boss. A transgressive intrusion of igneous rock like a stock or dome. The term is also applied to forms of less regular outline than the latter and is therefore of wider application (H).

Boulder. A detached rock mass, somewhat rounded or otherwise modified by abrasion in transport; 10 in. (256 mm) has been suggested as a convenient lower limit for diameter (N).

Boulder Clay. A tenacious unstratified deposit of glacial origin consisting of a hard matrix (usually rock flour) packed with subangular stones of varied sizes (after H).

Breccia. A clastic rock made of coarse angular or subangular fragments of varied or uniform composition (and of either exogenetic or endogenetic origin) (H).

Calcareous. An adjective applied to rocks containing calcium carbonate (N).

Chalk. A fine-grained somewhat friable foraminiferal limestone of Cretaceous age occurring widely in Britain and in northwestern Europe (H).

Chert. A more or less pure siliceous rock, occurring as independent formations and also as nodules and irregular concretions in formations (generally calcareous) other than the chalk. The fracture is generally splintery rather than concoidal (H).

Clastic. A term applied to rocks composed of fragmental material derived from pre-existing rocks or from the dispersed consolidation products of magmas (H).

Clay. A fine-grained unconsolidated material which has the characteristic property of being plastic when wet and which loses its plasticity and retains its shape upon drying or when heated (after R and N).

Cleavage. (1) The property of minerals . . . whereby they can be readily separated along planes parallel to certain possible crystal faces.

    (2) The property of rocks, such as slates, that have been subjected to orogenic pressure, whereby they can be split into thin sheets . . . (H).

Cobble. A rock fragment between 64 and 256 mm in diameter, rounded or otherwise abraded in the course of aqueous, aeolian, or glacial transport (N).

Conchoidal. A term used in descriptive mineralogy to describe the shell-like form of surface produced by the fracture of a brittle substance (G).

Concretions. Nodular or irregular concentrations of certain authigenic constituents of sedimentary rocks and tuffs . . . (H).

Conglomerate. A cemented clastic rock containing rounded fragments corresponding in their grade sizes to gravel (H).

Crystal. A body, generally solid but not necessarily so, whose component atoms are arranged in definite space lattices; crystal faces are a commonly developed outward expression of the periodic arrangement of atoms (H).

Cumulose Deposits. Sedentary accumulations of carbonaceous matter with very little detrital sediment (H).

Current- or Cross-bedding. A structure of sedimentary rocks, generally arenaceous, in which the planes of deposition lie obliquely to the planes separating the larger units of stratification (H).

Detritus. Fragmental material, such as sand and mud, derived from older rocks by disintegration. The deposits produced by the accumulation of detritus constitute the detrital sediments (H).

Diabase. A rock of basaltic composition, consisting essentially of labradorite and pyroxene, and characterized by ophitic texture. Rocks containing significant amounts of olivine are olivine diabases. In Great Britain basaltic rocks with ophitic texture are called *dolerites,* and the term *diabase* is restricted to altered dolerites (G).

Diastrophism. The process or processes by which the crust of the earth is deformed, and by which continents and ocean basins, plateaus and mountains, flexures and folds of strata, and faults are produced (G).

Diorite. A phanerocrystalline igneous rock composed of plagioclase and mafic minerals such as hornblende, biotite, and augite; hornblende is especially characteristic (H).

Dip. The angle of inclination of the plane of stratification with the horizontal plane (R).

Dolerite. American authors use the term *diabase* in a sense synonymous with dolerite. In Great Britain, dolerite is the name used for an igneous rock occurring as minor intrusions, consisting essentially of plagioclase and pyroxene, and distinguished from basalt by its coarser grain and the absence of glass (after H).

Dolomite. A carbonate rock, consisting predominately of the mineral dolomite (H and R) (*cf.* dolomitic limestone and magnesian limestone, in which dolomite and calcite are present, the latter predominating).

Dike. An injected wall-like intrusion, cutting across the bedding or other parallel structures of the invaded formations and having a thickness narrow in proportion to its length (H).

Ejectamenta. A general term for pyroclastic materials ejected from a volcanic vent (H).

Endogenetic. A term applied to geological processes originating within the earth and to rocks that owe their origin to such processes (H).

Epigene. A general term for geological processes originating at or near the surface of the earth (H).

Epigenetic. A term now generally applied to ore deposits of later origin than the rocks among which they occur (H).

Essential Minerals. The essential constituents of a rock are those minerals whose presence is necessary in it by definition (R).

Exfoliation. The "peeling" of a rock surface in sheets due to changes of temperature or to other causes (R).

Exogenetic. A term applied to geological processes originating at or near the surface of the earth and to rocks that owe their origin to such processes (H).

Faults. Abrupt breaks in the continuity of the beds or strata with the elevation or depression of beds on one side of the plane at the fault (R).

Felsite. An igneous rock, with or without phenocrysts, in which either the whole or the groundmass consists of cryptocrystalline aggregates of felsic minerals; quartz and orthoclase are those characteristically developed (H).

Felsitic. A term applied to the cryptocrystalline texture seen in the groundmass of quartz felsites and similar rocks (H).

Ferruginous. An adjective applied to rocks containing iron.

Flint. A more or less pure siliceous rock composed mainly of granular chalcedony together with a small proportion of opaline silica and occurring in nodules, irregular concretions, layers, and veinlike masses. The fracture is concoidal, whereas in *chert* a splintery fracture is more usual (H).

Foliation. A structure represented most characteristically in schists, due to the parallel disposition of layers or lines of one or more of the conspicuous minerals of the rock; the parallelism is not a direct consequence of stratification (H).

Formation. A term applied stratigraphically to a set of strata possessing a common suite of lithological and/or faunal characteristics (H).

Gabbro. A phanerocrystalline rock consisting of labradorite, or bytownite, and augite (generally diallage) (H).

Gneiss. A foliated or banded phanerocrystalline rock (generally, but not necessarily, felspathic and of granitic or dioritic composition) in which granular minerals, or lenticles and bands in which they predominate, alternate with schistose minerals, or lenticles or bands in which they predominate. The foliation of gneiss is more "open," irregular, or discontinuous than that of schist (H).

Granite. A phanerocrystalline rock, consisting essentially of quartz and alkali feldspars with any of the following: biotite, muscovite, and amphiboles and pyroxenes (H).

Granitic. A term applied to irregularly granular textures such as that of a non-porphyritic granite (H).

Gravel. An unconsolidated accumulation of rounded rock fragments predominantly larger than sand grains. Depending on the coarseness of the fragments, the material may be called *pebble gravel, cobble gravel,* or *boulder gravel* (after N).

Grit. A coarse sandstone of angular grain. Variation from the grain-size range of from $\frac{1}{2}$ to 1 mm in diameter should be indicated as coarse grit, fine grit, etc. (N).

Ground Water. A term that should be applied only to the basal or bottom water in the zone of rock fracture below the earth's surface, in which interstitial water occurs, i.e., in the zone of saturation (M).

Gumbo. A provincial term used to describe local varieties of sticky, highly plastic clay soil (after N).

Hardpan. A term to be avoided, in view of its wide and essentially popular local use for a wide range of materials (see page 15).

Holocrystalline. A term applied to igneous rocks completely made up of crystals (H).

Hypabyssal. A general term applied to minor intrusions, such as sills and dikes, and to the rocks of which they are made, to distinguish them from volcanic rocks and formations, on the one hand, and plutonic rocks and major intrusions such as batholiths, on the other (H).

Hypogene. A general term intended to include both plutonic and metamorphic classes of rocks, i.e., for rocks formed within the earth (H).

Igneous (Rocks). Those which have been formed or crystallized from molten magmas, the source of which has been the earth's interior (R).

Inclusion. A general term for foreign bodies (gas, liquid, glass, or mineral) enclosed by minerals; also extended in its English usage to connote *enclosures* of rocks and minerals within igneous rocks (H).

Indurated. A term technically restricted to compact rocks that have been hardened by the action of heat (H). Occasionally the term is applied also to sediments hardened by pressure and cementation.

Intermediate (Rocks). Applies to rocks intermediate in silica content between the *basic* and the *acidic* groups (R).

Intrusive (Rocks). Igneous rocks that have cooled and solidified from magma under the cover of the rock masses of the outer shell of the earth; they therefore become accessible to view only after they have been exposed by erosion of the overlying rock (after L).

Isostasy. The principle that above some level within the earth, presumably at a depth of some scores of kilometers, different segments of the crust, if of equal area, also have the same mass. The blocks thus balance one another (G).

Joints (Rock). Rock fractures on which there has been no appreciable displacement parallel with the walls. They may sometimes be characterized, according to their relation with the rock bedding, as *strike joints* and *dip joints* (after L).

Kaolin. A white, or slightly stained, clay, resulting from the decomposition of a highly felspathic rock and therefore also containing a variable proportion of other constituents derived from the parent rock (H).

Laccolith. A dome-shaped intrusion with both floor and roof concordant with the bedding planes of the invaded formations; the roof is arched upward as a result of the intrusion (H).

Laterite. A residual deposit, often concretionary, formed as a result of the decomposition of rocks by weathering and ground waters and consisting essentially of hydrated oxides of aluminum and iron (H).

Limestone. A general term for bedded rocks of exogenetic origin, consisting predominantly of calcium carbonate (H).

Lithology. The study of rocks as based on the megascopic observation of hand specimens. In its French usage, the term is synonymous with *petrography* (H).

Loam. A detrital deposit containing nearly equal proportions of sand, silt, and clay; these terms refer to the grade size of the particles (H).

Loess. A widespread deposit of silt or marl, a buff-colored, porous, but coherent deposit traversed by a network of generations of grass roots (H).

Macroscopic. See under *Megascopic.*

Mafic. A mnemonic term for the ferromagnesian and other nonfelsic minerals actually present in an igneous rock (H).

Magma. A comprehensive term for the molten fluids generated within the earth from which igneous rocks are considered to have been derived by crystallization or other processes of consolidation (H).

Magnesian Limestone. See under *Dolomite.*

Marble. A general term for any calcareous or other rock of similar hardness that can be polished for decorative purposes (petrologically restricted to granular crystalline limestones).

Marl. A calcareous clay, or intimate mixture of clay and particles of calcite or dolomite, usually fragments of shells. Marl in America is chiefly applied to incoherent sands, but in other countries it is also applied to compact, impure, limestones (G).

Megascopic. A general term, more appropriate than *macroscopic*, applied to observations made on minerals and rocks by means of the naked eye or pocket lens but not with a microscope (H).

Metamorphic Rocks. Rocks derived from preexisting rocks by mineralogical, chemical, and structural alterations due to endogenic processes; the alteration is sufficiently complete throughout the body of the rock to produce a well-defined new type (H).

Mica Schist. A schist composed essentially of micas and quartz, the foliation is mainly due to the parallel disposition of the mica flakes (H).

Mudstone. A general term (including silt stone, clay stone, and shale) to be used only when a more precise one is not possible (*cf. sandstone, limestone*) (N).

Muskeg. A Canadian term of Cree Indian origin, meaning a moss-covered muck or peat bog. In the Far North all swamps are called muskegs (G).

Oölite. A rock made up of spheriodal or ellipsoidal grains formed by the deposition of successive coats of calcium carbonate around a nucleus (H).

Ophitic. A term applied to microscopic rock texture to designate a mass of longish interlacing crystals, the spaces between which are filled with minerals of later crystallization (R).

Orogeny. The process of forming mountains, particularly by folding and thrusting (G).

Outcrops (of Rock). Those places where the underlying bedrock comes to the surface of the ground and is exposed to view (R).

Outlier. An isolated mass or detached remnant of younger rocks, or of rocks overthrust upon others, separated by erosion from the main mass to which they belong and now surrounded, areally, by older, or at least underlying, rocks; opposite of inlier (G).

Pebble. A rock fragment between 4 and 64 mm in diameter, which has been rounded or otherwise abraded by the action of water, wind, or glacial ice (after N).

Pegmatite. A term applied to graphic granite and extended to coarse-grained modifications of granite characterized by irregular segregation of particular minerals rather than by interpenetration (H).

Phanerocrystalline. A term applied to igneous rocks in which all the crystals of the essential minerals can be distinguished individually by the naked eye; contrasted with *aphanitic* (H).

Phenocryst. A term applied to isolated crystals visible to the unaided eye and lying in the mass of a rock of igneous origin (R).

Phreatic. Pertaining to *ground water* (M).

Phyllite. An argillaceous rock intermediate in metamorphic grade between slate and schist. The mica crystals impart a silky sheen to the surface of cleavage (or schistosity) (G).

Plutonic. A general term applied to major intrusions and to the rocks of which they are composed, suggestive of the depths at which they were formed in contradistinction to most minor intrusions and all volcanic rocks (H).

Porphyrite. A term applied to hypabyssal rocks of marked porphyritic structure and andesitic composition. The phenocrysts are generally plagioclase and mafic minerals, and the groundmass is holocrystalline (after H).

Porphyry. A term first given to an altered variety of porphyrite on account of its purple color and afterward extended by common association to all rocks containing conspicuous phenocrysts in a fine-grained or aphanitic groundmass. The resulting texture is described as *porphyritic* (H).

Puddingstone. A popular term for conglomerates, consisting of well-rounded pebbles set in an abundant matrix (H).

Pyroclasts. A general term for fragmental deposits of volcanic *ejectamenta*, including volcanic conglomerates, agglomerates, tuffs, and ashes (H).

Quartzite. A granulose metamorphic rock, representing a recrystallized sandstone, consisting predominantly of quartz. The name is also used for sandstones and grits cemented by silica that has grown in optical continuity around each fragment (H).

Regolith. A general term for the superficial blanket of denudation products that is widely distributed over the more mature "solid" rocks. The term includes weathering residues, alluvium, and aeolian and glacial deposits (H).

Rhyolite. A volcanic rock corresponding in chemical composition to granite and generally having small phenocrysts of quartz and orthoclase in a glassy or cryptocrystalline groundmass. Flow structure is commonly developed (H).

Rock Flour. A general term for finely comminuted rock material corresponding in grade to mud but formed by the grinding action of glaciers and ice sheets and therefore composed largely of unweathered mineral particles (H).

Rudaceous. A term applied to sedimentary rocks composed of coarsely grained detritus such as gravel, shingle, and pebbles (H).

Sand. Fine granular material derived from either the natural weathering or the artificial crushing of rocks, generally limited in diameter between 2 and 0.05 mm.

Sandstone. A cemented or otherwise compacted detrital sediment composed predominantly of quartz grains, the grades of the latter being those of sand. Varieties such as argillaceous, calcareous, and ferruginous are recognized according to the nature of the cementing material. Corresponding rocks of coarser grades are sometimes called *grits* (after H).

Schist. A general term for foliated metamorphic rocks, the structures of which are controlled by the prevalence of lamellar minerals such as micas—which have normally a flaky habit—or of stressed minerals crystallized in elongated forms rather than in the granular forms generally assumed (H).

Schistosity. The property of a foliated rock whereby it can be divided into thin flakes or lenticles (H).

Sedimentary (Rocks). A general term for loose and cemented sediments of detrital origin, generally extended to include all exogenetic rocks (H).

Shale. A laminated sediment, in which the constituent particles are predominantly of the clay type. The characteristic cleavage is that of bedding and such other secondary cleavage or fissility as is approximately parallel to bedding (after H and N).

Shingle. Coarse beach gravel, relatively free from fine material and commonly of loose texture (N).

Siliceous. Of or pertaining to silica; containing silica, or partaking of its nature. Containing abundant quartz (G).

Sill. A tabular sheet of igneous rock injected along the bedding planes of sedimentary or volcanic formations (H).

Silt. An unconsolidated clastic sediment, most of the particles of which are between 0.053 and 0.002 mm in diameter (G).

Slate. A general term for compact aphanitic rocks, formed from shales, mudstones, or volcanic ashes and having the property of easy fissility along planes independent of the original bedding (H).

Slickensides. Polished and grooved surfaces on rock faces that have been subjected to faulting (after L).

Soapstone. Rock consisting of the mineral talc or a closely related mineral species (R).

Stratum. A layer that is separable along bedding planes from layers above and below; the separation arises from a break in deposition or a change in the character of the material deposited (T).

Strike (of Rocks). The direction of the line of intersection of the plane of stratification with the horizontal plane (R).

Structure (of Rocks). A term reserved for the larger features of rocks; e.g., a layered or laminated *structure* generally indicates sedimentary origin (L).

Syenite. A term originally applied to hornblende granite, now connoting a phanerocrystalline rock composed essentially of alkali feldspars and one or more of the common mafic minerals; hornblende is especially characteristic (H).

Syngenetic. A term now generally applied to mineral or ore deposits formed contemporaneously with the enclosing rocks, as contrasted with epigenetic deposits, which are of later origin than the enclosing rocks (G).

Talus. A term used for the accumulation of fine, coarse, or mixed fragments and particles, fallen at or near the base of cliffs (R).

Texture (of Rocks). The appearance, megascopic or microscopic, seen on a smooth surface of a homogeneous rock or mineral aggregate due to the degree of crystallization, the size of the crystals, and the shapes and interrelations of the crystals or other constituents (H).

Till. The unstratified or little-stratified deposits of glaciers.

Tillite. A term applied to consolidated boulder clays formed during glacial epochs anterior to that of the Pleistocene (H).

Trap. An old Swedish name originally applied to igneous rocks that were neither coarsely crystalline, like granite, nor cellular and obviously volcanic, like pumice. The rocks so designated included basalts, dolerites, andesites, and porphyrites (types often grouped as *whinstones*); altered varieties of some of these, such as epidiorite and diabase (types grouped as *green stones*); and, finally, the mica traps, or lamprophyres (H). The word is often popularly used to describe local rock types and so is one to be generally avoided.

Trass. A local Italian name applied to pumiceous tuffs that are utilized for the manufacture of hydraulic cement (H).

Tuff. A rock formed of compacted pyroclastic fragments, some of which can generally be distinguished as such by the naked eye (H). The indurated equivalent of volcanic ash or dust (*cf. agglomerate*) (H and N).

Unconformity. Represents a break in the geologic sequence and is a surface of erosion or nondeposition separating two groups of strata (T).

Vadose. A term applied to seepage waters occurring below the surface and above the water table; contrasted with *phreatic* (H).

Vein. An irregular sinuous igneous injection or a tabular body of rock formed by deposition from solutions rich in water or other volatile substances (H).

Ventrifact. A wind-carved stone; a sandblasted pebble or larger fragment (N).

Water Table. The upper surface of a zone of saturation beneath the earth's crust, except where that surface is formed by an impermeable body (M).

Weathering. The destructive alteration and decay of rocks by exogenetic processes acting at the surface and down to the depth to which atmospheric oxygen can penetrate (H).

Whinstone. See under *trap*.

References.—The definitions given above have been taken (by permission) from or are based on the following authorities, indicated throughout the glossary by index letters. Practically all quoted definitions will be found to be linked with original usage, or other authorities, in the references used.

(G) "Glossary of Geology and Related Sciences," American Geological Institute, National Academy of Sciences, National Research Council, Washington, D.C., 1957.

(H) Holmes, A.: "The Nomenclature of Petrology," Thomes Murby & Co., London, 1920.

(L) LONGWELL, C. R., A. KNOPF, and R. F. FLINT: "Textbook of Geology," pt. 1, "Physical Geology," John Wiley & Sons, Inc., New York, 1932.

(M) For a full discussion of ground-water terminology, see MEINZER, O. E.: Outline of Groundwater Hydrology with Definitions, *U.S. Geol. Survey Water Supply Paper* 494, 1923, on which the three definitions given are based.

(N) Reports, from 1930 to 1938, of the Committee on Sedimentation of the Division of Geology and Geography of the National Research Council, Washington, in which will be found—in addition to much valuable information on sedimentation—studies of the nomenclature of various groups of sediments.

(R) RUNNER. D. G.: A Glossary of Geological Terms for the Highway Engineer (rev.), *Roads and Streets*, Chicago, May 1, 1937. See also BROWN, V. J., and D. G. RUNNER: "Engineering Terminology," Gillette Publishing Company, Chicago, 1938.

(T) TWENHOFEL, W. H.: "A Treatise on Sedimentation," 2d ed., The Williams & Wilkins Company, Baltimore, 1932.

Special Note—Although not listed above, the Glossary of Selected Geologic Terms, with Special Reference to Their Use in Engineering by W. L. STOKES and D. J. VARNES, *Colorado Sci. Soc. Proc.,* Denver, 1953, vol. 16, 165 pp., is a most useful publication; its contents are clearly indicated by its title. So also is "Geological Nomenclature, English-Dutch-French-German," ed. by A. A. G. Schieferdecker, Royal Geological and Mining Soc. of the Netherlands, J. Noorduijn en Zoon, 1959, 523 pp.

APPENDIX B

GEOLOGICAL SURVEYS OF THE WORLD

Brief details of most of the geological surveys of the English-speaking world are here presented as a convenience for civil engineers who may wish to get in touch with their local survey concerning either geological publications or the progress of any of their work in which the survey might be interested. Surveys of other countries are listed at the end, with the address of their headquarters. Great care has been taken in the preparation of this list; a copy of each note was submitted to the director of each survey mentioned. In view of the lapse of time between this check and publication, however, the accuracy of the information cannot be guaranteed. It is hoped that the particulars given will not only suggest sources of information useful to engineers but that they will also enable engineers to notify scientists of new excavation work which may provide information of great interest and inestimable value. The geological departments of all universities are also appreciative of advice of this nature.

Australia:

Commonwealth of Australia: Bureau of Mineral Resources, Geology, and Geophysics
Director: J. M. Rayner

The Bureau of Mineral Resources, Geology, and Geophysics is a division of the Department of National Development. It was established in 1946 on the recommendation of the Mining Industry Advisory Panel, a body consisting of representatives of commonwealth and state government departments and the mining industry. The work of the Bureau of Mineral Resources is primarily concerned with the mineral resources of Australia, and particularly the application of geology and geophysics in exploration for oil and minerals. It also undertakes basic investigations to develop methods of exploration, maintains geophysical observatories throughout Australia, in New Guinea, and in Antarctica, and carries out nationwide surveys and assessments of mineral resources.

The Bureau advises the Commonwealth government on scientific, technical, and administrative aspects of the mining industry and all aspects of the mineral economy of Australia, including the best utilization of mineral resources in the national interest. Geological and geophysical surveys are carried out by the Bureau in Commonwealth territories and in the various states by arrangements with the state government concerned. Fully equipped laboratories, libraries, and drafting offices are maintained, together with a geophysical workshop for design and construction of specialized equipment.

The principal offices of the Bureau of Mineral Resources are in Canberra (Headquarters, Operations Branch, Mineral Resources Branch and Geological Branch) and Melbourne (Geophysical Branch).

Publications. The results of the Bureau's work are presented in numerous publications, which include geological and geophysical maps, the Annual Review and Quarterly Review of the Australian Mineral Industry, and summary reports on specific metals and minerals important in the Australian economy. Bulletins and reports give the results of field and laboratory investigations.

Australia: New South Wales:

Geological Survey of New South Wales
Government Geologist: F. W. Booker
Headquarters: Department of Mines, Sydney

The discovery of gold in New South Wales in 1851 apparently led to the appointment of a government geologist, but it was not until a Department of Mines was created in 1874 that a geological survey came into being. The Survey staff now constitutes one branch of the Department of Mines. Associated with it are the Geological Survey Laboratory and a Mining and Geological Museum (both at Sydney) which are under the direction of the government geologist. In its work, the survey, although chiefly concerned with the development of the mineral resources of the state, carries out regional surveys which are published on a scale of either 1:63,360 or 1:253,440. Surveys are also made of coal fields and areas likely to contain subsurface waters. Geophysical surveys of suitable areas, mainly auriferous and stanniferous deep leads, are undertaken. The services of the Survey are in constant demand by the public and other government departments and advice on civil engineering matters with regard to foundations for dams, buildings, and bridges is often supplied. A large number of free assays of economic materials are made annually.

Publications. Annual reports from 1875 to 1952 included geological reports. Since 1952 a new series—technical reports—has been published in addition to annual reports and all geological reports are embodied in these journals. A mineral resources series is also issued as well as bulletins dealing with the mineral industry. Memoirs of the Survey are classified into general, paleontological, and ethnological issues. A series of records is also issued in addition to a large selection of maps. All publications are obtainable from the headquarters of the Survey in Sydney.

Australia: Queensland:

Geological Survey of Queensland
Chief Government Geologist: A. K. Denmead
Headquarters: Brisbane
District Office: Charters Towers

Founded in 1879, the Geological Survey of Queensland is a subdepartment of the Department of Development and Mines. Its functions have not been defined by statute, but its main activities are to investigate, by inspection and sometimes by diamond drilling, the state's mineral resources; to carry out regional geological mapping on the scale of 4 miles to an inch as well as detailed geological mapping of critical areas, in part in collaboration with the Federal Bureau of Mineral Resources; to evaluate prospects; to do consultative work for other government departments, particularly in engineering geology; to undertake paleontological and palynological research; and to study coal petrology.

Publications. Geological Survey of Queensland Publications 1–300 (publication was suspended from 1930 to 1954); geological maps of the state (various scales), and detailed maps of mineral fields.

Geological Survey of South Australia
Director of Mines and Government Geologist: T. A. Barnes
Headquarters: Department of Mines,
                                          169 Rundle Street, Adelaide

The Survey is a part of the Department of Mines and is interlocked with other branches; the general and clerical work is performed by one staff for all branches. The geologists of the Department, who constitute the Survey staff, are engaged mainly on economic work concerned with the development of the mineral resources of the state; they are also concerned with water-supply problems, since underground water sources are of great importance to this state. In addition to the economic work, systematic geological mapping is carried out and regional maps are published in scales of 1 in. = 1 mile and 1 in. = 4 miles. The Survey includes a geophysics section which applies gravity, magnetic, seismic, and other recognized methods to exploration. The Department carries out well-boring and diamond-drilling work, all under geological supervision, and its geologists are freely consulted on engineering matters.

Publications. In addition to the maps mentioned, regular publications include annual reports, a series of bulletins (on general or regional subjects), mining records, and reports of investigations; all may be obtained from the Department and from the Government Printer, King William Road, Adelaide.

Geological Survey of Tasmania
Chief Geologist: H. G. W. Keid
Headquarters: Department of Mines, Hobart

The Geological Survey of Tasmania was founded in 1907 as a division of the State Department of Mines. It carries out regional and economic geology, with study of areal and stratigraphical problems and investigations into mineral deposits and ground-water resources.

Publications. These include district bulletins, papers on mineral resources and underground water supplies; geological maps, and annual volumes of technical reports. Copies are obtainable from the Department of Mines, Hobart.

Geological Survey of Victoria
Director: D. E. Thomas
Headquarters: Department of Mines, Treasury Gardens,
                Melbourne

The Geological Survey of Victoria was founded in 1851 under A. R. C. Selwyn, shortly after gold had been discovered in the state. For the first 17 years, reconnaissance and detail surveys received attention. Then for a short time, the survey work ceased, and Selwyn received an appointment in Canada. On resumption of work early in the 1870s, the Survey devoted attention to areas of economic importance, chiefly gold fields, but areas of black and brown coal were also dealt with. In 1903, under J. W. Gregory, the Survey was reorganized. The objective was to achieve a more even balance of geological and mining surveys, and this program has been followed, according to financial support, to the present time. The Survey operates its own boring branch and laboratories and has a geological museum.

Publications. Eleven geological progress reports were published between 1874 and 1899; in the two years following, nine monthly progress reports appeared. From 1902 onward, regular bulletins, memoirs, and records have been issued. In addition, an extensive series of geological maps has been published. A Mining and Geological Journal, issued twice yearly since 1937, has taken the place of the records. Copies are obtainable from Survey headquarters and the Government Printer, Melbourne.

Australia: Western Australia:

Geological Survey of Western Australia
Government Geologist: H. A. Ellis
Headquarters: 26 Francis Street, Perth

Following individual geological investigations carried out mainly by five geologists between the years 1847 and 1895, three of whom worked officially as government geologists, the Geological Survey of Western Australia was created in 1896 for the purpose of investigating the geological structure, mineral resources, mining industries, and underground water supplies of the state. An excellent review of the work of this Survey will be found in a paper by Mr. A. Gibb Maitland, sometime government geologist, read before the West Australian Natural History Society on May 10, 1910.

Publications. Annual reports, bulletins (114 having already been issued on all branches of the Survey's work), and geological maps are published by the Survey; copies are obtainable from Survey headquarters.

British Guiana:

Geological Survey Department
Director: R. B. McConnell
Headquarters: Brickdam, Georgetown

Geological investigations were carried out by C. B. Brown and J. G. Sawkins between the years 1867 and 1873, mainly along the rivers, and Brown produced the first geological map of British Guiana. Later, more detailed reconnaissance was carried out under the direction of Sir J. B. Harrison, Director of Science and Agriculture, from 1889 until 1927, when the geological section of that department was taken over by the Department of Lands and Mines. In 1943 the Geological Survey Department was founded under the direction of S. Bracewell, who retired in 1952. It was very largely during the years 1927 to 1939, first under H. J. C. Conolly and later D. R. Grantham, that the foundations of the stratigraphy of British Guiana were laid. Since 1946 a large proportion of the cost of expansion of the Geological Survey Department has been contributed by grants from the Colonial Development and Welfare Fund.

Publications. Annual reports, bulletins (31 have been published to date) and geological maps are published; copies are obtainable from the Department Headquarters.

Canada:

Geological Survey of Canada
Director: J. M. Harrison
Headquarters: 601 Booth Street, Ottawa

The Geological Survey of Canada was founded in 1842, only 7 years after the Geological Survey of Great Britain and before the United States Geological Survey. In view of the undeveloped state of Canada a century ago, this is a notable achievement and it is also notable that the Geological Survey is the only federal scientific organization that has been continuously active from then until now.

In 1880, its headquarters were transferred from Montreal to Ottawa. In 1959, it moved into the new Geological Survey Building where additional laboratories permitted new lines of geological research to be undertaken.

The Geological Survey is a branch of the federal Department of Mines and Technical Surveys. Its work includes research into all branches of geological science from reconnaissance geological mapping to the study of the nature and origin of paleomagnetism and the geochemistry of ore deposits.

Publications. The results of the geological research are embodied in memoirs, bulletins, economic geology series reports, multicolor maps, and preliminary series maps and reports. Inquiries should be made to the Director, Geological Survey of Canada, Department of Mines and Technical Surveys, Ottawa.

Canada: Provinces:

The Canadian Provinces

As natural resources are now generally under the control of the respective provinces that make up the Dominion of Canada, it is to be expected that the provinces will be interested in geological work at least in so far as it is related to mining. This is generally the case, and the departments and chief officials are as follows:

Newfoundland: Department of Mines and Resources, Frederick Gover, Deputy Minister of Mines, St. John's

Nova Scotia: Department of Mines, Frank Shea, Geologist, Halifax

New Brunswick: Department of Lands and Mines, C. S. Clements, Director, Mines Branch, Fredericton

Quebec: Department of Mines, I. W. Jones, Director of Geological Surveys, Quebec City

Ontario: Department of Mines, M. E. Hurst, Provincial Geologist, Toronto

Manitoba: Department of Mines and Natural Resources, J. S. Richards, Director of Mines, Winnipeg

Saskatchewan: Department of Mineral Resources, D. Mode, Director, Mines Branch, Regina

Alberta: Department of Mines and Minerals, J. A. Dutton, Director of Mines, Edmonton

British Columbia: Department of Mines, P. J. Mulcahy, Deputy Minister, Victoria

Ceylon:

Geological Survey of Ceylon
Department of Mineralogy

The history of geological survey work in Ceylon dates back to 1902 when, under the auspices of the Imperial Institute of London a mineralogical survey was initiated. While the primary purpose of this survey was the investigation of economic minerals in the island, sporadic geological surveys were also carried out. In 1939 arrangements were made for the establishment of a comprehensive geological survey of the island, and the expert services of Dr. D. N. Wadia, who had at that time retired from the Geological Survey of India, were obtained for this purpose. A team of Ceylonese geologists, a mining engineer, chemists and technical staff, trained under various programs of aid, chiefly the Technical Assistance Scheme and the Colombo Plan, is now available for the systematic survey work of the island. Besides systematic geological surveys, mineral investigations are carried out. Exploration by means of diamond drilling got under way in the middle of 1958 with the aid of equipment given to the Department under the American aid program. The main program of drilling was concentrated on the iron-ore fields and on deposits of sedimentary lime-stone as raw material for cement manufacture. The Department has its own labora-tory for analytical, mineralogical, petrological, and ceramic testing, and also a geological museum.

Publications. Obtainable from the Publications Bureau, Colombo 1.

Cyprus:

Cyprus Geological Survey

Chief Geological Survey Officer: L. M. Bear

Headquarters: Nicosia

The Geological Survey of Cyprus was established in 1950; its main function is the examination of the mineral potential of the igneous rocks of Troodos. The scope of the work has since been widened to include a detailed geological map of the island, and geochemical prospecting of the mineralized zones. For this purpose the island has been arbitrarily divided into 19 areas generally varying in area from 150 to 250 sq miles. Field work is done on a scale of 1:5,000 and a memoir with colored geological map (scale 1:31,680) is prepared for each area. Consultative work is undertaken for other government departments and prospectors.

Publications. Seven memoirs have been published by the Survey, as well as a series of annual reports dating from 1955. Copies are obtainable from the Government Printer, Nicosia.

Federation of Malaya:

Geological Survey Department, Federation of Malaya

Director: J. B. Alexander

Headquarters: Ipoh Perak

A systematic geological survey of Malaya was begun when J. B. Scrivenor was ap-pointed geologist to the Federated Malay States government in September, 1903. When he retired in 1931, a preliminary general survey of the greater part of the Malay Peninsula had been completed, including the federated and unfederated states and the straits settlements. After World War II these states were consolidated into a federation that became an independent nation in August, 1957.

For many years, Malaya has been the largest tin producer in the world. Records of all prospecting done is kept by the Geological Survey, and these have proved to be most useful. A chemical laboratory is maintained for assay work. More than half the area of Malaya is still jungle. In spite of this, about a quarter of the country has been geologically mapped to a scale of 1:63,360, while mapping work is in progress over another quarter of the country. Advice is given by the Geological Survey to government and to the public not only on mining matters but also in connection with road location, dam and bridge foundations, water supply, and hydroelectric installations.

Publications: In addition to maps, the Department issues mapping bulletins, economic bulletins, memoirs, professional papers, and reports. All publications are obtainable from the Director at Geological Survey Headquarters, P.O. Box 1015, Ipoh.

Fiji:

Geological Survey of Fiji

Acting Chief Geologist: R. E. Houtz

Headquarters: Geological Survey, Carnavon Street, Suva, Fiji.

The Geological Survey was established under a Colonial Development and Welfare Fund grant in 1951 as a section of the Lands Department of Fiji. In 1958 the

Geological Survey became an independent department consisting of a chief geologist and four geologists. The basic purpose of the Survey is to produce a complete geological map of the colony and to encourage exploitation of Fiji's mineral resources. The Survey's activities are organized so that likely mineralized areas, discovered during regional mapping, are followed up by geophysical investigations by means of self-potential and resistivity methods. Promising ore bodies are then tested further with the departmental diamond drill. The Survey also maintains a library, a modern laboratory, and a seismological station. The facilities and technical knowledge of the Geological Survey are available to the general public as well as to the government.

Publications. A geological bulletin is published along with a colored map as each quarter-degree sheet is geologically mapped. A seismological bulletin is published twice yearly by Columbia University, New York, covering the monthly seismological bulletins compiled by the Survey. Annual reports are also published.

Ghana:

Geological Survey of Ghana

Director: D.A. Bates

Headquarters: P.O. Box M. 80, Accra, Ghana

The Department was founded in 1913, and from its inception it has been closely associated with mineral developments. It is engaged in geological mapping and investigations of the mineral resources of Ghana, and in investigations related to water supplies obtained by boring and by surface conservation. Important deposits of manganese ore, diamonds, and bauxite have been discovered by the Survey. Detailed surveys and reports are made on the chief mineral-bearing areas, and assistance and advice are given to mining companies, prospectors, government departments, and others. The Department is now fully equipped for geochemical and geophysical investigations, with central laboratories at Accra and regional laboratories at Kumasi and Saltpond. Use is made of aerial geophysical survey methods.

Publications. These center around annual reports. Bulletins and memoirs have also been issued on special subjects, and a series of bulletins describing systematic geological, geochemical, geophysical, and mineral mapping is in progress. All publications are issued by the Government Printing Office, Box 124, Accra, Ghana.

Great Britain:

Geological Survey of Great Britain

Director: C. J. Stubblefield

Headquarters: Geological Survey and Museum, Exhibition Road,
South Kensington, London, S.W. 7

As early as the year 1814, a geologist was appointed to assist in the work of the Trigonometrical Survey of Scotland; in 1832, a similar appointment was made for Ireland. Three years later, the idea of forming a geological survey of Great Britain was suggested by the Ordnance Survey; and on the recommendation of the distinguished geologists then consulted, Henry Thomas De la Beche was appointed in 1835 as the first director at the age of thirty-nine. He was the first of a distinguished company; later directors included Murchison, Ramsay, and Geikie. During its long history, the Survey has undergone several reorganizations, but its main functions today remain little different from those originally conceived, as expressed by Lyell in 1838: "as calculated to promote geological science . . . but also as a work of great potential utility, bearing on agriculture, mining, road-making, the formation of canals and railroads, and other branches of natural industry." Since 1919, it has been under the Department of Scientific and Industrial Research and is thus linked with other official research and scientific bodies, such as the Building

Research Station and the National Physical Laboratory. In 1947, the Geological Survey was given responsibility for the Geological Survey of Northern Ireland. Interesting accounts of the Survey are to be found in its centenary volume, "The First Hundred Years of the Geological Survey of Great Britain" by Sir John Flett (a former director), published in 1937 by H. M. Stationery Office, London, and in "Geological Survey of Great Britain" by Sir Edward Bailey (another director), published in 1952 by T. Murby, London.

Publications. These are naturally varied and extensive, including memoirs of different types, annual reports, and (in recent years) summaries of progress, in addition to geological maps and sections covering the whole of Great Britain to various scales. A full list of publications up to 1936 was published in 1937; stocks of publications however, were destroyed by enemy action in the Second World War. A list of available book publications is obtainable from H. M. Stationery Office, York House, Kingsway, London, W.C. 2. A list of available maps (many of which had to be reprinted) may be obtained from the Geological Survey and Museum.

India:

Geological Survey of India

Director: B. C. Roy
Headquarters: Geological Museum, Library and Office, Calcutta

The Geological Survey of India is one of the oldest in the world. A geologist was appointed to the staff of the Trigonometrical Survey of India in 1818, but the modern survey may be said to have started in 1845. The survey today has a strength of 408 technical personnel and maintains a well-equipped laboratory and a scientific library having a large collection of volumes, journals, and bulletins.

The Geological Survey of India is entrusted with the preparation of geological maps for the whole country, the exploration of mineral deposits by geophysical and geochemical prospecting and their assessment on a regional scale, tendering geological advice to important engineering projects, study of the ground-water resources and connected matters. The Survey is freely consulted by all state governments on mineral, engineering, and other problems.

A general outline of the functions of this Department is indicated in the articles in the *Indian Minerals* under the heading The Geological Survey of India and Its Work by M. S. Krishman, published in vol. 9, no. 2, April, 1955; and The Note of Geological Survey of India in National Planning by B. C. Roy, vol. 14, no. 1, January–March, 1960.

Publications. These consist of memoirs devoted to complete surveys, which deal with either a particular region or a mineral industry; records consisting of short papers and general geological subjects; *Palaeontologia Indica*, containing results of paleontological research carried out by the survey; bulletins (A and B series) on individual minerals and on problems of engineering geology, ground water, and geophysics; miscellaneous publications like the "Manual of Geology of India and Burma" and an extensive series of geological maps. Annual reviews of work carried out by the survey are published regularly in the *Indian Minerals*, a quarterly semipopular journal of the Department, which contains information on minerals and their uses.

Jamaica, West Indies:

Geological Survey Department

Director: V. A. Zans
Headquarters: 14–16 East Street, Kingston, Jamaica, W.I.

The Geological Survey of Jamaica, established as a separate Department in 1951, is concerned with the basic geological mapping of the island and the investigation of its mineral and ground-water resources. Other functions include advice and assistance to the government on geological matters, particularly those branches of the government and semigovernment service whose duties bear some relationship to the rocks, minerals, ground-water resources, and their development. Private enterprise is provided with information on various matters pertaining to the geology of the island as far as possible.

Publications. The Department publishes bulletins, reports, occasional papers, and maps covering various aspects of the geology of the island. The list of publications issued so far comprises 62 items, most of which are obtainable from the Government Printing Office and from the Department. The general geological map of Jamaica on the scale 1:250,000 is now available and geological sheets 1:50,000 are in preparation.

New Zealand:

The New Zealand Geological Survey
Director: R. W. Willett
Headquarters: Andrews Avenue, Lower Hutt

The New Zealand Geological Survey was founded in 1865 with Sir James Hector as director. His staff included only two or three geologists. The Survey was reorganized in 1904, when the publication of regional geological maps and bulletins began. For many years attached to the Mines Department, it has since 1927 been a branch of the Department of Scientific and Industrial Research. The present staff (1960) numbers 43 professional officers and 43 others. About one-third of New Zealand has been geologically mapped on a scale of 1 mile to the inch, and a program of mapping on a scale of approximately 4 miles to the inch (1:250,000 series) was initiated recently and is to be completed by about 1963. The Survey has petrological and paleontological laboratories. Economic geological work includes particularly the mapping of coal fields, while the major engineering geology work of recent years has been for large hydroelectric dams.

Publications (to October, 1960). These include annual reports from 1907 onward; 68 bulletins (mostly regional, some on economic minerals, some on research topics); memoirs (9 only; now discontinued); 32 paleontological bulletins; 1:63,360 series maps (1 only, this series began in 1959); 1:250,000 series maps, 5 (this series began in 1959 and will total 28 maps).

Nigeria:

Geological Survey of Nigeria
Director: R. R. E. Jacobson
Headquarters: Kaduna South, N. Nigeria

The Geological Survey personnel includes a headquarters staff based at Kaduna South, where, besides administrative offices, there are laboratories, library, museum, and a drawing office. The scientific and technical staff consists of 32 geologists including senior supervisory personnel; six scientific officers including two chemists, one petrologist, one mineral dresser, and two geophysicists; one mining geologist; and one driller. The Geological Survey is engaged in systematic geological sheet mapping in all the three regions of the Federation and also in the Southern Cameroons. It is also concerned with the investigation of minerals used in industry, and it cooperates with government agencies and with the public in the development of mineral resources and in the construction of engineering projects. An important additional task of the Geological Survey is the investigation of the mode of occurrence and distribution of ground water.

Publications. These consist of annual reports (1929 and onward), bulletins and occasional papers published periodically, and records of the Geological Survey (1954 and onward). Maps published include a map of the Nigerian tin fields, scale 1:250,000, and a geological map of Nigeria, scale 1:2,000,000. Copies may be obtained from the Director. A number of 1:100,000 and 1:250,000 geological sheets are in course of preparation.

Northern Rhodesia:

Geological Survey Department

Director: W. H. Reeve

Headquarters: P.O. Box R. W. 135, Ridgeway, Lusaka,
Northern Rhodesia

This Survey was established in 1950 under the directorship of W. H. Reeve, and since then, a systematic geological survey of Northern Rhodesia has been carried out. Prior to 1940, a large part of the territory had been geologically examined and prospected by or on behalf of concession holders, but some of these areas and others not previously examined have been or are being surveyed by the department. The primary task of the Geological Survey is, therefore, the regional mapping of the territory; the two main objectives are the elucidation of the geological structure and history and the discovery and examination of new mineral deposits. Discovery of new minerals or extensions of minerals previously found has taken place. Among these are rare-earth minerals and graphite. The industrialization of this territory has resulted in investigations of materials such as brick earths, glass sands, ceramic and road-making materials. The quest for clays, limestone, and building stones has been accelerated. The Department is in close liaison with the various mining groups in the territory.

Publications. These comprise the annual reports, records of the Geological Survey, reports, bulletins, occasional papers, technical reports, and maps. All publications are sold by this department and printed publications are also available from the Government Printer, P.O. Box 136, Lusaka.

Nyasaland:

Geological Survey of Nyasaland

Director: W. G. Aitken

Headquarters: Geological Survey Department,
Liwonde Road, Zomba

As with other African geological surveys, that of the Nyasaland Protectorate was an outcome of the First World War and was founded in 1918. One general purpose of the institution of such surveys was to initiate the search for minerals of special value economically. The staff of the Nyasaland Survey has always been small; and in 1931, as a retrenchment measure, the survey suspended its normal duties and concentrated on the development of water supplies. Since the last war, some expansion has been possible and systematic geological mapping has begun. A section of the survey is concerned with making preliminary assessments of mineral deposits, and although the exploitation of ground water is no longer the responsibility of this department, advice is still rendered on ground-water problems.

Publications. Over 60 publications have been issued, including annual reports, bulletins, memoirs, and other papers, copies of which are available from the Government Printer, Zomba.

Somali Republic:

Geological Survey of the Somali Republic

Chief Geologist: Vacancy

Headquarters: Hargeisa, Northern Region

The Geological Survey of the Somali Republic was founded in 1952 as the Geological Survey of the Somaliland Protectorate. It was a British Colonial Development and Welfare Scheme until independence on June 26, 1960. After the protectorate united with Somalia to form the Somali Republic, the Geological

Survey became responsible for the systematic mapping of the older rocks in both territories. Activities include preliminary reconnaissance mapping of basement rocks, more detailed investigations of areas of potential economic interest, and the investigation of subsurface water resources in the Northern Region.

Publications. These include three professional papers, three mineral resources pamphlets, and two memoir-type reports. The latter are the first two in a series of seven reports, the remainder of which are at present in the course of publication. Integrating many earlier reports, they cover the geology of the basement rocks of the Northern Region of the republic. Copies of these reports can be obtained either from the Survey Headquarters or from Crown Agents, 4 Millbank, London S.W. 1.

Southern Rhodesia:

Geological Survey of Southern Rhodesia
Director: F. L. Amm
Headquarters: Salisbury

The Southern Rhodesia Geological Survey Department was started in 1910 by the British South Africa Company, which owned the mineral rights, to assist in the development and exploitation of the mineral resources of the colony. It became a government department with the granting of responsible government in 1924. The British South Africa Company continued to assist with the financing of the Department until the purchase by the government of the mineral rights in April, 1933. A strong leaning toward the economic side of geology has accordingly been a feature of the Department's activities since its inception.

The headquarters of the Department is in Salisbury with branch offices at Bulawayo and Gwelo. Regional mapping is all undertaken from Salisbury while the branch offices deal entirely with economic geology. Geological mapping is done on a scale of 1:50,000 with the assistance of aerial photographs, for publication on 1:100,000. The results are published in bulletins consisting of a description of the geology of the area together with an economic section containing detailed accounts of all the economic deposits in the area. Economic geologists stationed at Salisbury, Bulawayo, and Gwelo function in the capacity of free consultants to the mining industry and through them the industry has access to the facilities at the Survey's headquarters, which contains the following sections: chemistry, mineralogical, spectrographic, photographic, and drawing office. In addition a library and a museum are open to the public.

Publications. These include 50 bulletins, 37 short reports, a mineral resources series of geological maps obtainable from the Geological Survey Office, P.O. Box 8039, Causeway, Salisbury.

Tanganyika:

Geological Survey Division, Ministry of Commerce and Industry, Tanganyika
Commissioner: J. W. Pallister
Headquarters: Dodoma

The Geological Survey of Tanganyika which was established in 1926 has grown into a well-equipped organization; its staff consists of 24 geologists divided into a regional mapping section, supervised by a principal geologist, and an economic geology section, headed by a chief mining geologist. The laboratory services, with a chief research officer, are staffed by seven chemists and assistant chemists, a metallurgist, a mineralogist, and a petrologist. There is also a full supporting staff in drawing office, records, stores, mechanical, and clerical sections.

The aim of the Survey is primarily to undertake the geological mapping of the territory by the production and publication of geological map sheets on a scale of 1:125,000, and to search for and develop the economic mineral resources by all modern techniques. Steps are being taken to speed up both mapping and economic mineral appraisal. The laboratories are well equipped with modern instruments to carry out chemical, mineralogical, and petrological work including X-ray crystallography, and the ore-dressing equipment can be used for investigations for mining interests in the territory.

Publications. The annual report is now published in two parts: a description of general progress and administration and the records of the Geological Survey, including technical and scientific papers. Other publications include bulletins, memoirs, short papers, and reports. A series of colored geological quarter-degree map sheets are accompanied by a brief geological description. A revised geological map of Tanganyika dated 1959 is also available. Copies of publications are available from the Office of the Commissioner for Geological Survey, Dodoma, or from the Government Printer, Dar es Salaam.

Uganda:

Geological Survey of Uganda
Director: A. Cawley
Headquarters: Entebbe

This survey was suggested in 1918 when E. J. Wayland was offered the post of geological adviser. He reached Uganda in January, 1919; in a few years, three more geologists joined the staff. The Survey was expanded after the Second World War and in June, 1960, the scientific staff included sixteen geologists, two chemists, a field officer, five associate chemists, a records officer, a spectrographer, a topographer, and drilling and borehole maintenance staff.

There is a program of regional mapping and mineral exploration in progress, and advice is also given on specific problems concerning mineralization, engineering, and materials. The Survey also superintends the drilling of water boreholes; some 3,000 have now been completed.

Well-equipped chemical, spectrographic, petrological, and mineral-dressing laboratories are maintained at headquarters.

Publications. Annual reports have been issued since 1920. In addition, a number of memoirs, occasional papers, and bulletins have been published. Maps at a scale of 1:100,000 are now being produced with explanatory reports. A 1:250,000 map series is also being compiled.

Union of South Africa:

Geological Survey of the Union of South Africa
(Geologiese Opname van die Unie van Suid-Afrika)
Director: F. C. Truter
Headquarters: Office of the Geological Survey, Pretoria

The Geological Survey of the Union of South Africa was founded in 1910. Prior to that date, geological work had been carried out by the Geological Commission of the Cape of Good Hope from 1896 until amalgamation in 1910 with the Geological Survey of the Transvaal, established in 1903; the two combined to form the Union Survey. In addition, work had been done by the state geologist of the South African Republic from 1897 to 1900 and by the Geological Survey of Natal and Zululand up to the year 1908. Functions of the present Survey, which is a division of the Department of Mines, include geological mapping, the investigation of mineral resources, the study of underground water problems, the examination of rocks and minerals for the public, the maintenance of a geological museum, paleontological, seismological, oceanographical, and geophysical research, and the investigation of the value of geophysical prospecting methods as applied to South African conditions.

Publications. Those of the older bodies, up to the year 1910, consisted generally of maps and annual reports. Publications since 1910 include sheet maps on the scales of 1:148,750, 1:238,000, and 1:125,000, accompanied by explanations, maps on the scale 1:250,000 without explanations, some annual reports, bulletins, handbooks, bibliographies of South African geology, information pamphlets, special publications, and a number of general and paleontological memoirs. Publications are obtainable from the Government Printer, Pretoria, but not from the Survey.

United Kingdom Protectorates, Dependencies, and Colonies:

The following parts of the British Commonwealth, some of which are in the process of achieving independence while this book is in press, so that their listing here may not be currently correct, have their geological survey work carried out through different agencies. Information on local geological conditions and operations can be obtained from the addresses noted:

Aden	Overseas Geological Surveys, London; Director of Public Works, Aden
Bahamas	Director of Public Works
Barbados	Director of Public Works
Bechuanaland	Geological Survey, Lobasti
Bermuda	Director of Public Works
Borneo	Geological Survey Department, British Territories in Borneo, Kuching, Sarawak
British Honduras	Geological Survey Department, British Guiana; Overseas Geological Surveys, London; Director of Surveys, British Honduras
British Solomon Islands	Senior Geologist, Box 62, Honiara, Guadalcanal
Cayman Islands	Superintendent of Works
Falkland Islands	Falkland Islands Dependencies Survey, Geological Dept., University of Birmingham, Birmingham 15
Gambia	Overseas Geological Surveys, London; Director of Public Works, Gambia
Gibraltar	Commissioner of Lands and Works
Gilbert and Ellice Islands	Superintendent of Works
Hong Kong	Prof. S. G. Davis, University of Hong Kong
Leeward Islands *Antigua* *St. Kitts-Nevis and Anguilla* *Montserrat* *British Virgin Islands*	Overseas Geological Surveys, London; Geological Survey Department, British Guiana
Malta	Director of Public Works
Mauritius	Director of Public Works and Surveys
St. Helena	Superintendent of Works
Seychelles	Superintendent of Public Works
Sierra Leone	Geological Survey Department, Freetown
Singapore	Ministry for Home Affairs
Swaziland	Geological Survey and Mines, P.O. Box 9, Mbabane
Trinidad	Ministry of Industry, Commerce, Tourism, and External Communications
Turks and Caicos Islands	Superintendent of Works

Windward Islands:

Government Geologist's Department, Windward Islands
Government Geologist: P. H. A. Martin-Kaye
Headquarters: Castries, St. Lucia, West Indies

The present geological surveys of the Windward Islands were instituted in 1956. They cover the southern Lesser Antillean islands of Grenada, St. Vincent, St. Lucia, and Dominica, together with a string of smaller islands, the Grenadines, which lie between Grenada and St. Vincent. The establishment consists of one geologist and assistants; there is a program of general geological mapping, with special investigations into ground-water supplies and any mineral occurrences of economic aspect. No publications have been produced, but specific enquiries may be directed to the Department.

In addition occasional studies are made as required in the Leeward and British Virgin Islands. Continuous surveys in these latter islands ceased in 1956 and "Reports on the Geology of the Leeward and British Virgin Islands" was subsequently published.

United States:

Geological Survey, United States Department of the Interior
Director: Thomas B. Nolan
Headquarters: Washington, D.C.

The Geological Survey of the United States was established on July 1, 1879, in response to an act of Congress passed on March 3 of that year. Prior to that date, considerable official geological survey work had been done by Federal organizations, and even more by the states. Among the earlier Federal surveys four were outstanding: (1) Geological Exploration of the Fortieth Parallel, conducted by Clarence King, for the War Department; (2) Geological and Geographical Survey of the Territories, conducted by F. V. Hayden under the direction of the Commissioner of the General Land Office; (3) Geographical and Geological Survey of the Rocky Mountain Region, conducted by John Wesley Powell, for the War Department; and (4) Geographical Survey West of the One Hundreth Meridian, conducted by Lt. George M. Wheeler of the Corps of Engineers under the jurisdiction of the War Department. Today, the Survey is most extensive in its scope, operations, and personnel. Survey publications are known to geologists throughout the world, and the Survey contains a most comprehensive collection of technical works in its fields.

The Survey is a bureau of the Department of the Interior, and five divisions—conservation, geologic, publications, topographic, and water resources—share its activities. An administrative division serves the entire Bureau. The Survey's main functions are defined by an act of March 3, 1879, which provided for "the classification of the public lands and the examination of the geological structure, mineral resources, and products of the national domain." Topographic mapping and chemical and physical researches were recognized as an essential part of the Survey's investigations and studies as authorized by its basic law, and were specifically provided for by Congress in 1888. Provision was made in 1894 for gauging the streams and determining the water supply of the United States. Recently, the Survey was assigned responsibilities in connection with supervision of activities of the Federal Petroleum Board in administering the act of Congress which prohibits interstate shipment of oil in violation of certain state oil and gas conservation laws. The Survey cooperates with various state geological surveys and municipalities through formal agreements and informal arrangements. It performs work for other Federal

U.S.A. State Geological Surveys

State	Name of survey	Director	Headquarters
Alabama...........	Geological Survey of Alabama	Dr. Walter B. Jones, State Geologist	University of Alabama
Arizona...........	Arizona Bureau of Mines, University of Arizona	Dr. J. D. Forrester, Dean and Director	University of Arizona, Tucson 25
Arkansas........	Arkansas Geological and Conservation Commission	Mr. Norman F. Williams, Geologist-Director	State Capitol, Little Rock
California........	Division of Mines, Department of Natural Resources	Dr. Ian Campbell, Chief	Ferry Building, San Francisco
Colorado.........	Colorado Metal Mining Fund Board	Mr. Robert S. Palmer, Executive Secretary	204 State Office Building, Denver
	Colorado Geological Survey	Mr. Walter E. Scott, Jr., Commissioner of Mines	State Museum Building, Denver
Connecticut.....	Connecticut Geological and Natural History Survey	Dr. J. W. Peoples, Director	Box U-45, Storrs
Delaware........	Delaware Geological Survey	Mr. Johan J. Groot, State Geologist	University of Delaware, Newark
Florida...........	Florida Geological Survey	Dr. Robert O. Vernon, Director	P.O. Box 631, Tallahassee
Georgia..........	Dept. of Mines, Mining and Geology, State Division of Conservation	Capt. Garland Peyton, Director	19 Hunter St. S.W., Atlanta 3
Idaho.............	Idaho Bureau of Mines and Geology	Dr. Earl F. Cook, Director	University of Idaho, Moscow
Illinois...........	State Geological Survey Division	Dr. John C. Frye, Chief	University of Illinois, Urbana
Indiana...........	Indiana Geological Survey, Department of Conservation	Mr. John B. Patton	Indiana University, Bloomington
Iowa..............	Iowa Geological Survey	Dr. H. Garland Hershey, Director and State Geologist	Geological Survey Building, Iowa City
Kansas...........	State Geological Survey	Dr. Frank C. Foley, State Geologist and Director	University of Kansas, Lawrence
Kentucky........	Kentucky Geological Survey	Dr. Wallace W. Hagan, Director and State Geologist	307 Mineral Industries Building, 120 Graham Ave., Lexington
Louisiana........	Louisiana Geological Survey	Mr. Leo W. Hough, State Geologist	P.O. Box 8847, Univ. Station, Baton Rouge 3

State	Official	Address
Maine	Mr. Robert G. Doyle, State Geologist	Department of Economic Development	State House, Augusta
Maryland	Dr. Joseph T. Singewald, Jr., Director	Department of Geology, Mines, and Water Resources, Board of Natural Resources	102 Latrobe Hall, Johns Hopkins Univ., Baltimore 18
Michigan	Mr. W. L. Daoust, State Geologist	Geological Survey Division, Department of Conservation	Lansing 26
Minnesota	Dr. G. M. Schwartz, Director	Minnesota Geological Survey	University of Minn., Minneapolis 14
Mississippi	Mr. Tracy W. Lusk, Director and State Geologist	Mississippi State Geological Survey	University of Mississippi
Missouri	Dr. Thomas R. Beveridge, State Geologist	Division of Geological Survey and Water Resources	P.O. Box 2500, Rolla
Montana	Dr. Edwin G. Koch, Director	Montana Bureau of Mines and Geology, Montana School of Mines	Butte
	Mr. W. S. March, Jr., State Geologist	Montana Bureau of Mines and Geology	Butte
Nebraska	Mr. Eugene C. Reed, Director and State Geologist	Conservation and Survey Division	University of Nebraska, Lincoln 8
Nevada	Dr. Vernon E. Scheid, Director	Nevada Bureau of Mines	University of Nevada, Reno
New Hampshire	Dr. T. R. Meyers, Geologist	New Hampshire State Planning and Development Commission	Conant Hall, Univ. of New Hampshire, Durham
New Jersey	Mr. Kemble Widmer, State Geologist	Bureau of Geology and Topography	520 East State St., Trenton 25
New Mexico	Mr. Alvin J. Thompson, Director	New Mexico Bureau of Mines and Mineral Resources	Socorro
New York	Dr. John G. Broughton, State Geologist	State Geological and Natural History Surveys	State Education Bldg., University of the State of New York, Albany 1
North Carolina	Dr. Jasper L. Stuckey, State Geologist	Division of Mineral Resources, Dept. of Conservation and Development	State Office Bldg., Raleigh
North Dakota	Dr. Wilson M. Laird, State Geologist	North Dakota Geological Survey	University of North Dakota, Grand Forks
Ohio	Mr. Ralph Bernhagen, Chief	Ohio Division of Geological Survey	155 South Oval Drive, Ohio State Univ., Columbus 10

U.S.A. State Geological Surveys (Continued)

State	Name of survey	Director	Headquarters
Oklahoma............	Oklahoma Geological Survey	Dr. Carl C. Branson, Director	Norman
Oregon..............	State Department of Geology and Mineral Industries	Mr. Hollis Dole, Director	1069 State Office Bldg., Portland 1
Pennsylvania........	Bureau of Topographic and Geologic Survey, Department of Internal Affairs	Dr. Carlyle Gray, State Geologist	Harrisburg
South Carolina......	Dept. of Geology, Mineralogy, and Geography	Dr. Laurence L. Smith, State Geologist	University of South Carolina, Columbia 19
South Dakota.......	State Geological Survey	Dr. Allen F. Agnew, State Geologist	State University, Lock Drawer 351, Vermillion
Tennessee...........	Division of Geology, Department of Conservation	Mr. W. D. Hardeman, State Geologist	G-5 State Office Bldg., Nashville 3
Texas...............	Bureau of Economic Geology	Dr. John T. Lonsdale, Director	University of Texas, Austin 12
Utah................	Utah Geological and Mineralogical Survey, College of Mines and Mineral Industries	Mr. Arthur L. Crawford, Director	University of Utah, Salt Lake City 2
Vermont............	State of Vermont Development Commission	Dr. Charles G. Doll, State Geologist	East Hall, Univ. of Vermont, Burlington
Virginia............	Dept. of Conservation and Economic Development, Division of Mineral Resources	Mr. James L. Calver, State Geologist	Natural Resources Bldg., Box 3667, Charlottesville
Washington.........	Division of Mines and Geology, Department of Conservation	Mr. Marshall Huntting, Supervisor	355 General Administration Bldg., Olympia
West Virginia.......	West Virginia Geological and Economic Survey	Dr. Paul H. Price, State Geologist	P.O. Box 879, Morgantown
Wisconsin..........	Geological and Natural History Survey	Mr. George F. Hanson, State Geologist	Science Hall, Univ. of Wisconsin, Madison 6
Wyoming...........	Geological Survey of Wyoming	Dr. Horace D. Thomas, State Geologist	University of Wyoming, Laramie

agencies as requested. *Science*, vol. 119, no. 3100 (May 28, 1954), and *The Scientific Monthly*, vol. 78, no. 6 (June, 1954) published articles on "The U.S. Geological Survey, 75 Years of Service to the Nation, 1879–1954."

Publications. The results of the Survey's investigations are published in its bulletins, professional papers, water-supply papers, and circulars; and its topographic, geologic, and hydrologic maps. Results of many investigations are published also by cooperating Federal and state agencies, and in technical and scientific journals. At the end of each fiscal year, the Survey makes a report to the Secretary of the Interior on its activities and progress during the previous year. Circulars are distributed without charge by the Survey; maps are sold by the Survey. Other reports are sold by the Superintendent of Documents, Washington.

United States: States:

Geological Surveys of the States

As will be seen from the foregoing list, a majority of the states maintain their own geological surveys, the functions of which are usually related to areal and economic geological problems. It is impossible to do more than list these surveys in this place, in view of their number. Many of them far surpass in size and achievement some of the more isolated surveys already mentioned in detail, but this uneven attention is felt to be desirable, as the state surveys are generally so well known, whereas those in more distant parts of the world are but little heard of in normal work. Tribute must be paid to the high standard of state geological survey publications and to their frequent use far outside state boundaries. State geological survey work may be said to have begun with surveys made in North Carolina in 1824. The first real state survey was that of Massachusetts, started in 1830 by Hitchcock.

Directory of Other Geological Surveys of the World:

This summary list is taken, by permission, from *AGI Data Sheet* 14, as revised, June, 1960, appearing in *Geotimes*, **5**, 33–34, 1960, published by the American Geological Institute, 2101 Constitution Ave., Washington 25, D.C.

North America:

Greenland:	Grønlands Geologiske Undersøgelse, Østervoldgade 7, København K, Danmark
Mexico:	Instituto de Geología, Universidad Nacional Autónoma de Mexico, Ciudad Universitaría, Mexico 20, D.F.

Central America and Caribbean Islands:

Costa Rica:	Departamento de Geología, Ciudad Universitaría, San José
Cuba:	Instituto Nacional de Investigaciones Científicas, Cerro 827, Havana
Dominican Republic:	Secretaria de Estado de Fomento, Dirección de Minería, Ciudad Trujillo
El Salvador:	Servicio Geólogico Nacional, 23 Avenida Norte No. 140, San Salvador
Guatemala:	Sección de Geología, Dirección General de Minería e Hidrocarburos, 10a. Calle 11–46, Zona 1, Guatemala City
Haiti:	Geological Survey, Department of Agriculture, Damiens près Port-au-Prince

Nicaragua: Servicio Geológico Nacional, Ministerio de Economía, Apartado Postal No. 1347, Managua, D.N.

Puerto Rico: Economic Development Administration, Department of Industrial Research, Mineralogy and Geology Section, Box 38, Roosevelt

South America:

Argentina: Direccion Nacional de Geologia y Mineria, Peru No. 562, Buenos Aires

Bolivia: Direccional General de Minas y Petroleo, Casilla 401, La Paz

Brazil: Departamento Nacional da Produção Mineral, Avenida Pasteur 404, Praia Vermelha, Rio de Janeiro

Chile: Instituto de Investigaciones Geológicas, Augustinas 785, 5.0 Piso, Casilla 10465, Santiago

Colombia: Servicio Geologico Nacional, Apartado Nacional No. 2504, Bogotá

Ecuador: Direccion General de Mineria y Petroleos, Ministerio de Econimía, Quito

French Guiana: Service des Mines, Cayenne

Paraguay: Direccion General de Minas y Petroleos, Tacuari 271, Asuncion

Peru: Instituto Nacional de Investigaciones y Fomento Mineros, Division de Geología Minera, Apartado 2559, Lima

Surinam: Geologisch Mijnbovwkundige Dienst, Paramaribo

Uruguay: Instituto Geologico del Uruguay, Calle J. Herrera y Obes, 1239, Montevideo

Venezuela: Ministerio de Minas e Hidrocarburos, Dirección de Geología, Torre Norte, Piso 19, Caracas

Europe:

Austria: Geologische Bundesanstalt, Rasumofsky-gasse 23, Vienna 111/40

Belgium: Service Géologique de Belgique, 13 rue Jenner, Parc Léopold, Brussels 4

Bulgaria: Direction des Mines, Ministère des Mines et des Richesses du Sous-sol, Sofia

Czechoslovakia: Ustrednz Ustav Geologicky, Hradebni 9, Prague

Denmark: Geological Survey of Denmark, Charlottenlund

Finland: Geologinen Tutkimuslaitos, Otaniemi

France: Service de la Carte Géologique de France, 62 Boulevard St. Michel, Paris 6

Germany: Bundesanstalt für Bodenforschung, Wiesenstrasse 1, Hannover

Greece: Institute for Geology and Subsurface Research, Ministry of Industry, 34 University Str., Athens

Hungary:	Magyar Allami, Földtani Intezet, Vorosilov-ut 14, Budapest XIV
Iceland:	Department of Geology and Geography, Museum of Natural History, P.O. Box 532, Reykjavik
Ireland:	Geological Survey, 14 Hume Street, Dublin
Italy:	Servizio Geologico d'Italia, Largo S. Susanna N. 13, Rome
Liechtenstein:	Geological Survey, Vaduz
Luxembourg:	Service Géologique, Direction des Ponts et Chaussées, 38 Blvd. de la Foire, Luxembourg
Netherlands:	Geological Survey, Spaarne 17, Haarlem
Norway:	Norges Geologiska Undersøkelse, Josefines gate 34, Oslo
Poland:	Centralny Urzad Geologii, Inst. Geol., UL. Jasna 6, Warsaw
Portugal:	Serviços Geológicos de Portugal, Rua da Academia das Ciencias 19—2°, Lisbon 2
Romania:	Comité Géologique de la R. P. Roumaine, Calea Victoriei 126, Bucuresti
Saar:	Service Géologique de la Sarre, 1, Triererstrass, Sarbrucken
Spain:	Instituto Geología y Minero de Espana, Rios Rosas 9, Madrid
Sweden:	Sveriges Geologiska Undersökning, Stockholm 50
Switzerland:	Geologische Kommission der Schweizerische, Naturforschende Gesellschaft, Basal Bernoullianum
Union of Soviet Socialist Republics:	Ministry of Geology, Moscow
Yugoslavia:	Institut de Géologia de l'Académie, Serbe des Sciences, Belgrade
Africa:	
Algeria:	Service de la Carte Geologique de l'Olgérie, 14 Boulevard Baudin, Algers
Angola:	Servico de Geología e Minas da Provincia de Angola, Avenida Marginal—C.P. 1260-C, Luanda
Cameroons:	Ministère de l'Economie Nationale, Direction des Mines et de la Géologie, Boite Postale 70, Yaounde
Egypt:	Geological Survey of Egypt, Dawawin Post Office, Cairo
Ethiopia:	Ministry of Mines and State Domain, P.O. Box 486, Addis Ababa
French Equatorial Africa:	Institut Equatorial de Recherches et d'Etat, Géologique et Minieres, B.P. 12, Brazzaville
French Somaliland:	Service des Travaux Publics de la Côte des Somalis, Djibouti

French West Africa:	Director, Fédérale des Mines et de la Géologie, Occidentale Francaise, Boite Postale No. 355, Dakar
Liberia:	Bureau of Natural Resources and Surveys, P.O. Box 145, Monrovia
Libya:	Mining Department, Ministry of National Economy, Tripoli
Madagascar:	Service Géologique, Direction des Mines et de la Géologie, B.P. 322, Tananarive
Morocco:	Service de la Carte Géologique, Direction des Mines, Sous Secrétariat d'Etat a Industrie et au Commerce, Rabat
Mozambique:	Servicos de Geología e Minas, P.O. Box 217, Lourenço Marques
Reunion:	Service des Travaux Publics, St. Denis
South-West Africa:	Geological Survey Section, Dept. of Water Affairs, Windhoek
Spanish West Africa:	Dirección General de Marruecos y Colonias, Paseo de la Castellane 5, Madrid, Spain
Sudan:	Geological Survey, P.O. Box 410, Khartoum
Togoland:	Service des Mines au Togo, Lome
Tunisia:	Service des Mines de l'Industrie et de l'Energie (Service Géologique), Tunis
Middle East:	
Iran:	Iranian Geological Survey, Ministry of Industry and Mines, Tehran
Iraq:	Geological Survey Department, Directorate of Mines, Ministry of Economics, Baghdad
Israel:	Geological Survey of Israel, Malkhei Israel Street, Jerusalem
Jordan:	Ministry of Economics, Amman
Lebanon:	Direction Générale des Travaux Publics, Beyrouth
Saudi Arabia:	Department of Mines and Petroleum, Jidda
Syria:	Geological Survey of Syria, Youssef el Azmeh Square, Damascus
Turkey:	Maden Tetkik ve Arama Enstitusu, Posta Kutusu 16, Ankara
Asia:	
Afghanistan:	Afghanistan Geological Survey, Darulaman, Kabul
Burma:	Burma Geological Department, 226 Dalhousi Street, P.O. Box 843, Rangoon
Cambodia:	Service des Mines, Phnom-Penh
China:	Chinese Ministry of Geology, Peking
Indonesia:	Geological Survey of Indonesia, Djalan Diponegoro 57, Bandung
Japan:	Geological Survey of Japan, 135 Hisamoto-cho, Kawasaki City

Pakistan:	Geological Survey of Pakistan, P.O. Box 15, Quetta
Philippines:	Geological Survey Division, Bureau of Mines, Manila
Taiwan:	Geological Survey of Taiwan, P.O. Box 31, Taipei
Thailand:	Geological Survey Division, Royal Department of Mines, Bangkok
Vietnam, Republic of:	Service Géologique, Direction Générale des Mines de Industrie, 59 Rue Gia-Lorg, Saigon

Australia and Pacific Islands:
New Caledonia:	Service des Mines, Noumea

APPENDIX C

GEOLOGICAL SOCIETIES, PERIODICALS, AND SOURCES OF INFORMATION

As with other branches of science, there is such a large volume of printed information on geology, accumulating at what appears to be a steadily increasing rate, that it has not always been easy to make sure that this store of useful knowledge was being used to full advantage in connection with individual problems. Fortunately, however, there are now available a number of guides to the literature, three series of bibliographies, and a series of geological abstracts serving North America, all of which can assist in the search for necessary information.

Guides to Literature:

PEARL, R. M.: "Guide to Geologic Literature," McGraw-Hill Book Company, Inc., New York, 1951.

HOWELL, J. V., A. I. LEVORSEN, R. H. DOTT, and J. W. WILDS: "Directory of Geological Material in North America," 2d ed., Am. Geological Inst., Washington, D.C., 1957.

Bibliographies:

"Bibliography and Index of Geology Exclusive of North America," published annually by the Geological Society of America. The first volume was published in 1933.

"Bibliography of North American Geology," published at regular intervals in the Bulletin series of the United States Geological Survey, 1785–1918, 1919–1928, 1928–1939, 1940–1949, and then issued annually.

"Annotated Bibliography of Economic Geology," published semiannually by the Economic Geology Publishing Co., Urbana, Ill., 1929–date.

Geological Abstracts:

First published by the Geological Society of America, these are now issued regularly by the American Geological Institute as "*Geoscience Abstracts.*" The possibility of an international abstracting service is being investigated.

In the study of the geology of locations in which they have to carry out their work, civil engineers may sometimes need to refer to geological publications other than those of their local geological survey. These will usually be the official proceedings of geological societies or geological journals. Since some civil engineers may be drawn to a study of pure geology, because of the contacts geology has with their own work, it may be useful to give particulars of the main geological societies and periodicals of the English-speaking world.

SOCIETIES

The Geological Society of London (Burlington House, London, W.C. 1, England). The Society is one of the oldest in existence devoted to one branch of science,

826

having been founded on Nov. 13, 1807. It publishes brief *Proceedings* and its well-known *Quarterly Journal.*

The Geological Society of America (419 West 117th St., New York). Founded in 1888, the Society is the North American counterpart of the London Society. It publishes a monthly *Bulletin, Annual Proceedings, Memoirs,* and *Special Papers.*

Attention has already been directed (see page 35) to the Engineering Geology Division of the GSA and to its useful publications.

The Society of Economic Geologists. The Society is accurately described by its name. It holds regular meetings in association with the Geological Society of America and the American Institute of Mining and Metallurgy. Closely linked with the Society is *Economic Geology,* an independent journal published eight times each year, again well described by its title. Business office for the journal is: Care of Illinois Geological Survey, Urbana.

International Geological Congress. The Congress meets every three years in different countries. Its *Proceedings* contain articles relating to geology and civil engineering.

There exist also many specialized and local geological societies such as the Geological Association of Canada, the American Association of Petroleum Geologists, and the Liverpool and Manchester Geological Societies in England, the existence of which will usually be known to engineers practicing in the respective districts or fields of work. Detailed mention may be made of the Geologists' Association of London, an essentially popular body which exists to "foster the progress and diffusion of the science of geology." It holds meetings in London and valuable field excursions not only in all parts of Great Britain but also on the continent of Europe. It publishes *Proceedings;* many engineers are members. No equivalent appears to exist in North America, although many local "natural history" societies have active geological sections.

PERIODICALS

In addition to the regular publications of the various geological societies and of journals that deal with special branches of pure and applied geology in the mining and petroleum fields, the following periodicals are of value to geologists and cover the whole science as their sphere of interest.

The Geological Magazine: a monthly journal, published in London by Dulau and Co., 29 Dover St., London, W. 1; it incorporates *The Geologist,* which was founded in 1864.

The American Journal of Science: a monthly journal, founded in 1818 by Benjamin Silliman, published at Yale University, New Haven, Conn.

The Journal of Geology: a semiquarterly journal, published by the University of Chicago Press, Chicago.

Geotechnique: a quarterly journal serving the field of soil mechanics, published by the Institution of Civil Engineers, London, S.W. 1.

Finally, it may be noted that valuable publications of geological interest, including some relating to applications in civil engineering, are to be found in the records of the great general scientific societies such as the Royal Society of Great Britain, the Royal Society of Canada, the American Association for the Advancement of Science, and the British association of the same nature. Scientific journals such as *Nature* and *Science* occasionally contain articles of relevant interest, and the proceedings of the various mining engineering institutions include some papers that touch upon geology as applied in civil engineering (as references listed in Appendix D will indicate).

APPENDIX D

REFERENCES CITED IN TEXT

For the convenience of readers, reference is made, whenever possible, to articles in readily accessible journals such as *Engineering News-Record* and *Civil Engineering* (London and New York), even though in many cases more complete descriptions are available in the proceedings of professional societies.

Chapter 1

1.1. DAWKINS, Boyd: On the Relation of Geology to Civil Engineering (James Forrest Lecture, 1898), *Inst. Civil Eng. Min. Proc. (London)*, **134**: 254–255 (1898).

1.2. McCALLUM, R. T.: The Opening-out of Cofton Tunnel, London, Midland, and Scottish Railway, *Inst. Civil Eng. Min. Proc. (London)*, **231**: 161 (1931).

1.3. GRUNER, H. E.: Hydro Electric Power Development on the Rhine (Special Lecture) *Inst. Civil Eng. (London)* (1935).

1.4. Contractors Win Suit to Recover Losses Due to Engineer's Misrepresentation, *Eng. News-Record (New York)*, **93**: 21 (1924).

1.5. WALKER, T. A.: "The Severn Tunnel; Its Construction and Difficulties, 1872–1887," R. Bentley and Son, London, 1888.

1.6. CARPMAEL, R.: Cementation in the Severn Tunnel, *Inst. Civil Eng. Min. Proc. (London)*, **234**: 277 (1933).

1.7. MOYE, D. G.: Engineering Geology for the Snowy Mountains Scheme, *Jour. Inst. Engs., Australia (Sydney, NSW)*, **30**: 287–298 (1955); see also **32**: 85–87 (1960).

1.8. PATON, John: The Glen Shira Hydro-Electric Project, *Proc. Inst. Civil Eng. (London)*, pt. I, **5**: 593–632 (1956).

1.9. The Work of the Royal Engineers in the European War 1914–1919: Geological Work on the Western Front, *The Secretary, Institution of Royal Engineers (Chatham, England)* (1922).

1.10. BROOKS, A. H.: The Use of Geology on the Western Front, *U.S. Geol. Survey Prof. Paper* 128d (1921).

1.11. DAVID, M. E.: "Professor David," Edward Arnold & Co., London, 1937. A fascinating biography.

1.12. See p. 28 of 1.9.

1.13. See p. 232 of 1.11.

1.14. See p. 256 of 1.11.

1.15. WOODRING, W. P.: Introductory Paper in The Bradley Volume, *Am. Jour. Sci.*, **258A**: 3 (1960).

1.16. WILMOT, Chester: "The Struggle for Europe," Fontana Books, Collins, London, 1959, p. 219. One of the best of the "war books."

1.17. See p. 410 of 1.16.

1.18. HYDE, J. E.: Geology of Camp Sherman Quadrangle, *Geol. Surv. of Ohio, Columbus, Bull.* 23, *Fourth Series* (1921).

1.19. STAMP, L. Dudley: "The Earth's Crust," George G. Harrap & Co., Ltd., London, 1951.

Chapter 2

2.1. PALLISER, Bernard: "Admirable Discourses," trans. by A. La Rocque, Univ. of Illinois Press, Urbana, 1957, pp. 148, 186.

2.2. For a vivid review of the history of geology see ADAMS, F. D.: "The Birth and Development of the Geological Sciences," Dover Publications, New York, 1954.

2.3. SHEPPARD, T: "William Smith, His Maps and Memoirs," A. Brown and Sons, Ltd., Hull, England, 1920.

2.4. KEITH, Sir A.: An African Garden of Eden, *John o'London's Weekly*, **35**: 890 (1934).

2.5. SINGER, C.: "A Short History of Scientific Ideas to 1900," Oxford University Press, New York, 1959. Highly commended to all readers interested in the history of science.

Chapter 3

3.1. LUCRETIUS, Titus Carus: "De Rerum Natura," bk. V, 306, trans. by W. H. D. ROUSE (Loeb Classical Library), quoted by F. D. ADAMS in 2.2, to which the writer gratefully acknowledges his debt.

3.2. MERRILL, G. P.: "Rocks, Rock Weathering and Soils," rev. ed., The Macmillan Company, New York, 1911.

3.3. EKBLAW, G. E., and R. E. GRIM: Some Geological Relations between the Constituents of Soil Materials and Highway Construction, *Illinois Geol. Survey Rept. Investigation*, **42** (1936).

3.4. CLARKE, F. W.: note in *Nature*, **89**: 334 (May 30, 1912).

3.5. CAPPS, S. R.: Rock Glaciers in Alaska, *Jour. of Geol.*, **18**: 359–375 (1910). See also **18**: 549–553.

3.6. See *The Journal of Glaciology*, Cambridge, England, for many papers on this and allied subjects.

3.7. RADFORTH, N. W.: A Suggested Classification of Muskeg for the Engineer, *Eng. Jour.*, **35**: 1199–1210 (1952).

3.8. BRYAN, K: Cryopedology: The Study of Frozen Ground and Intensive Frost Action with Suggestions on Nomenclature, *Am. Jour. Sci.*, **244**: 622–642 (September, 1946).

3.9. CRAWFORD, C. B., and R. F. LEGGET: Ground Temperature Investigations in Canada, *Eng. Journal*, **40**: 263–269 (1957).

3.10. LEGGET, R. F., H. B. DICKENS, and R. J. E. BROWN: Permafrost Investigations in Canada, *First Symp. on Arctic Geology, Calgary* (1960).

3.11. CHARLESWORTH, J. K.: "The Quaternary Era," 2 vols., Edward Arnold & Co., London, 1957.

Chapter 4

4.1. COLLIN, Alexandre: "Landslides in Clay" (1846), trans. by W. R. SCHRIEVER, Univ. Toronto Press, Toronto, 1956. The quotation consists of the closing words of this memorable book.

4.2. See pp. 77ff., chap. 7 of 4.1.

4.3.   Baker, Sir, B.: The Actual Lateral Pressure of Earthwork, *Inst. Civil Eng. Min. Proc. (London)*, **65**: 140 (1882).

4.4.   Bell, A. L. L.: The Lateral Pressure and Resistance of Clay and the Supporting Power of Clay Foundations, *Inst. Civil Eng. Min. Proc. (London)*, **199**: 233 (1916).

4.5.   Terzaghi, K.: In *Proc. First Int. Conf. on Soil Mech. and Found. Eng.*, **3**: 13, Cambridge, Mass. (1936).

4.6.   Guide to the Field Classification of Soils for Engineering Purposes, *Assoc. Comm. on Soil and Snow Mechanics, Tech. Memo.* 37, National Research Council, Ottawa (1955).

4.7.   Hubbard, M. K., and W. W. Rubey: Mechanics of Fluid Filled Porous Solids and Its Application to Overthrust Faulting; and Rubey, W. W., and M. K. Hubbard: Overthrust Belt in Geosynclinical Area of Western Wyoming in Light of Fluid Pressure Hypothesis, *Bull. Geol. Soc. Am.*, **70**: 115–166, 167–206 (1959).

4.8.   Legget, R. F.: Geotechnique: New Word, Old Science, *Trans. Geol. Assn. of Canada*, **12**: 13–19 (1960).

4.9.   Clevenger, W. A.: Experiences with Loess as Foundation Material, *Proc. Am. Soc. C.E.*, **82**: SM3, Paper 1025 (July, 1956).

4.10. Woods, K. B., R. W. Pryer, and W. J. Eden: Soil Engineering Problems on the Quebec, North Shore and Laborador Railway, *Bull. Am. Ry. Eng. Assoc.*, **60**: 669–688 (1959).

4.11. Legget, R. F., and W. J. Eden: Soil Problems in Mining on the Precambrian Shield, *Eng. Jour.*, **43**: 81–87 (November, 1960).

4.12. Eden, W. J.: A Laboratory Study of Varved Clay from Steep Rock Lake, Ontario, *Am. Jour. of Science*, **62**: 1223–1262 (1955).

4.13. Crawford, C. B.: Engineering Studies of Leda Clay, "Soils in Canada," University of Toronto Press, Toronto, 1961, pp. 200–217.

4.14. Pihlainen, J. A., and G. H. Johnston: Permafrost Investigations at Aklavik, 1953, *Div. of Building Research Tech. Paper* 16, Nat. Res. Council, Canada (1954).

4.15. For a useful review and good bibliography see Symposium on Airfield Construction on Overseas Soils, *Proc. Inst. Civ. Eng.*, **8**: 211–292 (1957).

4.16. Simon, P., and J. Vallee: The Souapiti Fall; The Konkouré Development, *Travaux*, no. 286, pp. 193–202 (1958).

4.17. Terzaghi, K.: Design and Performance of the Sasamua Dam, *Proc. Inst. Civil Eng.*, **9**: 369–394 (1958).

4.18. For a full discussion see Symposium on Physico-Chemical Properties of Soil: Clay Minerals, *Proc. Am. Soc. C.E.*, **84**: SM2, Papers 1998–2001 (April, 1959).

4.19. See p. 374 of 4.17.

4.20. Lee, C. H.: Sealing the Lagoon Lining at Treasure Island with Salt, *Trans. Am. Soc. C. E.*, **106**: 577–607 (1941).

4.21. Rominger, J. F., and P. C. Rutledge: Use of Soil Mechanics Data in Correlation and Interpretation of Lake Agassiz Sediments, *Jour. of Geol.*, **60**: 160–180 (1952).

4.22. Rominger, J. F.: Relationships of Plasticity and Grain Size of Lake Agassiz Sediments, *Jour. of Geol.*, **62**: 537–572 (1954).

4.23. Dreimanis, A.: Tills of Southern Ontario, "Soils in Canada," University of Toronto Press, Toronto, 1961, pp. 80–96.

4.24. See 4.13.

4.25. Fisk, H. N., and B. McClelland: Geology of Continental Shelf off Louisiana: Its Influence on Offshore Foundation Design, *Bull. Geol. Soc. Am.*, **70**: 1369–1394 (1959).

4.26. TERZAGHI, K.: Influence of Geological Factors on the Engineering Properties of Sediments, *Econ. Geology*, 50th Anniversary Volume, 557–618 (1955).

Chapter 5

5.1. ARISTOTLE: "Meteorologica," bk. I, 13, trans. by E. W. WEBSTER, Oxford University Press, New York. For this quotation I am also indebted to Dr. F. D. ADAMS through 2.2.

5.2. FIEDLER, A. G.: Importance of Ground Water in the National Economy, *Trans. Am. Soc. C.E.*, **123**: 776–791 (1958).

5.3. MEINZER, O. E.: The History and Development of Ground-water Hydrology, *Jour. Washington Acad. Sci.*, **24**: 6 (1934).

5.4. See 2.3.

5.5. JACK, R. Lockhart: The Geology of the County of Jervois . . . with Special Reference to Underground Water Supplies, *Geol. Survey South Australia Bull.* 3, p. 29 (1914).

5.6. SMITH, B.: Geological Aspects of Underground Water Supplies (Royal Society of Arts Cantor Lecture), *Water and Water Eng. (London)*, **38**: 223 (1936).

5.7. See 9.3.

5.8. Pumps and Weight Keep Hospital out of Hot Water, *Eng. News-Record (New York)*, **158**: 46–48 (June 20, 1957).

5.9. GREGORY, J. W.: The Origin and Distribution of Underground Waters, *Water and Water Eng. (London)*, **29**: 321 (1927).

5.10. SCOTT, F. W.: Pietermaritzburg–Riet Spruit Deviation, *Inst. Civil Eng. Min. Proc. (London)*, **207**: 229 (1921).

5.11. Discussion of Forster BROWN, E. O.: Underground Waters in the Kent Coal Field and Their Incidence in Mining Development, *Inst. Civil Eng. Min. Proc. (London)*, **215**: 77 (1923).

5.12. PARKER, C. G., and V. T. STRINGFIELD: Effects of Earthquakes, Trains, Tides, Winds and Atmospheric Pressure Changes on Water in the Geological Formations of Southern Florida, *Econ. Geology*, **45**: 441–460 (1950).

5.13. See 5.12.

5.14. Report of Discussion at British Association meeting in Aberdeen, *Water and Water Eng. (London)*, **36**: 623 (1934).

5.15. See p. 226 of 5.6.

5.16. HOFFMAN, John F.: Planning to Use Water for Air Conditioning Design, *Heating, Piping and Air Conditioning*, **29**: 96 (1957).

5.17. Hot Well Water Cooled for Use in City Distribution System, *Eng. News-Record (New York)*, **118**: 130 (1937).

5.18. Corrosiveness of Aqueduct Water Reduced by Gas Drainage, *Eng. News-Record (New York)*, **117**: 790 (1936); see also Drains Remove CO_2 from Tunnel, **120**: 885 (1938).

5.19. HATTON, T. C.: Ferrous Strata Develop CO_2 in Tunnel Shafts, *Eng. News-Record (New York)*, **89**: 706 (1922).

5.20. WYLLIE, J.: An Investigation of the Source of Arsenic in a Well, *Canadian Public Health Journal*, **28**: 128–135 (1937).

5.21. Boron Creates Special Problems in Los Angeles' Water Supply, *Eng. News-Record (New York)*, **125**: 113–114 (1940).

5.22. BESSEY, G. E., and F. M. LEA: The Distribution of Sulphates in Clay Soils and Ground Water, *Proc. Inst. Civil Eng.*, pt. I, pp. 159–181 (1953).

5.23. See p. 224 of 5.6.

5.24. DIXEY, F.: "A Practical Handbook of Water Supply," Thomas Murby & Co., London, 1931, p. 183.

5.25. McQueen, A. W. F., and R. C. McMordie: Soil Mechanics at the Shand Dam, *Eng. Jour.*, **23**: 161–177 (1940).

5.26. See p. 224 of 5.6

5.27. *Reports of the Interstate Conferences on Artesian Water:* no. 1: Sydney, 1912; no. 2: Brisbane, 1914; no. 3: Adelaide, 1921; no. 4: Perth, 1924; no. 5: Sydney, 1928. Issued by various state government printers.

5.28. Artesian Water Pressure Lifts Dam, *Eng. News-Record (New York)*, **123**: 485 (1939).

5.29. Banks, H. O., and R. C. Richter: Sea-water Intrusion into Ground-water Basins Bordering the Californian Coast and Inland Bays, *Trans. Am. Geophys. Un.*, **34**: 575 (1953).

5.30. Perlmutter, N. M., J. J. Geraghty, and J E. Upson: The Relation between Fresh and Salty Ground-water in Southern Nassau and South-eastern Queen's Counties, Long Island, New York, *Econ. Geol.*, **54**: 416–435 (1959).

5.31. Wentworth, C. K., A. C. Mason, and D. A. Davis: Salt-water Encroachment as Induced by Sea-level Excavation on Anguar Island, *Econ. Geol.*, **50**: 669–680 (1955).

5.32. Foose, R. M.: Ground Water Behavior in the Hershey Valley, *Bull. Geol. Soc. Am.*, **64**: 623–646 (1953).

5.33. Gibbings, Robert: "Coming down the Seine," J. M. Dent & Sons, Ltd., London, 1953. One of a delightful series of books by this author.

5.34. *The Observer (London)* Aug. 27, 1939.

5.35. Casteret, N.: "Ten Years under the Earth," Trans. by B. Mussey, J. M. Dent & Sons, Ltd., London, 1939.

5.36. Unusual Flood in Ohio Town, *Eng. News-Record (New York)*, **119**: 40 (1937).

5.37. Vertical Sewer System May Be Abolished, *Eng. News-Record (New York)*, **136**: 823 (1946).

5.38. Francis, J. L., and J. C. Allan: Driving a Mines Drainage Tunnel in North Wales, *Inst. Min. and Met., Trans. (London)*, **41**: 236 (1932).

5.39. Public Water Supply from Colliery, *Water and Water Eng. (London)*, **38**: 294 (1936).

5.40. Ground Water Pollution in California Points to Industrial Waste Discharge, *Eng. News-Record (New York)*, **137**: 785 (1946).

5.41. Harmon, B.: Contamination of Ground-water Resources, *Civil Eng.*, **11**: 345–348 (1941).

5.42. New Look at Acid Mine-drainage, *Eng. News-Record (New York)*, **164**: 61–62 (May 19, 1960); see also reports of the Ohio River Valley Water Sanitation Commission (Cincinnati, Ohio).

5.43. Bierschenk, W. H.: Hydrological Aspects of Radioactive Waste Disposal, *Proc. Am. Soc. C. E.*, SA6, Paper 1835 (November, 1958).

5.44. Nace, R. L.: Contributions of Geology to the Problems of Radioactive Waste Disposal (with bibliography), presented to 1959 Monaco Conference on this subject, rep. USGS (1959).

5.45. Marr, J. C.: Drainage by Means of Pumping from Wells in Salt River Valley, Arizona, *U.S. Dept. Agr. Dept. Bull.* 1456 (1926).

5.46. Agricultural Engineers Dedicate Monumenc to Tile Drainage Pioneer, *Agric. Eng. (St. Joseph, Mich.)*, **16**: 454–455 (1935).

5.47. Thornthwaite, C. W.: An Approach toward a Rational Classification of Climate, *Geograph. Review*, **38**: 55–94 (1948).

5.48. Meinzer, O. E.: Plants as Indicators of Ground Water, *U.S. Geol. Survey Water Supply Paper* 577 (1927).

5.49. ELLIS, A. J.: The Divining Rod; A History of Water Witching, *U.S. Geol. Survey Water Supply Paper* 416, 1934 (rep.).

5.50. Divination by Rods, *Water and Water Eng. (London)*, **34**: 147 (1932).

5.51. GREGORY, J. W.: Water Divining, *Water and Water Eng. (London)*, **29**: 453 (1927).

5.52. THOMSON, Sir J. J.: "Recollections and Reflections," G. Bell & Sons, Ltd., London, 1936, p. 160.

5.53. DE FRANCE, Vicomte Henri: "The Modern Dowser," G. Bell & Sons, Ltd., London, 1936.

5.54. See 5.49.

5.55. MEINZER, O. E., and N. D. STEARNS: A Study of Groundwater in the Pomperaug Basin, Connecticut, with Special Reference to Intake and Discharge, *U.S. Geol. Survey Water Supply Paper* 597(b) (1928).

5.56. MEINZER, O. E.: Outlines of Methods for Estimating Ground-water Supplies, *U.S. Geol. Survey Water Supply Paper* 638(c) (1932).

5.57. See p. 245 of 2.3.

Chapter 6

6.1. See pp. 217–218 of 2.1.

6.2. See 13.13.

6.3. JACOBY, H. S., and R. P. DAVIS: "Foundations of Bridges and Buildings," 2d ed., McGraw-Hill Book Company, Inc., New York, 1925, p. 385.

6.4. HUSBAND, J.: The San Francisco–Oakland Bay Bridge, *Structural Eng. (London)*, **14** (new ser.): 170 (1936).

6.5. For a general description of these works, see HALCROW, W. T.: The Lochaber Water Power, *Inst. Civil Eng. Min. Proc. (London)*, **231**: 31 (1931); costs in a personal communication from Sir William Halcrow.

6.6. CHAPMAN, L. J., and D. F. PUTNAM: "The Physiography of Southern Ontario," Univ. of Toronto Press, Toronto, 1951.

6.7. RAY, R. G., and W. A. FISCHER: Geology from the Air, *Science*, **126**: 725–735 (1957).

6.8. WOODS, K. B., J. E. HITTLE, and R. E. FROST: Correlation between Permafrost and Soils as Indicated by Aerial Photographs, *Proc. of Second Int. Conf. on Soil Mechanics and Foundation Engineering, Rotterdam*, **1**: 321–324 (June, 1948).

6.9. RADFORTH, N. W.: Muskeg Access, with Special Reference to Problems of the Petroleum Industry, *Trans. Can. Inst. Mining and Metallurgy, Petroleum and Natural Gas Div.*, **59**: 271–277 (1956).

6.10. MOLLARD, J. D., and H. E. DISHAW: Locating and Mapping Granular Construction Materials from Aerial Photographs. *Highway Res. Bd. Bull.* 180, 20–32, (1958).

6.11. "Field Manual of Soil Engineering," 3d ed., Mich. State Highway Dept., Lansing, Mich., 1952.

6.12. "Interpreting Geologic Maps for Engineering Purposes," folio of 6 maps; scale 1:62,500; prepared by Engineering Geology and Ground Water Branches, U.S. Geol. Survey, 1953.

6.13. See several references in 4.1.

6.14. Sampler for Hard-to-Hold Soils, *Eng. News-Record (New York)*, **137**: 366–367 (1946).

6.15. DOW, A. L.: Foundation Exploration in Deep Water, *Eng. News-Record (New York)*, **119**: 635 (1937).

6.16. PERKINS, R. L.: Floating Rig Takes Core Samples in Deep Swift Water, *Eng. News-Record (New York)*, **159**: 60–62 (Sept. 12, 1957).

6.17. TOMLINSON, M. J.: Geological Investigations (1958–59) for the Channel Tunnel Project, *The Times Science Review (London)*, **37**: 10–12 (Autumn, 1960); see also BRUCKSHAW, J. M., J. GOGUEL, H. J. B. HARDING, and R. MALCOR: The Work of the Channel Tunnel Group, *Proc. Inst. Civil Eng. (London)*, **18**: 149–178 (February, 1961). Special attention is directed to this notable paper, which appeared while this book was in press.

6.18. FORNWALD, W. L.: Recent Developments in Soil Sampling and Core Drilling, *Ninth Ann. Conf. on Geology as Appl. to Highway Eng. (Charlottesville)*, p. 31 (1958).

6.19. The Bore-hole Camera, *Eng. News-Record (New York)*, **150**: 39 (June 25, 1953).

6.20. JOHN, K.: Electronic Bore-hole Camera for T.V. Projection, *Civil Eng.*, **28**: 197–198 (1958).

6.21. POPE, R. J.: The Dalles Closure Dam, *Proc. Am. Soc. C.E.*, **84**: PO4, Paper 1738 (1958).

6.22. Diamond Drills Explore Rock Strata in Turnpike Tunnels, *Construction Methods*, **58**: 98 (April, 1943).

6.23. See 18.45.

6.24. See illustrated articles in *Construction Methods (New York)*, p. 36, April, 1932; p. 38, July, 1932. See also Redesign and Construction of Prettyboy Dam, *Eng. News-Record (New York)*, **111**: 63 (1933).

6.25. JOHNSTON, H. R.: Underground Exploration with Calyx Drills, *Eng. News-Record (New York)*, **120**: 436 (1938).

6.26. SCOTT, H. A.: Calyx Drill Aids Soft-ground Examination, *Eng. News-Record (New York)*, **137**: 102–104 (1946).

6.27. Big Calyx Drill Sinks 1,400 ft. Holes, *Construction Methods*, pp. 78–81 (August, 1947).

6.28. See 4.6.

6.29. LYNN, A. V., and R. RHOADES: Large Peg Model Reproduces Damsite Borings, *Eng. News-Record (New York)*, **124**: 372 (1940).

6.30. Look to Your Borings (Editorial), *Eng. News-Record (New York)*, **121**: 11 (1938).

6.31. U.S. Standard Form 23A, Art. 4 as rev. March, 1953.

Chapter 7

7.1. The author is indebted for many of the facts cited to JACOBS, J. A., R. D. RUSSELL, and J. T. WILSON: "Physics and Geology," McGraw-Hill Book Company, Inc., New York, 1959.

7.2. DYMOND, J., and W. WALES: Observations on the State of the Air, Winds, Weather Made at Prince of Wales Fort on the Northwest Coast of Hudson Bay in the Years 1768–1769, *Phil. Trans. Royal Soc. (London)*, **60**: 137 (1770).

7.3. JONES, O. T.: Geophysics (James Forrest Lecture, 1935), *Inst. Civil Eng. Min. Proc. (London)*, **240**: 699 (1936).

7.4. SHAW, H.: "Applied Geophysics," *Sci. Mus. Pub. (London)*, H. M. Stationery Office (1936); p. 43. Quotations made by permission of the Controller.

7.5. DOLMAGE, V.: Geology and Geophysics in Engineering, *The Canadian Eng. (Toronto)*, **67**: 19 (1931). See also *Eng. News-Record (New York)*, **105**: 364 (1930).

7.6. CROSBY, I. B., and S. F. KELLY: Electrical Subsoil Exploration and the Civil Engineer, *Eng. News-Record (New York)*, **102**: 270 (1929).

7.7. LEONARDON, E. G.: Electrical Exploration Applied to Geological Problems in Civil Engineering, *Geophysical Prospecting, AIME Trans.*, **97**: 99 (1932).

7.8.   Lugeon, M., and C. Schlumberger: The Electrical Study of Dam Foundations, *Water and Water Eng.* (*London*), **35**: 609 (1933) (rep. from *Mining Mag.*).

7.9.   Enslin, J. F.: Geophysics as an Aid to Foundation Engineering, *Trans. S. African Inst. of Civil Eng.*, **3**: 53–54 (1953).

7.10.   See p. 296 of 1.7.

7.11.   Wantland, D.: The Application of Geophysical Methods to Problems in Civil Engineering, *Bull. Can. Inst. Mining and Metallurgy*, **46**: 288–296 (May, 1953).

7.12.   See p. 294 of 7.11.

7.13.   Shepherd, E. R.: Subsurface Exploration by Earth Resistivity and Seismic Methods, *Public Roads* (*Washington*), **16**: 57 (1935).

7.14.   Wilcox, S. W.: Prospecting for Road Materials by Geophysics, *Eng. News-Record* (*New York*), **114**: 271 (1935).

7.15.   Tuttle, C. R.: Application of Seismology to Highway Engineering Problems, *Ninth Ann. Conf. on Geology as Appl. to Highway Eng.* (*Charlottesville*), pp. 49–59 (1958).

7.16.   Murphy, V. J.: Seismic Profiles Speed Quantity Estimates for Massachusetts Turnpike, *Civil Eng.*, **26**: 374–375 (1956).

7.17.   Hedstrom, H., and R. Kollert: Seismic Sounding of Shallow Depths, *Telus*, **1**: 24–36 (1949).

7.18.   See pp. 55–58 of 7.9 and Gough, D. I.: The Investigation of Foundations by the Seismic Method, *Trans. S. African Inst. of Civil Eng.*, **3**: 61–70 (1953).

7.19.   Wesley, R. H.: Geophysical Exploration in Michigan, *Econ. Geology*, **47**: 57–63 (1952).

7.20.   Bruckshaw, J. M., and F. Dixey: Ground Water Investigation by Geophysical Methods, *Water and Water Eng.* (*London*), **36**: 261 and 368 (1934) (rep. from *Mining Mag.*).

7.21.   Way, H. J. R.: Geophysical Prospecting for Water in Uganda, *The Mining Mag.* (*London*) (August, 1941).

7.22.   Geophysical Prospecting for Water, editorial in *South African Min. Eng. Jour.* (*Johannesburg*), **47**: 44 (1936).

Chapter 8

8.1.   It has been suggested that this reference to "slime" provided a clue to the discovery of oil in the Middle East.

8.2.   Mudge, M. R., C. W. Matthews, and J. D. Wells: Geology and Construction Material Resources of Morris County, Kansas, *U.S. Geol. Surv. Bull.* 1060-A (1958).

8.3.   See 5.25 and Legget, R. F.: An Enginering Study of Glacial Drift for an Earth Dam, near Fergus, Ontario, *Econ. Geology*, **37**: 531–556 (1942).

8.4.   Cummings, A. E., and R. B. Peck: Local Materials in High Andes Prove Suitable for Rolled-fill Dam, *Civil Eng.*, **23**: 293–296 (1953).

8.5.   High Earth Dam Plugs Narrow Canyon for Power, *Eng. News-Record* (*New York*), **164**: 44–49 (April 7, 1960).

8.6.   Rhodes. A. D.: Puddled-clay Cutoff Walls Stop Sea-water Infiltration, *Civil Eng.*, **21**: 71–73 (1951).

8.7.   Buzzell, D. A.: Fused Ceramic Material for Riprap on Keystone Dam, *Eng. News-Record* (*New York*), **120**: 787 (1938).

8.8.   Flett, Sir John S.: "The First Hundred Years of the Geological Survey of Great Britain," H. M. Stationery Office, London, 1937, p. 33.

8.9.   From personal communication from S. H. Ellis, Alfred Holt and Co., Liverpool, England.

8.10. Emery, K. O.: Weathering of the Great Pyramid, *Jour. of Sedimentary Petrology*, **30:** 140–143 (March, 1960).

8.11. Sorsbie, R. F.: "Geology for Engineers," Charles Griffin & Co., Ltd., London, 1911, p. 331.

8.12. See 15.23.

8.13. Fleming, A. G.: The Development of Special Portland Cements in Canada, *Eng. Jour. (Montreal)*, **16:** 215, 260 (1933).

8.14. Legget, R. F.: "Rideau Waterway," Univ. of Toronto Press, Toronto, 1955, pp. 49, 193.

8.15. See pp. 43–47 of 16.12.

8.16. Martin, R. E.: Construction Plant for Fontana Project, Part One, *Civil Eng.*, **13:** 533–536 (1943); and McKamey, J. B.: Aggregate Production at Fontana Dam, *Eng. News-Record (New York)*, **135:** 232–238 (1945).

8.17. Jewell, H. G.: Rock Riprap Replaces Porous Concrete Slope Protection at Santee-Cooper Project, *Civil Eng.*, **18:** 2–6 (1948).

8.18. McAdam, J. L.: "Remarks on the Present System of Road Making," 7th ed., Longman, Hurst, Rees, Orme and Brown, London, 1823.

8.19. Builders Save Millions on Two Faced-Rockfill Dams, *Eng. News-Record (New York)*, **159:** 38–44 (Aug. 29, 1957).

8.20. See pp. 43–47 of 16.12.

8.21. Swenson, E. G., and V. Chaly: Basis for Classifying Deleterious Characteristics of Concrete Aggregate Materials, *Jour. Am. Conc. Inst.*, **27:** 987–1002 (1956).

8.22. Cameron, K. M.: Public Works, *Eng. Jour. (Montreal, Canada)*, **20:** 297 (1937); and information from Mr. E. Viens, (then) Chief, Testing Laboratories, Department of Public Works, Ottawa.

8.23. Precast Window Frames Cover Hotel, *Eng. News-Record (New York)*, **163:** 38–40 (Oct. 22, 1959).

8.24. Davis, H. S.: High Density Concrete for Reactor Construction, *Civil Eng.*, **26:** 376–380 (1956); and Heavy Concrete Mixed in Transit, *Eng. News-Record (New York)*, **163:** 43–50 (1959).

8.25. McConnell, D., R. C. Mielenz, W. Y. Holland, K. T. Greene: Petrology of Concrete Affected by Cement-aggregate Reaction, *The Berkey Volume, Geol. Soc. of Am.*, 225–250 (1950).

8.26. Swenson, E. G.: A Canadian Reactive Aggregate Undetected by ASTM Tests, *ASTM, Bull.* 226, pp. 236–239 (December, 1957).

8.27. Disney, C. P., and R. F. Legget: "Modern Railroad Structures," McGraw-Hill Book Company, Inc., New York, 1949, pp. 181–202.

8.28. Perry, J. R.: Coral: A Good Aggregate in Concrete, *Eng. News-Record (New York)*, **135:** 174–180 (1945); and Narver, D. L.: Good Concrete Made with Coral and Sea Water, *Civil Eng.*, **24:** 654–658, 725–728 (1954).

8.29. Whitaker, T.: "Lightweight Concrete in America," Nat. Bldg. Studies, Special Report 13, London, 1953.

8.30. Cunney, C. A.: Blast Holes Shot into Volcanic Slag, *Civil Eng.*, **16:** 71 (1946).

8.31. Knight, P. G. K.: Pulverised Fuel Ash as a Construction Material, *Proc. Inst. Civil Eng. (London)*, **16:** 419–432 (1960).

8.32. Knight, B. H., and R. G. Knight: Rapid Staining in Granites used in Civil Engineering Work, *Jour. Inst. Civil Eng. (London)*, **9:** 545 (1938).

Chapter 9

9.1. For some of these historical notes the author is indebted to C. Prelini: "Tunnelling," 6th ed., D. Van Nostrand Company, Inc., Princeton, N.J., 1912.

9.2.   Information from the late R. S. Cole. See also DEAN, A. J.: The Lake Copais, Boeotia, Greece: Its Drainage and Development, *Jour. Inst. Civil Eng. (London)*, **5**: 287 (1937).

9.3.   Fox, F.: The Simplon Tunnel, *Inst. Civil Eng. Min. Proc. (London)*, **168**: 61 (1907).

9.4.   The Lötschberg-Simplon Railway and Its Construction, *The Engineer (London)*, **112**: 633 (1911).

9.5.   Mont Blanc Tunnel will be the World's "Longest" Shortcut, *Eng. News-Record (New York)*, **162**: 30–32 (Mar. 26, 1959).

9.6.   The Las Raices Tunnel, Chile, *Civil Eng. (London)*, **28**: 335 (1933).

9.7.   BERKEY, C. P., and J. F. SANBORN: Engineering Geology of the Catskill Water Supply, *Trans. Am. Soc. C. E. (New York)*, **86**: 1 (1923). See also BERKEY, C. P.: Geology of the New York (Catskill) Aqueduct, *N.Y. State Museum Bull.* 146 (1911). See also KEMP, J. T.: Geological Problems presented by the Catskill Aqueduct of the City of New York, *Jour. Canadian Min. Inst.*, **14**: 472 (1911).

9.8.   See for example, FLUHR, T. W.: Engineering Geology of the Delaware Aqueduct, *The Municipal Engs. Jour. (New York)*, **27**: 91–126 (1941).

9.9.   Driving the Queens Midtown Tunnel, *Eng. News-Record (New York)*, **124**: 29–34 (1940).

9.10.   Tunnel Looped under a Fault, *Eng. News-Record (New York)*, **119**: 220 (1937).

9.11.   NOBLE, CELIA B.: "The Brunels, Father and Son," Cobden-Sanderson, London, 1938, p. 80.

9.12.   KELL, J.: Pre-treatment of Gravel for Compressed Air Tunneling under the River Thames at Dartford, *The Chartered Civil Eng.*, pp. 3–7 (March, 1957).

9.13.   BOSCHEN, H. C.: Havana Traffic Tunnel Built in the Dry under Almendares River, *Civil Eng.*, **23**: 447–451 (1953).

9.14.   COREN, R. D.: Kanmon Highway Tunnel, Japan, *The Military Eng.*, **331**: 346–347 (September–October, 1957).

9.15.   Isambard Kingdom Brunel: 9th April 1806–15 Sept. 1859; a note in *Proc. Inst. Civil Eng. (London)*, **14**: N9 (November, 1959).

9.16.   WALKER, F. (ed.): "Daylight through the Mountain," The Eng. Inst. of Canada, Montreal, 1957.

9.17.   GLAESER, J. R.: Lining Concrete Pumped into Place, *Civil Eng.*, **23**: 753–757 (1953).

9.18.   LAWTON, F. L., and J. G. SUTHERLAND: Kemano Pressure Conduit Engineering Investigations, *Proc. Am. Soc. C. E.*, PO5, Paper 1396 (October, 1957).

9.19.   HOGG, A. D.: Some Engineering Studies of Rock Movement in the Niagara Area, *Eng. Geol. Case Histories*, **3**: 1–12, Geol. Soc. of Am. (1959).

9.20.   HASKINS, G.: The Construction, Testing and Strengthening of a Pressure Tunnel for the Water Supply of Sydney, N.S.W., *Inst. Civil Eng. Min. Proc. (London)*, **234**: 25 (1932).

9.21.   Information in personal communication from the Chief Engineer, New York Central Railroad Co.

9.22.   Information in personal communication from Le Chef du Service de la Voie et des Batiments du Sud-Est, S.N.C.F., Paris, France.

9.23.   See *Eng. News-Record (New York)*, **160**: 46 (June 5, 1958).

9.24.   Tunneling Machine Tackles Hard Rock, *Eng. News-Record (New York)*, **161**: 39 (Sept. 4, 1958).

9.25. Contractor Unveils New Tunneler, *Eng. News-Record (New York)*, **163**: 43–44 (Dec. 3, 1959).

9.26. WAHLSTROM, E. E.: Application of Geology to Tunneling Problems, *Trans. Am. Soc. C.E. (New York)*, **113**: 1310–1348 (1948).

9.27. KEAYS, R. H.: Construction Methods on the Moffatt Tunnel, *Trans. Am. Soc. C. E. (New York)*, **92**: 69 (1928).

9.28. ANDERSON, D.: The Construction of the Mersey Tunnel, *Jour. Inst. Civil Eng. (London)*, **2**: 473 (1936); BOSWELL, P. G. H.: The Geology of the New Mersey Tunnel, *Liverpool Geol. Soc. Proc.*, **17**: 160 (1937).

9.29. See pp. 255–256 of 1.3.

9.30. KEAYS, R. R.: Inflows Block Construction of Aqueduct Tunnel for Athens, Greece, *Eng. News-Record (New York)*, **106**: 978 (1931).

9.31. CROCKER, E. R.: Hottest, Wettest Tunnel Holed Through, *Civil Eng.*, **25**: 142–146 (1955); see also "Technical Record of Design and Construction of the Tecolote Tunnel," U.S. Bureau of Reclamation, Denver, Colo. (September, 1959).

9.32. See 1.6.

9.33. STICKLER, C. W., and A. ALLAN: Chemical Sealing Stops Leakage in Tunnels of Pennsylvania Turnpike, *Civil Eng.*, **24**: 722–724 (1954).

9.34. CLOOS, H.: "Conversation with the Earth," trans. by E. B. GARSIDE, Routledge & Kegan Paul, Ltd., London, 1954.

9.35. PEACH, B. N.: The Lochaber Water Power Scheme and Its Geological Aspect, *Water and Water Eng. (London)*, **32**: 71 (1930) (rep. from *Inst. Min. Eng. Trans.*). See also 6.5.

9.36. SCOTT, P. A., and J. I. CAMPBELL: Woodhead New Tunnel: Construction of a Three-mile Main Double-line Railway Tunnel, *Proc. Inst. Civil Eng.*, pt. I, **3**: 506–563 (1954).

9.37. "Report on the Collapse of Clifton Hall Tunnel," H. M. Stationery Office, Ministry of Transport and Civil Aviation, London, 1954.

9.38. Huge Underground Vaults Built Oiltight, *Eng. News-Record (New York)*, **135**: 873–877 (1945).

9.39. Oil Storage in Virgin Rock, *Civil Eng. and Pub. Wks. Review*, **47**: 311 (1952).

9.40. Subterranean Storehouses, *Imperial Oil Review*, p. 11, (June, 1955).

9.41. Carving out a Cavern through a "Needle's Eye," *Eng. News-Record (New York)*, **160**: 36–38 (Jan. 23, 1958).

9.42. CROWTHER, E.: An Underground Cavity as a Gasholder, *The New Scientist*, **6**: 1177–1179 (1959).

9.43. LAWTON, F. L.: Underground Hydro-electric Power Stations, *Eng. Jour.*, **42**: 33–51 (January, 1959).

9.44. MATTHIAS, F. T.: Kemano, Underground, *Eng. Jour.*, **37**: 1398–1412 (November, 1954); see also ROBERTS, C. M.: Underground Power Plants in Scotland, *Proc. Am. Soc. C.E. (New York)*, **84**: Paper 1675, PO3 (1958).

9.45. BOWMAN, W. G.: Swedes Make Rock Tunnel History, *Eng. News-Record (New York)*, **155**: 32–44 (Sept. 1, 1955).

9.46. Investigation of Alternative Aqueduct Systems to Serve Southern California, Appendix C; Procedure for Estimating Costs of Tunnel Construction, Cal. Dept. of Water Resources *Bull.* 78, 1959. See also summary: Tunnel Estimating Improved: Tied to Geology, *Eng. News-Record (New York)*, **163**: 64–70 (Dec. 17, 1959).

9.47. GRIEVE, W. G., and B. NEWMAN: "Tunnellers," H. Jenkins, London, 1936, p. 123.

9.48. Hydraulic Mining on Twin Cities Sewer Tunnels, *Eng. News-Record* (*New York*), **115**: 627 (1935).

Chapter 10

10.1. *Min. Proc. Inst. Civil Eng.* (*London*), **1**: 61 (1841).

10.2. LEGGET, R. F., and W. R. SCHRIEVER: Site Investigations for Canada's First Underground Railway, *Civil Eng. and Pub. Wks. Review*, **55**: 73–80 (1960).

10.3. WRIGHT, C. F.: "The Ice Age in North America," Bibliotheca Sacra Co., Oberlin, Ohio, 1911.

10.4. Just How Much Has It Really Cost? *Eng. News-Record* (*New York*), **158**: 31–32 (June 13, 1957).

10.5. See 1.2.

10.6. On-schedule at Niagara, *Eng. News-Record* (*New York*), **151**: 33–38 (Sept. 10, 1953).

10.7. CERUTTI, H. P.: Twin Conduits for Niagara, *Civil Eng.*, **30**: 50–53 (July, 1960).

10.8. See 4.1.

10.9. LEGGET, R. F.: Soil Engineering at Steep Rock Iron Mines, Ontario, Canada, *Proc. Inst. Civil Eng.*, **11**: 169–188 (1958).

10.10. LEGGET, R. F.: The Wellpoint System; Application to an Excavation in Waterlogged Ground in Canada, *Civil Eng.* (*London*), **31**: 229 (1936).

10.11. Information in personal communication from the late Thomas F. Moore, The Moretrench Corporation, Rockaway, N.J.

10.12. Wellpoints in a Pumped-sand Fill Facilitate Outfall Sewer Construction, *Eng. News-Record* (*New York*), **137**: 238–240 (1946).

10.13. GILL, T. C.: Wellpoints Dewater Denison Dam Closure Area, *Civil Eng.*, **16**: 108–110 (1946).

10.14. Draining Coarse Gravel with Wellpoints, *Eng. News-Record* (*New York*), **137**: 638–639 (1946).

10.15. WOOD, E. D.: Wellpoints Master Oölite, *Eng. News-Record* (*New York*), **152**: 35 (May 6, 1954).

10.16. PRUGH, B. J.: Anchorage Excavation Tests Versatility of Wellpoints, *Civil Eng.*, **24**: 580–582 (1954).

10.17. McHAFFIE, M. G.: Southhampton Docks Extension, *Jour. Inst. Civil Eng.* (*London*), **9**: 184 (1938).

10.18. WARREN, D. R.: Novel Construction Plan for Graving Dock Suggested by Soil Studies, *Civil Eng.*, **14**: 323–328 (1944).

10.19. THORESEN, S. A.: Shield-driven Tunnels near Completion under the Schelde at Antwerp, *Eng. News-Record* (*New York*), **110**: 827 (1933).

10.20. GOUGH, H. B.: A Wet Shaft Frozen Tight, *Eng. News-Record* (*New York*), **122**: 666–668 (1939).

10.21. Deep Freeze to Keep Shaft in the Dry, *Eng. News-Record* (*New York*), **163**: 25 (Sept. 3, 1959).

10.22. A New Interoceanic Railway in Central America, *Eng. News-Record* (*New York*), **88**: 474 (1927).

10.23. Tough Shale Bored and Sawed for Fort Peck Spillway Gate, *Eng. News-Record* (*New York*), **116**: 37 (1936).

10.24. Wheeler Dam Construction Enters Final Year, *Eng. News-Record* (*New York*), **115**: 259 (1935).

10.25. BRANNFORS, S.: Blasting without Removing the Overburden, *Civil Eng.*, **29**: 780–781 (1959).

10.26. NORTHWOOD, T. D., and A. T. EDWARDS: Experimental Blasting Studies on Structures, *The Engineer* (*London*), **210**: 538–546 (1960).

10.27. ANDERSON, A. P.: Some Studies of Drilling and Blasting in Highway Grading, *Public Roads (Washington)*, **12**: 293 (1932).

10.28. BLEE, C. E.: Drill Hole Size Tests at Hiwassee Dam, *Eng. News-Record (New York)*, **123**: 643 (1939).

10.29. Big Controlled Blast Makes Molehill out of Mountain, *Eng. News-Record (New York)*, **159**: 28–29 (Aug. 15, 1957).

10.30. Roofed-in Slate Quarry Now Stores Oil, *Eng. News-Record (New York)*, **153**: 24 (Sept. 16, 1954).

10.31. Cheap Levees by Hydraulic Fill at Lake Okeechobee, *Eng. News-Record (New York)*, **115**: 81 (1935).

10.32. LEGGET, R. F.: Development of a Pulpwood Shipping Harbour, Forestville, Quebec, *Eng. Jour.*, **36**: 1287–1294 (October, 1953); see also 10.9.

10.33. BURR, E.: Remove Subaqueous Ledge above Rapid Transit Tunnel, *Eng. News-Record (New York)*, **89**: 1021 (1922).

10.34. GWYTHER, R. D.: Improvements to St. Helier's Harbour, Jersey, *Inst. Civil Eng. Min. Proc. (London)*, **238**: 100 (1934).

10.35. HYZER, P. C., and H. E. HILL: Scheduling Equipment for Great Lakes Channel Dredging, *Civil Eng.*, **27**: 470–472 (1957).

10.36. BOWERS, N. A.: Submarine Drilling with Job-assembled Rig, *Eng. News-Record (New York)*, **134**: 580–583 (1945).

10.37. PHILLIPS, C.: Blasting Submarine Coral, *Eng. News-Record (New York)*, **136**: 779 (May 16, 1946).

10.38. COOKE-YARBOROUGH, S. S.: Making a Market out of a Swamp, *Eng. News-Record (New York)*, **163**: 48–50 (1959).

10.39. Jet-piercing Method Applied to Quarrying Aggregate, *Civil Eng.*, **23**: 609 (1953).

10.40. Toronto's Cover-then-Cut Subway, *Eng. News-Record (New York)*, **164**: 37–39 (1960). See also Bentonite Slurry Stabilizes Trench—Keeps Groundwater Out, *Eng. News-Record (New York)*, **164**: 42–46 (1960).

10.41. See, for example, Swords or Plowshares? *Eng. News-Record (New York)*, **161**: 25 (1958).

10.42. PRITCHARD, J. B.: We Found the Lost City, *Sat. Eve. Post* (Philadelphia), 230: 40–41, 87–88, 90 (1958).

Chapter 11

11.1. Information received from F. W. Furkert, New Zealand; also FURKERT, F. W.: Remedial Measures on the Arapuni Hydro-electric Scheme of Power Development on the Waikato River, New Zealand, *Inst. Civil Eng. Min. Proc. (London)*, **240**: 411 (1935).

11.2. COTTON, C. A.: For How Long Will Wellington Escape Destruction by Earthquakes? *N.Z. Jour. Sci. and Techn. (Wellington)*, **3**: 229–231 (1921).

11.3. ONGLEY, M.: Waikaremoana, *N.Z. Jour. of Sci. and Techn. (Wellington)*, **14**: 173–184 (1932).

11.4. BENSON, W. N.: Landslides and Their Relation to Engineering in the Dunedin District, New Zealand, *Econ. Geology*, **41**: 328–347 (1946); see also BENSON, W. N.: Landslides and Allied Features in the Dunedin District in Relation to Geological Structure, Topography, and Engineering, *Trans. Roy. Soc. N.Z. (Wellington)*, **70**: pt. 3, 249–263 (1940).

11.5. Natural Steam Turns the Wheels at New Zealand's Wairakei Power Plant, *Eng. News-Record (New York)*, **162**: 44 (1959); see also GRANGE, L. I.: "Geothermal Steam for Power in New Zealand," N.Z. Dept. Sci. and Ind. Research, Bull. 117, Wellington, 1955.

11.6. LONGWELL, C. R., A. KNOPF, and R. F. FLINT: "A Textbook of Geology,"
pt. I, Physical Geology, John Wiley & Sons, Inc., New York, 1932, p. 296.

11.7. HECK, N. H.: Earthquake History of the United States, U.S. Coast and
Geodetic Survey Special Pub. 149 (1928) in which original sources of information are listed.

11.8. LEGGET, R. F.: Earthquake Damage at Cornwall, Eng. Jour. (Montreal), 27:
572 (1944).

11.9. RICHTER, C. F.: "Elementary Seismology," W. H. Freeman & Co., Inc., San
Francisco, 1958.

11.10. "Report of the Special Committee for the Study of the Fukui Earthquake,
1948," National Research Council of Japan, 1950.

11.11. FURKERT, F. W.: The Effect of Earthquakes on Engineering Structures, Inst.
Civil Eng. Min. Proc. (London), 236: 344 (1933).

11.12. Arvin—Tehachapi Earthquake, Mineral Information Service (California),
vol. 5, no. 9 (Sept. 1, 1952).

11.13. SHERARD, J. L.: What the Earthquake Did to Hegben Dam, Eng. News-
Record (New York), 163: 26-27, (Sept. 10, 1959); see also BARNEY, K. R.:
Madison Canyon Slide, Civil Eng., 30: 72-75 (August, 1960).

11.14. MALLET, R.: "The Great Neapolitan Earthquake of 1857," 2 vols., 1862.

11.15. See 11.6.

11.16. Land Subsidence of 15 In. Follows Earthquake in Utah, Eng. News-Record
(New York), 114: 322 (1935).

11.17. See The Engineer (London), 51: 123 (1881).

11.18. MEINZER, O. E.: Compressibility and Elasticity of Artesian Aquifers, Econ.
Geology (New Haven, Conn.), 23: 263 (1928).

11.19. STOHSNET, E. E.: Santa Clara Valley Subsidence Has Now Reached 5 Feet,
Eng. News-Record (New York), 118: 479 (1937).

11.20. See, for example, NEEL, C. H.: Surface Subsidence at a Naval Shipyard, The
Military Engineer, no. 332, 432-435 (1957).

11.21. Water Buoys Land that Sank as Oil Was Removed, Eng. News-Record
(New York), 163: 26-27 (Nov. 12, 1959).

11.22. COLLINS, J. J.: New Type Seawall Built for Subsiding Lake Shore in
Venezuela, Eng. News-Record (New York), 114: 405 (1935).

11.23. LOCKWOOD, M. G.: Ground Subsides in Houston Area, Civil Eng., 24: 370-
373 (1954).

11.24. "Mining Subsidence," Inst. Civil Eng., London, 1959.

11.25. "Subsidence: Its Cause, Effect and Prevention," Pittsburgh Coal Co., Pittsburgh, Pa., 1957.

11.26. RICHEY, J. E.: Surface Effects of Mining Subsidence, Trans. Soc. of Eng.
(London), 55: 95-102 (1952).

11.27. News report in The Lancaster Guardian (Sept. 24, 1892) noted in The
Railway Magazine (April, 1958), and personal communication from
E. Scholes.

11.28. ECKEL, E. B. (ed.): "Landslides and Engineering Practice," Highway Research Board, Special Report 29, 1958.

11.29. ATWOOD, W. W.: Relation of Landslides and Glacial Deposits to Reservoir
Sites, U.S. Geol. Survey Bull. 685 (1918).

11.30. TERZAGHI, K.: Storage Dam Founded on Landslide Debris, Jour. Boston Soc.
C.E., 47: 64-94 (1960).

11.31. EMERSON, F. E.: 180 Ft. Dam Formed by Landslide in Gros Ventre Canyon,
Eng. News-Record (New York), 95: 467 (1925). See also ALDEN, W. C.:
Landslide and Flood at Gros Ventre, Wyoming, AIME Trans. (New York),
76: 347 (1927).

11.32. Information received privately from various Indian sources through Lt. Gen. Sir Harold Williams, Roorkee, India.

11.33. LADD, G. E.: Bank Slide in Deep Cut Caused by Drought, *Eng. News-Record (New York)*, **112**: 324 (1934).

11.34. Drainage Works at Lapworth, W. R., *The Railway Magazine*, **105**: 652 (September, 1959).

11.35. GORDON, G.: Arch Dam of Ice Stops Slide, *Eng. News-Record (New York)*, **118**: 211 (1937).

11.36. FOX, F.: "Sixty Three Years of Engineering," John Murray, London, 1924, p. 47.

11.37. NOLAN, T. R.: Slips and Washouts on the Hill Section of the Assam-Bengal Railway, *Inst. Civil Eng. Min. Proc. (London)*, **218**: 2 (1924).

11.38. DENNIS, T. H., and R. J. ALLAN: Slide Problem: Storms Do Costly Damage to State Highways Yearly, *California Highways and Public Works*, **10**: 1–3 (July 23, 1941).

11.39. MUIR WOOD, A. M.: Folkestone Warren Landslips: Investigations, 1948–1950, and VINER-BRADY, N. E. V.: Folkestone Warren Landslips: Remedial Measures, 1948–54; *Proc. Inst. Civil Eng. (London)*, **4**: pt. II, 410–466 (1955).

11.40. HILL, R. A.: Clay Stratum Dried Out to Prevent Landslips, *Civil Eng. (New York)*, **4**: 403 (1934); and from information in a personal communication from Mr. R. A. Hill.

11.41. See 4.1.

11.42. See 16.10.

11.43. WARD, W. H.: The Stability of Natural Slopes, *Geographical Jour. (London)*, **105**: 170–197 (1945).

11.44. SKEMPTON, A. W., and F. A. DELORY: Stability of Natural Slopes in London Clay, *Proc. Fourth Int. Conf. on Soil Mech. and Found. Eng. (London)*, **2**: 378–381 (1957).

11.45. MORUM, S. W. F.: The Treatment of Mud-runs in Bolivia, *Jour. Inst. Civil Eng. (London)*, **1**: 426 (1935).

11.46. Report of the Commission appointed to investigate Turtle Mountain, Frank, Alberta, *Canadian Geol. Survey Mem.* 27 (1912).

11.47. See p. 34 of 11.28.

11.48. SHREVE, R. L.: Geology of the Blackhawk Landslide, Lucerne Valley, California; Abstracts for Vancouver meeting, Cordilleran Section, *Geol. Soc. of Am. (New York)*, p. 41 (1960).

11.49. CARPMAEL, R.: Noteworthy Engineering Work on the Vriog Cliffs, near Barmouth, *G. W. Ry. Mag. (London)*, p. 118 (March, 1938). Information also from an unpublished paper by Mr. H. H. Reynolds, kindly loaned by Mr. Carpmael.

11.50. LEE, C. S.: Chalk Falls between Folkestone and Dover, *The Railway Magazine*, pp. 531–534 (October, 1940).

11.51. Penstocks and Power House Damaged as Result of Falling Boulder, *Eng. News-Record (New York)*, **136**: 934 (1946).

11.52. Tremor Triggers Niagara Rock Slide, *Eng. News-Record (New York)*, **156**: 27 (June 24, 1956).

11.53. HUSON, A., and A. COSTES: "Le Boulonnage des roches en souterrain," Editions Eyrolles, Paris, 1959.

11.54. Preventing Spalling at Glen Canyon Dam, *Civil. Eng.*, **28**: 958 (1958).

11.55. Slab Is Anchored to Wall of Canyon, *Eng. News-Record (New York)*, **151**: 25 (Dec. 17, 1953).

11.56. CHRISTMAN, H. E.: Bolts Stabilize High Rock Slopes, *Civil Eng.*, **30**: 98–99 (1960).

11.57. BJERRUM, L., and F. JØRSTAD: "Rockfalls in Norway," unpublished paper of the Norwegian Geotechnical Institute, Oslo, 1959.

Chapter 12

12.1. SAWTELL, H. E.: Foundations of the Boston, Mass., Parcel Post Building, *Jour. Boston Soc. C. E.*, **22**: 29 (1935).

12.2 PRENTIS, E. A., and L. WHITE: "Underpinning," rev. ed., Columbia University Press, New York, 1931, frontispiece.

12.3. DICKINSON, C. H.: Foundation Work Hampered by Soft Ground and Seamy Rock, *Eng. News-Record (New York)*, **99**: 424 (1927).

12.4. Information received privately from Dr. L. BJERRUM, Oslo.

12.5. PHILBRICK, S. S.: Cyclic Sediments and Engineering Geology, paper sub. to Int. Geog. Congress, Copenhagen 1960.

12.6. Tank Piers Carried 50 Ft. to Rock through Old Coal Mine, *Eng. News-Record (New York)*, **110**: 190 (1933).

12.7. KERR, L., and P. BROWN: Process Buildings over Faulted Rock, *Eng. News-Record (New York)*, **135**: 795–797 (1945).

12.8. CAMPBELL, C. W.: Chemicals Seal Foundation for New York Building, *Civil Eng.*, **27**: 693–697 (1957).

12.9. NOETZLI, F. A.: Multiple Arch Retaining Wall Damaged by Slip, *Eng. News-Record (New York)*, **98**: 146 (1927); also Cahuenga Pass Arch Retaining Wall Continues Slipping, **99**: 681 (1927).

12.10. MOHR, H. A.: Exploration of Soil Conditions and Sampling Operations, *Harvard University (Cambridge, Mass.) Graduate School Eng. Bull.* 208 (Soil Mechanics ser. 4) (June, 1937).

12.11. Undiscovered Substratum of Peat Complicates Foundation Job, *Eng. News-Record (New York)*, **91**: 192 (1923).

12.12. CRAWFORD, C. B.: Settlement Studies on the National Museum Building, Ottawa, Canada, *Proc. Third Int. Conf. on Soil Mech.*, **1**: 338–345 (1953).

12.13. Building on Soft Clay, *Eng. News-Record (New York)*, **123**: 692–695 (1939).

12.14. PIKE, C. W., and B. F. SAURIN: Buoyant Foundations in Soft Clay for Oil Refinery Structures at Grangemouth, *Proc. Inst. Civil Eng.*, pt. III, **1**: 301–334 (1952).

12.15. MASON, A. C.: Open-caisson Method Used to Erect Tokyo Office Building, *Civil Eng.*, **22**: 944–947 (1952).

12.16. Earth Compacts Earth for Cathedral Base, *Eng. News-Record (New York)*, **154**: 41 (April 28, 1955).

12.17. Modern Engineering to Save Mediaeval Tower, *Eng. News-Record (New York)*, **91**: 505 (1923).

12.18. SNOW, B. F.: Tracing Loss of Groundwater, *Eng. News-Record (New York)*, **117**: 1 (1936).

12.19. Drainage in Reverse at Copley Square, *Eng. News-Record (New York)*, **154**: 47 (Apr. 28, 1955).

12.20. Foundation of Fourteen-Story Building Replaced under Basement Floor, *Eng. News-Record (New York)*, **105**: 496–499 (1930).

12.21. Artificial Groundwater for Wood Piles, *Eng. News-Record (New York)*, **107**: 70 (1931).

12.22. See p. 196 of 11.36.

12.23. See 5.8.

12.24. Permanent Wellpoints Keep Sewage Tanks from Floating, *Eng. News-Record (New York)*, **150**: 47 (Mar. 26, 1953).

12.25. Site Dewatering Wells Stay Put to Control Uplift, *Eng. News-Record (New York)*, **152**: 36–39 (Apr. 1, 1954).

12.26. PARSONS, J. D.: Foundation Installation Requiring Recharging of Ground Water, *Proc. Am. Soc. C.E.*, CO2 Paper 2141, (September, 1959).

12.27. BOZOZUK, M., and K. N. BURN: Vertical Ground Movement near Trees, *Geotechnique (London)*, **10**: 19–32 (1960).

12.28. GIESECKE, F. E.: Columns and Walls Lifted by Swelling Clay under Floor, *Eng. News-Record (New York)*, **88**: 192 (1922).

12.29. OGDEN, P. H.: Adjustable Water Tanks at Heanor, *Civil Eng. (London)*, **33**: 131 (1938).

12.30. Building over Coal Mine Yields as Ground Settles, *Eng. News-Record (New York)*, **164**: 39 (Jan. 7, 1960).

12.31. BARACOS, A.: The Foundation Failure of the Transcona Elevator, *Eng. Journal*, **40**: 973–977 (1957).

12.32. Righting a Tilted Water Tower, *Eng. News-Record (New York)*, **105**: 300 (1930).

12.33. STANTON, Sir T. E.: Engineering Research, James Forrest Lecture, *Inst. Civil Eng. Min. Proc. (London)*, **232**: 400 (1923).

12.34. Consolidating the Foundations of the Leaning Tower of Pisa, *Civil Eng. (London)*, **31**: 289 (1936) (from *Schweizerische Bauzeitung*, **107**: 272). See also SPENCER, C. B.: Leaning Tower of Pisa, *Eng. News-Record (New York)*, **150**: 40–43 (Apr. 2, 1953).

12.35. See p. 413 of 2.2.

12.36. Information received privately from Lt. Gen. Sir Harold Williams, Roorkee, India.

12.37. THORNLEY, J. H., C. B. SPENCER, and P. ALBIN: Mexico's Palace of Fine Arts Settles 10 Ft.: Can It Be Stopped? *Civil Eng.*, **25**: 357–360, 707 (1955).

12.38. GILLETTE, D. H.: Washington Monument Facts Brought Up to Date, *Eng. News-Record (New York)*, **109**: 501–502 (1933).

12.39. DOHERTY, R. E.: The White House Made Safe, *Civil Eng.*, **22**: 482–488 (1952); see also BURMISTER, D. M.: Foundation Studies for the White House, *Columbia Eng. Quart.*, pp. 1–6 (March, 1952).

12.40. SCHROTER, G. A., and R. O. MAURSETH: Hillside Stability—the Modern Approach, *Civil Eng.*, **30**: 66–69 (June, 1960).

12.41. Information received privately from Mr. A. L. Baum, St. Louis, Mo.

12.42. A Geologic Challenge, *Geotimes*, p. 8 (November, 1957).

12.43. See 5.19. See also p. 8 of 12.2.

12.44. BERRY, C. S., and A. C. DEAN: The Constructional Works of the Battersea Power Station of the London Power Company, Ltd., *Inst. Civil Eng. Min. Proc. (London)*, **240**: 37 (1937); and EDMUNDS, F. H.: Some Gravel Filled Pipes in the London Clay at Battersea, *Geol. Survey Great Britain Summary of Progress*, 1930, pt. 2 (1931).

12.45. NOWSON, W. J. R.: The History and Construction of the Foundations of the Asia Insurance Building, Singapore, *Proc. Inst. Civil Eng.*, pt. I, **3**: 407–456 (1954).

12.46. "Some Data in Regard to Foundations in New Orleans and Vicinity," WPA and Board of State Eng., Louisiana (1937).

12.47. Committee on Foundations in Winnipeg, Manitoba, *Eng Jour. (Montreal)*, **20**: 827 (1937).

12.48. Boring Data from Greater Boston. *Jour. Boston Soc. C. E.*, **36**: 391–457 (1949); see also **37**: 355–404 (1950) and **38**: 389–422 (1951).

12.49. O'REILLY, M. J.: Subsurface Work in the Department of Public Works, *Mun. Engs. Jour. (New York)*, **40**: Spring issue (1954).

12.50. Drift Thickness Contours: City of Ottawa, Carleton County, *Geol. Surv. of Canada (Ottawa)*, map 13 (1959).

12.51. SCHLOCKER, J., D. H. RADBRUCH, and M. G. BONILLA: Geology of the San Francisco North Quadrangle, California, *U.S. Geol. Survey*, map I-272 (1958); see also LEE, C. H.: Building Foundations in San Francisco, *Proc. Am. Soc. C.E. (New York)*, **79**: Paper 325 (1953).

12.52. STANSFIELD, J.: The Pleistocene and Recent Deposits of the Island of Montreal, *Geol. Surv. of Can., Memoir* 73 (1915).

12.53. DARLING, W. D.: The Foundation Problem in the St. Peter Sandstone Lower Lock and Dam, St. Anthony Falls Project, Minneapolis, Minn., paper given at the 69th *Ann. Mtg. of the Geol. Soc. Am.* in Minneapolis (1956).

12.54. ALLEY, P. J.: Foundation Conditions in the Christchurch Metropolitan Area, *Proc. Second Aust.-New Zealand Conf. on Soil Mech. and Found. Eng.*, 34–38 (1956).

Chapter 13

13.1. BERKEY, C. P.: Responsibilities of the Geologist in Engineering Projects, *AIME Tech. Pub.* 215, p. 4 (1929).

13.2. For further historical notes, see PRELINI, C.: Some Dams of the Ancients, *Eng. News-Record (New York)*, **87**: 556 (1921).

13.3. Letter from L. J. Mensch in *Eng. News-Record (New York)*, **100**: 674 (1928).

13.4. LAPWORTH, H.: The Geology of Dam Trenches, *Assoc. Water Engs. Trans. (London)*, **16**: 25 (1911).

13.5. JUSTIN, J. D.: The Design of Earth Dams, *Trans. Am. Soc. C. E.*, *(New York)*, **87**: 1 (1924) (list on pp 133–134).

13.6. See p. 23 of 13.4. See also TAYLOR, T. U.: The Austin Dam, *U.S. Geol. Survey Water Supply Paper* 40 (1900).

13.7. McDONOUGH, C.: Historic Austin Dam Rebuilt, *Eng. News-Record (New York)*, **124**: 845–847 (1940); see also FREEMAN, G. L., and R. B. ALSOP: Underpinning Austin Dam, *Eng. News-Record (New York)*, **126**: 180–185 (1941).

13.8. RANSOME, F. L.: Geology of the St. Francis Dam Site, *Econ. Geology (New Haven, Conn.)*, **23**: 553 (1928).

13.9. Malpasset Dam on French Riviera Fails, *Civil Eng.*, **30**: 59 (1960); see also Preliminary Report on the Malpasset Dam, *The Engineer*, **209**: 812 (1960).

13.10. COYNE, A.: The Construction of Large Modern Dams, *Structural Eng. (London)*, **15** (new ser.): 70 (1937).

13.11. Tensioned Cables Will Strengthen Threatened Bombay Water Supply Dam, *Eng. News-Record (New York)*, **147**: 54–56 (July 5, 1951); see also **153**: 39 (Sept. 30, 1954).

13.12. MORRIS, S. S.: Steenbras Dam Strengthened by Post-tensioning Cables, *Civil Eng.*, **26**: 75–79 (1936).

13.13. McILDOWIE, G.: The Construction of the Silent Valley Reservoir, Belfast Water Supply, *Inst. Civil Eng. Min. Proc. (London)*, **239**: 465 (1936).

13.14. DEACON, G. F.: The Vyrnwy Works for the Water-supply of Liverpool, *Inst. Civil Eng. Min. Proc. (London)*, **126**: 24 (1896).

13.15. SUTHERLAND, R. A.: French Build High Dam in Narrow Limestone Canyon, *Eng. News-Record (New York)*, **115**: 706 (1935).

13.16. See 6.25.

13.17. Gorge Excavation Confirms Geological Assumptions, *Eng. News-Record (New York)*, **111**: 761 (1933). See also BERKEY, C. P.: Geology of Boulder and Norris Dam Sites, *Civil Eng. (New York)*, **5**: 24 (1935).

13.18. TWENHOFEL, W. H.: "A Treatise on Sedimentation," 2d ed., The Williams & Wilkins Company, Baltimore, 1932, p. 17.

13.19. FITZMAURICE, M.: The Nile Reservoir, Assuan, *Inst. Civil Eng. Min. Proc. (London)*, **152**: 71 (1903).

13.20. REEVES, F., and C. P. ROSS: A Geologic Study of the Madden Dam Project, Alhajuela, Canal Zone, *U.S. Geol. Survey Bull.* 821 (1931). See also KELLOG, F. H.: Clay Grouting at Madden Reservoir, *Eng. News-Record (New York)*, **109**: 395 (1932).

13.21. HAPP, S. C.: Treatment of Chalk Foundation with Bentonite Seams, Harlan County Dam, Nebraska, *Bull. Geol. Soc. Am.*, **61**: 1568 (1950).

13.22. BOWMAN, W. G.: The French Touch in Dams, *Eng. News-Record (New York)*, **146**: 33 (May 10, 1951).

13.23. RAO, K. L.: Engineering Problems in Recent River Valley Projects in India, *Proc. Inst. Civil Eng.*, **11**: 1–40 (1958).

13.24. MORRIS, S. B., and C. E. PEARCE: Concrete Gravity Dam for Faulted Mountain Area, *Eng. News-Record (New York)*, **113**: 823 (1934).

13.25. Earthquake-proof Dam in Chile, *Eng. News-Record (New York)*, **107**: 725 (1931).

13.26. Three Dams on San Andreas Fault Have Resisted Earthquakes, *Eng. News-Record (New York)*, **109**: 218 (1932). See also ECKART, N. A.: Development of San Francisco's Water Supply to Care for Emergencies, *Seismological Soc. America Bull.* 3, **27**: (1937).

13.27. Flexible Core for Dam in Earthquake Country, *Eng. News-Record (New York)*, **125**: 279 (1940).

13.28. See 13.24.

13.29. GOODALL, G E: Horizontal Joint Put in Arch Dam in Effort to Prevent Cracking, *Eng. News-Record (New York)*, **137**: 884–885 (1946).

13.30. Foundation Procedure at Owyhee Dam, *Eng. News-Record (New York)*, **106**: 178 (1931).

13.31. Unique Cutoff Construction and Arched Foundation Features of Rodriguez Dam, *Eng. News-Record (New York)*, **105**: 600 (1930). See also WILLIAMS, C. P.: Foundation Treatment at Rodriguez Dam, *Trans. Am. Soc. C. E., (New York)*, **99**: 295 (1935).

13.32. Joints Let Dam Flex with Soil Movements, *Eng. News-Record (New York)*, **161**: 32–33 (Nov. 6, 1958).

13.33. CHRISTIANS, G. W.: Asphalt Grouting under Hales Bar Dam, *Eng. News-Record (New York)*, **96**: 798 (1926); see also Stopping a River under a Dam, *Eng. News-Record (New York)*, **127**: 654–657 (1941); and FRINK, J. W.: Solution of Limestone Beneath Hales Bar Dam, *Jour. Geol.*, **53**: 137–139 (1945).

13.34. HINDS, J., and N. S. LONG: Oil No Boon in Foundations of Santa Felicia Dam, *Civil Eng.*, **25**: 220–223 (1955).

13.35. See 13.20.

13.36. See 13.14.

13.37. See 13.20.

13.38. WILBUR, E. M.: Grouting Checks Leakage in Earthfill Dam, *Eng. News-Record (New York)*, **115**: 499 (1935).

13.39. SLOCUM, H. S.: Asphalt Cutoff Wall at Claytor Dam, *Eng. News-Record (New York)*, **128**: 490–492 (1942).

13.40. BARNES, A. A.: Cementation of Strata below Reservoir Embankments, *Inst. Water Engs. Trans. (London)*, **32**: 42 (1927).

13.41. RANDS, H. A.: Grouting Cutoff for the Estacada Dam, *Trans. Am. Soc. C. E. (New York)*, **78**: 447 (1915)

13.42. Fox, J. R.: Precementation of a Reservoir Trench, *Inst. Wat. Engs. Trans. (London)*, **32**: 69 (1927).

13.43. TAYLOR, M.: Cementation of Abitibi Dam Foundations, *Canadian Eng. (Toronto)*, **66**: 5 (1934); and information from Mr. R. L. Hearn, Dominion Construction Corp., Toronto.

13.44. Thousands of Holes Grouted under Norris Dam, *Eng. News-Record (New York)*, **115**: 699 (1935).

13.45. Corewall Grouting at Chickamauga Dam, *Eng. News-Record (New York)*, **122**: 551–552 (1939).

13.46. Extensive Rock Grouting at Boulder Dam, *Eng. News-Record (New York)*, **114**: 795 (1935). See also MINEAR, V. L.: The Art of Pressure Grouting, *Reclamation Era (Washington)*, **27**: 56 (1937).

13.47. VOLUMARD, P., and R. DUBOST: The Saint-Pierrett Cognet Dam (The Drac Development), *Travaux*, no. 286, 5–15 (August, 1958).

13.48. BINNIE, G. M., J. G. CAMPBELL, N. H. GIMSON, P. F. F. LANCASTER-JONES, and G. A. GILLOTT: The Dokan Project: The Flood Disposal Works and the Grouted Cut-off Curtain, *Proc. Inst. Civil Eng.*, **14**: 157–204 (1959).

13.49. San Gabriel River Flood Control, *Eng. News-Record (New York)*, **114**: 113 (1935) (bibliography on p. 116).

13.50. California Dam Will Be Highest Earthfill, 730 Feet, *Eng. News-Record (New York)*, **161**: 24–25 (Dec. 4, 1958).

13.51. World's Highest Earth-fill Dam Completed, *Civil Eng.*, **28**: 840–845 (1958).

13.52. Processing Plant for Rock-Earth Dam, *Eng. News-Record (New York)*, **128**: 188–191 (1942).

13.53. CABANIUS, J., and R. MAIGRE: The Serre-Poncon Dam: The Durrance Development, *Travaux*, no. 286, 43–60 (August, 1958).

13.54. Merwin Hydro Project: *Guide for Western (U.S.) Tour*, International Congress on Large Dams, pp. 156–158 (1958).

13.55. STRENGE, K. O.: Noxon Rapids Dam Meets Extraordinary Geologic Conditions, *Civil Eng.*, **29**: 474–478 (1959).

13.56. MacKENZIE, I. D., and E. L. BROWN: Geological Features and Foundation Treatment at the Beechwood Development, *Eng. Journal*, **42**: 54–62 (1959); see also McFARLANE, H.: The Beechwood Earth-fill Dam, *Assoc. Comm. on Soil and Snow Mechanics*, *Tech. Memo. 63*, National Research Council, Ottawa, Canada (August, 1960).

13.57. Mining under Seminoe Dam, *Eng. News-Record (New York)*, **122**: 490–492 (1939).

13.58. Upward Mining of Cut-off Trenches, *Eng. News-Record (New York)*, **145**: 46–48 (July 20, 1950).

13.59. Caissons for a Cutoff Wall, *Eng. News-Record (New York)*, **125**: 761–764 (1940); see also **127**: 426–430 (1941).

13.60. SMITH, R.: At Oahe: Contractor Licks Slate by Building Backwards, *Eng. News-Record (New York)*, **163**: 42–43 (July 23, 1959).

Chapter 14

14.1. SMITH, William: On Retaining Water in the Rocks for Summer Use, *Phil. Mag. (London)* (new ser.), **1**: 415 (1827).

14.2. SWALES, J. K.: The Broomhead Reservoir, *Water and Water Eng. (London)*, **36**: 565 (1934).

14.3. Porosity of Reservoir Prevents Water Storage, *Eng. News-Record (New York)*, **96**: 561 (1926).

14.4. MACKIN, J. Hoover: "A Geologic Interpretation of the Failure of the Cedar Reservoir, Washington," Bull. 107, Eng. Expt. Sta., Univ. of Washington, Seattle, 1941.

14.5.   A Curious Water Wheel, *The Engineer (London)*, **142**: 590 (1926).

14.6.   Fox, Sir C. S.: Using Radioactive Isotopes to Trace Movement of Underground Waters, *Municipal Utilities*, **90**: no. 4, 30–32 (April, 1952).

14.7.   HALEVY, E., A. NIR, Y. HARPAZ, and S. MANDEZL: Use of Radioisotopes in Studies of Groundwater Flow, *Second UN Conf. on Peaceful Uses of Atomic Energy*, Paper 15/P/1613 (1958).

14.8.   STRANGE, W. L.: Reservoirs with High Earthen Dams in Western India, *Inst. Civil Eng. Min. Proc. (London)*, **132**: 137 (1898).

14.9.   COLLIER, B. C.: Sealing a Leaking Reservoir in Italian Apennines, *Eng. News-Record (New York)*, **108**: 293–294 (1932).

14.10. SCHMIDT, L. A.: Reservoir Leakage Stopped at Outlets, *Eng. News-Record (New York)*, **134**: 65–67 (1945).

14.11. Will Jamaica's Mona Reservoir Hold Water? *Eng. News-Record (New York)*, **162**: 42–43 (Mar. 5, 1959).

14.12. Information received from the (Sydney) Metropolitan Water, Sewage and Drainage Board, Australia; and WATERHOUSE, L. L., W. R. BROWNE, and D. G. MOYE: Preliminary Geological Investigations in Connection with the Proposed Warragamba Dam, N.S.W., *Jour. Inst. Eng. Australia (Sydney)*, **32**: 74–84 (1951); see also **32**: 85–97 (1960).

14.13. THOMSON, D. H.: Water and Water Power, *Liverpool Eng. Soc. Trans.*, **44**: 105 (1923).

14.14. LEGGET, R. F.: A "Perched" Reservoir in Northern Ontario, Canada, *Geotechnique*, **3**: 259–265 (1953).

Chapter 15

15.1.   Quoted in 16.12, from *Nat. History*, XXXVI, sec. 15.24. pp. 101–125.

15.2.   VAN ESVELD, W. H. C.: De Watervoorziening in die Oudheid, *Water en Gas*, p. 37 (Mar. 7, 1930).

15.3.   See, e.g., WIEGAND, T., and H. SCHEADER: "Priene," G. Reimer, Berlin, 1904.

15.4.   HERSCHEL, C.: "The Two Books on the Water Supply of the City of Rome of Sextus Julius Frontinus," Dana Estes and Co., Boston, 1899, p. 19.

15.5.   LAMBARDE: "Perambulation of Kent," (London) 1826, p. 152. Quoted in *Meteorological Mag. (London)*, (February, 1928).

15.6.   BOWMAN, J.: German Waterworks Practice, *Water and Water Eng. (London)*, **38**: 665 (1936).

15.7.   See discussion on p. 530 of 15.9.

15.8.   The New Filter Gallery at Des Moines, *Eng. News-Record (New York)*, **65**: 468 (1912); and information from the General Manager, Des Moines Water Works.

15.9.   GOURLAY, H. J. F.: The Water-supply of Kano, Northern Nigeria, *Inst. Civil Eng. Min. Proc. (London)*, **237**: 454 (1935).

15.10. McDANIELS, A. B.: Groundwater Cutoff Wall Provides New Water Supply, *Eng. News-Record (New York)*, **113**: 757 (1934).

15.11. See *Eng. News-Record (New York)*, **113**: 129, Hetch Hetchy Water Supply No. (1934); also publications of the city of San Francisco.

15.12. HINDS, J.: Colorado River Water for California, *Civil Eng. (New York)*, **7**: 573 (1937). See also **5**: 2 (1935).

15.13. *Karez:* R. D. S. THOMPSON: Capturing Water in the Desert, *Eng. News-Record (New York)*, **120**: 327 (1938). *Keghriz:* L'alimentation en eau des regions desertiques de la Perse et du Caucase, *L'Eau (Paris)*, p. 86 (1933).

15.14. CUMMINS, G. A.: Underground Water Circulation, *Water and Water Eng. (London)*, **38**: 319 (1936).

15.15. See 5.56.

15.16. JACK, R. Lockhart: Geological Structure and Other Factors in Relation to Underground Water Supply in Portions of South Australia, *Geol. Survey South Australia Bull.* 14 (1930).

15.17. See p. 28 of 5.5; p. 10 of 15.20.

15.18. See p. 224 of 5.6.

15.19. PARKER, P. á M: "The Control of Water," 2d ed., Routledge & Kegan Paul, Ltd., London, 1925, p. 207.

15.20. EAST, L. R.: Water Supply Problems in Australia, *Inst. Civil Eng. Selected Eng. Paper* 141 (*London*) (1933).

15.21. See bulletins of the Geological Survey of South Australia, e.g., JACK, R. Lockhart: Some Developments in Shallow Water Areas in the North East of South Australia, no. 11 (1925).

15.22. YOUNG, J. W.: Bituminous Surfacing Treatment of Portion of the Water Supply Catchment at Narrogin, Western Australia, *Civil Eng. and Pub. Wks. Review*, pp. 548–549 (August, 1941).

15.23. HALCROW, W. T., G. B. BROOK, and R. PRESTON: The Corrosive Attack of Moorland Water on Concrete, *Inst. Water Eng. Trans.* (*London*), **33**: 187 (1929).

15.24. See 13.13.

15.25. SUTER, R.: Engineering Report on the Water Supplies of Long Island, *New York State Cons. Dept. Div. Water Power and Control Bull. G.W.* 2 (1937).

15.26. Underground Water Storage in California's South Coastal Basin, *Eng. News-Record* (*New York*), **115**: 733 (1935).

15.27. Water Scheme for Nassau, Bahamas, *Civil Eng.* (*London*), **29**: 177 (1934); see also RIDDEL, J. O.: Excluding Salt Water from Inland Wells, *Civil Eng.* (*New York*), **3**: 383 (1933).

15.28. Skimming Fresh Water Off Salt, *Eng. News-Record* (*New York*), **156**: 47 (Mar. 15, 1956); see also STEARNS, N. D.: Wells for the Water of Hawaii, *Eng. News-Record* (*New York*), **118**: 450–452 (1937); see also Reports of the Honolulu Board of Water Supply.

Chapter 16

16.1. Quoted in GREGORY, J. W.: "The Story of the Road," Alexander MacLehose & Co., London, 1931.

16.2. BENNETT, F. J.: The Influence of Geology on Early Settlements and Roads, *Geol. Assoc. Proc.* (*London*), **10**: 372 (1888).

16.3. *The Times* (*London*) (Aug. 20, 1937).

16.4. ECKERMANN, J. P.: "Conversations of Goethe with Eckermann," Everyman Edition, J. M. Dent & Sons, Ltd., London, 1930, pp. 173–174.

16.5. READE, T. M.: The Advantage to the Engineer of a Study of Geology, *Liverpool Eng. Soc. Trans.*, **10**: 36 (1888).

16.6. See 8.14.

16.7. RINGERS, J. A.: Construction of the New Ijmuiden Lock, *Eng. News-Record* (*New York*), **104**: 769 (1930).

16.8. War Christens Belgium's Albert Canal, *Eng. News-Record* (*New York*), **124**: 729–732 (1940).

16.9. Recent figures from the Engineering and Construction Director, Panama Canal Company, Canal Zone.

16.10. Report of the Committee of the National Academy of Sciences on Panama Canal Slides, *Nat. Acad. Sci.* (*Washington*), *Mem.* 18 (1924).

16.11. ARNOLD, H. M.: Taking the Menace out of Contractors Hill, *Eng. News-Record* (*New York*), **154**: 34–36 (Feb. 24, 1955).

16.12. GEST, A. P.: "Engineering (Our Debt to Greece and Rome)," Longmans, Green & Co., New York, 1930.

16.13. ALLEN, C. J.: "Switzerland's Amazing Railways," Thomas Nelson & Sons, London and New York, 1953.

16.14. EMERSON, Col. Sir Rolf: A Project for Extending the Nigerian Railway into Bornu Province, *Proc. Inst. Civil Eng.*, **12**: 353–366 (1959).

16.15. SUPP, C. W. A.: Geological and Soils Engineering on Ohio Turnpike Project, *Fifth Conf. on Geology as Appl. to Highway Eng. (Columbus, Ohio)*, pp. 61–111 (1954).

16.16. See 16.2.

16.17. DENNY, C. S.: Late Quaternary Geology and Frost Phenomena along Alaska Highway, Northern British Columbia and South-eastern Yukon, *Bull. Geol. Soc. America*, **63**: 883–921 (1952).

16.18. "West Texas Geological Society Road Log, Del Rio, El Paso," W. Texas Geol. Soc., Midland, 1958.

16.19. See 16.1.

16.20. See 8.18.

16.21. BEAN, E. E.: Economic Geology and Highway Construction, *Econ. Geol.*, **16**: 215–221 (1921).

16.22. EKBLAW, G. E.: Twenty-five Years of Engineering Geology in Illinois, *Trans. Ill. State Acad. Sci.*, **46**: 7–16 (1953).

16.23. Memoir of S. E. HORNER, *Bull. Geol. Soc. Am.*, **65**: 119–122 (1954).

16.24. Annual Conferences on Geology as Applied to Highway Engineering have been held, with proceedings issued after each meeting by the host institution, at Richmond, Va. (1950, 1951), Lexington, Va. (1952), Charleston, W.Va. (1953), Columbus, Ohio (1954), Baltimore, Md. (1955), Raleigh, N.C. (1956), State College, Penn. (1957), Charlottesville, Va. (1958), and Atlanta, Ga. (1959).

16.25. Surveying and Sampling Soils for Highway Subgrades, ASTM D420–50, ASTM Book of Standards, vol. 4, pp. 1099–1107 (1958), *Am. Soc. for Testing Mats. (Philadelphia)* (1958).

16.26. BURTON, V. R.: Fill Settlement in Peat Marshes, *Public Roads (Washington)*, **7**: 233 (1927).

16.27. ALLEN, H., and A. W. JOHNSON: Adding Water to Subgrade Levels Up Pavement, *Eng. News-Record (New York)*, **113**: 464 (1934).

16.28. Information received privately from Dr. U. Soveri, Helsinki.

16.29. YOUNG, E. R., and R. T. PINCHBACK: Sand-Shell Admixture as Flexible Road Base, *Civil Eng.*, **11**: 286–287 (1941).

16.30. Heat Treatment of Soils as Base for Road Construction, *Commonwealth Eng. (Australia)*, **21**: 399 (1934).

16.31. Airfield Construction on Overseas Soil, a Symposium, *Proc. Inst. Civil Eng.*, **8**: 211–292 (1957).

16.32. Depressing a Highway in Unstable Soil, *Eng. News-Record (New York)*, **133**: 409–412 (1944).

16.33. Repair of Florida Pike Forced by Rain Effect, *Eng. News-Record (New York)*, **158**: 27 (Mar. 21, 1957).

16.34. SMITH, N. L.: Notable Dual Road Completed, *Eng. News-Record (New York)*, **121**: 45 (1938).

16.35. Quoted in WOODWARD, H. B.: "The Geology of Soils and Subsoils," Edward Arnold & Co., London, 1912.

16.36. Town Road Carved through Loess Bluffs, *Eng. News-Record (New York)*, **125**: 277–278 (1940); see also GWYNNE, C. S.: Terraced Highway Side Slopes in Loess, Southwestern Iowa, *Bull. Geol. Soc. Am.*, **61**: 1347–1354 (1950).

16.37. Big Freeway Will Link L.A., San Diego, Mexico, *Eng. News-Record* (*New York*), **161**: 30–36 (1958).

16.38. ELLIS, C. H.: "British Railway History 1830–1876," George Allen & Unwin, Ltd., London, 1954, p. 93.

16.39. O'DELL, A. C.: "Railways and Geography," Hutchison & Co. (Publishers), Ltd., London, 1956.

16.40. See p. 55 of 16.39.

16.41. A Natural Tunnel in Virginia, *The Railway Magazine*, 319 (September and October, 1946); See also WOODWARD, H. P.: Natural Bridge and Natural Tunnel, Virginia, *Jour. Geol.*, **44**: 604–616 (1936).

16.42. ELLIS, C. H.: "The Midland Railway," Ian Allan, Ltd., London, 1953, p. 98.

16.43. See p. 130 of 16.39.

16.44. See p. 55 of 16.39; also MACBRIDE, W. D.: The White Pass Route, *The Beaver* (*Winnipeg*), **285**: 18–23 (1954).

16.45. WAHRHAFTIG, C., and R. F. BLACK: Engineering Geology along Part of the Alaska Railway, *U.S. Geol. Surv. Prof. Paper* 293–8, 69–118 (1958).

16.46. Accident Investigation 2222, Bureau of Safety, Interstate Commerce Commission (in Summary 74).

16.47. See *The Railway Magazine*, **104**: 735 (October, 1958).

16.48. Information received privately from the Secretary for Railways, W. Australia.

16.49. Information received privately from Mr. J. R. Thomas (Assistant Engineer Signals), Great Northern Railway.

16.50. MORUM, S. W. F.: The Treatment of Mud-runs in Bolivia, *Jour. Inst. Civil Eng.* (*London*), **1**: 426 (1935).

16.51. See p. 24 of 16.13.

16.52. See pp. 25–26 of 16.13.

16.53. "Tangiwai Railway Disaster, Report of the Board of Inquiry," Wellington, N.Z., 1954; see also ODELL, N.E.: Mount Puapehu, New Zealand: Observations on Its Crater Lake and Glaciers, *Jour. Glaciology* (*Cambridge, England*), **2**: 601–605 (1955).

16.54. Rising Water Completes Circuit, Sounds Flood Alarm, *Eng. News-Record* (*New York*), **161**: 58–59 (Oct. 16, 1958).

16.55. MCLEOD, N. W.: Geology and Airfield Construction, "Soils in Canada," University of Toronto Press, Toronto, 1961, pp. 195–199.

16.56. Underground Channels Utilized for Airport Drainage, *Eng. News-Record* (*New York*), **130**: 498–499 (1943).

16.57. 10,000,000 Yd. Earthmoving Job Levels Hills for West Virginia Airport, *Construction Methods*, **186**: 86–90 (January, 1946).

16.58. CAMPBELL, F. B., and W. K. CHASE: Seabees Encounter Unusual Soils on Iwo Jima, *Civil Eng.*, **15**: 505–506 (1945).

16.59. See 16.31.

Chapter 17

17.1. See "British Bridges," Public Works, Roads and Transport Congress, London, 1933, p. 173.

17.2. See pp. 175–176 of 17.1.

17.3. WADDELL, J. A. L.: "Bridge Engineering," John Wiley & Sons, Inc., New York, 1916, vol. 2, p. 1544.

17.4. ALLEN, P.: The George's River Bridge, New South Wales, *Inst. Civil Eng. Min. Proc.* (*London*), **232**: 183 (1932).

17.5. MORAN, D.: Sampling and Soil Tests for Bay Bridge, San Francisco, *Eng. News-Record* (*New York*), **111**: 404 (1933). See also other articles in the same journal on other aspects of this bridge, e.g., PURCELL, C. H., C. E.

ANDREW, and G. B. WOODRUFF: Deep Open Caissons for Bay Bridge, **113**: 227 (1934).

17.6. In a personal communication from Mr. W. M. Scott of Winnipeg.

17.7. MILLARD, L. W.: The Mortimer E. Cooley Bridge, *Civil Eng. (New York)*, **7**: 617 (1937).

17.8. Tappan Zee Bridge: a Foundation Triumph, *Eng. News-Record (New York)*, **155**: 44–46 (Apr. 14, 1955).

17.9. BUCKTON, E. J., and H. J. FEREDAY: The Demolition of Waterloo Bridge, *Jour. Inst. Civil Eng. (London)*, **3**: 472 (1936). See also MACINTOSH, F. H.: Waterloo Bridge, *Building (London)* (April, 1932).

17.10. The Vaudreuil Rigid-frame Bridge, *The Engineer*, **150**: 160–161, 170 (Aug. 16, 1935).

17.11. MACKENZIE, C. J.: The Broadway Bridge, Saskatoon, *Eng. Jour. (Montreal, Canada)*, **17**: 3 (1934).

17.12. Bridging the St. Lawrence at the Ile d'Orleans, *Eng. News-Record (New York)*, **112**: 356 (1934).

17.13. Road Foundation Problems, *Civil Eng. (London)*, **32**: 442 (1937).

17.14. Mentioned in BROOKE-BRADLEY, H. E.: Bridge Foundations, *Struct. Eng. (London)*, **12**: (new ser.) 103 (1934), from older records.

17.15. SCOTT, P. A., and C. ROBERTS: The Volta Bridge, *Proc. Inst. Civil Eng. (London)*, **9**: 395–432 (1958).

17.16. PILKEY, O. H.: Arresting Abutment Shifting on a Bascule Bridge, *Eng. News-Record (New York)*, **108**: 725 (1932).

17.17. WENTHOLT, L. R.: The Construction of Two New Canals for Inland Navigation in the Netherlands, Special Lecture, *Inst. Civil Eng. (London)* (1935).

17.18. From a paper by W. T. EVERALL, Description of Several Unusual Structures Adopted in Bridge Construction (no. 160), kindly supplied by the Chief Engineer, N.W. Rly., India.

17.19. Described in The Strengthening of an L.M.S. Railway Bridge, *British Steel Piling Co., Ltd., Bull.* 4–1935; geological data kindly supplied by Messrs. W. H. Gyles and D. C. Bean.

17.20. FINCH, R. M., and A. GOLDSTEIN: Clifton Bridge, Nottingham: Initial Design Studies and Model Test, *Proc. Inst. Civil Eng. (London)*, **12**: 289–316 (1959).

17.21. SAVAGE, J. L.: Earthquake Studies for Pit River Bridge, *Civil Eng.*, **9**: 470–472 (1939).

17.22. Deck-girder Railroad Bridge Has Earthquake-resistant Features, *Eng. News-Record (New York)*, **134**: 120–121 (January, 1945).

17.23. See pp. 186, 190 of 17.1.

17.24. DEAN, A. W. H.: Construction of a Submergible Road-bridge over the Nerbudda River near Jubbulpore, Central Provinces, India, *Inst. Civil Eng. Min. Proc. (London)*, **239**: 178 (1936).

17.25. BORHEK, R.: Scouring of Foundations as a Cause of Bridge Failure, *Roads and Bridges*, **33**: 50–54 (August, 1943).

17.26. See p. 32 of 8.27.

17.27. ROLT, L. T. C.: Centenary of the Royal Albert Bridge, at Saltash, *The Railway Magazine*, **103**: 307–313 (May, 1959).

17.28. WOODRUFF, G. B.: An Overturned 19,000 Ton Caisson Successfully Salvaged, *Eng. News-Record (New York)*, **106**: 275 (1931).

17.29. BOULTON, G. O.: Construction of the Grey Street Bridge, Brisbane, Australia, *Civil Eng. (London)*, **26**: 55 (1931).

17.30. Failure to Clean Bottom Results in Defective Pier Bases, *Eng. News-Record (New York)*, **95**: 221 (1925).

17.31. Quoted on p. 167 of Gest, A. P.: "Engineering," 16.12, as from Vitruvius, bk. V, chap. 12, Harbours and Breakwaters.

17.32. Contractors Win River Battle, *Eng. News-Record (New York)*, **119**: 13 (1937).

17.33. Sinking Open Cofferdams through Glacial Drift, *Eng. News-Record (New York)*, **114**: 1 (1935).

17.34. Fighting Water in a Bridge Foundation, *Eng. News-Record (New York)*, **130**: 806–810 (1943).

17.35. Townsend, W. H.: Underground Water Supply Complicates Bridge Pier Construction, *Eng. News-Record (New York)*, **128**: 495–497 (1942).

17.36. Alexander, F. W.: Maintenance of Substructure of the Lethbridge Viaduct, *Eng. Jour. (Montreal, Canada)*, **17**: 523 (1934).

17.37. Mohr, C., and R. Haefeli: Umbau der Landquartbrücke der Rhätischen Bahn in Klosters, *Schweitzerische Bauzeitung*, **65**: 5–24, 32–37 (1947).

17.38. Two Railroad Bridge Failures Laid to Inadequate Inspection, *Eng. News-Record (New York)*, **111**: 687 (1933).

Chapter 18

18.1.   Smeaton, John: "A Narrative of the Building and a Description of the Construction of the Eddystone Lighthouse with Stone . . . ," printed by H. Hughs, sold by G. Nicol, London, 1791. An engineering classic.

18.2.   Carson, Rachel L.: "The Sea Around Us," Oxford University Press, New York, 1951.

18.3.   See p. 122 of 18.2.

18.4.   Stevenson, T.: "The Design and Construction of Harbours," 3d ed., A. and C. Black, Ltd., London, 1886. See pp. 49–52 for experiences at Wick.

18.5.   Hunt, I. A., and L. Bajorunas: The Effect of Seiches at Conneaut Harbor, *Proc. Am. Soc. C.E.*, WW2, Paper 2067 (June, 1959).

18.6.   Shepard, F. L.: "The Earth Beneath the Sea," Johns Hopkins Press, Baltimore, 1959.

18.7.   Fairbridge, R.: The Changing Level of the Sea, *Scientific American*, **202**: 70–79 (1960).

18.8.   How Far to the Bottom, *The New Scientist*, **7**: 515–516 (Mar. 3, 1960).

18.9.   Steers, J. A.: "The Coastline of England and Wales," Cambridge University Press, New York, 1946; see also Steers, J. A.: "The Sea Coast" (The New Naturalist Series), Collins, London, 1953, to both of which the author is indebted.

18.10. Third (and final) Report of the Royal Commission on Coast Erosion, H. M. Stationery Office, London, 1911.

18.11. Coode, Sir John: Description of the Chesil Bank, with Remarks upon Its Origin, the Causes Which Have Contributed to Its Formation, and upon the Movement of Shingle generally, *Min. Proc. Inst. Civil Eng. (London)*, **12**: 520–557 (1853).

18.12. Ridehalgh, H.: Shoreham Harbour Development, *Proc. Inst. Civil Eng. (London)*, **11**: 285–296 (1958).

18.13. Sheppard, T.: "The Lost Towns of the Yorkshire Coast . . . ," A. Brown and Sons, Ltd., London, 1912.

18.14. Sutton Bridge Dock, *The Railway Magazine*, **96**: 422 (1955).

18.15. Kirkpatrick, Sir C. R. S.: The Development of Harbour and Dock Engineering (Vernon Harcourt Lecture), *Inst. Civil Eng. (London)*, 1926.

18.16. Schlumerger, C., and P. J. M. Renaud: Étude géophysique sous marine exécutée dans le Port d'Alger, *Annales des Ponts et Chaussées*, **4**: (1935).

18.17. Buckton, E. J.: The Construction of Haifa Harbour, *Inst. Civil Eng. Min. Proc. (London)*, **239**: 544 (1936).

18.18. Ellson, G.: Dover Train-ferry Dock, *Jour. Inst. Civil Eng. (London)*, **7**: 223 (1937).

18.19. Quinn, A. de F.: Great Lakes Port for Shipping Taconite Built by Ore Industry, *Eng. News-Record (New York)*, **156**: 38–44 (Oct. 18, 1956).

18.20. Shaler, N. S.: The Geologic History of Harbors, *U.S. Geol. Survey*, 13th Ann. Rep, II, pp. 99–205 (1893).

18.21. Bemelmans, Ludwig: "Father, Dear Father," The Viking Press, Inc., New York, 1953. See p. 143 in a chapter titled "Cinderella Island": it is a pleasure to be able to refer to this charming book in this listing.

18.22. Hunter, W. H.: "Rivers and Estuaries," Longmans, Green & Co., Ltd., London, 1913.

18.23. Schijf, J. B.: Generalities on Coastal Processes and Protection, *Proc. Am. Soc. C.E.*, WW1, Paper 1976 (1959).

18.24. See 10.32.

18.25. Stanton, W. F., and A. G. Le Clercq: The Improvement of the Port of Valparaiso and Extension of the Breakwater, *Inst. Civil Eng. Min. Proc. (London)*, **233**: 199 (1931).

18.26. See 18.1.

18.27. Rutledge, P. C.: Design of Texas Towers Offshore Radar Stations, *Proc. Eighth Texas Conference on Soil Mech. and Found. Eng.* (1956).

18.28. Blume, J. A., and J. M. Keith: Rincon Offshore Island and Open Causeway, *Proc. Am. Soc. C.E.*, WW3, Paper 2170 (1959).

18.29. White, G. W., and W. H. Gould: Erosion of Lake Erie Shore, *Eng. Expt. News, Ohio State Univ.*, **17**: 3–10 (1945).

18.30. Forney, F. H., and G. A. Lynde: Beach Protection Engineers Attempt to Outwit Nature at Presque Isle Peninsula, *Civil Eng.*, **21**: 508–511 (1951); see also **28**: 172–175 (1958).

18.31. Escoffier, F. F.: Harrison County (Mississippi) Artificial Beach, *Trans. Am. Soc. C.E.*, **123**: 817–823 (1958).

18.32. Beach Erosion Studies by Federal Board, *Eng. News-Record (New York)*, **111**: 281 (1933).

18.33. Ash, W. C., and O. B. Rattenbury: Vizagapatam Harbour, *Jour. Inst. Civil Eng. (London)*, **1**: 235 (1935).

18.34. Spring, Sir Francis: Coastal Sand Travel near Madras Harbour, *Min. Proc. Inst. Civil Eng. (London)*, **194**: 153–239 (1913).

18.35. Howard, E. A.: Permeable Groins of Concrete Check Beach Erosion, *Eng. News-Record (New York)*, **114**: 594 (1935).

18.36. Duvivier, J: Coast Protection: Some Recent Works on the East Coast 1942–52, *Proc. Inst. Civil Eng. (London)*, **2**: pt. II, 510–531 (1953).

18.37. Harwood, F. L., and K. C. Wilson: An Investigation into a Proposal to Dispose of Power Station Ash by Discharging It into the Sea at Low Water, *Proc. Inst. Civil Eng. (London)*, **8**: 53–70 (1957).

18.38. Senour, C., and J. E. Bardes: Sand By-Passing Plant at Lake Worth Inlet, Florida, *Proc. Am. Soc. C.E.*, WW2, Paper 1980 (1959).

18.39. Wheeler, W. H.: "Tidal Rivers," Longmans, Green & Co., Ltd., London, 1893, p. 145.

18.40. See p. 365 of 18.39. Also Peel, C.: The Mersey Estuary, paper published by Manchester and District Association of Institution of Civil Engineers (England), 1926.

18.41. See p. 191 of 18.39. Also from information from personal communication with Mr. Billings Wilson, Assistant General Manager, The Port of New York Authority.

18.42. See p. 142 of 18.39.

18.43. See "The Addresses and Papers of James B. Eads," ed. by E. McHenry, Slawson and Co., St. Louis, Mo., 1884. See also papers by Corthell, E. L., in *Trans. Am. C. E. (New York)*.

18.44. Johnson, W. A.: Sedimentation of the Fraser River Delta, *Geol. Soc. Can. Mem.* 125 (no. 107 geol. ser.) (1912).

18.45. Dolmage, V., E. E. Mason, and J. W. Stewart: Demolition of Ripple Rock, *Trans. Can. Inst. Mining and Met.*, **61**: 382–395 (1958).

18.46. Terzaghi, K.: Varieties of Submarine Slope Failures, *Proc. Eighth Texas Conf. on Soil Mech. and Found. Eng.*, Austin, Tex., 1956.

18.47. Elmendorf, C. H., and Heezen, B. C.: Oceanographic Information for Engineering Submarine Cable Systems, *Bell System Tech. Jour.*, **36**: 1047–1093 (1957).

Chapter 19

19.1. Again I am indebted to Dr. F. D. Adams (see p. 339 of 2.2) for this significant quotation from "La composzione del Mondo," bk. 6, chap. 8.

19.2. Chatley, H.: The Hydraulics of Large Rivers, *Civil Eng. and Pub. Wks. Review*, **33**: 59–62 (February, 1938).

19.3. Flood Prevention and Other Hydraulic Problems in China, *The Engineer*, **166**: 278–280 (Sept. 9, 1938).

19.4. Todd, O. J.: A Runaway River Controlled, *Eng. News-Record (New York)*, **116**: 735–738 (1936).

19.5. Elliot, D. O.: "The Improvement of the Lower Mississippi River for Flood Control and Navigation," 3 vols., U.S. Waterways Experiment Station, Vicksburg, Miss., 1932.

19.6. Fisk, H. N.: "Geological Investigation of the Alluvial Valley of the Lower Mississippi River," Miss. River Commission, Vicksburg, Miss., 1944; see also Matthes, G. H.: Paradoxes of the Mississippi, *Scientific American*, **184**: 19–23 (April, 1951).

19.7. New Control Dams Remove Threat to Ol' Mississippi, *Eng. News-Record (New York)*, **164**: 32–36 (Jan. 7, 1960).

19.8. Crawford, R. C.: Missouri Basin, Inter-agency Committee, *Civil Eng.*, **16**: 64–65 (1946); see also **14**: 413–416 (1944).

19.9. Bringing the River to the Dry-land Bridge, *Eng. News-Record (New York)*, **154**: 25–26 (May 12, 1955).

19.10. See p. 65 of 11.6.

19.11. Gottschalk, L. C.: Effects of Soil Erosion on Navigation in Upper Chesapeake Bay, *Geograph. Review*, **35**: 221–238 (1945); see also Sedimentation in a Great Harbour, *Soil Conservation*, **10**: 3–12 (1944).

19.12. See 13.19.

19.13. Marr, N., C. G. Cline, and H. C. Woods: Flow Diversion at Niagara Falls, *Civil Eng.*, **13**: 321–324, 359–362, 403–406 (1943).

19.14. Butcher, A. D. D., and J. D. Atkinson: The Causes and Prevention of Bed Erosion, with Special Reference to the Protection of Structures Controlling Rivers and Canals, *Inst. Civil Eng. Min. Proc. (London)*, **235**: 175 (1934).

19.15. See Lane, E. W.: Retrogression of Levels in Riverbeds below Dams, *Eng. News-Record (New York)*, **112**: 836 (1934). See also original report dated Dec. 16, 1929, by the Islam Enquiry Committee into the Failure of the Islam Weir, S.V.P., Sept. 19, 1929, Lahore, India, 1930.

19.16. Keener, K. B.: Spillway Erosion at Grand Coulee Dam, *Eng. News-Record (New York)*, **133**: 41–47 (July 13, 1944).

19.17. Stevens, J. C.: Scour Prevention below Bonneville Dam, *Eng. News-Record (New York)*, **118**: 61–64 (Jan. 14, 1937); see also **154**: 36–39 (Apr. 21, 1955).

19.18.   DEINHART, A. V.: Chute Spillway Preserves St. Anthony Falls, *Civil Eng.*, **26**: 12–14 (1956).

19.19.   Seen at the display arranged for visitors to this plant on the Connecticut River, just south of Hanover, N.H.

19.20.   FORTIER, S., and H. F. BLANEY: Silt in the Colorado River and Its Relation to Irrigation, *U.S. Dept. Agr. Techn. Bull.* 67 (1928).

19.21.   VETTER, C. P.: Why Desilting Works for the All-American Canal, *Eng. News-Record (New York)*, **118**: 321 (1937).

19.22.   KENNEDY, R. G.: "Hydraulic Diagrams for Channels in Earth," 2d ed., Edinburgh, 1907.

19.23.   DUFOUR, H.: Le dessableur, les turbines et la production d'Energie de l'Usine de Marlengo, *La Houille Blanche*, pp. 1–8 (January– February, 1936).

19.24.   BAUMANN, P.: Control of Flood Debris in San Gabriel Area, *Civil Eng.*, **14**: 143–146 (1944).

19.25.   ALLEN, H. J.: Coal Fires Offset Cost of Culm Elimination, *Civil Eng.*, **16**: 395–397 (1946).

19.26.   LEVIN, P., and D. I. SMITH: Six-million-dollar Plant Recovers Fine Coal from Susquehanna River, *Civil Eng.*, **24**: 435–438 (1954).

19.27.   STEVENS, J. C.: The Silt Problem, *Trans. Am. Soc. C. E. (New York)*, **101**: 207 (1936).

19.28.   STEVENS, J. C.: Future of Lake Mead and Elephant Butte Reservoir, *Trans. Am. Soc. C. E.*, **111**: 1231 (1946).

19.29.   Filling of Lake Mead with Silt Estimated to Take 445 Years, *Eng. News-Record (New York)*, **145**: 34 (July 6, 1950).

19.30.   Removing Reservoir Silt by Sluicing Operations, *Eng. News-Record (New York)*, **127**: 20 (July 3, 1941).

19.31.   Dredge Cleans Waterworks Basin without Interrupting Services, *Eng. News-Record (New York)*, **137**: 314–315 (Sept. 5, 1946).

19.32.   MOBLEY, C. F.: Muck-filled Reservoir Behind 120 Foot Dam Is Cleared, *Eng. News-Record (New York)*, **160**: 40–42 (May 15, 1958).

19.33.   For some detailed figures, see BROWN, C. B.: Sediment Complicates Flood Control, *Civil Eng.*, **15**: 83–86 (1945).

19.34.   BENNETT, H. H.: Stilling the Dunes, *Soil Conservation*, **16**: 106–109 (1950).

19.35.   Grass Stabilizes Sand on 4,900 Acres of New York's Idlewild Airport, *Civil Eng.*, **18**: 22–23, 66 (1948).

19.36.   Biology and Engineering, *Proc. of Conference of Inst. Civil Engs.* in September, 1948, London, 1949.

19.37.   WINSOR, L. M.: The Barrier System of Flood Control, *Civil Eng.*, **8**: 675–678 (1938).

19.38.   Beaten by Birdies, *The Countryman (Idbury, England)*, **57**: 56–57 (1960). A quarterly highly recommended.

Chapter 20

20.1.   See *The Countryman*, **56**: 540 (1959).

20.2.   Based on YOUNG, E. C.: The Interaction between Technical Change on the Farm and Technical Change in Marketing and Distribution, *Proc. Ninth Inter. Conf. of Agric. Economists*, 1957, p. 166.

20.3.   SHAPLEY, H. (ed.): "Climatic Change," Harvard University Press, Cambridge, Mass., 1953.

20.4.   SHERLOCK, R. L.: "Man's Influence on the Earth," Butterworth & Co. (Publishers) Ltd., London, 1931.

20.5.   See *Proc. Sixth Technical Meeting of the International Union for the Con-*

servation of Nature and Natural Resources, pp. 119–184, London, 1957. Good bibliography.

20.6.   BLACK, R. F.: Some Problems in Engineering Geology caused in Permafrost in the Arctic Coastal Plain, Northern Alaska, *Arctic,* **10**: 230–240 (1957).

20.7.   VETTER, C. P.: Silt Problems in Lake Mead and Downstream on the Colorado River, paper read at S. W. Regional Meeting of Am. Geophys. Union, Feb. 8, 1952.

20.8.   CARDER, D. S.: Influence of Reservoir Loading on Earthquake Activity in the Boulder Dam Area, *Trans. Am. Geophys. Union,* **26**: 203 (1945); see also CARDER, D. S., and J. B. SMALL: ibid., **29**: 767–771 (1948); see also SMITH, W. O., C. P. VETTER, and G. B. CUMMINGS, Comprehensive Survey of Sedimentation in Lake Mead, 1948–49, *U.S. Geol. Survey Prof. Paper 295,* (1960).

20.9.   GOUGH, D. I.: Some Scientific Opportunities at Kariba Lake, *The New Scientist,* **7**: 1278–1280 (May 19, 1960).

20.10. Cairo to Study Qattara Hydro, *Eng. News-Record (New York),* **164**: 53 (Mar. 10, 1960).

20.11. For a fine outline of this entire project see "From Fisherman's Paradise to Farmer's Pride," Netherlands Govt. Inf. Service, 1959.

20.12. HAUSER, E. O.: Holland's New Weapon Against the Sea, *Saturday Evening Post* (Jan. 17, 1959); see also, "The Delta Plan," Information Dept., Ministry of Transport and Waterstaat, The Hague, April, 1958; see also The Delta Project—A Symposium, with papers by J. B. Schijf, J. J. Dronkers, and H. A. Ferguson, *Trans. Am. Soc. C. E.,* **125**: 1290–1303 (1960).

20.13. 1. *Australia:* See 5.27, Report of Fifth Conference, Government Printer, Sydney, 1929, p. 9.
2. *South Dakota:* MEINZER, O. E.: Progress in the Control of Artesian Water Supplies, *Eng. News-Record (New York),* **113**: 167 (1934).
3. *Paris:* LEMOINE, P., R. HUMERY, and R. SOYER: L'Appauvrissement de la nappe des sables vertes de la region parisienne, *Comptes rendus (Paris),* p. 1870 (May 23, 1934).
4. *Chicago:* BURDICK, C. B.: Ground Water as a Source of Supply, *Eng. News-Record (New York),* **105**: 398 (1930).
5. *London:* The Falling Water Level of the Chalk under London, *Water and Water Eng. (London),* **35**: 440 (1933).

20.14. MITCHELSON, A. T.: Conservation of Water through Recharge of the Underground Supply, *Civil Eng.,* **9**: 163–165 (1939).

20.15. LANE, D. A.: Artificial Storing of Groundwater by Spreading, *Jour. Am. Water Works Assoc.,* **28**: 1240 (1936).

20.16. L.A. to Expand Groundwater Recharge, *Eng. News-Record (New York),* **163**: 28 (Dec. 3, 1959).

20.17. LAVERTY, F. B.: Recharging Groundwater with Reclaimed Sewage Effluent, *Civil Eng.,* **28**: 585–587 (1958).

20.18. BONIFACE, E. S.: Some Experiments in Artificial Recharge in the Lower Lea Valley, *Proc. Inst. Civil Eng. (London),* **16**: 325–337 (1959).

20.19. For many examples, see 20.20.

20.20. MARCH, G. P.: "The Earth as Modified by Human Action," Scribner, Armstrong, and Co., New York, 1874, p. 241.

20.21. For a good general review see, JACKS, G. V., and R. O. WHYTE: "Vanishing Lands," Doubleday & Company, Inc., New York, 1939.

20.22. BENNETT, H. H: "Soil Conservation," McGraw-Hill Book Company, Inc., New York, 1939. A book strongly recommended for the attention of all readers.

NAME INDEX

PLACE INDEX

Names of countries listed in Appendix B are not included: places are listed generally under states and provinces for North America, but for the rest of the world under countries: natural features such as rivers and mountains are grouped with corresponding notations.

865

SUBJECT INDEX

874